APPLIED PARTIAL
DIFFERENTIAL
EQUATIONS

The Prindle, Weber & Schmidt Series in Mathematics

Althoen and Bumcrot, *Introduction to Discrete Mathematics*
Brown and Sherbert, *Introductory Linear Algebra with Applications*
Buchthal and Cameron, *Modern Abstract Algebra*
Burden and Faires, *Numerical Analysis*, Fourth Edition
Cullen, *Linear Algebra and Differential Equations*
Cullen, *Mathematics for the Biosciences*
Eves, *In Mathematical Circles*
Eves, *Mathematical Circles Adieu*
Eves, *Mathematical Circles Revisited*
Eves, *Mathematical Circles Squared*
Eves, *Return to Mathematical Circles*
Fletcher and Patty, *Foundations of Higher Mathematics*
Gantner and Gantner, *Trigonometry*
Geltner and Peterson, *Geometry for College Students*
Gilbert and Gilbert, *Elements of Modern Algebra*, Second Edition
Gobran, *Beginning Algebra*, Fourth Edition
Gobran, *College Algebra*
Gobran, *Intermediate Algebra*, Fourth Edition
Gordon, *Calculus and the Computer*
Hall, *Algebra for College Students*
Hall and Bennett, *College Algebra with Applications*, Second Edition
Hartfiel and Hobbs, *Elementary Linear Algebra*
Kaufmann, *Algebra for College Students*, Third Edition
Kaufmann, *Algebra with Trigonometry for College Students*, Second Edition
Kaufmann, *College Algebra*, Second Edition
Kaufmann, *College Algebra and Trigonometry*, Second Edition
Kaufmann, *Elementary Algebra for College Students*, Third Edition
Kaufmann, *Intermediate Algebra for College Students*, Third Edition
Kaufmann, *Precalculus*
Kaufmann, *Trigonometry*
Laufer, *Discrete Mathematics and Applied Modern Algebra*
Nicholson, *Elementary Linear Algebra with Applications*, Second Edition
Powers, *Elementary Differential Equations*
Powers, *Elementary Differential Equations with Boundary–Value Problems*
Powers, *Elementary Differential Equations with Linear Algebra*
Proga, *Arithmetic and Algebra*, Second Edition
Proga, *Basic Mathematics*, Second Edition
Rice and Strange, *Plane Trigonometry*, Fifth Edition
Schelin and Bange, *Mathematical Analysis for Business and Economics*, Second Edition
Strnad, *Introductory Algebra*
Swokowski, *Algebra and Trigonometry with Analytic Geometry*, Seventh Edition
Swokowski, *Calculus with Analytic Geometry*, Second Alternate Edition
Swokowski, *Calculus with Analytic Geometry*, Fourth Edition
Swokowski, *Fundamentals of Algebra and Trigonometry*, Seventh Edition
Swokowski, *Fundamentals of College Algebra*, Seventh Edition
Swokowski, *Fundamentals of Trigonometry*, Seventh Edition
Swokowski, *Precalculus: Functions and Graphs*, Sixth Edition
Tan, *Applied Calculus*, Second Edition

Tan, *Applied Finite Mathematics*, Third Edition
Tan, *Calculus for the Managerial, Life, and Social Sciences*, Second Edition
Tan, *College Mathematics*, Second Edition
Trim, *Applied Partial Differential Equations*
Venit and Bishop, *Elementary Linear Algebra*, Third Edition
Venit and Bishop, *Elementary Linear Alegbra*, Alternate Second Edition
Willard, *Calculus and Its Applications*, Second Edition
Wood and Capell, *Arithmetic*
Wood, Capell, and Hall, *Developmental Mathematics*, Fourth Edition
Wood and Capell, *Intermediate Algebra*
Zill, *A First Course in Differential Equations with Applications*, Fourth Edition
Zill, *Calculus with Analytic Geometry*, Second Edition
Zill, *Differential Equations with Boundary–Value Problems*, Second Edition

The Prindle, Weber & Schmidt Series in Advanced Mathematics

Brabenec, *Introduction to Real Analysis*
Eves, *Foundations and Fundamental Concepts of Mathematics*, Third Edition
Keisler, *Elementary Calculus: An Infinitesimal Approach*, Second Edition
Kirkwood, *An Introduction to Real Analysis*

APPLIED PARTIAL DIFFERENTIAL EQUATIONS

DONALD W. TRIM
THE UNIVERSITY OF MANITOBA

PWS PUBLISHING COMPANY
■ ■ ■ ■ ■ ■ ■ ■ ■ ■ BOSTON

PWS
Publishing Company

20 Park Plaza
Boston, Massachusetts 02116

 International Thomson Publishing
The trademark ITP is used under license.

Library of Congress Cataloging-in-Publication Data

Trim, Donald W.
  Applied partial differential equations

  Includes bibliography and index
1. Partial Differential Equations   I. Title
QA391.T890   1989   523.4'2   89-16753
ISBN 0-534-92134-5

Printed in the United States of America

94—10 9 8 7 6 5 4

Sponsoring Editor: Steve Quigley
Production Editor: S. London
Manufacturing Coordinator: Marcia Locke
Interior and Cover Designer: S. London
Interior Illustration: Lotus Art
Typesetter: Polyglot Pte. Ltd.
Cover Printer: Henry N. Sawyer Co., Inc.
Printer and Binder: The Maple-Vail Book Manufacturing Group

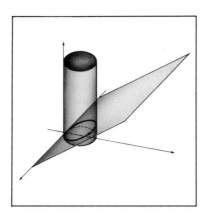

Preface

This text evolved, as have so many others, from notes used to teach partial differential equations to advanced undergraduate mathematics students and graduate engineering students. Major emphasis is placed on techniques for solving partial differential equations found in physics and engineering, but discussions on existence and uniqueness of solutions are also included. Every opportunity is taken to show that there may be more than one way to solve a particular problem and to discuss the advantages of each solution relative to the others. In addition, physical interpretations of mathematical solutions are stressed whenever possible.

Section 1.1 introduces partial differential equations and describes how initial boundary value problems are associated with such equations. To distinguish between physical assumptions leading to the various models of heat conduction, vibration, potential problems, and so forth, and the mathematical techniques used to solve these problems, models are developed in Sections 1.2–1.6, with no attempt at solutions. At this stage, the reader concentrates only on how mathematics describes physical phenomena. Once these ideas are firmly entrenched, it is then reasonable to proceed to various solution techniques. It has been our experience that confusion often arises when new mathematical techniques are prematurely applied to unfamiliar problems.

One of the most fundamental classical techniques for solving partial differential equations is that of separation of variables, which leads, in the simplest of examples, to trigonometric Fourier series. Chapter 2 develops the theory of Fourier series to the point where it is easily accessible to separation of variables in Chapter 3. Eigenfunction expansions are used to handle nonhomogeneities in this chapter. The examples in Chapter 3 also suggest the possibility of expansions other than trigonometric Fourier series, and these are discussed in detail through Sturm-Liouville systems in Chapter 4.

The reader can proceed in a variety of ways through Chapters 5–9. One obvious way is to follow the order of topics as presented. This begins in Chapter 5, with separation of variables on homogeneous problems that are more difficult than those encountered in Chapter 3. In this chapter we also illustrate how to verify series solutions of initial boundary value problems, and we discuss distinguishing properties of parabolic, elliptic, and hyperbolic partial differential equations. In Chapter 6, finite Fourier transforms are presented as an alternative to eigenfunction expansions for nonhomogeneous problems. In Chapter 7 we discuss homogeneous and nonhomogeneous problems on unbounded domains using separation of variables, Fourier integrals, and Fourier transforms. Chapters 8 and 9 essentially repeat material in Chapters 4, 5, 6, and 7, but in polar, cylindrical, and spherical coordinates.

For those who prefer to study bounded domain problems in polar, cylindrical, and spherical coordinates before considering problems on unbounded domains, we suggest one of three reorderings of sections in Chapters 5–9:

Chapter 8	Chapter 5	Chapter 5
Chapter 5 and Section 9.1	Chapter 6	Chapter 8
Chapter 6 and Section 9.2	Chapter 8	Section 9.1
Chapter 7 and Section 9.3	Sections 9.1 and 9.2	Chapter 6 and Section 9.2
	Chapter 7 and Section 9.3	Chapter 7 and Section 9.3

To work through most sections of the book, students require a first course in ordinary differential equations and an introduction to advanced calculus. Sections 10.3–10.5, which deal with Laplace transform solutions of initial boundary value problems, assume a working knowledge of complex variable theory. This chapter can also be adapted to the above schemes. Sections 10.1–10.4 can be covered at any time after Chapter 5. Section 10.5 requires material from Chapter 8.

Green's functions for ordinary and partial differential equations are discussed in Chapters 11 and 12. Green's functions for ordinary differential equations can be studied at any time. Chapter 12 utilizes separation techniques from Chapter 5 and Section 9.1.

We are of the opinion that exercises are of the utmost importance to a student's learning. There must be straightforward problems to reinforce fundamentals and more difficult problems to challenge enterprising students. We have attempted to provide more than enough of each type. Problems in each set of exercises are graded from easy to difficult, and answers to selected exercises are provided at the back of the book. Exercise sets in 16 sections (3.2, 3.3; 5.2, 5.3, 5.4; 6.2, 6.3; 7.2, 7.4; 9.1, 9.2, 9.3; 10.2, 10.4, 10.5; 11.4) stress applications. They have been divided into four parts:

Part A—Heat Conduction

Part B—Vibrations

Part C—Potential, Steady-State Heat Conduction, Static Deflections of Membranes

Part D—General Results

Students interested in heat conduction should concentrate on problems from Part A. Students interested in mechanical vibrations will find problems in Part B particularly appropriate. All students can profit from problems in Part C, since every problem therein, although stated in terms of one of the three applications, is easily interpretable in terms of the other two. We recommend the exercises in Part D to all students.

A student supplement containing solutions to many of the exercises is available from the author.

The author wishes to acknowledge the students who provided initial motivation for writing this book and the students who suffered through its many revisions. Appreciation is also expressed to the reviewers, who made many valuable suggestions:

Philip S. Crooke, Vanderbilt University; William E. Fitzgibbon, University of Houston; Herman Gollwitzer, Drexel University; Euel W. Kennedy, California Polytechnic State University; Gilbert Lewis, Michigan Technological University; Peter J. Olver, University of Minnesota at Minneapolis; William Smith, Brigham Young University; Monty Strauss, Texas Tech University, and Raymond D. Terry, California Polytechnic State University.

Finally, many thanks to the staff of PWS-KENT for their cooperation throughout the duration of this project.

D.W.T.

In memory of my father. Not many words passed between us, but we knew.

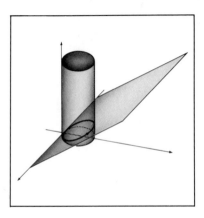

Contents

T W O

Fourier Series   69

T H R E E

Separation of Variables   102

F O U R

Sturm-Liouville Systems   141

F I V E

Solutions of Homogeneous Problems
by Separation of Variables   169

S I X

Finite Fourier Transforms and Nonhomogeneous Problems 221

S E V E N

Problems on Infinite Spatial Domains 252

E I G H T

Special Functions 287

N I N E

Problems in Polar, Cylindrical, and Spherical Coordinates 320

Laplace Transforms   351

Green's Functions for Ordinary Differential Equations   395

T W E L V E

Green's Functions for Partial Differential Equations   440

A P P E N D I X A

Convergence of Fourier Series A

A P P E N D I X B

Convergence of Fourier Integrals A-6

A P P E N D I X C

Vector Analysis A-10

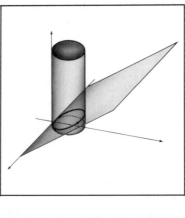

C H A P T E R

O   N   E

Derivation of Partial Differential Equations of Mathematical Physics

1.1 Introduction

A partial differential equation (PDE) is an equation that must be solved for an unknown function of at least two independent variables when the equation contains partial derivatives of the unknown function. For example, in Figure 1.1 we picture a circular rod of length L that at some initial time (say $t = 0$) has a constant temperature of $10°C$. Suppose that at time $t = 0$, the lateral side of the rod is insulated and the ends are suddenly heated to $100°C$ and maintained at this temperature thereafter. In Section 1.2 it is shown that the temperature U at points in the rod is a function of x and t only, $U = U(x, t)$, and that this function must satisfy the PDE

$$\frac{\partial U}{\partial t} = k \frac{\partial^2 U}{\partial x^2}, \tag{1a}$$

where k is a constant (the thermal diffusivity of the material in the rod). This PDE is called the *one-dimensional heat conduction equation*; it states that the temperature function $U(x, t)$ must have a first partial derivative with respect to t identical to k times its second partial derivative with respect to x.

1

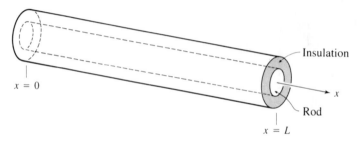

Figure 1.1

Other PDEs we shall consider include the one-dimensional wave equation for displacement $y(x, t)$ of vibrating strings,

$$\frac{\partial^2 y}{\partial t^2} = \frac{\tau}{\rho} \frac{\partial^2 y}{\partial x^2} \tag{2}$$

(Section 1.3); the three-dimensional Poisson's equation for potential $V(x, y, z)$,

$$\frac{\partial^2 V}{\partial x^2} + \frac{\partial^2 V}{\partial y^2} + \frac{\partial^2 V}{\partial z^2} = F(x, y, z) \tag{3}$$

(Section 1.6); and the beam-vibration equation for displacement $y(x, t)$,

$$\frac{w}{g} \frac{\partial^2 y}{\partial t^2} + EI \frac{\partial^4 y}{\partial x^4} = F(x, t) \tag{4}$$

(Section 1.5).

The *order* of a PDE is the highest-order partial derivative contained therein. Equations (1a), (2), and (3) are therefore second order, and equation (4) is fourth order.

Since partial derivatives of multivariable functions are ordinary derivatives with respect to one variable (the others being held constant), it might seem that the study of partial differential equations should be an easy extension of the theory for ordinary differential equations (ODEs). Such is not the case. Partial differential equations and ordinary differential equations are approached in fundamentally different ways. To understand why, recall that in your studies of ODEs it was customary to solve a certain class of equations and thereafter to deal with applications involving equations in this class. For example, a general solution of the second-order linear ODE

$$p \frac{d^2 y}{dt^2} + q \frac{dy}{dt} + ry = 0$$

is $y(t) = A y_1(t) + B y_2(t)$, where A and B are arbitrary constants and $y_1(t)$ and $y_2(t)$ are any two linearly independent solutions of the equation. Once $y_1(t)$ and $y_2(t)$ are known, every solution of the equation is of the form $A y_1(t) + B y_2(t)$ for some A and B. When such an equation is found in an application, say a vibrating mass–spring system or an LCR circuit, it is accompanied by two initial conditions that the solution $y(t)$ must satisfy. These conditions determine the values for A and B. What we are saying is that in applications, ODEs are often solved by first finding general solutions and then using subsidiary conditions to determine arbitrary constants.

It is very unusual to approach PDEs in this way, principally because arbitrary constants in general solutions of ODEs are replaced by arbitrary functions in PDEs, and determination of these arbitrary functions using subsidiary conditions is usually impossible. In other words, general solutions of PDEs are of limited utility in solving applied PDEs. [The one major exception is wave equation (2), and this particular situation is discussed in Section 1.7.] In general, then, it is necessary to consider a PDE and any extra conditions that accompany the equation simultaneously. We must proceed directly to a solution of the PDE and subsidiary conditions, as opposed to PDE first and subsidiary conditions later.

Subsidiary conditions that accompany PDEs are called initial or boundary conditions. For example, it is clear that the temperature function $U(x, t)$ for the rod in Figure 1.1 must also satisfy the *boundary conditions*

$$U(0, t) = 100, \tag{1b}$$

$$U(L, t) = 100, \tag{1c}$$

since the ends of the rod, $x = 0$ and $x = L$, are held at temperature $100°C$. In addition, $U(x, t)$ must satisfy the *initial condition*

$$U(x, 0) = 10, \tag{1d}$$

since its temperature at time $t = 0$ was $10°C$ throughout.

Partial differential equation (1a), boundary conditions (1b, c), and initial condition (1d) constitute the complete *initial boundary value problem* for temperature in the rod. It is more precise to describe the problem as follows:

$$\frac{\partial U}{\partial t} = k\frac{\partial^2 U}{\partial x^2}, \qquad 0 < x < L, \qquad t > 0, \tag{5a}$$

$$U(0, t) = 100, \qquad t > 0, \tag{5b}$$

$$U(L, t) = 100, \qquad t > 0, \tag{5c}$$

$$U(x, 0) = 10, \qquad 0 < x < L. \tag{5d}$$

All that we have done is affix intervals on which conditions (1) must be satisfied, but, perhaps unexpectedly, these intervals are all open. To see why this is the case, consider first PDE (5a). Physically, $U(x, t)$ is a function of one space variable x and the time variable t, but mathematically, it is simply a function of two independent variables x and t. It must satisfy PDE (5a) in some region of the xt-plane, and we take this region to be described by the inequalities $0 < x < L$ and $t > 0$ (Figure 1.2). By keeping these intervals open, we avoid discussing the PDE on the boundary of the region. Otherwise

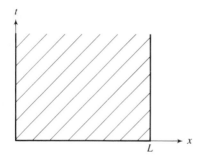

Figure 1.2

it would be necessary to consider one-sided derivatives with respect to x along $x = 0$ and $x = L$, one-sided derivatives with respect to t along $t = 0$, and both types of one-sided derivatives at $(0,0)$ and $(L,0)$. We take as a general principle that partial differential equations are always considered on open[†] regions.

Replacement of $t > 0$ and $0 < x < L$ in (5b–d) with $t \geq 0$ and $0 \leq x \leq L$ would lead to contradictions. Conditions (5b, c) would then require $U(x, t)$ to have values $U(0, 0) = U(L, 0) = 100$, whereas (5d) would demand that $U(0,0) = U(L,0) = 10$. By imposing boundary and initial conditions on open intervals, we eliminate such mathematical contradictions. Realize, however, that although (5) contains no mathematical contradictions, it is physically impossible to change the temperature of the ends of the rod instantaneously from $10°C$ to $100°C$, and yet (5) does demand this. We must therefore anticipate some type of anomaly in the solution to (5) near positions $x = 0$ and $x = L$ at times close to $t = 0$.

It is not always necessary to use open intervals for boundary and initial conditions. If the initial temperature in the rod were not constant but varied with x according to, say, $f(x) = 400x(L - x) + 100$, it would not be necessary to heat the ends of the rod suddenly to $100°C$ at time $t = 0$; they would already be at that temperature, since $f(0) = f(L) = 100$. It would be necessary only to maintain them at $100°C$ thereafter. In this case, it would be quite acceptable to replace the open intervals in (5b–d) with

$$U(0, t) = 100, \qquad t \geq 0,$$
$$U(L, t) = 100, \qquad t \geq 0,$$
$$U(x, 0) = 400x(L - x) + 100, \qquad 0 \leq x \leq L.$$

It will be our practice to state initial and boundary conditions on open intervals even when closed intervals are acceptable.

Example 1:   The ends of a violin string of length L are fixed on the x-axis at positions $x = 0$ and $x = L$. When the middle of the string is elevated to the position in Figure 1.3 and then released from rest (at time $t = 0$), subsequent displacements of particles of the string must satisfy PDE (2), where τ is the tension in the string and ρ is its linear density. What are the boundary and initial conditions for $y(x, t)$?

Figure 1.3

Solution: Since the ends of the string are fixed on the x-axis, boundary conditions are

$$y(0, t) = 0, \qquad t > 0$$

at $x = 0$ and
$$y(L, t) = 0, \qquad t > 0$$

at $x = L$.

[†] A region of the xy-plane is said to be open if about every point in the region there can be drawn a circle such that its interior contains only points of the region. A region in space is open if about every point in the region there can be drawn a sphere such that its interior contains only points of the region.

Because the string has the position shown in Figure 1.3 at time $t = 0$, $y(x, t)$ must satisfy the initial condition

$$y(x, 0) = \begin{cases} x/50 & 0 < x < L/2 \\ (L - x)/50 & L/2 < x < L \end{cases}.$$

In addition, the fact that the string is released from rest indicates that its velocity at time $t = 0$ is equal to zero. Since velocity is the time rate of change of displacement, the second initial condition is

$$\frac{\partial y(x, 0)}{\partial t} = 0, \qquad 0 < x < L.$$

There would be no conflict in replacing each of the open intervals in these four conditions with closed intervals.   ∎

In problem (5), boundary conditions (5b, c) specify the temperature of the rod at its ends, $x = 0$ and $x = L$. Likewise, in Example 1, the boundary conditions specify the displacement of the string at its ends. These are examples of what are called *Dirichlet* boundary conditions. A Dirichlet boundary condition specifies the value of the unknown function on a physical boundary. As another example, consider the two-dimensional version of Poisson's equation (3),

$$\frac{\partial^2 V}{\partial x^2} + \frac{\partial^2 V}{\partial y^2} = F(x, y), \qquad (x, y) \text{ in } R, \tag{6a}$$

for the region R in Figure 1.4. [$F(x, y)$ is a given function.] In compliance with our previous remarks, R is the open region consisting of all points interior to the bounding curve $\beta(R)$ but not including $\beta(R)$ itself. A Dirichlet boundary condition specifies the value for $V(x, y)$ on $\beta(R)$:

$$V(x, y) = G(x, y), \qquad (x, y) \text{ on } \beta(R), \tag{6b}$$

$G(x, y)$ some given function. Poisson's equation (6a) together with boundary condition (6b) is called a *boundary value problem*.

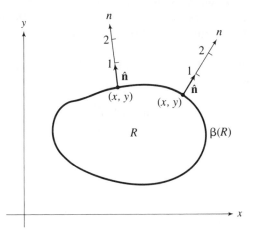

Figure 1.4

Two other types of boundary conditions arise frequently in applications—Neumann and Robin. A *Neumann* boundary condition for equation (6a) specifies the rate of change of $V(x, y)$ at points on $\beta(R)$ in a direction outwardly normal (perpendicular) to $\beta(R)$. We express this in the form

$$\frac{\partial V}{\partial n} = G(x, y), \qquad (x, y) \text{ on } \beta(R), \tag{7a}$$

where n is understood to be a measure of distance at (x, y) in a direction perpendicular to $\beta(R)$ (Figure 1.4). Because $\partial V/\partial n$ is in reality the directional derivative of V along the outward normal to $\beta(R)$, (7a) may be expressed in the equivalent form

$$\nabla V \cdot \hat{\mathbf{n}} = G(x, y), \qquad (x, y) \text{ on } \beta(R), \tag{7b}$$

where ∇V is the gradient of V at (x, y) and $\hat{\mathbf{n}}^\dagger$ is the unit outward normal vector to $\beta(R)$ at (x, y).

A *Robin* boundary condition is a linear combination of a Dirichlet and a Neumann condition. For equation (6a), it takes the form

$$l\frac{\partial V}{\partial n} + hV = G(x, y), \qquad (x, y) \text{ on } \beta(R), \tag{8a}$$

where l and h are nonzero constants. What is important is not the individual values of l and h but their ratio, l/h or h/l; division of (8a) by l or h leads to boundary conditions

$$\frac{\partial V}{\partial n} + \left(\frac{h}{l}\right)V = \frac{G(x, y)}{l}, \qquad (x, y) \text{ on } \beta(R) \tag{8b}$$

and

$$\left(\frac{l}{h}\right)\frac{\partial V}{\partial n} + V = \frac{G(x, y)}{h}, \qquad (x, y) \text{ on } \beta(R), \tag{8c}$$

both of which are equivalent to (8a). The advantage of (8a), however, is that solutions of problems with Dirichlet and Neumann boundary conditions are easily obtained from those with Robin conditions by specifying $l = 0$, $h = 1$ and $h = 0$, $l = 1$, respectively. Boundary conditions (6b), (7), and (8) are said to be *homogeneous* if $G(x, y) \equiv 0$; otherwise, they are said to be *nonhomogeneous*. Physical interpretations of Neumann and Robin boundary conditions are discussed in Sections 1.2–1.7.

Example 2:   What form do Robin boundary conditions take for the heat conduction problem described by equations (5a–d)?

Solution: At the end $x = L$ of the rod, the outward normal is in the positive x-direction. Consequently, at $x = L$, $\partial U/\partial n = \partial U/\partial x$, and the general Robin boundary condition there is

$$l_2 \frac{\partial U(L, t)}{\partial x} + h_2 U(L, t) = G_2(t), \qquad t > 0.$$

---

† A "ˆ" over a vector indicates that the vector is of unit length.

Because the outward normal at $x = 0$ is in the negative x-direction, it follows that $\partial U(0,t)/\partial n = -\partial U(0,t)/\partial x$, and a Robin boundary condition there takes the form

$$-l_1 \frac{\partial U(0,t)}{\partial x} + h_1 U(0,t) = G_1(t), \qquad t > 0. \qquad \blacksquare$$

In order that an (initial) boundary value problem adequately represent a physical situation, its solution should have certain properties. First, there should be a solution to the (initial) boundary value problem. Second, this solution should be unique; that is, the problem should not have more than one solution. For example, if problem (5) had more than one solution, how could it possibly be an accurate description of the temperature in the rod? Solutions should also have one further property, which we explain through problem (6). The solution of this problem depends on the functions $F(x, y)$ and $G(x, y)$. In practice, these quantities may not be known exactly; they may, for instance, be obtained from physical measurements. It would be reasonable to expect that small changes in either $F(x, y)$ or $G(x, y)$ should not appreciably affect $V(x, y)$. These three conditions lead to what is called a "well-posed" problem. An (initial) boundary value problem is said to be *well posed* if

(1) it has a solution;

(2) the solution is unique;

(3) the solution depends continuously on source terms and initial and boundary data (i.e., small changes in source terms and initial and boundary data produce small changes in the solution).

All stable physical situations should be modeled by well-posed problems.

In this book we discuss only existence and uniqueness of solutions; continuous dependence of solutions on source terms and subsidiary data is beyond our scope. Existence of solutions can be approached in two ways. One might be interested in knowing whether a particular initial boundary value problem has a solution but might not be at all interested in what the solution is. This is "existence" in its purest sense. Our approach is more pragmatic. We discuss different ways to solve (initial) boundary value problems, and if one of these methods succeeds in giving a solution to a problem, then clearly "existence" of a solution has been established. It is important to know that a problem has only one solution, however, since then, and only then, may we conclude that once *a* solution has been found, it must be *the* solution to the problem. Uniqueness is discussed in Sections 5.6–5.8.

In Sections 1.2–1.6 we derive partial differential equations that arise in physics and engineering. Each section is self-contained and may therefore be read independently of the others. This means that readers interested in heat conduction could study Section 1.2 and omit Section 1.3–1.6 without fear of missing any general ideas concerning PDEs. Likewise, readers interested in mechanical vibrations could omit Section 1.2 and 1.6 and concentrate on Sections 1.3–1.5.

Arising in many of these applications is the "Laplacian" of a function. The Laplacian of a function $V(x, y)$ of Cartesian coordinates x and y is defined as

$$\nabla^2 V = \frac{\partial^2 V}{\partial x^2} + \frac{\partial^2 V}{\partial y^2} \qquad \text{(9a)}$$

and, if $V(x, y, z)$ is a function of three variables, as

$$\nabla^2 V = \frac{\partial^2 V}{\partial x^2} + \frac{\partial^2 V}{\partial y^2} + \frac{\partial^2 V}{\partial z^2}. \tag{9b}$$

When a function is expressed in polar, cylindrical, or spherical coordinates, its Laplacian is more complicated to calculate. We list the formulas here, leaving verification to Exercises 9 and 10. In polar coordinates (r, θ) (Figure 1.5),

$$\nabla^2 V = \frac{\partial^2 V}{\partial r^2} + \frac{1}{r}\frac{\partial V}{\partial r} + \frac{1}{r^2}\frac{\partial^2 V}{\partial \theta^2}; \tag{10a}$$

in cylindrical coordinates (r, θ, z),

$$\nabla^2 V = \frac{\partial^2 V}{\partial r^2} + \frac{1}{r}\frac{\partial V}{\partial r} + \frac{1}{r^2}\frac{\partial^2 V}{\partial \theta^2} + \frac{\partial^2 V}{\partial z^2}; \tag{10b}$$

and in spherical coordinates (r, θ, ϕ) (Figure 1.6),

$$\nabla^2 V = \frac{\partial^2 V}{\partial r^2} + \frac{2}{r}\frac{\partial V}{\partial r} + \frac{1}{r^2 \sin \phi}\frac{\partial}{\partial \phi}\left(\sin \phi \frac{\partial V}{\partial \phi}\right) + \frac{1}{r^2 \sin^2 \phi}\frac{\partial^2 V}{\partial \theta^2}. \tag{10c}$$

The PDE obtained by setting the Laplacian of a function equal to zero,

$$\nabla^2 V = 0, \tag{11}$$

is called *Laplace's equation*.

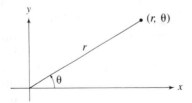

Figure 1.5

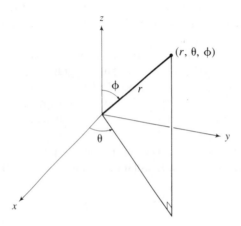

Figure 1.6

Exercises 1.1

On the regions in Exercises 1–7 what form do Dirichlet, Neumann, and Robin boundary conditions take for the PDE?

1. $\dfrac{\partial^2 V}{\partial x^2} + \dfrac{\partial^2 V}{\partial y^2} = F(x, y), \quad 0 < x < L, \quad 0 < y < L'$

2. $\dfrac{\partial^2 V}{\partial x^2} + \dfrac{\partial^2 V}{\partial y^2} + \dfrac{\partial^2 V}{\partial z^2} + V = F(x, y, z), \quad 0 < x < L, \quad y > 0, \quad z > 0$

3. $\dfrac{\partial^2 V}{\partial r^2} + \dfrac{1}{r}\dfrac{\partial V}{\partial r} + \dfrac{1}{r^2}\dfrac{\partial^2 V}{\partial \theta^2} = F(r, \theta), \quad 0 < r < r_0, \quad -\pi < \theta \le \pi, \quad (r, \theta) \text{ polar coordinates}$

4. $\dfrac{\partial^2 V}{\partial r^2} + \dfrac{1}{r}\dfrac{\partial V}{\partial r} + \dfrac{1}{r^2}\dfrac{\partial^2 V}{\partial \theta^2} = F(r, \theta), \quad 0 < r < r_0, \quad 0 < \theta < \pi$

5. $\dfrac{\partial^2 V}{\partial r^2} + \dfrac{1}{r}\dfrac{\partial V}{\partial r} + \dfrac{1}{r^2}\dfrac{\partial^2 V}{\partial \theta^2} + \dfrac{\partial^2 V}{\partial z^2} = F(r, \theta, z), \quad 0 < r < r_0, \quad -\pi < \theta \le \pi, \quad z > 0, \quad (r, \theta, z)$

   cylindrical coordinates

6. $\dfrac{\partial^2 V}{\partial r^2} + \dfrac{2}{r}\dfrac{\partial V}{\partial r} + \dfrac{1}{r^2 \sin \phi}\dfrac{\partial}{\partial \phi}\left(\sin \phi \dfrac{\partial V}{\partial \phi}\right) + \dfrac{1}{r^2 \sin^2 \phi}\dfrac{\partial^2 V}{\partial \theta^2} = F(r, \theta, \phi), \quad 0 < r < r_0,$

   $-\pi < \theta \le \pi, \quad 0 < \phi < \pi, \quad (r, \theta, \phi) \text{ spherical coordinates}$

7. Use the same PDE as in Exercise 6, but on the region

   $$0 < r < r_0, \quad -\pi < \theta \le \pi, \quad 0 < \phi < \frac{\pi}{2}.$$

8. When a boundary value problem (but *not* an initial boundary value problem) has a Neumann boundary condition on all parts of its boundary, it must satisfy a consistency condition. In this exercise, we derive this condition for two- and three-dimensional problems.

   (a) Consider the two-dimensional boundary value problem consisting of Poisson's equation (6a) and Neumann boundary condition (7a). Use Green's theorem in the plane to show that

   $$\oint_{\beta(R)} G(x, y)\, ds = \iint_R F(x, y)\, dA. \tag{12a}$$

   (Green's theorem is stated in Appendix C.) The left side of this equation is the line integral of $G(x, y)$ around the bounding curve $\beta(R)$, and the right side is the double integral of $F(x, y)$ over R. Thus, the "source term" $F(x, y)$ in (6a) and the boundary data $G(x, y)$ in (7a) cannot be specified independently; they must satisfy consistency condition (12a). Physical interpretations of this condition will be given later (see, for example, Exercise 23 in Section 1.2).

   (b) Show that the analog of (12a) for the three-dimensional boundary value problem

   $$\frac{\partial^2 V}{\partial x^2} + \frac{\partial^2 V}{\partial y^2} + \frac{\partial^2 V}{\partial z^2} = F(x, y, z), \qquad (x, y, z) \text{ in } V,$$

   $$\frac{\partial V}{\partial n} = G(x, y, z), \qquad (x, y, z) \text{ on } \beta(V)$$

   is

   $$\iint_{\beta(V)} G(x, y, z)\, dS = \iiint_V F(x, y, z)\, dV. \tag{12b}$$

   (You will need the divergence theorem from Appendix C.)

9. In this exercise we verify expression (10a) for the Laplacian in polar coordinates. Formula (10b) is then obvious.

   (a) Verify that when a function $V(x, y)$ is expressed in polar coordinates r and θ, its Cartesian derivatives $\partial V/\partial x$ and $\partial V/\partial y$ may be calculated according to

   $$\frac{\partial V}{\partial x} = \frac{\partial V}{\partial r}\frac{\partial r}{\partial x} + \frac{\partial V}{\partial \theta}\frac{\partial \theta}{\partial x}, \qquad \frac{\partial V}{\partial y} = \frac{\partial V}{\partial r}\frac{\partial r}{\partial y} + \frac{\partial V}{\partial \theta}\frac{\partial \theta}{\partial y}.$$

   (b) Obtain formulas for $\partial r/\partial x$, $\partial r/\partial y$, $\partial \theta/\partial x$, and $\partial \theta/\partial y$ from the relations $x = r\cos\theta$ and $y = r\sin\theta$ between polar and Cartesian coordinates, and use them to show that

   $$\frac{\partial V}{\partial x} = \cos\theta\frac{\partial V}{\partial r} - \frac{\sin\theta}{r}\frac{\partial V}{\partial \theta}, \qquad \frac{\partial V}{\partial y} = \sin\theta\frac{\partial V}{\partial r} + \frac{\cos\theta}{r}\frac{\partial V}{\partial \theta}.$$

   (c) Use the results in (b) to calculate the following expressions for second partial derivatives of V with respect to x and y:

   $$\frac{\partial^2 V}{\partial x^2} = \cos^2\theta\frac{\partial^2 V}{\partial r^2} + \frac{\sin^2\theta}{r}\frac{\partial V}{\partial r} + \frac{\sin^2\theta}{r^2}\frac{\partial^2 V}{\partial\theta^2}$$

   $$+ \frac{2\sin\theta\cos\theta}{r^2}\frac{\partial V}{\partial\theta} - \frac{2\sin\cos\theta}{r}\frac{\partial^2 V}{\partial r\,\partial\theta},$$

   $$\frac{\partial^2 V}{\partial y^2} = \sin^2\theta\frac{\partial^2 V}{\partial r^2} + \frac{\cos^2\theta}{r}\frac{\partial V}{\partial r} + \frac{\cos^2\theta}{r^2}\frac{\partial^2 V}{\partial\theta^2}$$

   $$- \frac{2\sin\theta\cos\theta}{r^2}\frac{\partial V}{\partial\theta} + \frac{2\sin\theta\cos\theta}{r}\frac{\partial^2 V}{\partial r\,\partial\theta}.$$

   (d) Finally, add the results in (c) to obtain (10a).

10. Use the technique of Exercise 9 to obtain (10c).

1.2 Heat Conduction

In this section we develop the mathematics necessary to describe conductive heat flow in various physical media—rods, plates, and three-dimensional bodies. We could begin with one-dimensional flow, such as that in the rod of Figure 1.1, and generalize later to plates and volumes. Alternatively, we could begin with three-dimensional heat flow and specialize later to plates and rods. We find the latter approach more satisfactory; it does not require special physical apparatus to ensure heat flow in only one or two directions. Furthermore, the mathematical and physical quantities that describe heat flow have units that are more natural in a three-dimensional setting.

When we consider temperature at various points in some body (say the human body), seldom is it constant; temperature normally varies from point to point and changes with time. Experience has shown that when temperature does vary, heat flows by conduction. Heat can flow by other means as well, namely by convection and by radiation. Heat received by the earth from the sun is due to *radiation*. We do not consider heat transfer by radiation in this book. The engine of a car illustrates the difference between convective and conductive heat flow. In order to keep the engine

cool, water carries heat from the engine to the radiator through hoses; it is the
of the water that transfers heat from engine to radiator. This is called *convec*
transfer. Heat will also pass through the walls of the engine to be dissipated into   ... .
The process by which heat is moved from molecule to molecule in the engine wall is
called heat transfer by *conduction*; it is due to vibrations of molecules, the vibrations
increasing with higher and higher temperatures. In this book we discuss only heat
transfer by conduction. To describe conductive heat flow in a medium, and ultimately
obtain a PDE that determines temperature in the medium, we introduce the heat flux
vector:

> **The heat flux vector q(r, t) is a vector function of position r and time t. Its direction corresponds
> to the direction of heat flow at position r and time t, and its magnitude is equal to the amount of
> heat per unit time crossing unit area normal to the direction of q.**

This vector, which has units of watts per square meter (W/m^2), is defined at every
point in a conducting medium except possibly at sources or sinks of heat (Figure 1.7).

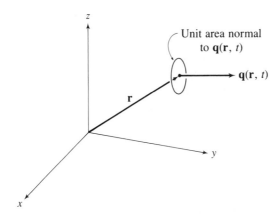

Figure 1.7

A medium is said to be *isotropic* if, when any point within it is heated, heat spreads
out equally in all directions. In other words, isotropic media have no preferred
directions for heat flow. It has been shown experimentally that in an isotropic medium,
heat flows in the direction in which temperature decreases most rapidly, and the
amount of heat flowing in that direction is proportional to the rate of change of
temperature in that direction. This is called *Fourier's law of heat conduction*. Mathematically, if $U(\mathbf{r}, t)$ is the temperature distribution in the medium, then its gradient,
∇U, points in the direction in which the function U increases most rapidly and $|\nabla U|$
is the maximum rate of increase. Consequently, Fourier's law of heat conduction in
an isotropic medium can be stated vectorially as

$$\mathbf{q}(\mathbf{r}, t) = -\kappa \nabla U; \tag{13}$$

where $\kappa > 0$ is the "constant" of proportionality called the *thermal conductivity* of the
medium. It has units of watts per meter per degree Kelvin or Celsius (W/mK). In general, thermal conductivity may depend both on the temperature of and the position in
the medium. If, however, the range of temperature is "limited" (and we shall consider
only this case), the variation of κ with temperature is negligible and κ becomes a

Table 1.1

Thermal Properties of Some Materials

Material	Density (kg/m^3)	Specific Heat (Ws/kgK)	Thermal Conductivity (W/mK) at 273 K	Thermal Diffusivity (m^2/s)
Copper	8950	381	390	114×10^{-6}
Mild steel	7884	460	45	12.4×10^{-6}
Pyrex glass	2413	837	1.18	0.584×10^{-6}
Water	1000	1000	0.600	0.600×10^{-6}
Asbestos	579	1047	0.15	0.247×10^{-6}

function of position only, $\kappa = \kappa(\mathbf{r})$. The medium is said to be *homogeneous* if κ is independent of position, in which case κ becomes a numerical constant. Rough values for thermal conductivities of various homogeneous materials are given in Table 1.1. The larger the value of κ, the more readily the material conducts heat. Other thermal properties are also included.

To obtain a PDE governing temperature in a medium, we consider an imaginary surface S bounding a portion of the medium of volume V (Figure 1.8). Heat is added to (or removed from) V in two ways—across S and by internal heat sources or sinks. When $g(\mathbf{r}, t)$ is the amount of heat generated (or removed) per unit time per unit volume at position $\mathbf{r}$ and time t, the total heat generation per unit time within V is expressed by the triple integral

$$\iiint_V g(\mathbf{r}, t)\, dV. \tag{14}$$

The amount of heat flowing into V through S per unit time is given by the surface integral on the left side of the equation

$$\iint_S \mathbf{q} \cdot (-\hat{\mathbf{n}})\, dS = \iint_S \kappa \nabla U \cdot \hat{\mathbf{n}}\, dS, \tag{15}$$

where $\hat{\mathbf{n}}$ is the unit outward-pointing normal to S. Equation (13) has been used to obtain the integral on the right. The total heat represented by (14) and (15) changes the temperature of points (x, y, z) in V by an amount $\partial U/\partial t$ in unit time. The heat requirement for this change is

$$\iiint_V \frac{\partial U}{\partial t} s\rho\, dV, \tag{16}$$

where ρ and s are the density and specific heat of the medium. (Specific heat is the amount of heat required to produce unit temperature change in unit mass.) Energy balance requires that (16) be equal to (14) plus (15):

$$\iiint_V \frac{\partial U}{\partial t} s\rho\, dV = \iiint_V g(\mathbf{r}, t)\, dV + \iint_S \kappa \nabla U \cdot \hat{\mathbf{n}}\, dS, \tag{17}$$

and when the divergence theorem (see Appendix C) is applied to the surface integral, the result is

$$\iiint_V \left(\rho s \frac{\partial U}{\partial t} - g(\mathbf{r}, t) - \nabla \cdot (\kappa \nabla U) \right) dV = 0. \tag{18}$$

For this integral to vanish for an arbitrary volume V, in particular for an arbitrarily small volume, the integrand must vanish at each point of V; that is, U must satisfy the PDE

$$\rho s \frac{\partial U}{\partial t} - g(\mathbf{r}, t) - \nabla \cdot (\kappa \nabla U) = 0. \tag{19}$$

In actual fact, this conclusion is correct only when we know that the integrand in (18) is a continuous function throughout V. When this is not the case, (19) may not be valid at every point of V. It will, however, be true in each subregion of V in which the integrand is continuous. Since (18) must be valid even when its integrand is discontinuous, it is a more general statement of energy balance than (19).

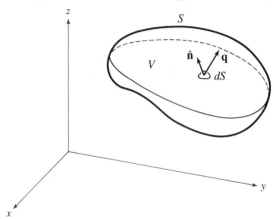

Figure 1.8

Equation (19) is the PDE for heat conduction in an isotropic medium. If the medium is also homogeneous, we define $k = \kappa/(s\rho)$ as the *thermal diffusivity* of the medium, in which case (19) reduces to

$$\boxed{\frac{\partial U}{\partial t} = k \left(\nabla^2 U + \frac{g(\mathbf{r}, t)}{\kappa} \right).} \tag{20}$$

The units of k are meters squared per second (m^2/s); typical values are given in Table 1.1.

Accompanying the PDE of heat conduction in any given problem will be initial and/or boundary conditions. An initial condition describes the temperature throughout the extent of the medium, R, at some initial time (usually $t = 0$):

$$U(\mathbf{r}, 0) = f(\mathbf{r}), \qquad \mathbf{r} \text{ in } R, \tag{21}$$

$f(\mathbf{r})$ some given function of position.

The three types of boundary conditions that we consider are those introduced in Section 1.1—Dirichlet, Neumann, and Robin. A Dirichlet condition prescribes temperature on the boundary $\beta(R)$ of R:

$$U = F(\mathbf{r}, t), \qquad \mathbf{r} \text{ on } \beta(R), \qquad t > 0, \tag{22}$$

$F(\mathbf{r}, t)$ a given function.

Sometimes in applications we know that a certain amount of heat is being conducted across $\beta(R)$; that is, we know that the heat flux vector $\mathbf{q}$ on $\beta(R)$ is normal to $\beta(R)$, and its magnitude is specified (Figure 1.9). Suppose in this situation that we represent $\mathbf{q}$ on $\beta(R)$ by $\mathbf{q} = q(\mathbf{r}, t)\hat{\mathbf{n}}$, where $q(\mathbf{r}, t)$ is the component of $\mathbf{q}$ in direction $\hat{\mathbf{n}}$ (q is negative when heat is added to R and positive when heat is extracted). Fourier's law (13) on $\beta(R)$ yields

$$q\hat{\mathbf{n}} = -\kappa \nabla U, \qquad \mathbf{r} \text{ on } \beta(R), \qquad t > 0, \tag{23}$$

and scalar products with $\hat{\mathbf{n}}$ give

$$\frac{\partial U}{\partial n} = -\frac{q(\mathbf{r}, t)}{\kappa}, \qquad \mathbf{r} \text{ on } \beta(R), \qquad t > 0. \tag{24}$$

In other words, specification of heat flow across $\beta(R)$ leads to a Neumann boundary condition. In particular, if a bounding surface is insulated, the heat flux vector thereon vanishes and consequently that surface satisfies a homogeneous Neumann boundary condition

$$\frac{\partial U}{\partial n} = 0, \qquad \mathbf{r} \text{ on } \beta(R), \qquad t > 0. \tag{25}$$

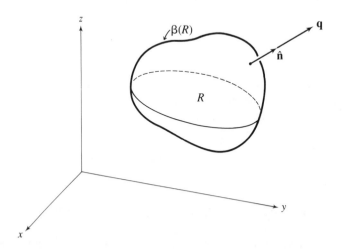

Figure 1.9

A Robin boundary condition is a linear combination of a Dirichlet and a Neumann condition:

$$l\frac{\partial U}{\partial n} + hU = F(\mathbf{r}, t), \qquad \mathbf{r} \text{ on } \beta(R), \qquad t > 0. \tag{26}$$

Dirichlet and Neumann boundary conditions are obtained by setting l and h, respectively, equal to zero. To show that Robin boundary conditions are physically realistic, suppose the conducting material transfers heat to or from a surrounding medium according to Newton's law of cooling (heat transfer proportional to temperature difference). Then

$$-\kappa \frac{\partial U}{\partial n} = \mu(U - U_m), \qquad \mu > 0, \qquad \mathbf{r} \text{ on } \beta(R), \qquad t > 0, \tag{27a}$$

where U_m is the temperature of the surrounding medium, or

$$\kappa \frac{\partial U}{\partial n} + \mu U = \mu U_m = F(\mathbf{r}, t), \qquad \mathbf{r} \text{ on } \beta(R), \qquad t > 0. \tag{27b}$$

The constant of proportionality μ is called the *surface heat transfer coefficient*. This is clearly a Robin condition. Homogeneous Robin conditions

$$\kappa \frac{\partial U}{\partial n} + \mu U = 0, \qquad \mathbf{r} \text{ on } \beta(R), \qquad t > 0 \tag{28}$$

describe heat transfer according to Newton's law of cooling to media at temperature zero.

The initial boundary value problem of heat conduction in a homogeneous, isotropic medium can thus be stated as

$$\frac{\partial U}{\partial t} = k\left[\nabla^2 U + \frac{g(\mathbf{r}, t)}{\kappa}\right], \qquad \mathbf{r} \text{ in } R, \qquad t > 0, \tag{29a}$$

$$\text{Boundary conditions, if applicable,} \tag{29b}$$

$$\text{Initial condition } U(\mathbf{r}, 0) = f(\mathbf{r}), \ \mathbf{r} \text{ in } R, \text{ if applicable.} \tag{29c}$$

If boundary conditions (29b) and heat sources $g(\mathbf{r}, t)$ in (29a) are independent of time, there may exist solutions of (29a, b) that are also independent of time. Such solutions are called *steady-state* solutions; they satisfy

$$\nabla^2 U = -\frac{g(\mathbf{r})}{\kappa}, \qquad \mathbf{r} \text{ in } R, \tag{30a}$$

$$\text{Boundary conditions, if applicable.} \tag{30b}$$

For example, suppose a conducting sphere of radius a (Figure 1.10) has at time $t = 0$ some temperature distribution $f(r, \theta, \phi)$, where r, θ, and ϕ are the spherical coordinates shown in Figure 1.6. If the sphere is suddenly packed on the outside with perfect insulation, and no heat generation occurs within the sphere, the temperature distribution $U(r, \theta, \phi, t)$ thereafter must satisfy the initial boundary value problem

$$\frac{\partial U}{\partial t} = k\nabla^2 U, \qquad 0 < r < a, \qquad 0 < \phi < \pi, \quad -\pi < \theta \le \pi, \quad t > 0, \tag{31a}$$

$$\frac{\partial U(a, \theta, \phi, t)}{\partial r} = 0, \qquad 0 \le \phi \le \pi, \quad -\pi < \theta \le \pi, \qquad t > 0, \tag{31b}$$

$$U(r, \theta, \phi, 0) = f(r, \theta, \phi), \quad 0 \le r < a, \qquad 0 \le \phi \le \pi, \quad -\pi < \theta \le \pi. \tag{31c}$$

Steady-state solutions $U(r, \theta, \phi)$ for this problem, if there are any, must satisfy

$$\nabla^2 U = 0, \qquad 0 < r < a, \qquad 0 < \phi < \pi, \qquad -\pi < \theta \leq \pi, \qquad \text{(32a)}$$

$$\frac{\partial U(a, \theta, \phi)}{\partial r} = 0, \qquad 0 \leq \phi \leq \pi, \qquad \pi < \theta \leq \pi. \qquad \text{(32b)}$$

Obviously, a solution of (32) is $U = C$, C any constant whatsoever. Thus, constant functions are steady-state solutions for problem (31). We can realize the physical significance of steady-state solutions and determine a useful value for C if we return to initial boundary value problem (31). Physically it is clear that because no heat can enter or leave the sphere, heat will eventually redistribute itself until the temperature at every point in the sphere becomes the same constant value. [In Section 9.1 we prove that the value of this constant is the average value $\bar{U}$ of $f(r, \theta, \phi)$ over the sphere.] In other words, the useful steady-state solution will be $U = \bar{U}$. Later we shall see that the solution of (31) contains two parts. One is the steady-state (time-independent) part $U = \bar{U}$; the other is a transient (time-dependent) part that describes the transition from initial temperature $f(r, \theta, \phi)$ to final temperature $\bar{U}$.

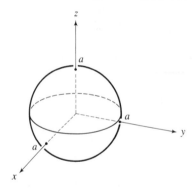

Figure 1.10

When $g(\mathbf{r})$ in Poisson's equation (30a) is identically zero (i.e., no internal heat generation occurs within R), the PDE reduces to Laplace's equation. Problem (30) then reads

$$\nabla^2 U = 0, \qquad \mathbf{r} \text{ in } R, \qquad \text{(33a)}$$

$$\text{Boundary conditions, if applicable.} \qquad \text{(33b)}$$

Problems (30) and (33) are called boundary value problems rather than initial boundary value problems, since no initial conditions are present.

Example 3:   Formulate the initial boundary value problem for the temperature in a cylindrical rod with insulated sides and with flat ends at $x = 0$ and $x = L$. The end at $x = 0$ is kept at temperature $60°C$; the end at $x = L$ is insulated; and at time $t = 0$ the temperature distribution throughout the rod is $f(x)$, $0 \leq x \leq L$. Assume no internal heat generation. Are there steady-state solutions for this problem?

Solution: Notwithstanding the fact that the rod is three-dimensional, we note that because all cross sections are identical, the sides are insulated, and the initial temperature distribution is a function of x alone, heat flows only in the x-direction. In other words, the heat conduction problem is one-dimensional, namely

$$\frac{\partial U}{\partial t} = k\frac{\partial^2 U}{\partial x^2}, \qquad 0 < x < L, \qquad t > 0,$$

$$U(0, t) = 60, \qquad t > 0,$$

$$\frac{\partial U(L, t)}{\partial x} = 0, \qquad t > 0,$$

$$U(x, 0) = f(x), \qquad 0 < x < L.$$

Steady-state solutions $\psi(x)$ for this problem must satisfy

$$\frac{d^2\psi}{dx^2} = 0, \qquad 0 < x < L,$$

$$\psi(0) = 60, \qquad \psi'(L) = 0.$$

The general solution of this ODE is $\psi(x) = Ax + B$, and the boundary conditions require that

$$60 = B, \qquad 0 = A;$$

that is, $\psi(x) = 60$. After a very long time, the temperature in the rod will become 60°C throughout. ∎

Exercises 1.2

1. (a) A cylindrical, homogeneous, isotropic rod has flat ends at $x = 0$ and $x = L$ and insulated sides. Initially the temperature distribution in the rod is a function of x only, and heat generation at points x in the rod takes place uniformly over the cross section at x. Apply an energy balance to a segment of the rod from a fixed point $x = a$ to an arbitrary value x to show that the PDE governing temperature $U(x, t)$ in the rod is

$$\frac{\partial U}{\partial t} = k\frac{\partial^2 U}{\partial x^2} + \frac{k}{\kappa}g(x, t),$$

where $g(x, t)$ is the amount of heat per unit volume per unit time generated at position x and time t.

   (b) What form do Robin boundary conditions take at $x = 0$ and $x = L$?

In Exercises 2–19, set up, but do not solve, an (initial) boundary value problem for the required temperature. Assume that the medium is isotropic and homogeneous.

2. A cylindrical rod has flat ends at $x = 0$ and $x = L$ and insulated sides. At time $t = 0$ its temperature is a function $f(x)$, $0 \leq x \leq L$, of x only. If both ends are kept at 100°C for $t > 0$, formulate the initial boundary value problem for temperature $U(x, t)$ in the rod for $0 < x < L$ and $t > 0$.

3. Repeat Exercise 2 except that the end at $x = 0$ is insulated.

4. Repeat Exercise 2 except that the temperature at end $x = L$ is changed from 0°C to 100°C at a constant rate over a period of T seconds and maintained at 100°C thereafter.

5. Repeat Exercise 2 except that heat is transferred according to Newton's law of cooling from the ends $x = 0$ and $x = L$ into media at temperatures U_0 and U_L, respectively.

6. Repeat Exercise 2 except that both ends are insulated and at each point in the rod heat is generated at a rate $g(x, t)$ per unit volume per unit time. What is $g(x, t)$ if heat generation is q calories per cubic centimeter per minute over that part of the rod between $x = L/4$ and $x = 3L/4$ and is zero otherwise?

7. Repeat Exercise 2 except that heat is added to the end $x = 0$ at a constant rate $Q_0 > 0$ W/m^2 uniformly over the end and is removed at a variable rate $Q_L(t) > 0$ W at $x = L$ uniformly over the end.

8. The top and bottom of a horizontal rectangular plate $0 \le x \le L, 0 \le y \le L'$ are insulated. At time $t = 0$ its temperature is a function $f(x, y)$ of x and y only. If the edges $x = 0$ and $y = L'$ are kept at 50°C for $t > 0$ and the edges $y = 0$ and $x = L$ are insulated, formulate the initial boundary value problem for temperature $U(x, y, t)$ in the plate for $0 < x < L, 0 < y < L'$, and $t > 0$.

9. Repeat Exercise 8 except that along $y = 0$ heat is transferred according to Newton's law of cooling into a medium with temperature $f_1(t)$, and heat is generated at a rate $e^{\alpha t}$ joules per cubic meter per second at every point in the plate for the first T seconds.

10. The top and bottom of a horizontal circular plate $0 \le r \le r_0, -\pi < \theta \le \pi$ are insulated. At time $t = 0$ its temperature is a function $f(r, \theta)$ of polar coordinates r and θ only. For $t > 0$, heat is transferred along its edge according to Newton's law of cooling into a medium at temperature zero, and heat is generated at constant rate q W/m^3 inside the ring $0 < r_1 < r < r_2 < r_0$. Formulate the initial boundary value problem for temperature in the plate.

11. A right circular cylinder of length L and radius r_0 has its axis along the z-axis with flat faces in the planes $z = 0$ and $z = L$. At time $t = 0$ its temperature is a function $f(r, \theta)$ of r and θ only. For $t > 0$, faces $z = 0$ and $z = L$ are insulated, and $r = r_0$ is kept at temperature $f_1(\theta, t)$. Formulate the initial boundary value problem for temperature in the cylinder.

12. Repeat Exercise 11 except that $f(r, \theta)$ is replaced by $f(r, \theta, z)$.

13. Repeat Exercise 11 except that the ends $z = 0$ and $z = L$ are kept at 100°C for $t > 0$ and the cylindrical side is insulated.

14. Repeat Exercise 11 except that heat is transferred according to Newton's law of cooling from the top and cylindrical faces into air at temperature 20°C. Initially, temperature is a function $f(r)$ of r only.

15. Repeat Exercise 11 except that the initial temperature is a function $f(r)$ of r only and $r = r_0$ is kept at temperature $f_1(t)$.

16. The top and bottom of a horizontal semicircular plate $0 \le r \le r_0, 0 \le \theta \le \pi$ are insulated. At time $t = 0$, its temperature is $f(r, \theta)$. For $t > 0$, the curved edge of the plate is insulated, but along the straight edge, heat is added at a constant rate $q > 0$ W/m^2. Formulate the initial boundary value problem for temperature in the plate.

17. Repeat Exercise 16 except that along $r = r_0$, heat is extracted at a constant rate $q > 0$ W/m^2 and along the straight edge, heat is exchanged according to Newton's law of cooling with an environment at constant temperature U_0.

18. A sphere of radius r_0 has an initial temperature ($t = 0$) of 100°C. If, for $t > 0$, it transfers heat according to Newton's law of cooling to an environment at constant temperature 10°C, what is the initial boundary value problem for temperature in the sphere?

19. A hemisphere of radius r_0 has its flat face in the xy-plane. The curved face of the sphere is insulated. If the heat flux vector on the face $z = 0$ is $\mathbf{q} = f(r, \theta)\hat{\mathbf{k}}$, formulate the boundary value

problem for steady-state temperature in the hemisphere. Can $f(r, \theta)$ be arbitrarily specified? [See Exercise 8(b) in Section 1.1.]

20. A homogeneous, isotropic rod with insulated sides has its ends $x = 0$ and $x = L$ held at temperatures U_0 and U_L, respectively. If no heat is generated in the rod, can there be a steady-state temperature distribution in the rod?

21. Heat is added (or removed) at the ends $x = 0$ and $x = L$ of a homogeneous, isotropic rod with insulated sides at constant rates q_0 and q_L, respectively. Can there be a steady-state temperature distribution in the rod?

22. Discuss each of the following statements for temperature in a homogeneous, isotropic rod with insulated sides:

    (a) If temperature at points in the rod changes in time, heat must flow in the rod.

    (b) If heat flows in the rod, temperature at points in the rod must change in time.

23. (a) Suppose there is a steady-state temperature distribution in a region R of the xy-plane that satisfies Poisson's equation $\nabla^2 U = -g(x, y)/\kappa$. Suppose further that the boundary condition on the boundary $\beta(R)$ of R is of Neumann type, $\partial U/\partial n = f(x, y)$ for (x, y) on $\beta(R)$. Use the result of Exercise 8 in Section 1.1 (or Green's theorem) to show that $f(x, y)$ and $g(x, y)$ must satisfy the consistency condition

$$\oint_{\beta(R)} f(x, y)\, ds = \iint_R -\frac{g(x, y)}{\kappa}\, dA.$$

What is the physical significance of this requirement?

    (b) What is the three-dimensional analog of the result in (a)?

24. In Exercise 1 we developed the one-dimensional heat conduction equation based on energy balance for a small segment of the rod. In this exercise we use the PDE to discuss energy balance for the entire rod. Multiply the PDE in Exercise 1 by $A\kappa/k$ (A is the cross-sectional area of the rod), integrate with respect to x over the length $0 \le x \le L$ of the rod, and integrate with respect to t from $t = 0$ to an arbitrary value of t, to obtain the following result:

$$\int_0^L A\rho s U(x, t)\, dx - \int_0^L A\rho s U(x, 0)\, dx$$
$$= \int_0^t A\kappa \frac{\partial U(L, t)}{\partial x}\, dt - \int_0^t A\kappa \frac{\partial U(0, t)}{\partial x}\, dt + \int_0^t \int_0^L A g(x, t)\, dx\, dt.$$

Interpret each term in this equation physically, and hence deduce that the equation is a statement of energy balance for the rod.

25. Repeat Exercise 24 to obtain an energy balance for a volume V using PDE (20).

26. (a) The inside temperature of a flat wall is a constant $U_{in}°$C and the outside temperature is a constant $U_{out}°$C. If the wall is considered as part of an infinite slab that is in a steady-state temperature situation, find an expression for the amount of heat lost through an area A of the wall per unit time. Is this expression inversely proportional to the thickness of the wall?

    (b) Evaluate the result in (a) if A is $15\ \text{m}^2$, the thickness of the wall is 10 cm, the thermal conductivity of the material in the wall is 0.11 W/mK, $U_{out} = -20°$C, and $U_{in} = 20°$C.

27. (a) Steam is passed through a pipe with inner radius r_{in} and outer radius r_{out}. The temperature of the inner wall is a constant $U_{in}°$C and that on the outer wall is a constant $U_{out}°$C. If the pipe is considered part of an infinitely long pipe that is in a steady-state temperature situation, find an expression for the amount of heat per unit area per unit time flowing radially outward.

(b) How much heat (per second) is lost at the outer surface of the pipe in a section 2 m long if $r_{in} = 3.75$ cm, $r_{out} = 5.0$ cm, $U_{in} = 205°C$, $U_{out} = 195°C$, and $\kappa = 54$ W/mK?

(c) Illustrate that the same amount of heat is transferred through the inner wall of the section. Must this be the case?

28. A homogeneous, isotropic rod with insulated sides has temperature $\sin(n\pi x/L)$, n a positive integer, at time $t = 0$. For time $t > 0$ its ends at $x = 0$ and $x = L$ are held at temperature $0°C$.

(a) Find the initial boundary value problem for temperature in the rod and verify that a solution is

$$U(x, t) = e^{-n^2\pi^2 kt/L^2} \sin\frac{n\pi x}{L}.$$

(b) Find the rate of heat flow across cross sections of the rod at $x = 0$, $x = L/2$, and $x = L$ by calculating

$$\lim_{x \to 0^+} q(x, t), \qquad q\left(\frac{L}{2}, t\right), \qquad \lim_{x \to L^-} q(x, t).$$

(c) Calculate limits of the heat flows in (b) as $t \to 0^+$ and $t \to \infty$.

29. (a) When two media with different thermal conductivities κ_1 and κ_2 are brought into intimate contact, heat flows from the hotter to the cooler medium. Assuming that heat transfer follows Newton's law of cooling, show that the following boundary conditions must be satisfied by the temperatures in the media at the interface:

$$-\kappa_1 \frac{\partial U(0-)}{\partial n} = \mu[U(0-) - U(0+)],$$

$$\kappa_2 \frac{\partial U(0+)}{\partial n} = \mu[U(0+) - U(0-)], \qquad -\kappa_1 \frac{\partial U(0-)}{\partial n} = -\kappa_2 \frac{\partial U(0+)}{\partial n},$$

where n is a coordinate perpendicular to the interface with positive direction from medium 1 into medium 2. Are these conditions independent?

(b) What do these conditions become in the event that μ is so high that there is essentially no resistance to heat flow across the interface?

30. (a) A homogeneous, isotropic sphere of radius R is heated uniformly from heat sources within at the rate of Q watts per cubic meter. Heat is transferred to a surrounding medium at constant temperature U_m according to Newton's law of cooling until a steady-state situation is achieved. Find the steady-state temperature distribution in the sphere.

(b) What is the initial boundary value problem for temperature in the sphere for $t > 0$ if the heat sources are turned off at time $t = 0$ and the steady-state situation has been achieved?

31. A thin wire of uniform cross section radiates heat from its sides (not ends) at a rate per unit area per unit time that is proportional to the difference between the temperature of the wire on its surface and that of its surroundings. It follows that variations in temperature should occur over cross sections of the wire. In many applications, these variations are sufficiently small that they may be considered negligible. In such a case, temperature at points in the wire is a function of time t and only one space variable along the wire, which we take as x, $U = U(x, t)$. Temperature problems of this type are called *thin-wire problems*. By considering heat flow into, and out of, the segment of the wire from a fixed point $x = a$ to an arbitrary x, show that the PDE for thin-wire problems is

$$\frac{\partial U}{\partial t} = k\frac{\partial^2 U}{\partial x^2} - h(U - U_m) + \frac{k}{\kappa}g(x, t),$$

where $h > 0$ is a constant and U_m is the temperature of the medium surrounding the wire.

32. Heat generation within a rod can be effected by passing an electric current along the length of the rod. Show that when the current is I,

$$g(x, t) = \frac{I^2}{A^2\sigma},$$

where σ is the electrical conductivity of the material of the rod and A is its cross-sectional area.

33. A cylindrical pipe of inner and outer radii a and b is sufficiently long that end effects may be neglected. The temperature of the inner wall is a constant U_a, and heat is transferred at the outer wall to a medium at constant temperature $U_m < U_a$ with surface heat transfer coefficient μ.

(a) Find U as a function of r when the steady-state situation has been achieved.

(b) Show that the amount of heat flowing radially through a unit length of the pipe at any radius $a < r < b$ is

$$\frac{2\pi\mu\kappa b(U_a - U_m)}{\kappa + \mu b\ln(b/a)}.$$

34. A long, straight wire of circular cross section has thermal conductivity κ and carries a current I. Surrounding the wire is insulation with thermal conductivity κ^*, $b - a$ units thick. If r is a radial coordinate measured from the center of the wire, the wire occupies the region $0 < r < a$, and the insulation, $a < r < b$. Heat transfer takes place at $r = b$ into a medium at constant temperature U_m with surface heat transfer coefficent μ^*. Find the steady-state temperature $U(r)$ in the wire and insulation under the assumption that $U(r)$ must be continuous at $r = a$. [*Hint:* See Exercise 32 for $g(r)$ and Exercise 29 for the additional boundary condition at the wire-insulation interface.

35. Repeat Exercise 34 except that continuity of $U(r)$ at $r = a$ is replaced by the condition that heat transfer from the wire to the insulation occurs according to Newton's law of cooling with surface heat transfer coefficient μ.

1.3 Transverse Vibrations of Strings; Longitudinal and Angular Vibrations of Bars

In this section we discuss three vibration problems that all give rise to the same mathematical representation.

Transverse Vibrations of Strings

A perfectly flexible string (such as, perhaps, a violin string) is stretched tightly between two fixed points $x = 0$ and $x = L$ on the x-axis (Figure 1.11). Suppose the string is somehow set into motion in the xy-plane (possibly by pulling vertically on the midpoint of the string and then releasing it). Our objective is to study the subsequent motion of the string. When the string is very taut and displacements are small, horizontal displacements of particles of the string are negligible compared with vertical displacements; that is, displacements may be taken as purely transverse, representable in the form $y(x, t)$.

Figure 1.11

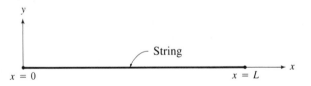

Figure 1.12

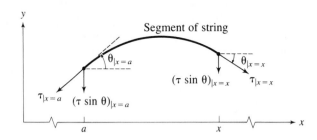

To find a PDE for $y(x, t)$, we analyze the forces on a segment of the string from a fixed position $x = a$ to an arbitrary position x (Figure 1.12). We denote by $\tau(x, t)$ the magnitude of the tension in the string at position x and time t. Because the string is perfectly flexible, tension in the string is always in the tangential direction of the string. This means that the y-component of the resulting force due to tension at the ends of the segment is $(\tau \sin \theta)_{|x=x} - (\tau \sin \theta)_{|x=a}$. We group all other forces acting on the segment into one function by letting $F(x, t)$ be the y-component of the sum of all external forces acting on the string per unit length in the x-direction. The total of all external forces acting on the segment then has y-component

$$\int_a^x F(\zeta, t) \, d\zeta.$$

Newton's second law states that the time rate of change of the momentum of the segment of the string must be equal to the resultant force thereon:

$$\frac{\partial}{\partial t} \left(\int_a^x \frac{\partial y(\zeta, t)}{\partial t} \rho(\zeta, t) \sqrt{1 + \left(\frac{\partial y(\zeta, t)}{\partial x} \right)^2} \, d\zeta \right)$$

$$= (\tau \sin \theta)_{|x=x} - (\tau \sin \theta)_{|x=a} + \int_a^x F(\zeta, t) \, d\zeta, \tag{34}$$

where $\rho(x, t)$ is the density of the string (mass per unit length). The quantity $\sqrt{1 + [\partial y(\zeta, t)/\partial x]^2} \, d\zeta$ is the length of string that projects onto a length $d\zeta$ along the x-axis. Multiplication by $\rho(\zeta, t)\partial y(\zeta, t)/\partial t$ gives the momentum of this infinitesimal length of string, and integration yields the momentum of that segment of the string from $x = a$ to an arbitrary position x. If we differentiate this equation with respect to x, we obtain

$$\frac{\partial}{\partial t}\left(\rho\frac{\partial y}{\partial t}\sqrt{1+\left(\frac{\partial y}{\partial x}\right)^2}\right) = \frac{\partial}{\partial x}(\tau\sin\theta) + F(x,t). \tag{35}$$

When vibrations of the string are such that the slope of the displaced string, $\partial y/\partial x$, is very much less than unity (and this is the only case that we consider), the radical may be dropped from the equation and $\sin\theta$ approximated by $\tan\theta = \partial y/\partial x$. The resulting PDE for $y(x,t)$ is

$$\frac{\partial}{\partial t}\left(\rho\frac{\partial y}{\partial t}\right) = \frac{\partial}{\partial x}\left(\tau\frac{\partial y}{\partial x}\right) + F(x,t). \tag{36}$$

For most applications, both the density of and the tension in the string may be taken as constant, in which case (36) reduces to

$$\boxed{\frac{\partial^2 y}{\partial t^2} = c^2\frac{\partial^2 y}{\partial x^2} + \frac{F}{\rho}, \qquad c^2 = \frac{\tau}{\rho}.} \tag{37}$$

This is the mathematical model for small transverse vibrations of a taut string; it is called the *one-dimensional wave equation*. In its derivation we have assumed that the slope of the string at every point is always very much less than 1 and that tension and density are constant.

When the only external force acting on the string is gravity, $F(x,t)$ takes the form

$$F = \rho g, \qquad g < 0. \tag{38}$$

Other possibilities include a damping force proportional to velocity,

$$F = -\beta\frac{\partial y}{\partial t}, \qquad \beta > 0; \tag{39}$$

and a restoring force proportional to displacement,

$$F = -ky, \qquad k > 0. \tag{40}$$

Accompanying the wave equation will be initial and/or boundary conditions. Initial conditions describe the displacement and velocity of the string at some initial time (usually $t = 0$):

$$y(x,0) = f(x), \qquad x \text{ in } I, \tag{41a}$$

$$\frac{\partial y(x,0)}{\partial t} = y_t(x,0)^\dagger = g(x), \qquad x \text{ in } I, \tag{41b}$$

where I is the interval over which the string is stretched. In Figure 1.11, I is $0 < x < L$, but other intervals are also possible. Interval I also dictates the number of boundary conditions. There are three possibilities, depending upon whether the string is of finite

---

† Subscripts are often used to denote partial derivatives. In (41b), y_t denotes $\partial y/\partial t$. In a similar way, we may use the notation y_{tt} in place of $\partial^2 y/\partial t^2$.

length, of "semi-infinite" length, or of "infinite" length. If the string is of finite length, the interval I is customarily taken as $0 < x < L$ and two boundary conditions result, one at each end. The string is said to be of semi-infinite length, or the problem is semi-infinite, if the string has only one end that satisfies some prescribed condition. The interval I in this case is always chosen as $0 < x < \infty$, and the one boundary condition is at $x = 0$. The string is said to be of infinite length, or the problem is infinite, if the string has no ends. In this case interval I becomes $-\infty < x < \infty$ and there are no boundary conditions.

It might be argued that there is no such thing as a semi-infinitely long or infinitely long string, and we must agree. There are, however, situations in which the model of a semi-infinite or infinite string is definitely advantageous. For example, suppose a fairly long string (with ends at $x = 0$ and $x = L$) is initially at rest along the x-axis. Suddenly, something disturbs the string at its midpoint, $x = L/2$ (perhaps it is struck by an object). The effect of this disturbance travels along the string in both directions toward $x = 0$ and $x = L$. Before the disturbance reaches $x = 0$ and $x = L$, the string reacts exactly as if it had no ends whatsoever. If we are interested only in these initial disturbances, and consideration of the "infinite" problem provides straightforward explanations, it is an advantage to analyze the "infinite" problem rather than the finite one.

We consider only three types of boundary conditions at an end of the string—Dirichlet, Neumann, and Robin. When the string has an end at $x = 0$, a Dirichlet boundary condition takes the form

$$y(0, t) = f_1(t), \qquad t > 0. \tag{42a}$$

It states that the end $x = 0$ of the string is caused by some external mechanism to perform the vertical motion described by $f_1(t)$. Similarly, if the string has an end at $x = L$, a Dirichlet condition

$$y(L, t) = f_2(t), \qquad t > 0 \tag{42b}$$

indicates that this end has a vertical displacement described by $f_2(t)$. For the string in Figure 1.11, $f_1(t) = f_2(t) = 0$.

Instead of prescribing the motion of the end $x = 0$ of the string, suppose that this end is attached to a mass m (Figure 1.13) and, furthermore, that motion of the mass is restricted to be vertical by a containing tube. The vertical component of the tension of the string acting on m at $x = 0$ is $\tau(0, t) \sin \theta$, which for small slopes can be approximated by

$$\tau(0, t) \sin \theta \approx \tau(0, t) \tan \theta = \tau(0, t) \frac{\partial y(0, t)}{\partial x}. \tag{43}$$

Consequently, when Newton's second law is applied to the motion of m,

$$m \frac{\partial^2 y(0, t)}{\partial t^2} = \tau(0, t) \frac{\partial y(0, t)}{\partial x} + f_1(t), \qquad t > 0, \tag{44}$$

where $f_1(t)$ represents the y-component of all other forces acting on m.

If m is sufficiently small that it may be taken as negligible (for instance, as with a very light loop around a vertical rod), this equation takes the form

$$\frac{\partial y(0,t)}{\partial x} = -\frac{1}{\tau(0,t)} f_1(t), \qquad t > 0, \tag{45}$$

a Neumann boundary condition. In particular, if the massless end of the string is free to slide vertically with no forces acting on it except tension in the string, it satisfies a homogeneous Neumann condition

$$\frac{\partial y(0,t)}{\partial x} = 0. \tag{46}$$

What this equation says is that when the end of a taut string is free of external forces, the slope of the string there will always be zero.

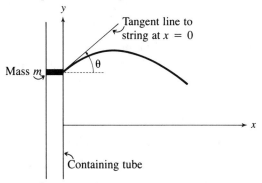

Figure 1.13

Similarly, if the string has a massless end at $x = L$ that is subjected to a vertical force with component $f_2(t)$, the boundary condition there is once again Neumann:

$$\frac{\partial y(L,t)}{\partial x} = \frac{1}{\tau(L,t)} f_2(t), \qquad t > 0. \tag{47}$$

What we have shown, then, is that Neumann boundary conditions result when the ends of the string, taken as massless, move vertically under the influence of forces that are specified as functions of time.

Robin boundary conditions, which are linear combinations of Dirichlet and Neumann conditions, arise when the ends of the string are attached to springs that are unstretched on the x-axis (Figure 1.14). When this is the case at $x = 0$, equation (44) becomes

$$m\frac{\partial^2 y(0,t)}{\partial t^2} = \tau(0,t)\frac{\partial y(0,t)}{\partial x} - ky(0,t) + f_1(t), \tag{48}$$

where $f_1(t)$ now represents all external forces acting on m other than the spring and tension in the string. For a massless end ($m = 0$) and constant tension τ, (48) takes the form

$$-\tau\frac{\partial y}{\partial x} + ky = f_1(t), \qquad x = 0, \qquad t > 0. \tag{49a}$$

Similarly, attaching the end $x = L$ to a spring gives the Robin condition

$$\tau\frac{\partial y}{\partial x} + ky = f_2(t), \qquad x = L, \qquad t > 0. \tag{49b}$$

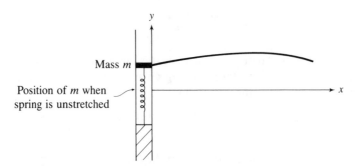

Figure 1.14

The initial boundary value problem for the vibrating string consists of the one-dimensional wave equation together with two initial conditions and/or zero, one, or two boundary conditions:

$$\frac{\partial^2 y}{\partial t^2} = c^2 \frac{\partial^2 y}{\partial x^2} + \frac{F(x,t)}{\rho}, \qquad x \text{ in } I, \qquad t > 0, \tag{50a}$$

Boundary conditions, if applicable, (50b)

$$y(x,0) = f(x), \qquad x \text{ in } I, \text{ if applicable}, \tag{50c}$$

$$y_t(x,0) = g(x), \qquad x \text{ in } I, \text{ if applicable}. \tag{50d}$$

When the boundary conditions and external force F are independent of time, there may exist solutions of (50a, b) that are also independent of time. Such solutions, called *static deflections*, satisfy the boundary value problem

$$\frac{d^2 y}{dx^2} = -\frac{F(x)}{\tau}, \qquad x \text{ in } I, \tag{51a}$$

Boundary conditions. (51b)

No vibrations occur; the string remains in static equilibrium under the forces present. We shall see that the solution of (50) divides into two parts: the static deflection part plus a second part that represents vibrations about the static solution.

Example 4:   Formulate the initial boundary value problem for transverse vibrations of a string stretched tightly along the x-axis between $x = 0$ and $x = L$. The end $x = 0$ is free to move without friction along a vertical support, and the end $x = L$ is fixed on the x-axis. Initially, the string is released from rest at a position described by the function $f(x)$, $0 \leq x \leq L$. Take gravity into account. Are there static deflections for this problem?

Solution: The initial boundary value problem for displacements $y(x,t)$ of points in the string is

$$\frac{\partial^2 y}{\partial t^2} = c^2 \frac{\partial^2 y}{\partial x^2} - 9.81, \qquad 0 < x < L, \qquad t > 0,$$

$$\frac{\partial y(0,t)}{\partial x} = 0, \qquad t > 0,$$

$$y(L,t) = 0, \qquad t > 0,$$

$$y(x,0) = f(x), \qquad 0 < x < L,$$

$$\frac{\partial y(x,0)}{\partial t} = 0, \qquad 0 < x < L.$$

The PDE is a result of equations (37) and (38), and the boundary condition at $x = 0$ is equation (46). Static deflections must satisfy

$$0 = c^2 \frac{d^2 y}{dx^2} - 9.81, \qquad 0 < x < L,$$

$$y'(0) = 0, \qquad y(L) = 0,$$

the solution of which is

$$y(x) = \frac{9.81}{2c^2}(x^2 - L^2)$$

(Figure 1.15). This is the position that the string would occupy were it to hang motionless under gravity. Notice, in particular, that the parabola has zero slope at its free end, $x = 0$.

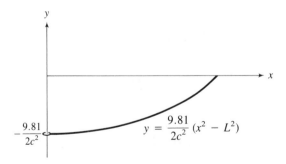

Figure 1.15

It is a standard example in ODEs to find the shape of a string that hangs between two points under the influence of gravity. The solution, called a *catenary*, is a hyperbolic cosine function, not a parabola as derived in Example 4. The difference lies in the assumptions leading to the ODEs describing the two situations. In Example 4, it is assumed that tension τ in the string is constant, and this leads to the differential equation $d^2 y/dx^2 = 9.81\rho/\tau$ for static deflections. For the catenary problem, the string is not sufficiently taut that tension is constant. This leads to the differential equation $d^2 y/dx^2 = (9.81\rho/\tau)\sqrt{1 + (dy/dx)^2}$, where τ is tension at only the lowest point in the string.

Longitudinal Vibrations of Bars

In Figure 1.16 we show a circular bar of natural length L lying along the x-axis. Suppose that the end $x = 0$ is clamped at that position and the end $x = L$ is struck with a hammer. This will set up longitudinal vibrations in the bar. We show that the one-dimensional wave equation, which describes transverse vibrations of a taut string, also describes these longitudinal vibrations of the bar. Although we have drawn the bar in a horizontal position, it could equally well be vertical. We denote by x the positions of cross sections of the bar when the bar is in an unstrained state, and we denote by $y(x, t)$ the positions of cross sections relative to their unstrained positions (Figure 1.17). It is assumed that cross sections remain plane during vibrations.

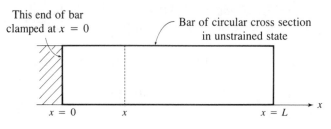

Figure 1.16

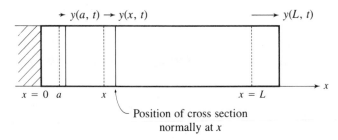

Figure 1.17

Consider the segment of the bar that in an unstrained state occupies the region between $x = a$ (a some fixed number) and an arbitrary position x. At time t, this segment is stretched an amount $y(x, t) - y(a, t)$. Hooke's law states that the force exerted across the segment due to this extension (or compression) is given by

$$AE\left(\frac{y(x, t) - y(a, t)}{x - a}\right), \tag{52}$$

where A is the cross-sectional area of the bar and E is Young's modulus of elasticity of the material in tension and compression. It follows (by limits as $x \to a$) that the internal force exerted on the face at $x = a$ by that part of the bar to its right at time t has component

$$AE\frac{\partial y(a, t)}{\partial x}. \tag{53}$$

[The internal force on the face at $x = a$ due to that part of the bar to its left has component $-AE\partial y(a, t)/\partial x$.]

We now apply Newton's second law to the motion of the above segment of the bar:

$$AE\frac{\partial y(x, t)}{\partial x} - AE\frac{\partial y(a, t)}{\partial x} + \int_a^x F(\zeta, t)A\, d\zeta = \frac{\partial}{\partial t}\left(\int_a^x \frac{\partial y(\zeta, t)}{\partial t}\rho(\zeta, t)A\, d\zeta\right), \tag{54}$$

where $\rho(x, t)$ is the density of the bar (mass per unit volume) and $F(x, t)$ is the x-component of all external forces acting on the bar per unit volume. It is assumed that these external forces are constant over each cross section of the bar. Differentiation of this equation with respect to x and division by A give

$$E\frac{\partial^2 y}{\partial x^2} + F(x,t) = \frac{\partial}{\partial t}\left(\rho\frac{\partial y}{\partial t}\right). \tag{55}$$

In most applications, ρ can be taken as constant, in which case (55) reduces to the one-dimensional wave equation

$$\boxed{\frac{\partial^2 y}{\partial t^2} = c^2\frac{\partial^2 y}{\partial x^2} + \frac{F(x,t)}{\rho}, \qquad c^2 = \frac{E}{\rho}.} \tag{56}$$

Initial conditions that accompany PDE (56) describe the displacement and velocity of cross sections of the bar at some initial time, usually $t = 0$ [see equations (41a, b)]. Boundary conditions must also be specified. When the bar is of finite length $(0 < x < L)$, two boundary conditions occur, one at each end. If the bar is of semi-infinite length $(0 < x < \infty)$, only the end $x = 0$ satisfies a boundary condition; and when the bar is of infinite length, no boundary conditions are present. Dirichlet boundary conditions are of form (42a, b); they specify displacements $y(0,t)$ and $y(L,t)$ of the ends of the bar. Neumann boundary conditions result when longitudinal forces that are prescribed functions of time are applied to the faces of the bar. To see this, note that the force exerted on the face $x = 0$ by the bar (to the right) is $AE\partial y(0,t)/\partial x$. Consequently, if the end $x = 0$ of the bar is subjected to an external force with x-component $f_1(t)$, then taking the face as massless, Newton's second law for the face gives

$$AE\frac{\partial y(0,t)}{\partial x} + f_1(t) = 0 \tag{57a}$$

or

$$\frac{\partial y(0,t)}{\partial x} = -\frac{1}{AE}f_1(t), \qquad t > 0, \tag{57b}$$

a Neumann condition. Similarly, if the bar has an end at $x = L$ with external force $f_2(t)$, the Neumann boundary condition there is

$$\frac{\partial y(L,t)}{\partial x} = \frac{1}{AE}f_2(t), \qquad t > 0. \tag{58}$$

Homogeneous Neumann boundary conditions describe free ends.

Were we to attach the end of the bar at $x = 0$ to the origin by a spring (of constant $k > 0$) so that the spring were unstretched when the end is at $x = 0$, (57a) would be replaced by

$$AE\frac{\partial y(0,t)}{\partial x} - ky(0,t) = 0, \qquad t > 0$$

or

$$-AE\frac{\partial y(0,t)}{\partial x} + ky(0,t) = 0, \qquad t > 0. \tag{59a}$$

This is a homogeneous Robin condition. Similarly, when end $x = L$ is attached to a spring, the resulting boundary condition is the homogeneous Robin condition

$$AE\frac{\partial y(L,t)}{\partial x} + ky(L,t) = 0, \qquad t > 0. \tag{59b}$$

The initial boundary value problem for longitudinal displacements in the bar consists of the one-dimensional wave equation (56) together with two initial conditions and zero, one, or two boundary conditions, a problem identical to that for string vibrations.

Angular Vibrations of Bars

Angular vibrations of a bar also give rise to the above mathematical problem. Let x denote distance from some fixed reference point to cross sections of a cylindrical elastic bar (Figure 1.18). At time t, the angular displacement of the section labeled x from its torque-free position is denoted by $y(x, t)$, where it is assumed that in each cross section, lines that are radial in the bar before torque is applied remain straight after the bar is twisted. At this time, the segment of the bar between a and x has its right face twisted relative to its left face by an amount $y(x, t) - y(a, t)$. The torque exerted across the element is then

$$IE\left(\frac{y(x,t) - y(a,t)}{x - a}\right), \tag{60}$$

where I is the moment of inertia of the cross-sectional area about the axis of the bar and E is Young's modulus of elasticity of the material in shear. It follows (by limits) that the internal torque exerted on the face at $x = a$ by that part of the bar to its right at time t is

$$IE\frac{\partial y(a,t)}{\partial x}. \tag{61}$$

[The internal torque on the face at $x = a$ due to that part of the bar to its left is $-IE\partial y(a, t)/\partial x$.]

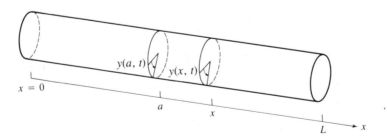

Figure 1.18

If, in addition, an external torque per unit length $\tau(x, t)$ acts, and $\rho(x, t)$ is the density (mass per unit volume) of the bar, then the PDE for angular vibrations of the bar can be obtained from Newton's second law applied to the element between a and x:

$$IE\frac{\partial y(x,t)}{\partial x} - IE\frac{\partial y(a,t)}{\partial x} + \int_a^x \tau(\zeta,t)\,d\zeta = \frac{\partial}{\partial t}\left(\int_a^x I\rho(\zeta,t)\frac{\partial y(\zeta,t)}{\partial t}\,d\zeta\right). \tag{62}$$

Differentiation of this equation with respect to x and division by I give

$$E\frac{\partial^2 y}{\partial x^2} + \frac{\tau(x,t)}{I} = \frac{\partial}{\partial t}\left(\rho\frac{\partial y}{\partial t}\right). \tag{63}$$

When ρ is constant, (63) reduces to the one-dimensional wave equation

$$\boxed{\frac{\partial^2 y}{\partial t^2} = c^2\frac{\partial^2 y}{\partial x^2} + \frac{\tau(x,t)}{\rho I}, \qquad c^2 = \frac{E}{\rho}.} \tag{64}$$

Accompanying this PDE will be two initial conditions and/or zero, one, or two boundary conditions.

Exercises 1.3

In Exercises 1–12, set up, but do not solve, an (initial) boundary value problem for the required displacement. Assume that density of and tension in the string are constant (or that Young's modulus and density are constant in the bar).

1. A taut string has its ends fixed at $x = 0$ and $x = L$ on the x-axis. It is given an initial displacement at $t = 0$ of $f(x)$, $0 \le x \le L$ and initial velocity $g(x)$, $0 \le x \le L$. Formulate the initial boundary value problem for displacement $y(x,t)$ of the string for $0 < x < L$ and $t > 0$.

2. Repeat Exercise 1 except that the end at $x = L$ is free to slide without friction along a vertical support.

3. Repeat Exercise 1 where oscillations take place in a medium that creates a damping force proportional to velocity and the ends of the string are elastically connected to the x-axis. Furthermore, do not neglect the weight of the string.

4. Repeat Exercise 1 except that a vertical force $F(t) = \cos \omega t$, $t > 0$, acts on the end $x = 0$ of the string and the string is initially at rest along the x-axis.

5. Repeat Exercise 3 except that the force $F(t)$ in Exercise 4 also acts on the end $x = 0$.

6. A horizontal cylindrical bar is originally at rest and unstrained along the x-axis between $x = 0$ and $x = L$. For time $t > 0$, the left end is fixed and the right end is subjected to a constant elongating force per unit area F parallel to the bar. Formulate the initial boundary value problem for displacements $y(x,t)$ of cross sections of the bar.

7. A bar of unstrained length L is clamped along its length, turned to the vertical position, and hung from its end $x = 0$. At time $t = 0$, the clamp is removed and gravity is therefore permitted to act on the bar. Formulate an initial boundary value problem for displacements $y(x,t)$ of cross sections of the bar.

8. Repeat Exercise 7 except that the top of the bar is attached to a spring with constant k. Let $x = 0$ correspond to the top of the bar when the spring is in the unstretched position at $t = 0$.

9. The ends of a taut string are fixed at $x = 0$ and $x = L$ on the x-axis. The string is initially at rest

along the x-axis, then is allowed to drop under its own weight. Formulate an initial boundary value problem for displacements of the string. What are the static deflections for this string?

10. Repeat Exercise 9 except that motion takes place in a medium that creates a damping force proportional to velocity.

11. Repeat Exercise 9 except that the end of the string at $x = L$ is looped around a smooth vertical support and a constant vertical force F_L acts on this loop. What are the static deflections for the string?

12. An unstrained elastic bar falls vertically under gravity with its axis vertical. When its velocity is v (which we take as time $t = 0$), it strikes a solid object and remains in contact with it thereafter. Formulate an initial boundary value problem for displacements of cross sections of the bar.

13. A cylindrical bar has unstrained length L. If it is hung vertically from one end so that no oscillations occur, what is its length?

14. The bar in Exercise 13 is hung from a spring with constant $k > 0$. How far below $x = 0$ (the position of the lower end of the spring in the unstretched position) will the lower end of the bar lie?

15. Verify that Robin and Neumann conditions at $x = L$ take the forms (49b) and (47) for massless ends.

16. The end $x = 0$ of a horizontal bar of length L is kept fixed, and the other end has a mass m attached to it. The mass m is then subjected to a horizontal periodic force $F = F_0 \sin \omega t$. If the bar is initially unstrained and at rest, set up the initial boundary value problem for longitudinal displacements in the bar.

17. The one-dimensional wave equation (37) for vibrations of a taut string was derived by applying Newton's second law to a segment of the string. In this exercise, we use the PDE to discuss energy balance for the entire string (assumed finite in length).

    (a) Multiply the PDE by $\partial y/\partial t$, integrate the result with respect to x over the length of the string $0 \le x \le L$, and use integration by parts to obtain

    $$\frac{1}{2} \int_0^L \left[\frac{\partial}{\partial t} \left(\frac{\partial y}{\partial t} \right)^2 + c^2 \frac{\partial}{\partial t} \left(\frac{\partial y}{\partial x} \right)^2 \right] dx = c^2 \left\{ \frac{\partial y}{\partial x} \frac{\partial y}{\partial t} \right\}_0^L + \int_0^L \frac{F(x,t)}{\rho} \frac{\partial y}{\partial t} dx.$$

    (b) Integrate the result in (a) with respect to time from $t = 0$ to an arbitrary t to show that

    $$\int_0^L \frac{\rho}{2} \left(\frac{\partial y}{\partial t} \right)^2 dx + \int_0^L \frac{\tau}{2} \left(\frac{\partial y}{\partial x} \right)^2 dx = \int_0^L \frac{\rho}{2} \left(\frac{\partial y(x,0)}{\partial t} \right)^2 dx$$

    $$+ \int_0^L \frac{\tau}{2} \left(\frac{\partial y(x,0)}{\partial x} \right)^2 dx$$

    $$+ \int_0^t \left(\tau \frac{\partial y(L,t)}{\partial x} \right) \frac{\partial y(L,t)}{\partial t} dt$$

    $$+ \int_0^t \left(-\tau \frac{\partial y(0,t)}{\partial x} \right) \frac{\partial y(0,t)}{\partial t} dt$$

    $$+ \int_0^t \int_0^L F(x,t) \frac{\partial y}{\partial t} dx \, dt.$$

    Interpret each of these terms physically and thereby conclude that the equation is a statement of work-energy balance. It is often called the "energy equation" for the string.

18. Show that when the cross-sectional area of the bar in Figure 1.16 varies with position, equation (56) is replaced by

$$\frac{\partial^2 y}{\partial t^2} = \frac{c^2}{A(x)}\frac{\partial}{\partial x}\left(A(x)\frac{\partial y}{\partial x}\right) + \frac{F(x,t)}{\rho}, \qquad c^2 = \frac{E}{\rho},$$

provided expression (53) still gives forces across cross sections of the bar.

19. A bar of unstrained length L is clamped at end $x = 0$. For time $t < 0$, it is at rest, subjected to a force with x-component F distributed uniformly over the other end. If the force is removed at time $t = 0$, formulate the initial boundary value problem for subsequent displacements in the bar.

20. In this exercise we derive the PDE for small vibrations of a suspended heavy cable. Consider a heavy cable of uniform density ρ (mass/length) and length L suspended vertically from one end. Take the origin of coordinates at the position of equilibrium of the lower end of the cable and the positive x-axis along the cable. Denote by $y(x,t)$ small horizontal deflections of points in the cable from equilibrium.

(a) Apply Newton's second law to a segment of the cable to obtain the PDE for small deflections

$$\frac{\partial^2 y}{\partial t^2} = -g\frac{\partial}{\partial x}\left(x\frac{\partial y}{\partial x}\right) + \frac{F}{\rho},$$

where $g < 0$ is the acceleration due to gravity and F is the y-component of all external horizontal forces per unit length in the x-direction.

(b) What boundary condition must $y(x,t)$ satisfy?

1.4 Transverse Vibrations of Membranes

In this section we study vibrations of perfectly flexible membranes stretched over regions of the xy-plane (Figure 1.19). When the membrane is very taut and displacements are small, the horizontal components of these displacements are negligible compared with vertical components; that is, displacements may be taken as purely transverse, representable in the form $z(x,y,t)$.

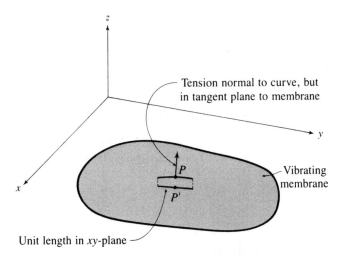

Figure 1.19

In discussing transverse vibrations of strings, tension played an integral role. No less important is the tension in a membrane. Suppose a line of unit length is drawn in any direction at a point P' in the xy-plane and projected onto a curve on the membrane (Figure 1.19). The material on one side of the curve exerts a force on the material on the other side, the force acting normal to the curve and in the tangent plane of the surface at P. This force is called the tension τ of the membrane.

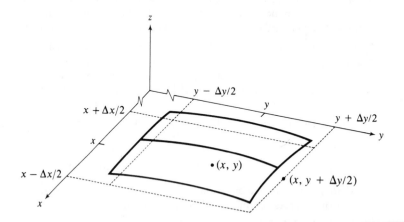

Figure 1.20

To obtain a PDE for displacements $z(x, y, t)$ of the membrane, we examine forces acting on an element of the membrane that projects onto a small rectangle in the xy-plane (Figure 1.20). The vertical component of the tension force on the element is obtained by taking vertical components of the tensions on the boundaries. The tension at the point on the membrane corresponding to the point $(x, y + \Delta y/2)$ in the xy-plane acts in the tangential direction of the curve

$$x = x \quad \text{(fixed)}, \quad y = y, \quad z = z(x, y, t),$$

namely,

$$\left(0, 1, \frac{\partial z}{\partial y}\right)_{|(x, y + \Delta y/2, t)} \tag{65}$$

A unit vector in this direction is

$$\frac{(0, 1, \partial z/\partial y)}{\sqrt{1 + (\partial z/\partial y)^2}}_{|(x, y + \Delta y/2, t)} \tag{66}$$

When vibrations of the membrane are such that $\partial z/\partial y$ is very much less than unity (and we consider only this case), the denominator in (66) may be approximated by 1, and (66) is replaced by (65). The vertical component of the tension force acting along that part of the boundary containing the point $(x, y + \Delta y/2, z)$ may therefore be approximated by

$$\tau_{|(x, y + \Delta y/2, t)}\left(0, 1, \frac{\partial z}{\partial y}\right)_{|(x, y + \Delta y/2, t)} \Delta x \cdot \hat{\mathbf{k}} = \left(\tau \frac{\partial z}{\partial y}\right)_{|(x, y + \Delta y/2, t)} \Delta x. \tag{67}$$

A similar analysis may be made on the remaining three boundaries, resulting in a total vertical force on the element (due to tension) of approximately

$$\left[\left(\tau\frac{\partial z}{\partial y}\right)_{|(x,\,y+\Delta y/2,\,t)} - \left(\tau\frac{\partial z}{\partial y}\right)_{|(x,\,y-\Delta y/2,\,t)}\right]\Delta x$$

$$+ \left[\left(\tau\frac{\partial z}{\partial x}\right)_{|(x+\Delta x/2,\,y,\,t)} - \left(\tau\frac{\partial z}{\partial x}\right)_{|(x-\Delta x/2,\,y,\,t)}\right]\Delta y. \tag{68}$$

When Newton's second law (force equals time rate of change of momentum) is applied to this element of the membrane, the result is

$$\left[\left(\tau\frac{\partial z}{\partial y}\right)_{|(x,\,y+\Delta y/2,\,t)} - \left(\tau\frac{\partial z}{\partial y}\right)_{|(x,\,y-\Delta y/2,\,t)}\right]\Delta x$$

$$+ \left[\left(\tau\frac{\partial z}{\partial x}\right)_{|(x+\Delta x/2,\,y,\,t)} - \left(\tau\frac{\partial z}{\partial x}\right)_{|(x-\Delta x/2,\,y,\,t)}\right]\Delta y$$

$$+ F\,\Delta x\,\Delta y = \frac{\partial}{\partial t}\left(\rho\frac{\partial z}{\partial t}\Delta x\,\Delta y\right), \tag{69}$$

where ρ is the density of the membrane (mass per unit area) and F is the sum of all vertical external forces on the membrane per unit area in the xy-plane. If we divide both sides of this equation by $\Delta x\,\Delta y$ and take limits as Δx and Δy approach zero,

$$\lim_{\substack{\Delta x\to 0 \\ \Delta y\to 0}}\frac{\partial}{\partial t}\left(\rho\frac{\partial z}{\partial t}\right) = \lim_{\Delta y\to 0}\frac{\left(\tau\frac{\partial z}{\partial y}\right)_{|(x,\,y+\Delta y/2,\,t)} - \left(\tau\frac{\partial z}{\partial y}\right)_{|(x,\,y-\Delta y/2,\,t)}}{\Delta y}$$

$$+ \lim_{\Delta x\to 0}\frac{\left(\tau\frac{\partial z}{\partial x}\right)_{|(x+\Delta x/2,\,y,\,t)} - \left(\tau\frac{\partial z}{\partial x}\right)_{|(x-\Delta x/2,\,y,\,t)}}{\Delta x} + F$$

or

$$\frac{\partial}{\partial t}\left(\rho\frac{\partial z}{\partial t}\right) = \frac{\partial}{\partial y}\left(\tau\frac{\partial z}{\partial y}\right) + \frac{\partial}{\partial x}\left(\tau\frac{\partial z}{\partial x}\right) + F. \tag{70}$$

For most applications, both the density of and the tension in the membrane may be taken as constant, in which case (70) reduces to

$$\boxed{\frac{\partial^2 z}{\partial t^2} = c^2\left(\frac{\partial^2 z}{\partial x^2} + \frac{\partial^2 z}{\partial y^2}\right) + \frac{F}{\rho}, \qquad c^2 = \frac{\tau}{\rho}.} \tag{71}$$

This is the PDE for transverse vibrations of the membrane, called the *two-dimensional wave equation*.

For an external force due only to gravity,

$$F = \rho g, \qquad g < 0; \tag{72}$$

for a damping force proportional to velocity,

$$F = -\beta \frac{\partial z}{\partial t}, \qquad \beta > 0; \tag{73}$$

and for a restoring force proportional to displacement,

$$F = -kz, \qquad k > 0. \tag{74}$$

Initial conditions that accompany (71) describe the displacement and velocity of the membrane at some initial time (usually $t = 0$):

$$z(x, y, 0) = f(x, y), \qquad (x, y) \text{ in } R, \tag{75a}$$

$$\frac{\partial z(x, y, 0)}{\partial t} = g(x, y), \qquad (x, y) \text{ in } R, \tag{75b}$$

where R is the region in the xy-plane onto which the membrane projects. A Dirichlet boundary condition for (71) prescribes the value of $z(x, y, t)$ on the boundary $\beta(R)$ of R,

$$z(x, y, t) = f(x, y, t), \qquad (x, y) \text{ on } \beta(R), \qquad t > 0, \tag{76}$$

$f(x, y, t)$ some given function.

Suppose instead that the edge of the membrane can move vertically and that it is subjected to an external vertical force $f(x, y, t)$ per unit length. The edge is also acted on by the tension in the membrane, and the magnitude of the z-component of the tension acting across a unit length along $\beta(R)$ is $|\tau \partial z/\partial n|$, where n is a coordinate measuring distance in the xy-plane normal to $\beta(R)$ (Figure 1.21). Consequently, if we take the edge of the membrane as massless, Newton's second law for vertical components of forces on an element ds of $\beta(R)$ gives

$$-\left(\tau \frac{\partial z}{\partial n} \right)_{|\beta(R)} ds + f(x, y, t)\, ds = 0 \tag{77a}$$

or

$$\frac{\partial z}{\partial n} = \frac{1}{\tau} f(x, y, t), \qquad (x, y) \text{ on } \beta(R), \qquad t > 0. \tag{77b}$$

This is a nonhomogeneous Neumann boundary condition. When the only force acting on the edge of the membrane is that due to tension, $z(x, y, t)$ must satisfy a homogeneous Neumann condition,

$$\frac{\partial z}{\partial n} = 0, \qquad (x, y) \text{ on } \beta(R), \qquad t > 0. \tag{78}$$

Another possibility is to have the edge of the membrane elastically attached to the xy-plane in such a way that the restoring force per unit length along $\beta(R)$ is proportional to displacement. Then, according to (77a),

$$-\left(\tau \frac{\partial z}{\partial n} \right) ds + [-kz + f(x, y, t)]\, ds = 0, \qquad (x, y) \text{ on } \beta(R), \qquad t > 0, \tag{79a}$$

where $k > 0$, and $f(x, y, t)$ now represents all external forces acting on $\beta(R)$ other than tension and the restoring force. Equation (79a) can be written in the equivalent form

$$\tau \frac{\partial z}{\partial n} + kz = f(x, y, t), \qquad (x, y) \text{ on } \beta(R), \qquad t > 0, \tag{79b}$$

a Robin condition.

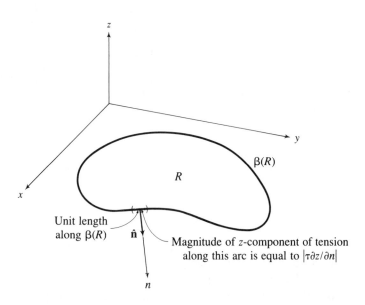

Figure 1.21

The initial boundary value problem for displacements in the membrane is

$$\frac{\partial^2 z}{\partial t^2} = c^2 \left(\frac{\partial^2 z}{\partial x^2} + \frac{\partial^2 z}{\partial y^2} \right) + \frac{F(x, y, t)}{\rho}, \qquad (x, y) \text{ in } R, \qquad t > 0, \tag{80a}$$

$$\text{Boundary conditions,} \tag{80b}$$

$$z(x, y, 0) = f(x, y), \qquad (x, y) \text{ in } R, \tag{80c}$$

$$z_t(x, y, 0) = g(x, y), \qquad (x, y) \text{ in } R. \tag{80d}$$

If boundary conditions (80b) and external force $F(x, y, t)$ are independent of time, there may exist solutions of (80a, b) that are also independent of time. Such solutions, called *static deflections*, satisfy Poisson's equation

$$\nabla^2 z = -\frac{F(x, y)}{\tau} \tag{81a}$$

and   Boundary conditions.   (81b)

If, in addition, no external forces are present, the PDE reduces to Laplace's equation

$$\nabla^2 z = 0. \tag{82}$$

An important technique in solving the two-dimensional wave equation is the method of separation of variables, a method we shall deal with at length in Section 3.2. In this method it is assumed that displacement can be separated into a function of x and y multiplied by a function of time t, $z(x, y, t) = u(x, y)T(t)$. Substitution of this into equation (80a) when $F \equiv 0$ gives

$$u(x, y)\frac{d^2 T}{dt^2} = c^2\left(\frac{\partial^2 u}{\partial x^2}T(t) + \frac{\partial^2 u}{\partial y^2}T(t)\right)$$

or

$$\frac{1}{T}\frac{d^2 T}{dt^2} = \frac{c^2}{u}\left(\frac{\partial^2 u}{\partial x^2} + \frac{\partial^2 u}{\partial y^2}\right). \qquad (83)$$

Because the left side of this equation is a function of only t and the right side is a function of x and y, it follows that each must be equal to a constant, say $-k$. Then $u(x, y)$ must satisfy

$$\frac{c^2}{u}\left(\frac{\partial^2 u}{\partial x^2} + \frac{\partial^2 u}{\partial y^2}\right) = -k$$

or

$$\boxed{\nabla^2 u + \frac{k}{c^2}u = 0.} \qquad (84)$$

This equation is called the two-dimensional *Helmholtz equation*. In the present context, it is also called the *reduced wave equation*. In essence, it describes the amplitude of the oscillations of each point in the membrane; $T(t)$ contains the time dependence of the vibrations. Boundary conditions for the wave equation will yield boundary conditions for the Helmholtz equation.

Exercises 1.4

In Exercises 1–7, set up, but do not solve, an (initial) boundary value problem for the required displacement. Assume that density of and tension in the membrane are constant.

1. A vibrating circular membrane of radius r_1 is given an initial displacement $f(r, \theta)$ and zero initial velocity. If its edge $r = r_1$ is fixed on the xy-plane, formulate an initial boundary value problem for subsequent displacements of the membrane. Assume that no external forces act on the membrane.

2. Repeat Exercise 1 except that $f(r, \theta)$ is replaced by $f(r)$.

3. A circular membrane of radius r_1 is in a static position with radial lines $\theta = 0$ and $\theta = \alpha$ clamped on the xy-plane. If the displacement of the edge $r = r_1$ is $f(\theta)$ for $0 \le \theta \le \alpha$, formulate the boundary value problem for displacement in the sector $0 < \theta < \alpha$. Would there be any restriction on $f(\theta)$?

4. Repeat Exercise 3 except that gravity acts on the membrane.

5. Repeat Exercise 1 except that gravity, as well as a damping force proportional to velocity, acts on the membrane.

6. A rectangular membrane is initially ($t = 0$) at rest over the region $0 \le x \le L$, $0 \le y \le L'$ in the xy-plane. For time $t > 0$, a periodic force per unit area $\cos \omega t$ acts at all points in the membrane.

If the edge of the membrane is fixed on the xy-plane, formulate an initial boundary value problem for displacements of the membrane.

7. Repeat Exercise 6 except that the boundaries $x = 0$ and $x = L$ are elastically connected to the xy-plane and the boundaries $y = 0$ and $y = L'$ are forced to exhibit motion described by $f_1(x, t)$ and $f_2(x, t)$, respectively.

8. A circular membrane of radius r_2 has its edge $r = r_2$ fixed on the xy-plane. If gravity and tension are the only forces acting on the membrane, what are the static deflections of points of the membrane?

9. In this exercise we replace gravity in Exercise 8 with an arbitrary (but continuous) function $f(r)$; that is, assume that the only forces acting on the membrane are tension and a force per unit area with y-component $f(r)$.

   (a) What is the boundary value problem for static deflections $z(r)$ of the membrane?

   (b) Show that $z'(r)$ must be of the form

   $$z'(r) = \frac{-1}{r\tau} \int rf(r)\, dr.$$

   (c) Express the antiderivative in (b) as a definite integral

   $$z'(r) = \frac{-1}{r\tau} \int_0^r uf(u)\, du$$

   and integrate once more to find $z(r)$ in the form

   $$z(r) = \frac{1}{\tau}\left(\int_0^{r_2} \int_0^v \frac{u}{v} f(u)\, du\, dv - \int_0^r \int_0^v \frac{u}{v} f(u)\, du\, dv \right).$$

   (d) Interchange orders of integration to obtain

   $$z(r) = \frac{1}{\tau}\left(\int_0^{r_2} uf(u) \ln\left(\frac{r_2}{u}\right) du - \int_0^r uf(u) \ln\left(\frac{r}{u}\right) du \right).$$

   (e) Verify that the result in (d) yields the solution to Exercise 8 when $f(r) = \rho g$.

   (f) Find deflections when $f(r) = k(r - r_2)$, $k > 0$ a constant.

10. The two-dimensional wave equation (71) was derived by applying Newton's second law to a segment of the membrane. In this exercise we use the PDE to discuss energy balance for the entire membrane.

   (a) Multiply (71) by $\partial z/\partial t$ and integrate over the region R in the xy-plane onto which the membrane projects to show that

   $$\iint_R \frac{1}{2}\frac{\partial}{\partial z}\left(\frac{\partial z}{\partial t}\right)^2 dA = c^2 \iint_R \frac{\partial z}{\partial t}\left(\frac{\partial^2 z}{\partial x^2} + \frac{\partial^2 z}{\partial y^2}\right) dA + \iint_R \frac{F(x, y, t)}{\rho}\frac{\partial z}{\partial t}\, dA.$$

   (b) Verify that for z a function of x, y, and t,

   $$\frac{\partial z}{\partial t}\nabla^2 z = \nabla \cdot \left(\frac{\partial z}{\partial t}\nabla z\right) - \frac{1}{2}\frac{\partial}{\partial t}|\nabla z|^2,$$

   and use this identity together with Green's theorem to rewrite the result in (a) in the form

   $$\frac{1}{2}\iint_R \left[\frac{\partial}{\partial t}\left(\frac{\partial z}{\partial t}\right)^2 + c^2\frac{\partial}{\partial t}|\nabla z|^2\right] dA = c^2 \oint_{\beta(R)} \frac{\partial z}{\partial t}\frac{\partial z}{\partial n}\, ds + \iint_R \frac{F(x, y, t)}{\rho}\frac{\partial z}{\partial t}\, dA.$$

(c) Integrate the result in (b) with respect to time from $t = 0$ to an arbitrary t to obtain

$$\iint_R \left[\frac{\rho}{2}\left(\frac{\partial z}{\partial t}\right)^2 + \frac{\tau}{2}|\nabla z|^2 \right] dA = \iint_R \left[\frac{\rho}{2}\left(\frac{\partial z(x,y,0)}{\partial t}\right)^2 + \frac{\tau}{2}|\nabla z(x,y,0)|^2 \right] dA$$

$$+ \int_0^t \oint_{\beta(R)} \left(\tau\frac{\partial z}{\partial n} \right)\frac{\partial z}{\partial t}\, ds\, dt + \int_0^t \iint_R F(x,y,t)\frac{\partial z}{\partial t}\, dA\, dt.$$

Interpret each term in this result physically, and hence obtain a physical interpretation of the equation as a whole. It is often called the "energy equation" for the membrane.

1.5 Transverse Vibrations of Beams

In this section we study vertical oscillations of horizontal beams (Figure 1.22). It is assumed that the beam is symmetric about the xy-plane and that all cross sections (which would be plane in the absence of any loading) remain plane during vibrations. Displacements are then described by the position $y(x,t)$ of the neutral axis.

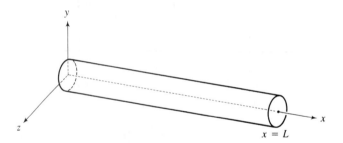

Figure 1.22

Stretches and compressions in various parts of the beam lead to internal forces and moments. It has been shown experimentally that the bending moment $M(x,t)$ on the right face of the cross section of the beam at position x due to the rest of the beam to its right is related to the signed curvature $\kappa(x,t)$ of the neutral axis by the equation

$$M = EI\kappa, \tag{85}$$

where $E = E(x) > 0$ is Young's modulus of elasticity (depending on the material in the beam) and $I = I(x)$ is the moment of inertia of the cross section of the beam (Figure 1.23). It is shown in elementary calculus that

$$\kappa = \frac{\partial^2 y/\partial x^2}{\left[1 + \left(\dfrac{\partial y}{\partial x}\right)^2 \right]^{3/2}}, \tag{86}$$

but if we assume that vibrations produce only small slopes, then $\partial y/\partial x \ll 1$, and we may take

$$\kappa = \frac{\partial^2 y}{\partial x^2}. \tag{87}$$

Consequently, for vibrations producing small slopes, bending moments are related to curvature by

$$M(x,t) = EI \frac{\partial^2 y}{\partial x^2}. \tag{88}$$

Since $\partial^2 y/\partial x^2$ is positive when the beam is concave upward (as in Figure 1.23), it follows that M must be positive on the right face for the direction shown. The moment on the left face of the same cross section due to the material in the beam on its left is therefore $-M(x,t) = -EI\partial^2 y/\partial x^2$.

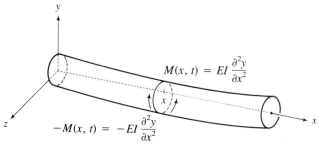

Figure 1.23

Shear forces also act on any cross section. We denote by $Q(x,t)$ the y-component of the shear force acting on the right face of the cross section at position x due to that part of the beam to its right. Then $-Q(x,t)$ is the shear force acting on the left face. Shear and bending moments are related. To see how, we apply Newton's second law for rotational motion of a segment of the beam from a fixed value $x = a$ to an arbitrary value x (Figure 1.24); the sum of all moments of all forces on the segment must equal the moment of inertia multiplied by the angular acceleration. Since motion about the line $x = \bar{x}$ through the center of mass of the segment is strictly translational, moments about $x = \bar{x}$ yield

$$0 = M(x,t) - M(a,t) + (x - \bar{x})Q(x,t) - (a - \bar{x})Q(a,t)$$
$$+ \int_a^x (\zeta - \bar{x})F(\zeta,t)\,d\zeta, \tag{89}$$

where $F(x,t)$ is the sum of all vertical forces on the beam per unit x-length. Differentiation of this equation with respect to x gives

$$0 = \frac{\partial M(x,t)}{\partial x} + (x - \bar{x})\frac{\partial Q(x,t)}{\partial x} + \left(1 - \frac{\partial \bar{x}}{\partial x}\right)Q(x,t) + Q(a,t)\frac{\partial \bar{x}}{\partial x}$$
$$+ \int_a^x -\frac{\partial \bar{x}}{\partial x}F(\zeta,t)\,d\zeta + (x - \bar{x})F(x,t). \tag{90}$$

If we now take limits as x approaches a, $\bar{x}$ approaches a also, and

$$0 = \frac{\partial M(a,t)}{\partial x} + Q(a,t). \tag{91}$$

Because a is arbitrary, we obtain the following relationship between shear and bending moments:

$$Q(x,t) = -\frac{\partial M(x,t)}{\partial x}. \tag{92}$$

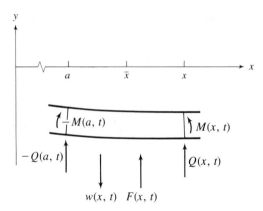

Figure 1.24

$w(x, t) \quad F(x, t)$

Vibrations of the beam are determined by the interactions of the internal bending moments and shear forces with the exterior loading $w(x, t)$ per unit x-length (including the weight of the beam) and all external forces $F(x, t)$ per unit x-length (including loading). The function $w(x, t)$ is the y-component of the loading and as such is negative, while $F(x, t)$, the y-component of all external forces, may be positive, negative, or zero. To describe these interactions, we apply Newton's second law to the vertical translational motion of the segment of the beam in Figure 1.24:

$$\frac{\partial}{\partial t}\left(\int_a^x \frac{\partial y(\zeta, t)}{\partial t}\frac{w}{g}\, d\zeta\right) = \int_a^x F(\zeta, t)\, d\zeta + Q(x, t) - Q(a, t), \qquad (g < 0). \qquad (93)$$

The integral on the left is the momentum of the segment—$w\, d\zeta/g$ is the mass of an element of the beam of length $d\zeta$ along the x-axis, and multiplication by velocity $\partial y\,(\zeta, t)/\partial t$ gives momentum. The integral on the right is the sum of all external forces on the segment, and $Q(x, t)$ and $Q(a, t)$ are the shear forces on the faces at x and a, respectively. Differentiation of this equation with respect to x gives

$$\frac{\partial}{\partial t}\left(\frac{w}{g}\frac{\partial y}{\partial t}\right) = F(x, t) + \frac{\partial Q}{\partial x}. \qquad (94)$$

Substitutions for $\partial Q/\partial x$ and M from equations (92) and (88) yield the PDE satisfied by transverse vibrations of the beam:

$$\frac{\partial}{\partial t}\left(\frac{w}{g}\frac{\partial y}{\partial t}\right) + \frac{\partial^2}{\partial x^2}\left(EI\frac{\partial^2 y}{\partial x^2}\right) = F(x, t). \qquad (95)$$

When E and I are independent of x and $w(x, t)$ is independent of t, the PDE can be written in the simplified form

$$\boxed{\frac{w}{EIg}\frac{\partial^2 y}{\partial t^2} + \frac{\partial^4 y}{\partial x^4} = \frac{F}{EI}.} \qquad (96)$$

In many applications, the internal forces in the beam are so large that the effect of F is negligible. In such cases, (96) may be replaced by the "homogeneous"[†] equation

---

[†] A general definition of what it means for a PDE to be homogeneous is given in Section 3.1.

$$\frac{w}{EIg}\frac{\partial^2 y}{\partial t^2} + \frac{\partial^4 y}{\partial x^4} = 0. \tag{97}$$

This is illustrated in Exercise 5, where it is shown that when $F(x)$ is due only to the weight of the beam itself, static deflections are very small.

Accompanying (96) or (97) will be two initial conditions that describe the displacement and velocity of the beam at some initial time (usually $t = 0$):

$$y(x, 0) = f(x), \qquad 0 < x < L, \tag{98a}$$

$$y_t(x, 0) = g(x), \qquad 0 < x < L. \tag{98b}$$

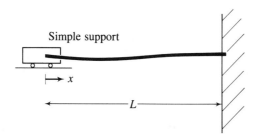

Simple support

x

L

Figure 1.25

Various types of boundary conditions may exist at each end of the beam. If the end $x = 0$ is "simply supported" (Figure 1.25), displacement and curvature (moment) there are both zero:

$$y(0, t) = 0, \qquad \frac{\partial^2 y(0, t)}{\partial x^2} = 0. \tag{99}$$

If this end is "built in" horizontally (Figure 1.26), displacement and slope vanish:

$$y(0, t) = 0, \qquad \frac{\partial y(0, t)}{\partial x} = 0. \tag{100}$$

Finally, if this end is "free" (Figure 1.27), curvature and shear are both zero:

$$\frac{\partial^2 y(0, t)}{\partial x^2} = 0, \qquad \frac{\partial^3 y(0, t)}{\partial x^3} = 0. \tag{101}$$

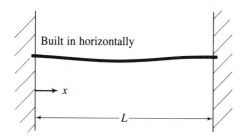

Built in horizontally

x

L

Figure 1.26

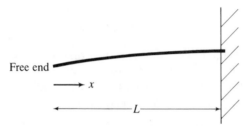

Figure 1.27

Similar conditions exist at the end $x = L$.

Exercises 1.5

In Exercises 1–4, set up, but do not solve, an (initial) boundary value problem for the required displacement. Assume that Young's modulus E and the moment of inertia I of the cross section of the beam are both constant.

1. A horizontal beam of length L has flat ends at $x = 0$ and $x = L$. At time $t = 0$, it is at rest but its neutral axis is deflected according to the function $f(x)$, $0 \le x \le L$. It is then released from this position. The left end of the beam is built in horizontally, and the right end is free.

2. Repeat Exercise 1 except that both ends are simply supported on the x-axis.

3. Repeat Exercise 1 except that a mass m is distributed uniformly along the beam and both ends are built in horizontally.

4. A beam of length L is clamped horizontally at $x = 0$ and is cantilevered (not supported) at $x = L$. For time $t < 0$, it is deflected, but motionless, under a downward force of magnitude F at $x = L$ and its own weight. At time $t = 0$, this force is removed. [*Hint:* In the static situation, the boundary conditions at $x = L$ are $y''(L) = 0$ and $y'''(L) = F/(EI)$.]

5. In this exercise we illustrate that for small external forces, the nonhomogeneous term $[F/(EI)]$ in equation (96) may be neglected.

    (a) What is the boundary value problem for static deflections of a beam of length L, simply supported at both ends? Solve this problem when the external force is constant.

    (b) Suppose now that F is due only to the weight of the beam itself. Find the maximum deflection of the beam using the following data:

    $$E = 2.1 \times 10^{11} \, \text{N/m}^2, \qquad \rho = 7.85 \times 10^3 \, \text{kg/m}^3, \qquad L = 5 \, \text{m},$$
    $$I = 6.5 \, \text{kg} \cdot \text{m}^2, \qquad \text{Cross-sectional area} = 0.02 \, \text{m}^2.$$

    (c) What constant force (per unit x-length) over the beam would create a maximum deflection of 1 cm? How large is this compared with the weight per unit length of the beam?

6. Show that when the ends of the beam in Exercise 5 are clamped horizontally, the maximum deflection is only one-fifth that for the simply supported beam.

1.6 Electrostatic Potential

When two positive point charges Q and q are r units apart in free space, Coulomb's law states that each repels the other with a force whose magnitude is

$$F = \frac{qQ}{4\pi\varepsilon_0 r^2},\tag{102}$$

where ε_0 is the permittivity of free space. The force on unit charge q due to Q is called the electric field intensity

$$\mathbf{E} = \frac{Q}{4\pi\varepsilon_0 r^3}\mathbf{r},\tag{103}$$

where $\mathbf{r}$ is the vector from Q to $q = 1$ (Figure 1.28). It is straightforward to show that the curl and divergence of this vector field vanish:

$$\nabla \times \mathbf{E} = \mathbf{0},\tag{104a}$$

$$\nabla \cdot \mathbf{E} = 0.\tag{104b}$$

A vanishing curl implies the existence (in a suitably defined domain not containing Q) of a potential function V satisfying

$$\mathbf{E} = -\nabla V.\tag{105}$$

Combine this with (104b), and we find that V must satisfy Laplace's equation

$$\nabla^2 V = 0.\tag{106}$$

For such a simple charge distribution, it is easily shown [from (105)] that to an additive constant,

$$V = \frac{Q}{4\pi\varepsilon_0 r}.\tag{107}$$

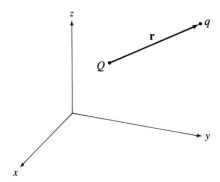

Figure 1.28

When Q is replaced by a distribution of charge with density σ in some region of free space (or other medium), determination of a potential function is more complex. In this case we appeal to Maxwell's equations, which govern all electromagnetic fields. In a static situation, Maxwell's equations still require the electric field intensity $\mathbf{E}$ to satisfy

(104a), in which case the potential function V associated with the field is once again defined by (105). Unfortunately, however, we do not know $\mathbf{E}$ (as we did for the point charge) and therefore cannot solve (105) for V. To find an equation determining V that does not contain $\mathbf{E}$, we use another of Maxwell's equations that requires the electric displacement $\mathbf{D}$ to satisfy

$$\mathbf{V} \cdot \mathbf{D} = \sigma \tag{108}$$

at each point in the medium. When the medium is isotropic with constant permittivity ε, then $\mathbf{D}$ and $\mathbf{E}$ are related by

$$\mathbf{D} = \varepsilon \mathbf{E}, \tag{109}$$

and hence $\mathbf{E}$ must satisfy

$$\mathbf{V} \cdot \mathbf{E} = \frac{\sigma}{\varepsilon}. \tag{110}$$

Between equations (105) and (110) we may eliminate $\mathbf{E}$, the result being Poisson's equation

$$\boxed{\nabla^2 V = -\frac{\sigma}{\varepsilon}.} \tag{111}$$

In other words, the electrostatic potential function V associated with an electrostatic field $\mathbf{E}$ must satisfy (111) at every point interior to the charge distribution. At points outside the charge distribution, σ vanishes and V satisfies Laplace's equation (106).

Equations (106) and (111) are not, by themselves, sufficient to determine V. It is necessary to specify boundary conditions as well. A Dirichlet boundary condition specifies $V(x, y, z)$ on the bounding surface $\beta(R)$ of the medium:

$$V(x, y, z) = f(x, y, z), \qquad (x, y, z) \text{ on } \beta(R), \tag{112}$$

$f(x, y, z)$ a given function. A Neumann boundary condition prescribes the directional derivative of $V(x, y, z)$ normal to the bounding surface:

$$\frac{\partial V}{\partial n} = \mathbf{V}V \cdot \hat{\mathbf{n}} = f(x, y, z), \qquad (x, y, z) \text{ on } \beta(R), \tag{113}$$

where $\hat{\mathbf{n}}$ is the unit outward normal to $\beta(R)$. Since $\mathbf{V}V = -\mathbf{E}$, it follows that specification of the electrostatic force on a bounding surface yields a Neumann boundary condition. If a bounding surface is free of electrostatic forces, it satisfies a homogeneous Neumann boundary condition.

A Robin boundary condition is a linear combination of a Dirichlet and a Neumann condition:

$$l\frac{\partial V}{\partial n} + hV = f(x, y, z), \qquad (x, y, z) \text{ on } \beta(R). \tag{114}$$

Dirichlet and Neumann boundary conditions are obtained by setting l and h equal to zero, respectively.

Exercises 1.6

In Exercises 1 and 2, set up, but do not solve, a boundary value problem for the required potential.

1. Region R in space is bounded by the planes $x = 0$, $y = 0$, $x = L$, and $y = L'$. If the planes $y = 0$ and $x = 0$ are held at zero potential, whereas $x = L$ and $y = L'$ are maintained at a potential of 100, what is the boundary value problem for potential in R?

2. Repeat Exercise 1 except that a uniform charge (with density σ) is spread over the volume $L/4 \leq x \leq 3L/4$, $L'/4 \leq y \leq 3L'/4$.

3. A region R of space has a subregion $\bar{R}$ occupied by charge with density $\sigma(x, y, z)$ coulombs per cubic meter, assumed continuous (Figure 1.29). Consider the function $V(x, y, z)$ defined by

$$V(x, y, z) = \iiint_{\bar{R}} \frac{\sigma(X, Y, Z)}{4\pi\varepsilon_0 \sqrt{(x - X)^2 + (y - Y)^2 + (z - Z)^2}} \, dZ \, dY \, dX.$$

Coordinates (X, Y, Z) identify points in $\bar{R}$.

(a) When (x, y, z) is in R but not in $\bar{R}$, $V(x, y, z)$ is clearly well defined. By using spherical coordinates originating at (x, y, z) for integration variables, show that when (x, y, z) is in $\bar{R}$, the improper integral converges. In other words, $V(x, y, z)$ is well defined throughout all R.

(b) By interchanging the order of differentiations with respect to x, y, and z and integrations with respect to X, Y, and Z, show that when (x, y, z) is in R, but not in $\bar{R}$, $V(x, y, z)$ satisfies Laplace's equation (106).

To prove that $V(x, y, z)$ satisfies Poisson's equation (111) when (x, y, z) is in $\bar{R}$ requires the theory of "generalized functions." Parts of this theory are introduced in Chapters 11 and 12, but the development is not carried far enough to permit verification of the integral as a solution to Poisson's equation. This is not really a problem, however, because the integral representation of $V(x, y, z)$ is of limited utility anyway. Seldom can the integral be evaluated in closed form. In addition, the integral does not take into account any boundary conditions that may be present, and there is no obvious way to modify the integral in order to encompass boundary conditions.

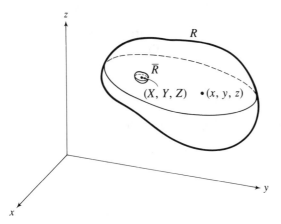

Figure 1.29

1.7 General Solutions of Partial Differential Equations

When boundary and/or initial conditions accompany an ODE, we often find a general solution and then use the subsidiary conditions to determine the arbitrary constants.

This procedure seldom works for PDEs. Arbitrary constants in ODEs are replaced by arbitrary functions in PDEs, and to use initial and/or boundary conditions to determine these functions is usually impossible. We give one very simple example to illustrate the direction the analysis might take in using a general solution for a PDE to solve an initial boundary value problem. The one-dimensional vibration problem

$$\frac{\partial^2 y}{\partial t^2} = c^2 \frac{\partial^2 y}{\partial x^2}, \qquad 0 < x < L, \qquad t > 0, \tag{115a}$$

$$y(0, t) = 0, \qquad t > 0, \tag{115b}$$

$$y(L, t) = 0, \qquad t > 0, \tag{115c}$$

$$y(x, 0) = f(x), \qquad 0 < x < L, \tag{115d}$$

$$y_t(x, 0) = g(x), \qquad 0 < x < L, \tag{115e}$$

describes free oscillations of a taut string with fixed ends. For consistency, we assume that the initial displacement and velocity functions satisfy $f(0) = g(0) = f(L) = g(L) = 0$. By changing independent variables according to $v = x + ct$ and $\eta = x - ct$ and denoting $y[x(v, \eta), t(v, \eta)]$ by $w(v, \eta)$, the wave equation (115a) is replaced by

$$\frac{\partial^2 w}{\partial v \partial \eta} = 0 \tag{116}$$

(see Exercise 1 for details). The general solution of this PDE is

$$w(v, \eta) = F(v) + G(\eta), \tag{117}$$

where F and G are arbitrary but continuous functions with continuous first derivatives. As a result, the general solution of (115a) is

$$y(x, t) = F(x + ct) + G(x - ct). \tag{118}$$

It now remains to determine the exact form of these functions. Application of initial conditions (115d) and (115e) requires that

$$f(x) = F(x) + G(x), \qquad 0 < x < L,$$

$$g(x) = cF'(x) - cG'(x), \qquad 0 < x < L.$$

When the first of these is differentiated with respect to x and combined with the second,

$$F'(x) = \frac{1}{2c}[cf'(x) + g(x)]$$

and therefore

$$F(x) = \frac{1}{2}f(x) + \frac{1}{2c}\int_0^x g(\zeta)\, d\zeta + D,$$

$$G(x) = \frac{1}{2}f(x) - \frac{1}{2c}\int_0^x g(\zeta)\, d\zeta - D$$

(D an arbitrary constant). When x is replaced by $x + ct$ in $F(x)$ and by $x - ct$ in $G(x)$, we obtain

$$y(x, t) = \frac{1}{2} f(x + ct) + \frac{1}{2c} \int_0^{x+ct} g(\zeta)\, d\zeta + D$$

$$+ \frac{1}{2} f(x - ct) - \frac{1}{2c} \int_0^{x-ct} g(\zeta)\, d\zeta - D$$

$$= \frac{1}{2}[f(x + ct) + f(x - ct)] + \frac{1}{2c} \int_{x-ct}^{x+ct} g(\zeta)\, d\zeta. \tag{119}$$

At first sight, (119) would seem to be the complete solution of (115), but this would be very strange, since boundary conditions (115b, c) have not been used, and the solution of an initial boundary value problem cannot be independent of its boundary conditions. The reason that (119) is not a complete solution is that f and g are defined only for $0 \le x \le L$, and yet for (119) to represent $y(x, t)$ for all x and t, these functions must be defined for all real numbers. The boundary conditions will show us how to extend the domains of f and g beyond the interval $0 \le x \le L$. Boundary condition (115b) demands that

$$0 = \frac{1}{2}[f(ct) + f(-ct)] + \frac{1}{2c} \int_{-ct}^{ct} g(\zeta)\, d\zeta,$$

and this equation is satisfied if we separately set

$$f(ct) + f(-ct) = 0, \qquad \int_{-ct}^{ct} g(\zeta)\, d\zeta = 0.$$

These imply that $f(x)$ and $g(x)$ must be extended from their original domain of definition $0 \le x \le L$ as odd functions. The functions are now defined for $-L \le x \le L$. Finally, boundary condition (115c) at $x = L$ is satisfied if we choose

$$0 = f(L + ct) + f(L - ct), \qquad 0 = \int_{L-ct}^{L+ct} g(\zeta)\, d\zeta.$$

These imply that the odd extensions of f and g must also be $2L$-periodic, and this completes definitions of f and g for all real arguments.

The function in (119) can now be used to calculate the position of the string for any x in $0 < x < L$ and any time $t > 0$; it is called *d'Alembert's solution* of initial boundary value problem (115).

As was stated earlier, this is a particularly simple example, and analyses of this type are not usually possible. For this reason, it is unusual to solve initial boundary value problems by finding a general solution for the PDE and attempting to use initial and/or boundary conditions to determine the arbitrary functions. More direct methods must be devised.

Notwithstanding the fact that general solutions of PDEs are seldom of use in solving initial boundary value problems, d'Alembert's solution (119) of (115) provides considerable insight into the behavior of vibrating strings that are free of external forces. Consider first a taut string that at time $t = 0$ is released from rest $[g(x) \equiv 0]$ from the position in Figure 1.30(a) $[f(x) = 0$ for $|x - L/2| \geq L/16]$. This is not a particularly realistic initial displacement in view of the assumptions in Section 1.3 that displacements and slopes must be small. But because our discussion is independent of $f(x)$, we have purposely exaggerated the initial shape in order that our graphical representations be unmistakable. According to d'Alembert's solution (119), subsequent displacements of the string are defined by

$$y(x,t) = \frac{1}{2}[f(x + ct) + f(x - ct)], \tag{120}$$

and it is quite simple to obtain a pictorial history of the string using this function. For any given time t, the graph of $f(x + ct)/2$ is one-half that of $f(x)$ translated ct units to the left; $f(x - ct)/2$ is one-half of $f(x)$ shifted ct units to the right. The position of the string at this particular time is the sum of these two graphs. We have shown this procedure for the times $t = L/(64c)$, $L/(32c)$, $3L/(64c)$, $L/(16c)$, and $L/(8c)$ in Figures 1.30(b), (c), (d), (e), and (f), respectively. The dotted curves represent $f(x + ct)/2$, the dashed curves $f(x - ct)/2$, and the solid curves $y(x,t)$.

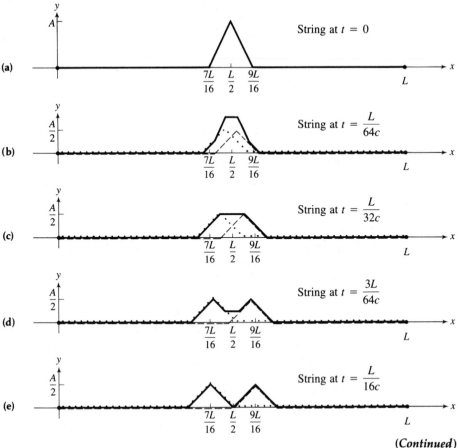

Figure 1.30

(Continued)

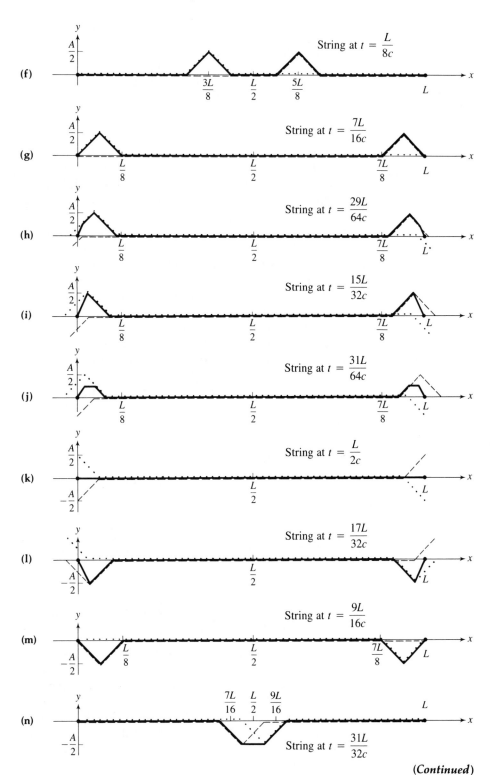

Figure 1.30
(*Continued*)

(*Continued*)

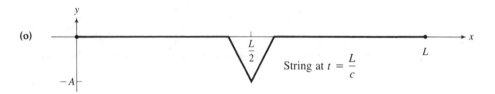

Figure 1.30
(*Continued*)

In Figures 1.30(g), (h), (i), (j), and (k), where we have continued this graphical construction at times $t = 7L/(16c)$, $29L/(64c)$, $15L/(32c)$, $31L/(64c)$, and $L/(2c)$, respectively, we have used the fact that $f(x)$ must be extended as an odd, $2L$-periodic function. At $t = L/(2c)$, the string is completely horizontal. Figures 1.30(l), (m), (n), and (o) show the string at four additional times. This procedure clearly yields the position of the string at any required time.

What is most interesting is that these graphs suggest the following physical description for the motion of the string. Figures 1.30(a)–(g) indicate that the initial deflection $f(x)$ in the string divides into two parts, each equal to one-half of $f(x)$, one traveling to the left with velocity $-c$ and the other traveling to the right with velocity c. Figures 1.30(h)–(o) suggest that when these disturbances reach the fixed ends of the string at time $7L/(16c)$, they are reflected there with a reversal of sign. The reflected disturbance then combines with the original disturbance to yield the total deflection. Reflected disturbances then travel toward one another at speed c, eventually combining at time $t = L/c$ to give a disturbance identical to that in Figure 1.30(a), but with a reversal in sign.

For times $t > L/c$, the disturbances separate again, travel to the ends of the string, are reflected there, and recombine at $t = 2L/c$ to yield the initial position in Figure 1.30(a).

For times $t > 2L/c$, the two disturbances continue to travel back and forth along the string, interfering constructively near the center of the string and destructively at the ends.

All of these things happen very quickly. For instance, if the tension in a 1-m string with density $\rho = 2.0$ g/m is 50 N, then $2L/c = 0.0126$. Thus, the initial displacement separates into two parts, and these two disturbances travel twice the length of the string and recombine to give the initial displacement in 0.0126 s. In other words, all of this happens $1/0.0126 = 79$ times each second, too fast for the human eye, but not for sophisticated cameras.

Example 5:   Find the position of the string described by (120) at time $t = 1023L/(32c)$ when $f(x)$ is as shown in Figure 1.30(a).

Solution: In each time interval of length $2L/c$ after $t = 0$, the initial disturbance separates into two parts; each part travels to an end of the string and is reflected, then travels to the other end of the string and is reflected, and the parts then recombine to form $f(x)$ once again. Since $1023L/(32c) = 15(2L/c) + 63L/(32c)$, the position of the string at time $t = 1023L/(32c)$ is identical to that at $t = 63L/(32c)$. But this is 63/64 of the time for a complete cycle; that is, the two waves will be in the positions shown in Figure 1.31(a). These are combined to give the position of the string in Figure 1.31(b).

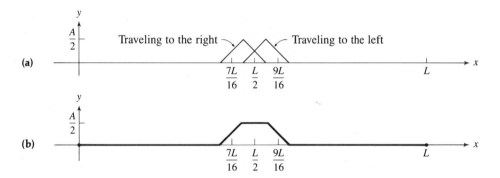

Figure 1.31

An alternative procedure is to write (120) at $t = 1023L/(32c)$ in the form

$$y\left(x, \frac{1023L}{32c}\right) = \frac{1}{2}\left[f\left(x + \frac{1023L}{32}\right) + f\left(x - \frac{1023L}{32}\right)\right]$$

$$= \frac{1}{2}\left[f\left(x + 16(2L) - \frac{L}{32}\right) + f\left(x - 16(2L) + \frac{L}{32}\right)\right]$$

$$= \frac{1}{2}\left[f\left(x - \frac{L}{32}\right) + f\left(x + \frac{L}{32}\right)\right],$$

since $f(x)$ is $2L$-periodic $[f(x + 2L) = f(x)]$. These functions are shown in Figure 1.31(a) and added in 1.31(b). ∎

The above discussion and example have illustrated that the motion of a string with initial displacement $f(x)$ as shown in Figure 1.30(a) and zero initial velocity is easily described. For more complicated functions $f(x)$, such as in Figure 1.32, the principles are the same; the only difference is that reflections at the ends of the string begin immediately. Examples of this are given in Exercises 3 and 4.

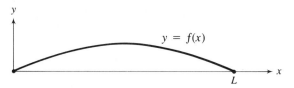

Figure 1.32

These ideas may also be extended to the situation in which the string is given a nonzero initial velocity $g(x)$, but no initial displacement, $f(x) \equiv 0$. In this case, (119) yields

$$y(x, t) = \frac{1}{2c} \int_{x-ct}^{x+ct} g(\zeta) \, d\zeta \tag{121a}$$

as the displacement of the string at position x and time t. Suppose, for example, that

$$g(x) = \begin{cases} 0 & 0 \le x < 7L/16 \\ k & 7L/16 < x < 9L/16, \\ 0 & 9L/16 < x \le L \end{cases}$$

where $k > 0$ is a constant (Figure 1.33). (It is not obviously so, but such an initial velocity can be achieved by striking that part of the string $7L/16 < x < 9L/16$ with a hammer.)

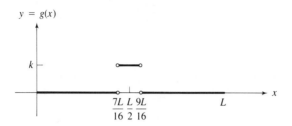

Figure 1.33

If we denote by $G(x)$ the antiderivative

$$G(x) = \frac{1}{2c} \int_0^x g(\zeta)\, d\zeta,$$

$y(x,t)$ can be expressed in the form

$$y(x,t) = G(x + ct) - G(x - ct), \tag{121b}$$

where, because $g(x)$ is extended as an odd, $2L$-periodic function [Figure 1.34(a)], the graph of $G(x)$ is as shown in Figure 1.34(b). The position of the string at any given time can now be obtained by the (destructive) combination of the left-traveling wave $G(x + ct)$ and the right-traveling wave $G(x - ct)$. Results are shown for various times in Figure 1.35.

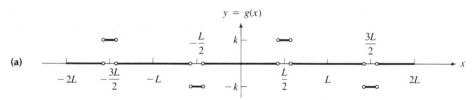

(a)

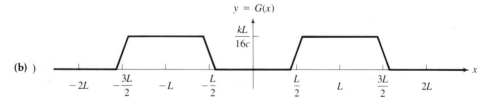

(b)

Figure 1.34

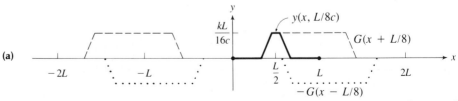

(a)

Figure 1.35

(Continued)

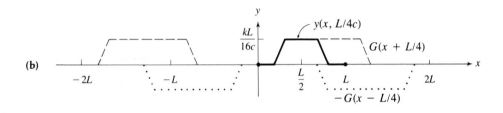

(b)

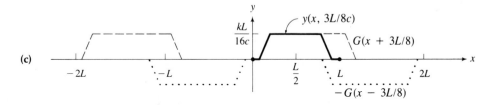

(c)

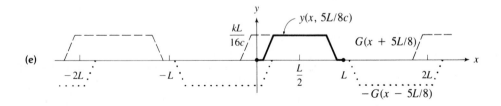

(d)

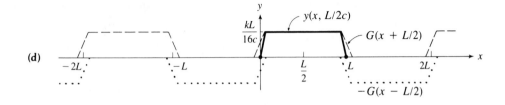

(e)

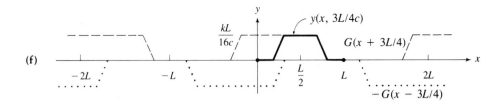

(f)

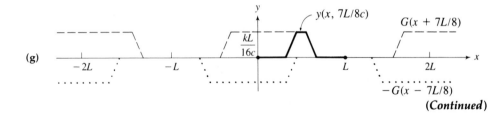

(g)

Figure 1.35
(*Continued*)

(*Continued*)

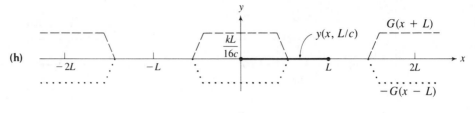

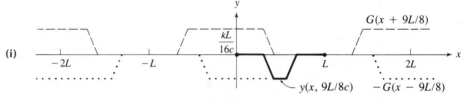

Figure 1.35
(Continued)

When a string has both an initial displacement $f(x)$ and an initial velocity $g(x)$, graphical techniques may still be used to determine the solution of (115). We express $y(x,t)$ in the form $y(x,t) = u(x,t) + v(x,t)$, where $u(x,t)$ and $v(x,t)$ satisfy the problems

$$\frac{\partial^2 u}{\partial t^2} = c^2 \frac{\partial^2 u}{\partial x^2} \qquad \frac{\partial^2 v}{\partial t^2} = c^2 \frac{\partial^2 v}{\partial x^2}$$

$$u(0,t) = 0 \qquad\qquad v(0,t) = 0$$

$$u(L,t) = 0 \qquad\qquad v(L,t) = 0$$

$$u(x,0) = f(x) \qquad\quad v(x,0) = 0$$

$$u_t(x,0) = 0 \qquad\qquad v_t(x,0) = g(x).$$

Exercises 1.7

1. Show that the transformation of independent variables $v = x + ct$ and $\eta = x - ct$ replaces the wave equation (115a) with (116).

2. Determine the position of the string in Figure 1.30(a) when (a) $t = L/c$; (b) $t = 21L/(8c)$.

3. Use the graphical techniques of this section to determine the displacements of a string with zero initial velocity and initial displacement

$$f(x) = \begin{cases} x/8 & 0 \le x \le L/2 \\ (L - x)/8 & L/2 \le x \le L \end{cases}$$

at the following times:

(a) $t = L/(8c)$ (b) $t = L/(4c)$ (c) $t = 3L/(8c)$ (d) $t = L/(2c)$

(e) $t = 5L/(8c)$ (f) $t = 3L/(4c)$ (g) $t = 7L/(8c)$ (h) $t = L/c$

4. Repeat Exercise 3 with $f(x) = \sin(2\pi x/L)$, $0 \le x \le L$.

5. Use the graphical techniques of this section to determine the displacements of a string with zero initial displacement and initial velocity

$$g(x) = \begin{cases} 0 & 0 \le x < L/4 \\ 1 & L/4 < x < 3L/4 \\ 0 & 3L/4 < x \le L \end{cases}$$

for the times in Exercise 3.

6. Repeat Exercise 5 with

$$g(x) = \begin{cases} 0 & 0 \le x < L/8 \\ 1 & L/8 < x < 3L/8 \\ 0 & 3L/8 < x < 5L/8. \\ 1 & 5L/8 < x < 7L/8 \\ 0 & 7L/8 < x \le L \end{cases}$$

1.8 Classification of Second-Order Partial Differential Equations

The material in this section is not essential at this point in our discussions. It can be considered at any time, since it is neither a prerequisite for subsequent discussions nor dependent on them. We include it here because it acts somewhat as a justification for the approach that we take in the remainder of the book. We intend solving the initial boundary value problems in Sections 1.2–1.6 using the techniques of separation of variables; Fourier transforms, both finite and infinite; Laplace transforms; and Green's functions. Second-order PDEs play a prominent role in these problems; the only application we have seen so far that gives rise to a PDE that is not second order is that for beam vibrations. What we illustrate here is that all linear second-order PDEs (we define this term shortly) are basically of three types. These types correspond generally to Poisson's equation, the wave equation, and the heat conduction equation. Consequently, once we learn how to apply the above techniques to these three equations, we have essentially learned how to handle all second-order linear equations.

For purposes of classification, it is not necessary to restrict consideration to linear equations. The classification is also valid for equations that are linear only in their second derivatives. Such equations, in two independent variables, are of the form

$$a(x, y)u_{xx} + b(x, y)u_{xy} + c(x, y)u_{yy} = f(x, y, u, u_x, u_y), \tag{122}$$

where f is any function of its arguments whatsoever. It is assumed that a, b, and c have continuous first partial derivatives in some domain D and that these coefficient functions do not all vanish simultaneously. We classify such PDEs into one of three types—elliptic, parabolic, or hyperbolic—and each type of PDE displays characteristics quite distinct from the others. This classification is stated as follows:

Partial differential equation (122) is said to be hyperbolic at a point (x, y) if

$$b^2 - 4ac > 0; \tag{123a}$$

parabolic at a point (x, y) if

$$b^2 - 4ac = 0; \tag{123b}$$

and elliptic at a point (x, y) if

$$b^2 - 4ac < 0. \tag{123c}$$

This classification is a pointwise one so that a PDE may change its type from point to point. The one-dimensional wave equation (37) is hyperbolic at all points; the one-dimensional heat conduction equation in Example 3 of Section 1.2 is parabolic; and Poisson's equation (6a) is elliptic.

We shall show that by means of a change of independent variables

$$v = v(x, y), \qquad \eta = \eta(x, y), \tag{124}$$

PDE (122) can be transformed into simpler forms. We require that functions $v(x, y)$ and $\eta(x, y)$ have continuous second partial derivatives in D and that the Jacobian

$$\frac{\partial(v, \eta)}{\partial(x, y)} \neq 0 \tag{125}$$

in order that the original variables x and y be retrievable:

$$x = x(v, \eta), \qquad y = y(v, \eta). \tag{126}$$

When we replace x and y by v and η, we denote the dependent variable by $w(v, \eta) = u[x(v, \eta), y(v, \eta)]$. It follows, then, that $u(x, y) = w[v(x, y), \eta(x, y)]$, and chain rules for partial derivatives permit us to express derivatives of $u(x, y)$ with respect to x and y in terms of derivatives of w with respect to v and η:

$$u_x = w_v v_x + w_\eta \eta_x, \qquad u_y = w_v v_y + w_\eta \eta_y$$

and
$$u_{xx} = (w_{vv} v_x + w_{v\eta} \eta_x) v_x + w_v v_{xx} + (w_{\eta v} v_x + w_{\eta\eta} \eta_x) \eta_x + w_\eta \eta_{xx},$$

$$u_{xy} = (w_{vv} v_y + w_{v\eta} \eta_y) v_x + w_v v_{xy} + (w_{\eta v} v_y + w_{\eta\eta} \eta_y) \eta_x + w_\eta \eta_{xy},$$

$$u_{yy} = (w_{vv} v_y + w_{v\eta} \eta_y) v_y + w_v v_{yy} + (w_{\eta v} v_y + w_{\eta\eta} \eta_y) \eta_y + w_\eta \eta_{yy}.$$

The PDE in w as a function of v and η equivalent to (122) is therefore

$$(av_x^2 + bv_x v_y + cv_y^2) w_{vv} + [2av_x \eta_x + b(v_x \eta_y + v_y \eta_x) + 2cv_y \eta_y] w_{v\eta}$$
$$+ (a\eta_x^2 + b\eta_x \eta_y + c\eta_y^2) w_{\eta\eta} + (av_{xx} + bv_{xy} + cv_{yy}) w_v$$
$$+ (a\eta_{xx} + b\eta_{xy} + c\eta_{yy}) w_\eta = f[x(v, \eta), y(v, \eta), w, w_v v_x + w_\eta \eta_x, w_v v_y + w_\eta \eta_y]$$

or
$$\alpha w_{vv} + \beta w_{v\eta} + \gamma w_{\eta\eta} = F(v, \eta, w, w_v, w_\eta), \tag{127a}$$

where
$$\alpha = av_x^2 + bv_x v_y + cv_y^2,$$

$$\beta = 2av_x \eta_x + b(v_x \eta_y + v_y \eta_x) + 2cv_y \eta_y, \tag{127b}$$

$$\gamma = a\eta_x^2 + b\eta_x \eta_y + c\eta_y^2$$

and
$$F(v, \eta, w, w_v, w_\eta) = f[x(v, \eta), y(v, \eta), w, w_v v_x + w_\eta \eta_x, w_v v_y + w_\eta \eta_y]$$
$$- (av_{xx} + bv_{xy} + cv_{yy}) w_v$$
$$- (a\eta_{xx} + b\eta_{xy} + c\eta_{yy}) w_\eta. \tag{127c}$$

It is a simple exercise to show that

$$\beta^2 - 4\alpha\gamma = (b^2 - 4ac) \left(\frac{\partial(v, \eta)}{\partial(x, y)} \right)^2, \tag{128}$$

a result that proves that our classification of PDEs is invariant under a real transformation of independent variables.

We now suppose that PDE (122) is of the same type at every point (x, y) in D and show that hyperbolic PDEs can be transformed into the *canonical* form

$$w_{v\eta} = F(v, \eta, w, w_v, w_\eta); \tag{129a}$$

parabolic PDEs can be transformed into the canonical form

$$w_{vv} = F(v, \eta, w, w_v, w_\eta); \tag{129b}$$

and elliptic PDEs can be transformed into the form

$$w_{vv} + w_{\eta\eta} = F(v, \eta, w, w_v, w_\eta). \tag{129c}$$

Hyperbolic Equations

For hyperbolic PDEs, we claim the existence of a transformation (124) that reduces the PDE to canonical form (129a). This is possible if functions $v(x, y)$ and $\eta(x, y)$ can be found to satisfy

$$0 = \alpha = av_x^2 + bv_xv_y + cv_y^2, \tag{130a}$$

$$0 = \gamma = a\eta_x^2 + b\eta_x\eta_y + c\eta_y^2 \tag{130b}$$

or

$$0 = a\left(\frac{v_x}{v_y}\right)^2 + b\frac{v_x}{v_y} + c, \tag{131a}$$

$$0 = a\left(\frac{\eta_x}{\eta_y}\right)^2 + b\frac{\eta_x}{\eta_y} + c; \tag{131b}$$

that is, the ratios v_x/v_y and η_x/η_y must satisfy the same equation,

$$a\lambda^2 + b\lambda + c = 0. \tag{132}$$

Since $b^2 - 4ac > 0$, there are two distinct solutions, $\lambda_1 = \lambda_1(x, y)$ and $\lambda_2 = \lambda_2(x, y)$, of this quadratic. Consequently, when functions $v(x, y)$ and $\eta(x, y)$ satisfy the first-order PDEs

$$v_x = \lambda_1(x, y)v_y, \qquad \eta_x = \lambda_2(x, y)\eta_y, \tag{133}$$

the PDE in w as a function of v and η is reduced to the form

$$\beta w_{v\eta} = F(v, \eta, w, w_v, w_\eta). \tag{134}$$

Since $\beta^2 - 4\alpha\gamma = \beta^2 = (b^2 - 4ac)[\partial(v, \eta)/\partial(x, y)]^2 \neq 0$, we may divide by β and obtain the canonical form for a hyperbolic PDE.

Because of the form of PDEs (133), solutions can be obtained with ODEs. Indeed, suppose the ordinary differential equation

$$\frac{dy}{dx} = -\lambda_1(x, y) \tag{135}$$

has a solution defined implicitly by

$$v(x, y) = C_1. \tag{136}$$

Then each curve in this one-parameter family has slope defined by

$$v_x + v_y \frac{dy}{dx} = 0 \qquad \text{or} \qquad \frac{dy}{dx} = -\frac{v_x}{v_y}. \tag{137}$$

Consequently, when (135) is solved in form (136), function $v(x, y)$ satisfies the PDE

$$\frac{v_x}{v_y} = \lambda_1(x, y). \tag{138}$$

The curves defined implicitly by (136) are called *characteristic curves* for the hyperbolic PDE; they are determined by the coefficients a, b, and c in the equation.

Similarly, the ODE

$$\frac{dy}{dx} = -\lambda_2(x, y) \tag{139}$$

defines a one-parameter family of curves

$$\eta(x, y) = C_2, \tag{140}$$

also called characteristic curves, and $\eta(x, y)$ is a solution of $\eta_x = \lambda_2(x, y)\eta_y$.

Each of the families $v(x, y) = C_1$ and $\eta(x, y) = C_2$ forms a covering of the domain of the xy-plane in which the PDE is hyperbolic (Figure 1.36). Furthermore, at no point can the particular curves from each family share a common tangent (else $\lambda_1 = \lambda_2$ at that point).

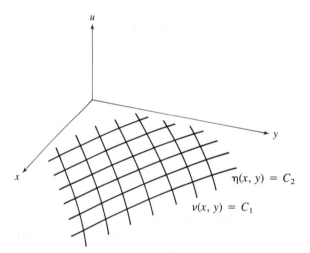

Figure 1.36

Under the transformation $v = v(x, y)$, $\eta = \eta(x, y)$, regarded as a mapping from the xy-plane to the $v\eta$-plane, curves along which v and η are constant in the xy-plane become coordinate lines in the $v\eta$-plane. Since these are precisely the characteristic curves, we conclude that when a hyperbolic PDE is in canonical form, coordinate lines are characteristic curves for the PDE. In other words, characteristic curves of a hyperbolic PDE are those curves to which the PDE must be referred as coordinate curves in order that it take on canonical form.

Example 6:   Show that the one-dimensional wave equation

$$\frac{\partial^2 y}{\partial t^2} - \frac{\tau}{\rho}\frac{\partial^2 y}{\partial x^2} = \frac{1}{\rho}F(x, t, y, y_x, y_t)$$

is hyperbolic, and find an equivalent equation in canonical form.

Solution: Since $b^2 - 4ac = 4\tau/\rho > 0$, the PDE is hyperbolic. Characteristic curves can be found by solving the ODE

$$\frac{dx}{dt} = -\lambda(x, t),$$

where $\lambda(x, t)$ satisfies $\lambda^2 - \tau/\rho = 0$. From the equations

$$\frac{dx}{dt} = -\lambda_1 = -\sqrt{\frac{\tau}{\rho}} \quad \text{and} \quad \frac{dx}{dt} = -\lambda_2 = \sqrt{\frac{\tau}{\rho}},$$

we obtain the characteristic curves

$$x = -\sqrt{\frac{\tau}{\rho}}t + C_1, \qquad x = \sqrt{\frac{\tau}{\rho}}t + C_2.$$

It follows, then, that the transformation

$$v = x + \sqrt{\frac{\tau}{\rho}}t, \qquad \eta = x - \sqrt{\frac{\tau}{\rho}}t$$

will reduce the wave equation to canonical form in $w(v, \eta)$:

$$\frac{\partial^2 w}{\partial v \partial \eta} = \frac{-1}{4\tau}F\left(x(v, \eta),\, t(v, \eta),\, w,\, w_v + w_\eta,\, \sqrt{\frac{\tau}{\rho}}w_v - \sqrt{\frac{\tau}{\rho}}w_\eta\right). \qquad \blacksquare$$

Notice that when $F \equiv 0$ in this example, the canonical form for the one-dimensional wave equation $y_{tt} - (\tau/\rho)y_{xx} = 0$ is

$$\frac{\partial^2 w}{\partial v \partial \eta} = 0.$$

This is precisely equation (116) of Section 1.7, but now we see the origin of the transformation $v = x + ct$ and $\eta = x - ct$.

If $\psi(v)$ and $\phi(\eta)$ are any two (twice continuously differentiable) functions of the canonical variables v and η, then

$$\psi_x = \psi'(v)v_x = \lambda_1(x, y)v_y\psi'(v) = \lambda_1(x, y)\psi_y,$$
$$\phi_x = \phi'(\eta)\eta_x = \lambda_2(x, y)\eta_y\phi'(\eta) = \lambda_2(x, y)\phi_y.$$

Thus, $\psi[v(x, y)]$ and $\phi[\eta(x, y)]$ also satisfy (133), and it follows that any transformation of the form

$$\psi = \psi[v(x, y)], \qquad \phi = \phi[\eta(x, y)] \tag{141}$$

also reduces the PDE to canonical form (in ψ and ϕ).

Finally, notice that if we set $r = v + \eta$, $s = v - \eta$, and $f(r, s) = w[v(r, s), \eta(r, s)]$, then

$$w_v = f_r r_v + f_s s_v = f_r + f_s$$

and

$$w_{v\eta} = f_{rr} r_\eta + f_{rs} s_\eta + f_{sr} r_\eta + f_{ss} s_\eta$$
$$= f_{rr} - f_{rs} + f_{sr} - f_{ss} = f_{rr} - f_{ss}.$$

Consequently, the PDE in $f(r, s)$ corresponding to (129a) is

$$f_{rr} - f_{ss} = F[v(r, s), \eta(r, s), f, f_r + f_s, f_r - f_s]; \tag{142}$$

this is sometimes used as a canonical form for hyperbolic equations.

Parabolic Equations

Parabolic equations can be transformed into canonical form (129b) by (124) if functions $v(x, y)$ and $\eta(x, y)$ can be found to satisfy

$$0 = \beta = 2av_x\eta_x + b(v_x\eta_y + v_y\eta_x) + 2cv_y\eta_y, \tag{143a}$$
$$0 = \gamma = a\eta_x^2 + b\eta_x\eta_y + c\eta_y^2. \tag{143b}$$

The second equation can be written in the form

$$0 = a\left(\frac{\eta_x}{\eta_y}\right)^2 + b\left(\frac{\eta_x}{\eta_y}\right) + c \tag{144}$$

so that η_x/η_y must satisfy

$$0 = a\lambda^2 + b\lambda + c. \tag{145}$$

Since $b^2 - 4ac = 0$, there is exactly one solution $\lambda = \lambda(x, y)$ of this quadratic, and $\eta(x, y)$ must therefore satisfy the first-order PDE

$$\eta_x = \lambda(x, y)\eta_y. \tag{146}$$

When $\eta(x, y)$ is so defined, $\gamma = 0$ and, from (128),

$$0 = (b^2 - 4ac)\left(\frac{\partial(v, \eta)}{\partial(x, y)}\right)^2 = \beta^2 - 4\alpha\gamma = \beta^2.$$

Thus, β must also vanish, and PDE (127a) in the parabolic case reduces to

$$\alpha w_{vv} = F(v, \eta, w, w_v, w_\eta). \tag{147}$$

Since $\alpha \neq 0$ (why?), we may divide to obtain the canonical form (129b) for a parabolic PDE.

We may obtain $\eta(x, y)$ by writing the solutions of the ODE

$$\frac{dy}{dx} = -\lambda(x, y) \tag{148}$$

in the form

$$\eta(x, y) = C. \tag{149}$$

The curves in this one-parameter family are called characteristic curves for the parabolic PDE. Parabolic PDEs therefore have only one family of characteristic curves. Notice that no mention of v has been made throughout the discussion. It follows that the canonical form for parabolic PDEs is obtained for arbitrary $v(x, y)$, except that $v(x, y)$ must be chosen to yield a nonvanishing Jacobian (125).

Example 7:   Is the one-dimensional heat conduction equation

$$k\frac{\partial^2 U}{\partial x^2} = \frac{\partial U}{\partial t} - \frac{k}{\kappa}g(x, t)$$

parabolic?

Solution: The equation is already in canonical form for a parabolic PDE.   ∎

Example 8:   Show that the PDE

$$x^2 u_{xx} - 2xy u_{xy} + y^2 u_{yy} = x^2 + u_y$$

is parabolic, and find an equivalent PDE in canonical form.

Solution: Because $b^2 - 4ac = (-2xy)^2 - 4(x^2)(y^2) = 0$, the PDE is everywhere parabolic. Characteristic curves can be found by solving

$$\frac{dy}{dx} = -\lambda(x, y)$$

where $\lambda(x, y)$ satisfies

$$0 = x^2\lambda^2 - 2xy\lambda + y^2 = (x\lambda - y)^2.$$

Consequently, we solve

$$\frac{dy}{dx} = -\frac{y}{x},$$

the solution of which can be written in the form $xy = C$. We choose therefore $\eta(x, y) = xy$, and $v(x, y)$ is arbitrary except that the Jacobian $\partial(v, \eta)/\partial(x, y) \neq 0$. If we choose $v(x, y) = y$, then

$$\frac{\partial(v, \eta)}{\partial(x, y)} = \begin{vmatrix} 0 & 1 \\ y & x \end{vmatrix} = -y \neq 0 \quad \text{(except along the x-axis).}$$

Instead of using (127) to write the PDE in $w(v, \eta)$ equivalent to the original equation in $u(x, y)$, let us perform the transformation. To do this, we require the following partial derivatives:

$$u_x = w_v v_x + w_\eta \eta_x = y w_\eta, \qquad u_y = w_v v_y + w_\eta \eta_y = w_v + x w_\eta,$$
$$u_{xx} = y(w_{\eta v} v_x + w_{\eta\eta}\eta_x) = y^2 w_{\eta\eta},$$
$$u_{xy} = w_\eta + y(w_{\eta v} v_y + w_{\eta\eta}\eta_y) = w_\eta + y w_{\eta v} + xy w_{\eta\eta},$$
$$u_{yy} = w_{vv} v_y + w_{v\eta}\eta_y + x(w_{\eta v} v_y + w_{\eta\eta}\eta_y) = w_{vv} + 2x w_{v\eta} + x^2 w_{\eta\eta}.$$

Substitution of these into the PDE for $u(x, y)$ along with $x = \eta/v$ and $y = v$ gives

$$\frac{\eta^2}{v^2} v^2 w_{\eta\eta} - 2\frac{\eta}{v} v \left(w_\eta + v w_{\eta v} + \frac{\eta}{v} v w_{\eta\eta} \right) + v^2 \left(w_{vv} + 2\frac{\eta}{v} w_{\eta v} + \frac{\eta^2}{v^2} w_{\eta\eta} \right)$$

$$= \frac{\eta^2}{v^2} + w_v + \frac{\eta}{v} w_\eta.$$

Thus, the PDE equivalent to the given equation is

$$w_{vv} = \frac{1}{v^4} [\eta^2 + v^2 w_v + \eta v(1 + 2v) w_\eta],$$

valid in any domain not containing points on the x-axis (for which $v = 0$).   ■

Elliptic Equations

Transformation (124) reduces an elliptic PDE to canonical form (129c) if functions $v(x, y)$ and $\eta(x, y)$ can be found to satisfy

$$0 = 2av_x\eta_x + b(v_x\eta_y + v_y\eta_x) + 2cv_y\eta_y, \tag{150a}$$

$$0 = a(v_x^2 - \eta_x^2) + b(v_x v_y - \eta_x\eta_y) + c(v_y^2 - \eta_y^2). \tag{150b}$$

For hyperbolic PDEs, $v(x, y)$ and $\eta(x, y)$ satisfied first-order PDEs that were separated one from the other. Similarly, $\eta(x, y)$ in the parabolic case satisfied a first-order equation that was independent of $v(x, y)$. Unfortunately, equations (150) for $v(x, y)$ and $\eta(x, y)$ are mixed; both unknowns appear in both equations. In an attempt to separate them, we multiply the first by the complex number i and add to the second to give

$$a(v_x + i\eta_x)^2 + b(v_x + i\eta_x)(v_y + i\eta_y) + c(v_y + i\eta_y)^2 = 0.$$

This equation can be solved for two possible values of the ratio

$$\frac{v_x + i\eta_x}{v_y + i\eta_y} = \frac{-b \pm \sqrt{b^2 - 4ac}}{2a} = \frac{-b \pm i\sqrt{4ac - b^2}}{2a} \tag{151}$$

(since $b^2 - 4ac$ is known to be negative). Real and imaginary parts of equation (151) give

$$v_x = \frac{-bv_y - (\pm)\eta_y\sqrt{4ac - b^2}}{2a}, \qquad \eta_x = \frac{-b\eta_y \pm v_y\sqrt{4ac - b^2}}{2a} \tag{152}$$

or $$2av_x + bv_y = -(\pm)\eta_y\sqrt{4ac - b^2}, \qquad \pm v_y\sqrt{4ac - b^2} = 2a\eta_x + b\eta_y. \tag{153}$$

These are linear equations in v_x and v_y that have the following solutions in terms of the partial derivatives η_x and η_y:

$$v_x = -\frac{2c\eta_y + b\eta_x}{\pm\sqrt{4ac - b^2}}, \qquad v_y = \frac{2a\eta_x + b\eta_y}{\pm\sqrt{4ac - b^2}}. \tag{154}$$

These equations (called the Beltrami equations) are equivalent to (150), but they still form a mixed set of equations in the sense that v and η appear in both. A second-order

PDE for $\eta(x, y)$ is evidently

$$\frac{\partial}{\partial x}\left(\frac{2a\eta_x + b\eta_y}{\sqrt{4ac - b^2}}\right) = \frac{\partial}{\partial y}\left(-\frac{2c\eta_y + b\eta_x}{\sqrt{4ac - b^2}}\right). \tag{155}$$

If this equation is solved for $\eta(x, y)$ and then used to determine $v(x, y)$, the original PDE in u is transformed to the form

$$\alpha w_{vv} + \alpha w_{\eta\eta} = F(v, \eta, w, w_v, w_\eta). \tag{156}$$

Since $0 < (b^2 - 4ac)[\partial(v, \eta)/\partial(x, y)]^2 = \beta^2 - 4\alpha\gamma = -4\alpha^2$, it follows that $\alpha \neq 0$, and the elliptic PDE can be obtained in canonical form (129c).

The only difficulty with this procedure is that in general, PDE (155) for $\eta(x, y)$ may not be significantly easier to solve than the original PDE in $u(x, y)$. Instead, notice that the form of equation (151) suggests that we define a complex function $\phi(x, y)$ of two real variables x and y,

$$\phi(x, y) = v(x, y) + i\eta(x, y), \tag{157}$$

in which case $v(x, y)$ and $\eta(x, y)$ can be retrieved as the real and imaginary parts of $\phi(x, y)$. It is clear that $\phi(x, y)$ must satisfy one of the equations

$$\frac{\phi_x}{\phi_y} = \frac{-b \pm i\sqrt{4ac - b^2}}{2a}. \tag{158}$$

To solve either one of these complex PDEs for $\phi(x, y)$, we employ the same technique used for hyperbolic and parabolic equations: we consider the ordinary differential equation

$$\frac{dy}{dx} = \frac{b + i\sqrt{4ac - b^2}}{2a} \tag{159}$$

[or $dy/dx = (b - i\sqrt{4ac - b^2})/(2a)$] for y as a function of x. Because the right side is complex, we must (temporarily) regard x and y as complex variables. If we obtain a solution in the form

$$\phi(x, y) = C, \tag{160}$$

then

$$\frac{dy}{dx} = -\frac{\phi_x}{\phi_y} = \frac{b + i\sqrt{4ac - b^2}}{2a}, \tag{161}$$

clearly indicating that $\phi(x, y)$ is the required function. Real and imaginary parts of ϕ (once again regarding x and y as real) give $v(x, y)$ and $\eta(x, y)$.

Because x and y in (159) are considered complex, elliptic PDEs do not have real characteristic curves.

Example 9:   Find regions in which

$$u_{xx} + x^2 u_{yy} = y u_y$$

is elliptic, and find an equivalent PDE in canonical form.

Solution: Since $b^2 - 4ac = -4x^2$, the PDE is elliptic in any region that does not contain points on the y-axis. To find a transformation that will reduce the PDE to canonical form, we set

$$\frac{dy}{dx} = -\lambda(x, y),$$

where $\lambda(x, y)$ is one of the complex solutions of $\lambda^2 + x^2 = 0$. If we choose $\lambda = -ix$, then

$$\frac{dy}{dx} = ix$$

and $y = ix^2/2 + C$. The transformation functions v and η are the real and imaginary parts of $y - ix^2/2$,

$$v(x, y) = y, \qquad \eta(x, y) = \frac{-x^2}{2}.$$

With this transformation,

$$u_x = w_v v_x + w_\eta \eta_x = -xw_\eta, \qquad u_y = w_v v_y + w_\eta \eta_y = w_v,$$

$$u_{xx} = -w_\eta - x(w_{v\eta}v_x + w_{\eta\eta}\eta_x) = -w_\eta + x^2 w_{\eta\eta},$$

$$u_{yy} = w_{vv}v_y + w_{v\eta}\eta_y = w_{vv}.$$

Substitution of these into the original PDE gives

$$w_{vv} + w_{\eta\eta} = \frac{-1}{2\eta}(w_\eta + vw_v).$$

Had we chosen to set $dy/dx = -ix$, the transformation would have been $v(x, y) = y$, $\eta(x, y) = x^2/2$, and the equivalent PDE would have been

$$w_{vv} + w_{\eta\eta} = \frac{1}{2\eta}(w_\eta + vw_v). \qquad \blacksquare$$

To summarize our results, all second-order PDEs in two independent variables that are linear in their second derivatives can be classified as hyperbolic, parabolic, or elliptic. The one-dimensional wave equation is hyperbolic, the one-dimensional heat equation is parabolic, and the two-dimensional Poisson's equation is elliptic. We can therefore discover properties of all second-order PDEs in two independent variables that are linear in second derivatives by analyzing vibrating strings, heat conduction in rods, and two-dimensional electrostatic problems. Each type of equation has properties distinct from the others; properties of hyperbolic equations differ from those of parabolic equations, and these in turn differ from those of elliptic equations. For instance, in Section 1.7 we saw that a disturbance (more generally, information) is transmitted by the wave equation (a hyperbolic equation) at finite speed. Information (in the form of heat) is transmitted infinitely fast by the heat equation (see Section 5.6). Elliptic equations represent static or steady-state situations. Other properties of hyperbolic, parabolic, and elliptic equations are discussed throughout the book, particularly in Sections 5.6–5.8. Problems associated with these equations are even characterized differently; all three are accompanied by boundary conditions, but the wave equation has two initial conditions, the heat equation has one, and Poisson's equation has none.

Second-order PDEs in more than two independent variables can also be classified into types, including parabolic, elliptic, and hyperbolic. However, it is not usually possible to reduce such equations to simple canonical forms. One instance in which a canonical form is possible is for PDEs with constant coefficients. We shall not discuss the classification and canonical forms here, but we should point out that in this classification, the three-dimensional Laplace equation is elliptic, the multidimensional wave equation is hyperbolic, and the multidimensional heat equation is parabolic.

Exercises 1.8

In Exercises 1–4, classify the PDE as hyperbolic, parabolic, or elliptic and find an equivalent PDE in canonical form.

1. $u_{xx} + 2u_{xy} + u_{yy} = u_x - xu_y$

2. $u_{xx} + 2u_{xy} + 5u_{yy} = 3u_x - yu$

3. $3u_{xx} + 10u_{xy} + 3u_{yy} = 0$

4. $u_{xx} + 6u_{xy} + u_{yy} = 4uu_x$

In Exercises 5–11, determine where the PDE is hyperbolic, parabolic, and elliptic. Illustrate each region graphically in the xy-plane.

5. $u_{xx} + 2yu_{xy} + 5u_{yy} = 15x + 2y$

6. $x^2 u_{xx} + 4yu_{yy} = u$

7. $x^2 yu_{xx} + xyu_{xy} - y^2 u_{yy} = 0$

8. $xyu_{xx} -- xu_{xy} + u_{yy} = uu_x + 3$

9. $(\sin x)u_{xx} + (2\cos x)u_{xy} + (\sin x)u_{yy} = 0$

10. $(x \ln y)u_{xx} + 4u_{yy} = u_x - 3xyu$

11. $u_{xx} + xu_{xy} + yu_{yy} = 0$

12. Find a PDE in canonical form equivalent to the PDE in Example 8 that is valid in regions not containing points on the y-axis.

13. **(a)** Show that the Tricomi PDE

$$yu_{xx} + u_{yy} = 0$$

is hyperbolic when $y < 0$, parabolic when $y = 0$, and elliptic when $y > 0$.

(b) Find an equivalent PDE in canonical form when $y < 0$.

(c) Find an equivalent PDE in canonical form when $y > 0$.

(d) Find an equivalent PDE in canonical form when $y = 0$.

14. Find regions in which

$$x^2 u_{xx} + 4u_{yy} = u$$

is hyperbolic, parabolic, and elliptic. In each such region, find an equivalent PDE in canonical form.

15. Show that

$$y^2 u_{xx} - 2xyu_{xy} + x^2 u_{yy} = 0$$

is everywhere parabolic. Find an equivalent PDE in canonical form valid in regions not containing points on the x-axis.

16. Show that

$$u_{xx} + x^2 u_{xy} - \left(\frac{x^2}{2} + \frac{1}{4}\right) u_{yy} = 0$$

is hyperbolic in the entire xy-plane. Find its characteristic curves and illustrate them geometrically.

17. Show that the PDE

$$x u_{xy} + y u_{yy} = 0$$

is hyperbolic when $x \neq 0$. Find an equivalent PDE in canonical form.

18. **(a)** A second-order PDE in two independent variables x and y is said to be linear if it is of the form

$$a u_{xx} + b u_{xy} + c u_{yy} + d u_x + e u_y + f u = g(x, y),$$

where a, b, c, d, e, and f are functions of x and y only. Show that when these coefficients are constants, the canonical forms for hyperbolic, parabolic, and elliptic equations remain linear with constant coefficients:

$$w_{v\eta} + p w_v + q w_\eta + r w = g \quad \text{(hyperbolic)},$$
$$w_{vv} + p w_v + q w_\eta + r w = g \quad \text{(parabolic)},$$
$$w_{vv} + w_{\eta\eta} + p w_v + q w_\eta + r w = g \quad \text{(elliptic)}.$$

(b) Prove that in the case of a hyperbolic equation, the first-derivative terms w_v and w_η can be eliminated by a change of dependent variable

$$v(v, \eta) = e^{\varepsilon v + \rho \eta} w(v, \eta)$$

for appropriate constants ε and ρ.

(c) Verify that the transformation in (b) can be used to eliminate first derivatives for elliptic equations also.

(d) Show that the transformation in (b) will eliminate w_v and w for a parabolic equation when $q \neq 0$ and will eliminate w_v and w_η when $q = 0$.

In Exercises 19–21, use the results of Exercise 18 to find simplified canonical representations for the PDE.

19. $u_{xx} + 2u_{xy} + 5u_{yy} = 3u_x$

20. $u_{xx} + 6u_{xy} + u_{yy} = 4u_x$

21. $u_{xx} + 2u_{xy} + u_{yy} = u_x - u_y$

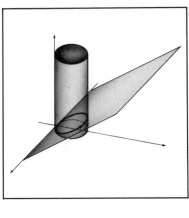

Fourier Series

2.1 Fourier Series

Power series play an integral part in real (and complex) analysis. Given a function $f(x)$ and a point $x = a$, it is investigated to what extent $f(x)$ can be expressed in the form

$$f(x) = \sum_{n=0}^{\infty} a_n(x - a)^n.$$

Perhaps one of the most important uses of such series (and one that we require in Chapter 8) is the solution of linear ODEs with variable coefficients. In this chapter we introduce a new type of series called a *Fourier series*; such series are indispensable to the study of PDEs. Fourier series are used in a theoretical way to determine properties of solutions of PDEs and in a practical way to find explicit representations of solutions. Some of the terminology associated with Fourier series is borrowed from ordinary vectors; in addition, many of the ideas in Fourier series have their origin in vector analysis. A quick review of pertinent ideas from vector analysis will therefore facilitate later comparisons and help to solidify underlying concepts in the new theory.

The Cartesian components of a vector $\mathbf{v}$ in space are three scalars v_x, v_y, and v_z such that $\mathbf{v} = v_x\hat{\mathbf{i}} + v_y\hat{\mathbf{j}} + v_z\hat{\mathbf{k}}$. Formulas for these components are

$$v_x = \mathbf{v} \cdot \hat{\mathbf{i}}, \qquad v_y = \mathbf{v} \cdot \hat{\mathbf{j}}, \qquad v_z = \mathbf{v} \cdot \hat{\mathbf{k}}. \tag{1}$$

These expressions are very simple, and the reason for this is that the basis vectors $\hat{\mathbf{i}}, \hat{\mathbf{j}},$ and $\hat{\mathbf{k}}$ are orthonormal; that is, they are mutually orthogonal (or perpendicular) and have length 1. Given different basis vectors, say $\mathbf{e}_1 = \hat{\mathbf{i}} + \hat{\mathbf{j}}, \mathbf{e}_2 = \hat{\mathbf{i}} - \hat{\mathbf{j}},$ and $\mathbf{e}_3 = 3\hat{\mathbf{k}},$ which remain orthogonal, it is still possible to express $\mathbf{v}$ in terms of the $\mathbf{e}_j,$

$$\mathbf{v} = v_1\mathbf{e}_1 + v_2\mathbf{e}_2 + v_3\mathbf{e}_3. \tag{2}$$

However, because the $\mathbf{e}_j$ do not have length 1, component formulas (1) must be replaced by somewhat more complicated expressions. Scalar products of (2) with $\mathbf{e}_1, \mathbf{e}_2,$ and $\mathbf{e}_3$ give

$$v_1 = \frac{\mathbf{v} \cdot \mathbf{e}_1}{|\mathbf{e}_1|^2}, \qquad v_2 = \frac{\mathbf{v} \cdot \mathbf{e}_2}{|\mathbf{e}_2|^2}, \qquad v_3 = \frac{\mathbf{v} \cdot \mathbf{e}_3}{|\mathbf{e}_3|^2}. \tag{3}$$

Were the $\mathbf{e}_j$ not orthogonal, expressions for components would be even more complicated, but we have no need for such generality here.

Thus, when an orthogonal basis is used for vectors, equations (3) yield components, and when the basis is orthonormal, the simpler expressions (1) prevail.

We now generalize these ideas to functions. When two functions $f(x)$ and $g(x)$ are defined on the interval $a \leq x \leq b,$ their *scalar product* with respect to a weight function $w(x)$ is defined as

$$\int_a^b w(x)f(x)g(x)\,dx. \tag{4}$$

This definition is much like the definition of the scalar product of ordinary vectors, $\mathbf{u} \cdot \mathbf{v} = u_x v_x + u_y v_y + u_z v_z,$ provided we think of a function as having an infinite number of components, its values at the points in the interval $a \leq x \leq b.$ Corresponding components of $f(x)$ and $g(x)$ are then multiplied together and added in (4). The weight function in scalar products (1) and (3) is unity; definition (4) is more general; it permits a variable weight function $w(x).$ Corresponding to the test for orthogonality of nonzero vectors $\mathbf{u}$ and $\mathbf{v},$ namely $\mathbf{u} \cdot \mathbf{v} = 0,$ we make the following definition for orthogonality of functions.

Definition

Two nonzero functions $f(x)$ and $g(x)$ are said to be orthogonal on the interval $a \leq x \leq b$ with respect to the weight function $w(x)$ if their scalar product vanishes:

$$\int_a^b w(x)f(x)g(x)dx = 0. \tag{5}$$

A sequence of functions $\{f_n(x)\} = f_1(x), f_2(x), \ldots$ is said to be orthogonal on $a \leq x \leq b$ with respect to $w(x)$ if every pair of functions is orthogonal:

$$\int_a^b w(x)f_n(x)f_m(x)\,dx = 0, \quad \text{when } n \neq m. \tag{6}$$

For example, since

$$\int_0^{2\pi} \sin nx \sin mx \, dx = \int_0^{2\pi} \frac{1}{2}(\cos(n-m)x - \cos(n+m)x) \, dx$$

$$= \frac{1}{2}\left\{ \frac{\sin(n-m)x}{n-m} - \frac{\sin(n+m)x}{n+m} \right\}_0^{2\pi} = 0,$$

the sequence of functions $\{\sin nx\}$ is orthogonal on the interval $0 \le x \le 2\pi$ with respect to the weight function $w(x) \equiv 1$. The sequence is also orthogonal with the same weight function on the interval $0 \le x \le \pi$.

By analogy with geometric vectors, where $|\mathbf{v}|^2 = \mathbf{v} \cdot \mathbf{v}$, we regard the scalar product of a function $f(x)$ with itself as the square of its length; that is, we define the *length* $\|f(x)\|$ of a function on the interval $a \le x \le b$ with respect to the weight function $w(x)$ as

$$\|f(x)\| = \sqrt{\int_a^b w(x)[f(x)]^2 \, dx}. \tag{7}$$

A sequence of functions $\{f_n(x)\}$ is said to be *orthonormal* on $a \le x \le b$ with respect to the weight function $w(x)$ if

$$\int_a^b w(x) f_n(x) f_m(x) \, dx = \begin{cases} 1 & n = m \\ 0 & n \ne m \end{cases}. \tag{8}$$

Condition (8) therefore requires the functions $f_n(x)$ to be mutually orthogonal and of unit length.

Any orthogonal sequence can be made orthonormal simply by dividing each function by its length; that is, when $\{f_n(x)\}$ is orthogonal, $\{f_n(x)/\|f_n(x)\|\}$ is orthonormal. For example, since

$$\int_0^\pi (\sin nx)^2 \, dx = \frac{\pi}{2},$$

the sequence $\{\sqrt{2/\pi} \sin nx\}$ is orthonormal with respect to the weight function $w(x) \equiv 1$ on $0 \le x \le \pi$.

With these preliminaries out of the way, we are now ready to consider Fourier series. In the theory of Fourier series, it is investigated to what extent a function $f(x)$ can be represented in an infinite series of the form

$$\frac{a_0}{2} + \sum_{n=1}^{\infty} \left(a_n \cos\frac{n\pi x}{L} + b_n \sin\frac{n\pi x}{L} \right), \tag{9}$$

where a_n and b_n are constants. The 2 in the first term of this series is included simply as a matter of convenience. (The formula for a_n, $n > 0$, will then include a_0 as well.)

Because $\cos(n\pi x/L)$ and $\sin(n\pi x/L)$ have period $2L/n$, it follows that any function $f(x)$ expressible in form (9) must necessarily be of period $2L$ (or of a period that evenly

---

† The notation $\{F(x)\}_a^b$ to represent $F(b) - F(a)$ is useful in evaluating definite integrals.

divides $2L$). That many $2L$-periodic functions can be expressed in this form is to a large extent attributable to the fact that the sine and cosine functions satisfy the following theorem.

Theorem 1

The set of functions $\{1, \cos(n\pi x/L), \sin(n\pi x/L)\}$ is orthogonal over the interval $0 \leq x \leq 2L$ with respect to the weight function $w(x) = 1$. Furthermore,

$$\int_0^{2L} 1^2 \, dx = 2L; \qquad \int_0^{2L} \left(\cos\frac{n\pi x}{L}\right)^2 dx = \int_0^{2L} \left(\sin\frac{n\pi x}{L}\right)^2 dx = L. \qquad (10)$$

(See Exercise 15 for a proof of this result.)

It follows that the functions $\{1/\sqrt{2L}, (1/\sqrt{L})\cos(n\pi x/L), (1/\sqrt{L})\sin(n\pi x/L)\}$ are orthonormal with respect to the weight function $w(x) = 1$ on the interval $0 \leq x \leq 2L$.

Suppose we neglect for the moment questions of convergence and formally set

$$f(x) = \frac{a_0}{2} + \sum_{n=1}^{\infty}\left(a_n \cos\frac{n\pi x}{L} + b_n \sin\frac{n\pi x}{L}\right). \qquad (11)$$

Just as v_x, v_y, and v_z are the components of $\mathbf{v}$ with respect to the basis vectors $\hat{\mathbf{i}}, \hat{\mathbf{j}}$, and $\hat{\mathbf{k}}$ in $\mathbf{v} = v_x\hat{\mathbf{i}} + v_y\hat{\mathbf{j}} + v_z\hat{\mathbf{k}}$, we regard the coefficients $a_0/2, a_n$, and b_n as components of $f(x)$ with respect to the basis functions $1, \cos(n\pi x/L)$, and $\sin(n\pi x/L)$. If we integrate both sides of (11) from $x = 0$ to $x = 2L$, and formally interchange the order of integration and summation on the right, we obtain

$$\int_0^{2L} f(x) \, dx = \frac{a_0}{2}(2L).$$

Thus,
$$a_0 = \frac{1}{L}\int_0^{2L} f(x) \, dx; \qquad (12a)$$

that is, if (11) is to hold, the constant term $a_0/2$ must be the average value of $f(x)$ over the interval $0 \leq x \leq 2L$. When we multiply both sides of equation (11) by $\cos(k\pi x/L)$, integrate from $x = 0$ to $x = 2L$, and once again interchange the order of integration and summation,

$$\int_0^{2L} f(x)\cos\frac{k\pi x}{L}\, dx = \int_0^{2L} \frac{a_0}{2}\cos\frac{k\pi x}{L}\, dx$$

$$+ \sum_{n=1}^{\infty}\left(\int_0^{2L} a_n \cos\frac{n\pi x}{L}\cos\frac{k\pi x}{L}\, dx + \int_0^{2L} b_n \sin\frac{n\pi x}{L}\cos\frac{k\pi x}{L}\, dx\right)$$

$$= a_k(L) \quad \text{(by the orthogonality of Theorem 1).}$$

Thus,
$$a_n = \frac{1}{L}\int_0^{2L} f(x)\cos\frac{n\pi x}{L}\, dx, \qquad n > 0. \qquad (12b)$$

Similarly,
$$b_n = \frac{1}{L}\int_0^{2L} f(x)\sin\frac{n\pi x}{L}\, dx. \qquad (12c)$$

We have found, therefore, that *if* $f(x)$ can be represented in form (11), and *if* the series is suitably convergent, coefficients a_n and b_n must be calculated according to (12). What we must answer is the converse question: If a_n and b_n are calculated according to (12), does series (11) converge to $f(x)$? Does it converge pointwise, uniformly, or in any other sense? When a_0, a_n, and b_n are calculated according to (12), the right side of (11) is called the *Fourier series* of $f(x)$. Numbers a_0, a_n, and b_n are called the *Fourier coefficients* of $f(x)$; they are, as we have already suggested, components of $f(x)$ with respect to the basis functions 1, $\cos(n\pi x/L)$, and $\sin(n\pi x/L)$.

Theorem 2, which follows shortly, guarantees that series (11) essentially converges to $f(x)$ when $f(x)$ is piecewise continuous and has a piecewise continuous first derivative. A function $f(x)$ is *piecewise continuous* on an interval $a \le x \le b$ if the interval can be divided into a finite number of subintervals inside each of which $f(x)$ is continuous and has finite limits as x approaches either end point of the subinterval from the interior. A $2L$-periodic function is said to be piecewise continuous if it is piecewise continuous on the interval $0 \le x \le 2L$. Figure 2.1(a) illustrates a $2L$-periodic function that is piecewise continuous; its discontinuities at $x = c$ and $x = d$ are finite. Because the discontinuity at $x = c$ in Figure 2.1(b) is not finite, this function is not piecewise continuous.

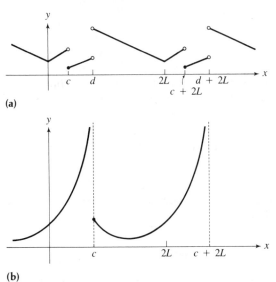

(a)

(b)

Figure 2.1

A function $f(x)$ is said to be *piecewise smooth* on an interval $a \le x \le b$ if $f(x)$ and $f'(x)$ are both piecewise continuous therein. A $2L$-periodic function is piecewise smooth if it is piecewise smooth on $0 \le x \le 2L$. The periodic functions in Figure 2.2 are both continuous: that in Figure 2.2(a) is piecewise smooth; that in Figure 2.2(b) is not. The $2L$-periodic function in Figure 2.3 is piecewise smooth.

Theorem 2

The Fourier series of a periodic, piecewise continuous function $f(x)$ converges to $[f(x+) + f(x-)]/2$ at any point at which $f(x)$ has both a left and right derivative.

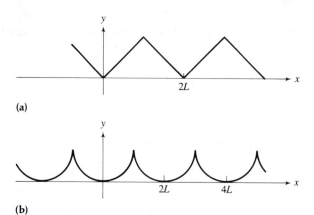

(a)

(b)

Figure 2.2

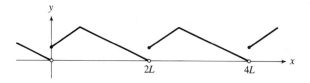

Figure 2.3

By $f(x+)$ we mean the right-hand limit of $f(x)$ at x, $\lim_{\varepsilon \to 0+} f(x + \varepsilon)$. Similarly, $f(x-) = \lim_{\varepsilon \to 0+} f(x - \varepsilon)$. The proof of this theorem is very lengthy; it requires verification of a number of preliminary results that, although interesting in their own right, detract from the flow of our discussion. We have therefore included the proof as Appendix A following Chapter 12.

Since functions that are piecewise smooth must have right and left derivatives at all points, we may state the following corollary to Theorem 2.

Corollary

When $f(x)$ is a periodic, piecewise smooth function, its Fourier series converges to $[f(x+) + f(x-)]/2$.

For such functions, we therefore write

$$\frac{f(x+) + f(x-)}{2} = \frac{a_0}{2} + \sum_{n=1}^{\infty} \left(a_n \cos\frac{n\pi x}{L} + b_n \sin\frac{n\pi x}{L} \right),$$

(13a)

where

$$a_n = \frac{1}{L} \int_0^{2L} f(x) \cos\frac{n\pi x}{L}\, dx, \qquad b_n = \frac{1}{L} \int_0^{2L} f(x) \sin\frac{n\pi x}{L}\, dx.$$

(13b)

There is nothing sacrosanct about the limits $x = 0$ and $x = 2L$ on the integrals in (13b); all that is required is integration over one full period of length $2L$. In other words, expressions (13b) could be replaced by

$$a_n = \frac{1}{L}\int_c^{c+2L} f(x)\cos\frac{n\pi x}{L}\,dx, \qquad b_n = \frac{1}{L}\int_c^{c+2L} f(x)\sin\frac{n\pi x}{L}\,dx, \qquad \text{(13c)}$$

where c is any number whatsoever.

If we make the agreement that at any point of discontinuity, $f(x)$ shall be defined (or redefined if necessary) as the average of its right- and left-hand limits, (13a) may be replaced by

$$f(x) = \frac{a_0}{2} + \sum_{n=1}^{\infty}\left(a_n\cos\frac{n\pi x}{L} + b_n\sin\frac{n\pi x}{L}\right). \qquad \text{(14)}$$

For example, the Fourier series of the function $f(x)$ in Figure 2.1(a) converges to the function in Figure 2.4; $f(x)$ must be defined as the average of its right- and left-hand limits at $x = d + 2nL$ and redefined as the average of its right- and left-hand limits at $x = c + 2nL$.

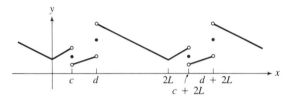

Figure 2.4

Example 1:   Find the Fourier series of the function $f(x)$ that is equal to x for $0 < x < 2L$ and is $2L$-periodic.

Solution: According to (13b), the Fourier coefficients are

$$a_0 = \frac{1}{L}\int_0^{2L} x\,dx = \frac{1}{L}\left\{\frac{x^2}{2}\right\}_0^{2L} = 2L;$$

$$a_n = \frac{1}{L}\int_0^{2L} x\cos\frac{n\pi x}{L}\,dx$$

$$= \frac{1}{L}\left\{\frac{Lx}{n\pi}\sin\frac{n\pi x}{L} + \frac{L^2}{n^2\pi^2}\cos\frac{n\pi x}{L}\right\}_0^{2L} = 0, \qquad n > 0;$$

$$b_n = \frac{1}{L}\int_0^{2L} x\sin\frac{n\pi x}{L}\,dx$$

$$= \frac{1}{L}\left\{-\frac{Lx}{n\pi}\cos\frac{n\pi x}{L} + \frac{L^2}{n^2\pi^2}\sin\frac{n\pi x}{L}\right\}_0^{2L} = -\frac{2L}{n\pi}, \qquad n > 0.$$

We may therefore write

$$f(x) = L + \sum_{n=1}^{\infty} -\frac{2L}{n\pi}\sin\frac{n\pi x}{L} = L\left(1 - \frac{2}{\pi}\sum_{n=1}^{\infty}\frac{1}{n}\sin\frac{n\pi x}{L}\right),$$

provided we define $f(x)$ as L at its points of discontinuity $x = 2nL$ (Figure 2.5).

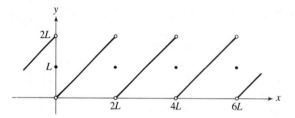

Figure 2.5

Example 2:   Find the Fourier series of the function $f(x)$ that is equal to x^2 for $-L \leq x \leq L$ and is of period $2L$.

Solution: In this example, it is more convenient to integrate over the interval $-L \leq x \leq L$. In other words, we use (13c) with $c = -L$ to calculate the Fourier coefficients:

$$a_0 = \frac{1}{L} \int_{-L}^{L} x^2 \, dx = \frac{1}{L} \left\{ \frac{x^3}{3} \right\}_{-L}^{L} = \frac{2L^2}{3};$$

$$a_n = \frac{1}{L} \int_{-L}^{L} x^2 \cos \frac{n\pi x}{L} \, dx$$

$$= \frac{1}{L} \left\{ \frac{Lx^2}{n\pi} \sin \frac{n\pi x}{L} + \frac{2L^2 x}{n^2 \pi^2} \cos \frac{n\pi x}{L} - \frac{2L^3}{n^3 \pi^3} \sin \frac{n\pi x}{L} \right\}_{-L}^{L}$$

$$= \frac{4L^2 (-1)^n}{n^2 \pi^2}, \qquad n > 0;$$

$$b_n = \frac{1}{L} \int_{-L}^{L} x^2 \sin \frac{n\pi x}{L} \, dx$$

$$= \frac{1}{L} \left\{ \frac{-Lx^2}{n\pi} \cos \frac{n\pi x}{L} + \frac{2L^2 x}{n^2 \pi^2} \sin \frac{n\pi x}{L} + \frac{2L^3}{n^3 \pi^3} \cos \frac{n\pi x}{L} \right\}_{-L}^{L}$$

$$= 0, \qquad n > 0.$$

Because $f(x)$ is continuous for all x (Figure 2.6), we may write

$$f(x) = \frac{L^2}{3} + \sum_{n=1}^{\infty} \frac{4L^2 (-1)^n}{n^2 \pi^2} \cos \frac{n\pi x}{L} = \frac{L^2}{3} + \frac{4L^2}{\pi^2} \sum_{n=1}^{\infty} \frac{(-1)^n}{n^2} \cos \frac{n\pi x}{L}.$$

This Fourier series can be used to find the sum of the series $\sum_{n=1}^{\infty} 1/n^2$. When we set $x = L$, and note that $f(L) = L^2$,

$$L^2 = \frac{L^2}{3} + \frac{4L^2}{\pi^2} \sum_{n=1}^{\infty} \frac{(-1)^n}{n^2} \cos n\pi$$

$$= \frac{L^2}{3} + \frac{4L^2}{\pi^2} \sum_{n=1}^{\infty} \frac{1}{n^2}.$$

This equation can be solved for

$$\sum_{n=1}^{\infty} \frac{1}{n^2} = \frac{\pi^2}{4L^2} \left(L^2 - \frac{L^2}{3} \right) = \frac{\pi^2}{6}.$$

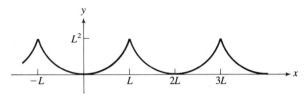

Figure 2.6

Example 3:   Find the Fourier series for the 2π-periodic function $f(x)$ in Figure 2.7.

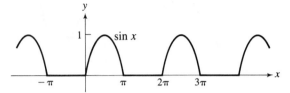

Figure 2.7

Solution: With $L = \pi$ in (13b),

$$a_0 = \frac{1}{\pi} \int_0^{2\pi} f(x)\,dx = \frac{1}{\pi} \int_0^{\pi} \sin x\,dx = \frac{1}{\pi}\{-\cos x\}_0^{\pi} = \frac{2}{\pi};$$

$$a_n = \frac{1}{\pi} \int_0^{2\pi} f(x)\cos nx\,dx = \frac{1}{\pi} \int_0^{\pi} \sin x \cos nx\,dx$$

$$= \frac{1}{\pi} \begin{cases} \left\{\dfrac{1}{2}\sin^2 x\right\}_0^{\pi} & n = 1 \\[2ex] \left\{\dfrac{\cos(n-1)x}{2(n-1)} - \dfrac{\cos(n+1)x}{2(n+1)}\right\}_0^{\pi} & n > 1 \end{cases}$$

$$= \begin{cases} 0 & n = 1 \\[2ex] -\dfrac{[1+(-1)^n]}{\pi(n^2-1)} & n > 1 \end{cases};$$

$$b_n = \frac{1}{\pi} \int_0^{2\pi} f(x)\sin nx\,dx = \frac{1}{\pi} \int_0^{\pi} \sin x \sin nx\,dx$$

$$= \frac{1}{\pi} \begin{cases} \left\{\dfrac{x}{2} - \dfrac{\sin 2x}{4}\right\}_0^{\pi} & n = 1 \\[2ex] \left\{\dfrac{\sin(n-1)x}{2(n-1)} - \dfrac{\sin(n+1)x}{2(n+1)}\right\}_0^{\pi} & n > 1 \end{cases}$$

$$= \begin{cases} \dfrac{1}{2} & n = 1 \\[2ex] 0 & n > 1 \end{cases}.$$

Because $f(x)$ is continuous for all x, we may write

$$f(x) = \frac{1}{\pi} + \sum_{n=2}^{\infty} -\frac{[1+(-1)^n]}{\pi(n^2-1)} \cos nx + \frac{1}{2}\sin x.$$

Terms in the series vanish when n is odd. To display only the even terms, we replace n by $2n$:

$$f(x) = \frac{1}{\pi} + \frac{1}{2}\sin x - \frac{2}{\pi} \sum_{n=1}^{\infty} \frac{\cos 2nx}{4n^2 - 1}.$$

■

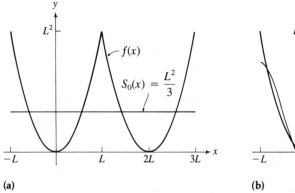

(a)

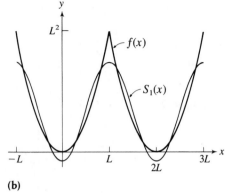

(b)

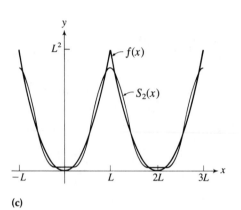

(c)

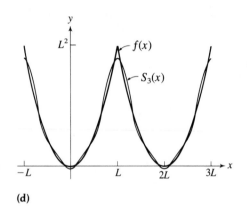

(d)

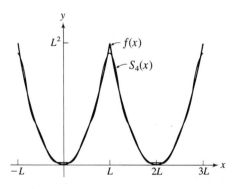

(e)

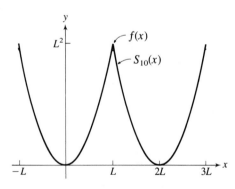

(f)

Figure 2.8

When we write (14), we mean that the sequence of partial sums $\{S_n(x)\}$ of the series on the right converges to $f(x)$ for all x; that is, were we to plot the functions in the sequence

$$S_0(x) = \frac{a_0}{2},$$

$$S_1(x) = \frac{a_0}{2} + \left(a_1 \cos \frac{\pi x}{L} + b_1 \sin \frac{\pi x}{L} \right),$$

$$S_2(x) = \frac{a_0}{2} + \left(a_1 \cos \frac{\pi x}{L} + b_1 \sin \frac{\pi x}{L} \right)$$

$$+ \left(a_2 \cos \frac{2\pi x}{L} + b_2 \sin \frac{2\pi x}{L} \right),$$

and so forth, their graphs should resemble more and more closely that of $f(x)$. Figure 2.8 illustrates this fact with the partial sums $S_0(x), S_1(x), S_2(x), S_3(x), S_4(x)$, and $S_{10}(x)$ for the function $f(x)$ in Example 2. Graphs are plotted only for $-L \le x \le 3L$; they are extended periodically outside this interval.

Figure 2.9 illustrates the same partial sums for the function $f(x)$ in Example 1, but convergence in this case is much slower. This is easily explained by the fact that the Fourier coefficients in Example 2 have a factor n^2 in the denominator, whereas in Example 1 the factor is only n. Figure 2.9 also indicates a property of all Fourier series at points of discontinuity of the function $f(x)$. On either side of the discontinuity, the partial sums eventually overshoot $f(x)$, and this overshoot does not diminish in size as more and more terms of the Fourier series are included. This is known as the Gibbs phenomenon; it states that for large n, $S_n(x)$ overshoots the curve at a discontinuity by about 9% of the size of the jump in the function.

Entire books have been written on Fourier series and their properties; some of these properties are developed in Section 2.3. For most of our discussions on partial differential equations, we require the basic ideas of pointwise convergence (contained in Theorem 2) and the ability to differentiate Fourier series. The following theorem indicates conditions that permit Fourier series to be differentiated term by term.

Theorem 3

If $f(x)$ is a continuous function of period $2L$ with piecewise continuous derivatives $f'(x)$ and $f''(x)$, the Fourier series of $f(x)$,

$$f(x) = \frac{a_0}{2} + \sum_{n=1}^{\infty} \left(a_n \cos \frac{n\pi x}{L} + b_n \sin \frac{n\pi x}{L} \right),$$

can be differentiated term by term to yield

$$f'(x) = \frac{f'(x+) + f'(x-)}{2} = \frac{\pi}{L} \sum_{n=1}^{\infty} n \left(-a_n \sin \frac{n\pi x}{L} + b_n \cos \frac{n\pi x}{L} \right). \tag{15}$$

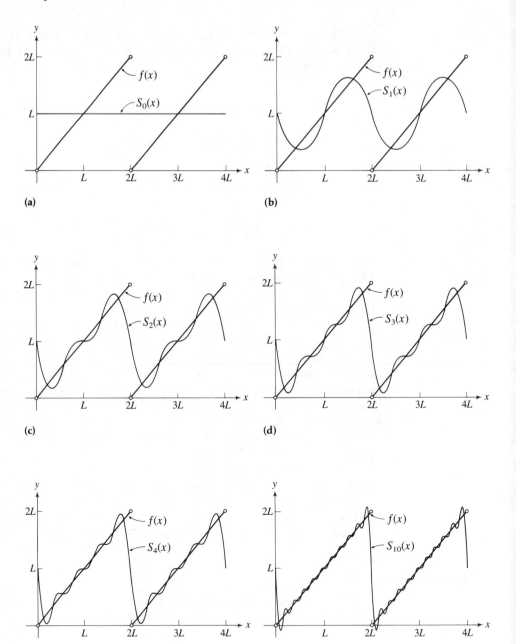

Figure 2.9

(a)

(b)

(c)

(d)

(e)

(f)

Proof: Because $f'(x)$ is piecewise smooth, its Fourier series converges to $[f'(x+) + f'(x-)]/2$ for each x,

$$\frac{f'(x+) + f'(x-)}{2} = \frac{A_0}{2} + \sum_{n=1}^{\infty}\left(A_n \cos\frac{n\pi x}{L} + B_n \sin\frac{n\pi x}{L}\right),$$

where $A_n = \frac{1}{L}\int_0^{2L} f'(x)\cos\frac{n\pi x}{L}\,dx = \frac{1}{L}\left\{f(x)\cos\frac{n\pi x}{L}\right\}_0^{2L} + \frac{n\pi}{L^2}\int_0^{2L} f(x)\sin\frac{n\pi x}{L}\,dx$

$= \frac{n\pi}{L}b_n,\qquad n > 0;$

$$B_n = \frac{1}{L}\int_0^{2L} f'(x)\sin\frac{n\pi x}{L}\,dx = \frac{1}{L}\left\{f(x)\sin\frac{n\pi x}{L}\right\}_0^{2L} - \frac{n\pi}{L^2}\int_0^{2L} f(x)\cos\frac{n\pi x}{L}\,dx$$

$= \frac{-n\pi}{L}a_n;$

$$A_0 = \frac{1}{L}\int_0^{2L} f'(x)\,dx = \frac{1}{L}\{f(x)\}_0^{2L} = 0.$$

Consequently,

$$\frac{f'(x+) + f'(x-)}{2} = \frac{\pi}{L}\sum_{n=1}^{\infty} n\left(-a_n\sin\frac{n\pi x}{L} + b_n\cos\frac{n\pi x}{L}\right).\qquad\blacksquare$$

Example 4:   The function in Figure 2.10(a) is the derivative of the function in Figure 2.7 (for Example 3). Find its Fourier series.

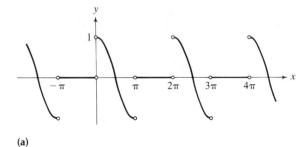

(a)

(b)

Figure 2.10

Solution: The function $f(x)$ in Figure 2.7 is continuous and has Fourier series

$$f(x) = \frac{1}{\pi} + \frac{1}{2}\sin x - \frac{2}{\pi}\sum_{n=1}^{\infty}\frac{\cos 2nx}{4n^2 - 1}.$$

Since $f'(x)$ and $f''(x)$ are piecewise continuous, we may differentiate this series term by term and write

$$f'(x) = \frac{1}{2}\cos x - \frac{2}{\pi}\sum_{n=1}^{\infty}\frac{-2n\sin 2nx}{4n^2 - 1}$$

$$= \frac{1}{2}\cos x + \frac{4}{\pi}\sum_{n=1}^{\infty}\frac{n}{4n^2 - 1}\sin 2nx,$$

provided we understand that $f'(x)$ is the function in Figure 2.10(b), that is, provided we define $f'(n\pi) = (-1)^n/2$. ∎

Integration formulas (13b) for Fourier coefficients almost invariably involve integration by parts. These integrations can be combined by using what is called the complex form for a Fourier series. With the expressions $\cos\theta = (e^{i\theta} + e^{-i\theta})/2$ and $\sin\theta = (e^{i\theta} - e^{-i\theta})/(2i)$, we may express the Fourier series of a function $f(x)$ in the form

$$f(x) = \frac{a_0}{2} + \sum_{n=1}^{\infty}\left(a_n\cos\frac{n\pi x}{L} + b_n\sin\frac{n\pi x}{L}\right)$$

$$= \frac{a_0}{2} + \sum_{n=1}^{\infty}\left(a_n\frac{e^{n\pi xi/L} + e^{-n\pi xi/L}}{2} + b_n\frac{e^{n\pi xi/L} - e^{-n\pi xi/L}}{2i}\right)$$

$$= \frac{a_0}{2} + \sum_{n=1}^{\infty}\left(\frac{a_n + ib_n}{2}\right)e^{-n\pi xi/L} + \sum_{n=1}^{\infty}\left(\frac{a_n - ib_n}{2}\right)e^{n\pi xi/L}$$

$$= \frac{a_0}{2} + \sum_{n=1}^{\infty}\left(\frac{a_n + ib_n}{2}\right)e^{-n\pi xi/L} + \sum_{n=-1}^{-\infty}\left(\frac{a_{-n} - ib_{-n}}{2}\right)e^{-n\pi xi/L}$$

or

$$f(x) = \sum_{n=-\infty}^{\infty} c_n e^{-n\pi xi/L}, \tag{16a}$$

where $c_0 = a_0/2$, $c_n = (a_n + ib_n)/2$ when $n > 0$ and $c_n = (a_{-n} - ib_{-n})/2$ when $n < 0$. It is straightforward to verify using formulas (13b) that for all n,

$$c_n = \frac{1}{2L}\int_0^{2L} f(x) e^{n\pi xi/L}\,dx. \tag{16b}$$

This is called the *complex form* of Fourier series (13). Its compactness is evident, and only one integration is required to determine the complex Fourier coefficients c_n. In addition, Fourier coefficients a_n and b_n are easily extracted as real and imaginary parts of c_n (see Exercises 22–26).

Exercises 2.1

In Exercises 1–14, find the Fourier series for the function $f(x)$. Draw graphs of $f(x)$ and the function to which the series converges in Exercises 1–8, 13, and 14.

1. $f(x) = 3x + 2$, $0 < x < 4$, $f(x + 4) = f(x)$

2. $f(x) = 2x^2 - 1$, $0 \le x < 2L$, $f(x + 2L) = f(x)$

3. $f(x) = 2x^2 - 1$, $-L \le x \le L$, $f(x + 2L) = f(x)$

4. $f(x) = 3x$, $0 < x \le 2L$, $f(x + 2L) = f(x)$

5. $f(x) = 3x$, $-L < x \le L$, $f(x + 2L) = f(x)$

6. $f(x) = \begin{cases} 2(L - x) & 0 \le x \le L \\ x - L & L < x < 2L \end{cases}$, $f(x + 2L) = f(x)$

7. $f(x) = \begin{cases} 2 & 0 < x < 1 \\ 1 & 1 < x < 2, \\ 0 & 2 < x < 3 \end{cases}$ $f(x + 3) = f(x)$

8. $f(x) = \begin{cases} x & 0 \le x \le 2 \\ 2 & 2 \le x \le 4, \\ 6 - x & 4 \le x \le 6 \end{cases}$ $f(x + 6) = f(x)$

9. $f(x) = 1 + \sin x - \cos 2x$

10. $f(x) = 2\cos x - 3\sin 10x + 4\cos 2x$

11. $f(x) = \cos^2 2x$

12. $f(x) = 3\cos 2x \sin 5x$

13. $f(x) = e^x$, $0 < x < 4$, $f(x + 4) = f(x)$

14. $f(x) = \begin{cases} \sin x & 0 \le x \le \pi \\ -2\sin x & \pi \le x \le 2\pi \end{cases}$, $f(x + 2\pi) = f(x)$

15. Verify that the functions in Theorem 1 are indeed orthogonal.

16. A student was once heard to say that the Fourier series of a periodic function is not unique. For example, in Example 1 the Fourier series of the function in Figure 2.5 was found. The student stated that this function also has period $4L$ and therefore has a Fourier series of the form

$$f(x) = \frac{a_0}{2} + \sum_{n=1}^{\infty} \left(a_n \cos \frac{n\pi x}{2L} + b_n \sin \frac{n\pi x}{2L} \right).$$

Is this series indeed different from that found in Example 1?

In Exercises 17–21, find the complex Fourier series for the given function.

17. The function in Example 2.

18. The function in Exercise 13.

19. The function in Exercise 7.

20. $f(x) = \begin{cases} 1 & 0 < x < L \\ -1 & L < x < 2L \end{cases}$, $f(x + 2L) = f(x)$

21. $f(x) = \begin{cases} x & 0 < x < L \\ 2L - x & L < x < 2L \end{cases}$, $f(x + 2L) = f(x)$

In Exercises 22–26, find the trigonometric Fourier series for the given function by calculating complex Fourier coefficients c_n and then taking real and imaginary parts.

22. The function in Example 2.

23. The function in Exercise 8.

24. The function in Exercise 7.

25. The function in Exercise 2.

26. The function in Exercise 6.

27. Is

$$f(x) = \sum_{n=-\infty}^{\infty} d_n e^{n\pi xi/L}$$

where

$$d_n = \frac{1}{2L} \int_0^{2L} f(x) e^{-n\pi xi/L} \, dx$$

an alternative to equation (16) for the complex form of the Fourier series of a function $f(x)$? How is d_n related to a_n and b_n in this case?

28. A function $f(x)$ is said to be *odd-harmonic* if $f(x + L) = -f(x)$.

(a) Prove that such a function is $2L$-periodic.

(b) Illustrate an odd-harmonic function graphically.

(c) Show that the Fourier series for an odd-harmonic function takes the form

$$f(x) = \sum_{n=1}^{\infty} \left[a_{2n-1} \cos \frac{(2n-1)\pi x}{L} + b_{2n-1} \sin \frac{(2n-1)\pi x}{L} \right],$$

where

$$a_{2n-1} = \frac{2}{L} \int_0^L f(x) \cos \frac{(2n-1)\pi x}{L} \, dx$$

and

$$b_{2n-1} = \frac{2}{L} \int_0^L f(x) \sin \frac{(2n-1)\pi x}{L} \, dx.$$

2.2 Fourier Sine and Cosine Series

When $f(x)$ is a $2L$-periodic, piecewise smooth function, it has a Fourier series representation as in (13a) with coefficients defined by (13b). If, in addition, $f(x)$ is an even function, it is a simple exercise to show that its Fourier coefficients satisfy

$$a_n = \frac{2}{L} \int_0^L f(x) \cos \frac{n\pi x}{L} \, dx, \qquad b_n = 0 \qquad \textbf{(17b)}$$

(see, for instance, Example 2). Thus, the Fourier series of an even function has only cosine terms,

$$f(x) = \frac{a_0}{2} + \sum_{n=1}^{\infty} a_n \cos \frac{n\pi x}{L}, \qquad \textbf{(17a)}$$

and is called a *Fourier cosine series*.

When $f(x)$ is an odd function, its Fourier coefficients are

$$a_n = 0, \qquad b_n = \frac{2}{L} \int_0^L f(x) \sin \frac{n\pi x}{L} \, dx, \qquad \textbf{(18b)}$$

and therefore the Fourier series of an odd function has only sine terms,

$$f(x) = \sum_{n=1}^{\infty} b_n \sin \frac{n\pi x}{L}, \tag{18a}$$

and is called a *Fourier sine series*.

Example 5:   Find the Fourier series for the function $f(x)$ in Figure 2.11.

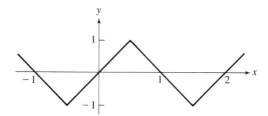

Figure 2.11

Solution: Because $f(x)$ is an odd function of period 2, its Fourier series must be a sine series

$$f(x) = \sum_{n=1}^{\infty} b_n \sin n\pi x$$

with coefficients

$$b_n = \frac{2}{1} \int_0^1 f(x) \sin n\pi x \, dx = 2 \int_0^{1/2} 2x \sin n\pi x \, dx + 2 \int_{1/2}^1 -2(x-1) \sin n\pi x \, dx$$

$$= 4 \left\{ \frac{-x}{n\pi} \cos n\pi x + \frac{1}{n^2\pi^2} \sin n\pi x \right\}_0^{1/2}$$

$$- 4 \left\{ \frac{-(x-1)}{n\pi} \cos n\pi x + \frac{1}{n^2\pi^2} \sin n\pi x \right\}_{1/2}^1$$

$$= \frac{8}{n^2\pi^2} \sin \frac{n\pi}{2}.$$

Because $f(x)$ is continuous for all x, the Fourier series of $f(x)$ converges to $f(x)$ for all x; that is,

$$f(x) = \sum_{n=1}^{\infty} \frac{8}{n^2\pi^2} \sin \frac{n\pi}{2} \sin n\pi x = \frac{8}{\pi^2} \sum_{n=1}^{\infty} \frac{(-1)^{n-1}}{(2n-1)^2} \sin(2n-1)\pi x. \qquad \blacksquare$$

Example 6:   Find the Fourier series for the function $f(x)$ in Figure 2.12.

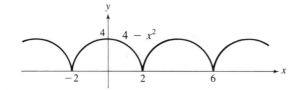

Figure 2.12

Solution: Because $f(x)$ is an even function of period 4, its Fourier series must be a cosine series

$$f(x) = \frac{a_0}{2} + \sum_{n=1}^{\infty} a_n \cos\frac{n\pi x}{2}$$

with coefficients

$$a_0 = \frac{2}{2}\int_0^2 (4 - x^2)\,dx = \left\{4x - \frac{x^3}{3}\right\}_0^2 = \frac{16}{3};$$

$$a_n = \frac{2}{2}\int_0^2 (4 - x^2)\cos\frac{n\pi x}{2}\,dx$$

$$= \left\{\frac{2}{n\pi}(4 - x^2)\sin\frac{n\pi x}{2} - \frac{8x}{n^2\pi^2}\cos\frac{n\pi x}{2} + \frac{16}{n^3\pi^3}\sin\frac{n\pi x}{2}\right\}_0^2$$

$$= \frac{16(-1)^{n+1}}{n^2\pi^2}.$$

Because $f(x)$ is continuous for all x, we may write

$$f(x) = \frac{8}{3} + \sum_{n=1}^{\infty} \frac{16(-1)^{n+1}}{n^2\pi^2}\cos\frac{n\pi x}{2}$$

$$= \frac{8}{3} + \frac{16}{\pi^2}\sum_{n=1}^{\infty} \frac{(-1)^{n+1}}{n^2}\cos\frac{n\pi x}{2}.$$

Alternatively, we could have noted that this function is 4 minus the function in Example 2 when L is set equal to 2. Hence,

$$f(x) = 4 - \left(\frac{2^2}{3} + \frac{4(2)^2}{\pi^2}\sum_{n=1}^{\infty} \frac{(-1)^n}{n^2}\cos\frac{n\pi x}{2}\right)$$

$$= \frac{8}{3} + \frac{16}{\pi^2}\sum_{n=1}^{\infty} \frac{(-1)^{n+1}}{n^2}\cos\frac{n\pi x}{2}. \qquad \blacksquare$$

Because we have treated Fourier sine and cosine series as special cases of the full Fourier series in Section 2.1, they have been approached from the following point of view: *Can an even (or odd) 2L-periodic function f(x) be expressed in a Fourier series of form (17a) [or (18a)]?*

When sine and cosine series are used to solve (initial) boundary value problems, they arise in a different way. Sine series arise from a need to answer the following question: *Suppose a function f(x) is defined for $0 < x < L$ and is piecewise smooth for $0 \le x \le L$. Is it possible to represent f(x) in a series of the form*

$$f(x) = \sum_{n=1}^{\infty} b_n \sin\frac{n\pi x}{L} \tag{19}$$

valid for $0 < x < L$?

Notice that $f(x)$ is not odd and it is not periodic; it is defined only between $x = 0$ and $x = L$. But by appropriately extending $f(x)$ outside the interval $0 < x < L$, we shall indeed be able to write it in form (19). First, we recognize that (19) resembles (18a), the Fourier sine series of an odd function. We therefore extend the domain of definition of $f(x)$ to include $-L < x < 0$ by demanding that the extension be odd; that is, we define $f(x) = -f(-x)$ for $-L < x < 0$. For example, if $f(x)$ is as shown in Figure 2.13(a), it is extended as shown in Figure 2.13(b). Next, we know that series (18a) represents a $2L$-periodic function. We therefore extend the domain of definition of $f(x)$ beyond $-L < x < L$ by making it $2L$-periodic [Figure 2.13(c)].

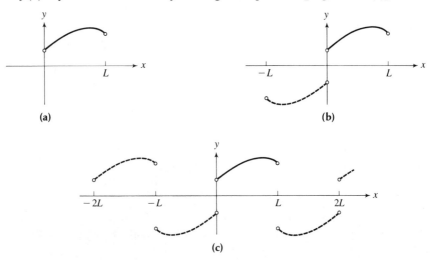

(a)   (b)

(c)

Figure 2.13

We have now extended $f(x)$, which was originally defined only for $0 < x < L$, to an odd, $2L$-periodic function. Because $f(x)$ was piecewise smooth on $0 \le x \le L$, the extended function is piecewise smooth for all x. As a result, the extended function can be represented in a Fourier sine series (18a), with coefficients defined by (18b), and this series converges to the average value of right- and left-hand limits at every point. Since the extension of $f(x)$ to an odd, periodic function does not affect its original values on $0 < x < L$, it follows that the Fourier sine series of this extension must represent $f(x)$ on $0 < x < L$. Thus, we should calculate the coefficients in (19) according to (18b). Finally, we should note that the series will converge to 0 at $x = 0$ and $x = L$.

In summary, when we are required to express a function $f(x)$, defined for $0 < x < L$, in form (19), we use the Fourier sine series of the odd, $2L$-periodic extension of $f(x)$.

In a similar way, if we are required to express a function $f(x)$, piecewise smooth on $0 \le x \le L$, in the form

$$f(x) = \frac{a_0}{2} + \sum_{n=1}^{\infty} a_n \cos \frac{n\pi x}{L}, \qquad 0 < x < L, \tag{20}$$

we use the Fourier cosine series of the even, $2L$-periodic extension of $f(x)$. For the function $f(x)$ in Figure 2.13(a), this extension is as shown in Figure 2.14. The series will converge to $\lim_{x \to 0^+} f(x)$ and $\lim_{x \to L^-} f(x)$ at $x = 0$ and $x = L$, respectively.

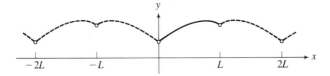

Figure 2.14

Example 7:   Find coefficients b_n so that

$$1 + 2x = \sum_{n=1}^{\infty} b_n \sin \frac{n\pi x}{3}$$

for all x in the interval $0 < x < 3$.

Solution: Constants b_n must be the coefficients in the Fourier sine series of the extension of $1 + 2x$ to an odd function of period 6 (Figure 2.15). According to (18b),

$$b_n = \frac{2}{3} \int_0^3 f(x) \sin \frac{n\pi x}{3} dx = \frac{2}{3} \int_0^3 (1 + 2x) \sin \frac{n\pi x}{3} dx$$

$$= \frac{2}{3} \left\{ \frac{-3}{n\pi} (1 + 2x) \cos \frac{n\pi x}{3} + \frac{18}{n^2 \pi^2} \sin \frac{n\pi x}{3} \right\}_0^3 = \frac{2}{n\pi} [1 + 7(-1)^{n+1}].$$

Consequently,

$$1 + 2x = \frac{2}{\pi} \sum_{n=1}^{\infty} \frac{1 + 7(-1)^{n+1}}{n} \sin \frac{n\pi x}{3}, \qquad 0 < x < 3.$$

At $x = 0$ and $x = 3$, the series does not converge to $1 + 2x$; it converges to zero, the average value of right- and left-hand limits of the odd, periodic extension of $1 + 2x$.

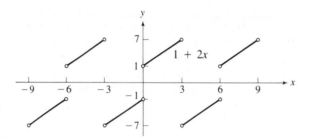

Figure 2.15

Example 8:   Find coefficients a_n so that

$$1 + 2x = \frac{a_0}{2} + \sum_{n=1}^{\infty} a_n \cos \frac{n\pi x}{3}$$

for all x in the interval $0 < x < 3$.

Solution: The constants a_n must be the coefficients in the Fourier cosine series of the extension of $1 + 2x$ to an even function $f(x)$ of period 6 (Figure 2.16). According to (17b),

$$a_0 = \frac{2}{3} \int_0^3 f(x) dx = \frac{2}{3} \int_0^3 (1 + 2x) dx = \frac{2}{3} \left\{ x + x^2 \right\}_0^3 = 8;$$

$$a_n = \frac{2}{3} \int_0^3 f(x) \cos \frac{n\pi x}{3} dx = \frac{2}{3} \int_0^3 (1 + 2x) \cos \frac{n\pi x}{3} dx$$

$$= \frac{2}{3} \left\{ \frac{3}{n\pi} (1 + 2x) \sin \frac{n\pi x}{3} + \frac{18}{n^2 \pi^2} \cos \frac{n\pi x}{3} \right\}_0^3 = \frac{12}{n^2 \pi^2} [(-1)^n - 1].$$

Consequently,

$$1 + 2x = 4 + \frac{12}{\pi^2} \sum_{n=1}^{\infty} \frac{(-1)^n - 1}{n^2} \cos \frac{n\pi x}{3}.$$

Terms in the series vanish when n is even. To display only the odd terms, we replace n by $2n - 1$ and sum from $n = 1$ to infinity:

$$1 + 2x = 4 - \frac{24}{\pi^2} \sum_{n=1}^{\infty} \frac{1}{(2n - 1)^2} \cos \frac{(2n - 1)\pi x}{3}, \qquad 0 < x < 3.$$

At $x = 0$ and $x = 3$, the series converges to 1 and 7, respectively (these being the average of right- and left-hand limits of the even, periodic extension), so that the series actually represents $1 + 2x$ for $0 \le x \le 3$. ∎

Figure 2.16

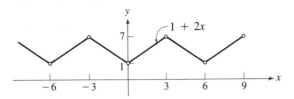

Exercises 2.2

In Exercises 1–5, find the Fourier series for the function $f(x)$. Draw graphs of $f(x)$ and the function to which the series converges in Exercises 2–5.

1. $f(x) = 2 \sin 4x - 3 \sin x$

2. $f(x) = |x|, \quad -\pi < x < \pi, \quad f(x + 2\pi) = f(x)$

3. $f(x) = \begin{cases} x & -4 \le x \le 4 \\ 8 - x & 4 \le x \le 12 \end{cases}, \quad f(x + 16) = f(x)$

4. $f(x) = 2x^2 - 1, \quad -L \le x \le L, \quad f(x + 2L) = f(x)$

5. $f(x) = \begin{cases} \cos x & -\pi/2 \le x \le \pi/2 \\ 0 & \pi/2 < x < 3\pi/2 \end{cases}, \quad f(x + 2\pi) = f(x)$

In Exercises 6–10, expand $f(x)$ in terms of the functions $\{\sin(n\pi x/L)\}$.

6. $f(x) = -x, \quad 0 < x < L$

7. $f(x) = \begin{cases} 1 & 0 < x < L/3 \\ 0 & L/3 < x < 2L/3 \\ -1 & 2L/3 < x < L \end{cases}$

8. $f(x) = \begin{cases} L/4 & 0 \le x \le L/4 \\ L/2 - x & L/4 < x \le L/2 \\ x - L/2 & L/2 < x < 3L/4 \\ L/4 & 3L/4 \le x \le L \end{cases}$

9. $f(x) = \sin(\pi x/L)\cos(\pi x/L)$

10. $f(x) = Lx - x^2, \quad 0 < x < L$

In Exercises 11–15, expand $f(x)$ in terms of the functions $\{1, \cos(n\pi x/L)\}$.

11. $f(x) = -x, \quad 0 < x < L$

12. $f(x) = \sin(\pi x/L)\cos(\pi x/L), \quad 0 < x < L$

13. $f(x) = Lx - x^2, \quad 0 < x < L$

14. $f(x) = 1, \quad 0 < x < L$

15. $f(x) = \begin{cases} 1 & 0 < x < L/2 \\ 0 & L/2 < x < L \end{cases}$

16. Find the Fourier series for the function $f(x) = |\sin x|$ by using the fact that the function has period π. What series is obtained if a period of 2π is used?

17. Under what additional condition is it possible to express a function $f(x)$ that is piecewise smooth on $0 \leq x \leq L$ in the form

$$ f(x) = \sum_{n=1}^{\infty} a_n \cos \frac{n\pi x}{L}? $$

18. Illustrate with graphs that when a function $f(x)$ defined on the interval $0 \leq x \leq L$ is continuous (from the right) at $x = 0$,

    (a) the Fourier cosine series of the even, $2L$-periodic extension of $f(x)$ always converges to $f(0)$ at $x = 0$;

    (b) the Fourier sine series of the odd, $2L$-periodic extension of $f(x)$ converges to $f(0)$ at $x = 0$ if and only if $f(0) = 0$.

    Are similar statements correct at $x = L$?

19. Suppose that $f(x)$ is continuous on the interval $0 \leq x \leq L$ with piecewise continuous derivatives $f'(x)$ and $f''(x)$.

    (a) Show that the Fourier sine series of the odd, $2L$-periodic extension $f_o(x)$ of $f(x)$ can be differentiated term by term to give a cosine series that converges to $[f_o'(x+) + f_o'(x-)]/2$ if $f(0) = f(L) = 0$. Does the differentiated series converge to $f'(0+)$ at $x = 0$ and $f'(L-)$ at $x = L$ when $f(0) = f(L) = 0$?

    (b) Show that the Fourier cosine series of the even, $2L$-periodic extension $f_e(x)$ of $f(x)$ can always be differentiated term by term to give a sine series that converges to $[f_e'(x+) + f_e'(x-)]/2$. Does the differentiated series converge to $f'(0+)$ at $x = 0$ and $f'(L-)$ at $x = L$?

20. **(a)** Find the Fourier series for the function

$$ f(x) = \begin{cases} x & 0 < x < L \\ 2L - x & L < x < 2L \end{cases}, \qquad f(x + 2L) = f(x). $$

    Use this result to find Fourier series for the following functions:

    (b) $f_1(x) = L - |x|, \quad -L \leq x \leq L, \quad f(x + 2L) = f(x)$

    (c) $f_2(x) = 2L - |2L - x|, \quad 0 < x < 4L, \quad f(x + 4L) = f(x)$

    (d) $f_3(x) = x, \quad -L < x < L, \quad f(L + x) = f(L - x), \quad f(x + 4L) = f(x)$

21. **(a)** A function $f(x)$ is said to be odd and odd-harmonic if it satisfies the conditions

$$ f(-x) = -f(x), \qquad f(L + x) = f(L - x). $$

    Show that such a function is $4L$-periodic.

    (b) Illustrate an odd, odd-harmonic function graphically. Is it symmetric about the line $x = L$?

    (c) Show that the Fourier series of an odd, odd-harmonic function takes the form

$$ f(x) = \sum_{n=1}^{\infty} b_n \sin \frac{(2n - 1)\pi x}{2L} $$

where

$$ b_n = \frac{2}{L} \int_0^L f(x) \sin \frac{(2n - 1)\pi x}{2L} \, dx. $$

22. (a) A function $f(x)$ is said to be even and odd-harmonic if it satisfies the conditions

$$f(-x) = f(x), \qquad f(L+x) = -f(L-x).$$

Show that such a function is $4L$-periodic.

(b) Illustrate an even, odd-harmonic function graphically. Is it antisymmetric about the line $x = L$?

(c) Show that the Fourier series of an even, odd-harmonic function takes the form

$$f(x) = \sum_{n=1}^{\infty} a_n \cos \frac{(2n-1)\pi x}{2L}$$

where
$$a_n = \frac{2}{L} \int_0^L f(x) \cos \frac{(2n-1)\pi x}{2L} \, dx.$$

2.3 Further Properties of Fourier Series

In Sections 2.1 and 2.2 we dealt with point-by-point convergence of Fourier series. In this section, and again in Chapter 5, uniform convergence of Fourier series is of considerable importance. It is appropriate, therefore, to give a brief review of uniform convergence, but we do so in a general setting rather than in the restrictive environment of Fourier series.

A series of functions $\sum_{n=1}^{\infty} u_n(x)$ converges to (or has sum) $S(x)$ if its sequence of partial sums $\{S_n(x)\}$ converges to $S(x)$. This is true if, given any $\varepsilon > 0$, there exists an integer N such that $|S_n(x) - S(x)| < \varepsilon$ whenever $n > N$. Usually N is a function of ε and x; in particular, the choice of N may vary from x to x. What this means is that convergence of $\{S_n(x)\}$ to $S(x)$ may be faster for some x's than for others. If it is possible to find an N, independent of x, such that $|S_n(x) - S(x)| < \varepsilon$ for all $n > N$ and all x in some interval I, then $\sum_{n=1}^{\infty} u_n(x)$ is said to converge *uniformly* to $S(x)$ in I. The word "uniform" is perhaps a misnomer. When N is independent of x, convergence is not necessarily uniformly fast for all x's; the rate of convergence may still vary from x to x. What we can say is that convergence does not become indefinitely slow for some x's in I. In practice, what often happens is that there is an x_0 in I at which convergence is slowest; for all other x's, convergence is more rapid than at this x_0. In this case, convergence is uniform. The most widely used test for uniform convergence of a series is the Weierstrass M-test.

Theorem 4 (Weierstrass M-Test)

If a convergent series of (positive) constants $\sum_{n=1}^{\infty} M_n$ can be found such that $|S_n(x)| \leq M_n$ for each n and all x in I, then $\sum_{n=1}^{\infty} u_n(x)$ is uniformly convergent in I.

An excellent example to illustrate these ideas is the geometric series $\sum_{n=0}^{\infty} x^n$. It is well known that this series converges to $1/(1-x)$ on the interval $-1 < x < 1$. In Figure 2.17 we show the five partial sums $S_1(x) = 1$, $S_2(x) = 1 + x$, $S_3(x) = 1 + x + x^2$, $S_4(x) = 1 + x + x^2 + x^3$, and $S_5 = 1 + x + x^2 + x^3 + x^4$, as well as $S(x) = 1/(1-x)$. They indicate that convergence of the partial sums $S_n(x)$ to $S(x)$ is rapid for values of x close to zero, but as x approaches ± 1, convergence becomes much slower. We can demonstrate this algebraically by noting that

$$S(x) - S_n(x) = \frac{1}{1-x} - \frac{1-x^n}{1-x} = \frac{x^n}{1-x}.$$

This is the difference between the sum of the series and its nth partial sum. As x approaches 1, the difference becomes very large; near $x = -1$, it oscillates back and forth between numbers close to $\pm 1/2$.

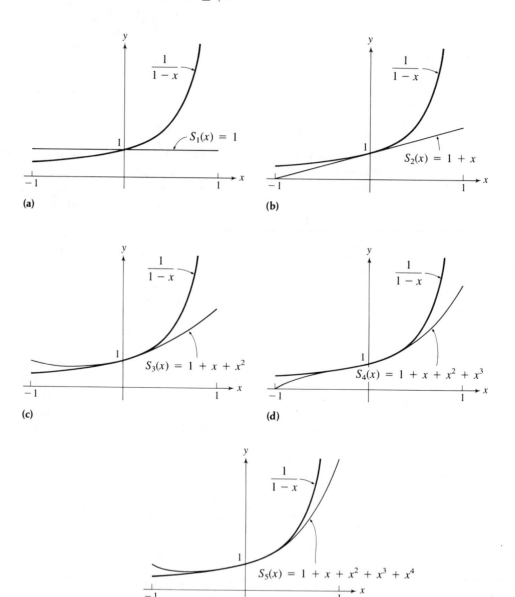

Figure 2.17

When x is confined to the interval $|x| \le a < 1$, we can state that $|x^n| \le a^n$, and since $\sum_{n=0}^{\infty} a^n$ converges, it follows that the geometric series $\sum_{n=0}^{\infty} x^n$ converges uniformly on $|x| \le a < 1$. Convergence is slowest at $x = a$; at all other points in $|x| \le a$, it converges more rapidly than it does at $x = a$. The series does not, however, converge uniformly on the interval $|x| < 1$; convergence becomes indefinitely slow as $x \to \pm 1$.

The Weierstrass M-test is easily generalized to series whose terms are functions of more than one variable. For example, $\sum_{n=1}^{\infty} u_n(x, y)$ is uniformly convergent for points (x, y) in a region R of the xy-plane if there exists a convergent series of constants $\sum_{n=1}^{\infty} M_n$ such that for each n and all (x, y) in R, $|u_n(x, y)| \le M_n$.

Series of the following form arise in almost all phases of our work:

$$\sum_{n=1}^{\infty} X_n(x) Y_n(y),$$

that is, series in which each term is a function $X_n(x)$ of x multiplied by a function $Y_n(y)$ of y. We find Abel's test useful in establishing uniform convergence of such series.

Theorem 5 (Abel's Test)

A series $\sum_{n=1}^{\infty} X_n(x) Y_n(y)$ converges uniformly in a region $\bar{R}$ of the xy-plane if:

(1) the series $\sum_{n=1}^{\infty} X_n(x)$ converges uniformly with respect to x for all x such that (x, y) is in $\bar{R}$;

(2) the functions $Y_n(y)$ are uniformly bounded[†] for all y such that (x, y) is in $\bar{R}$;

(3) for each y such that (x, y) is in $\bar{R}$, the sequence of constants $\{Y_n(y)\}$ is nonincreasing.

As further explanation of these conditions, suppose $\bar{R}$ is the "closed" region in Figure 2.18 consisting of the area R inside the curve plus the bounding curve $\beta(R)$. Condition (1) requires $\sum_{n=1}^{\infty} X_n(x)$ to be uniformly convergent for $a \le x \le b$. Conditions (2) and (3) must be satisfied for $c \le y \le d$. Of course, the roles of $X_n(x)$ and $Y_n(y)$ could be reversed.

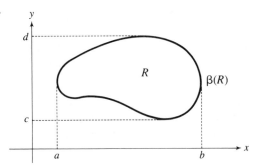

Figure 2.18

It is a well-known fact that the sum of finitely many continuous functions is a continuous function. On the other hand, the sum of infinitely many continuous

---

[†] A sequence of functions $\{Y_n(y)\}$ is said to be uniformly bounded on an interval I if there exists a constant M such that $|Y_n(y)| \le M$ for all x in I and all n.

functions may not be a continuous function. Fourier series are prime examples; each term in a Fourier series is continuous, but the sum of the terms may well be discontinuous (see Example 1). When convergence is uniform, the following result indicates that this cannot happen.

Theorem 6

A uniformly convergent series of continuous functions must converge to a continuous function.

This means that convergence of the Fourier series of a discontinuous function cannot be uniform over any interval that contains a point of discontinuity.

In many applications of series, it is necessary to integrate a series term by term. According to the following theorem, this is possible when the series converges uniformly.

Theorem 7

When a series $\sum_{n=1}^{\infty} u_n(x)$ of continuous functions converges uniformly to $S(x)$ on an interval $a \leq x \leq b$,

$$\int_a^b S(x)\,dx = \sum_{n=1}^{\infty} \int_a^b u_n(x)\,dx. \tag{21}$$

More important to our discussions of Fourier series and partial differential equations are sufficient conditions for term-by-term differentiability of a series. These are given in the next theorem.

Theorem 8

Suppose $\sum_{n=1}^{\infty} u_n(x) = S(x)$ for $a \leq x \leq b$. Then

$$S'(x) = \sum_{n=1}^{\infty} u_n'(x), \qquad a \leq x \leq b, \tag{22}$$

provided each $u_n'(x)$ is continuous for $a \leq x \leq b$ and the series $\sum_{n=1}^{\infty} u_n'(x)$ is uniformly convergent on $a \leq x \leq b$.

In the remainder of this section we discuss properties of Fourier series, which, although not directly related to partial differential equations, provide a better understanding of the manner in which Fourier series represent functions. We begin with the following result.

Theorem 9 (Bessel's Inequality)

If $f(x)$ is a piecewise continuous function on $0 \leq x \leq 2L$, its Fourier coefficients must satisfy the inequality

$$\frac{a_0^2}{2} + \sum_{k=1}^{n} (a_k^2 + b_k^2) \leq \frac{1}{L} \int_0^{2L} [f(x)]^2\,dx. \tag{23}$$

Proof: When

$$S_n(x) = \frac{a_0}{2} + \sum_{k=1}^{n} \left(a_k \cos\frac{k\pi x}{L} + b_k \sin\frac{k\pi x}{L} \right)$$

is the nth partial sum of the Fourier series of $f(x)$, orthogonality of the sine and cosine functions can be used to evaluate

$$\int_0^{2L} [f(x) - S_n(x)]^2 \, dx = \int_0^{2L} [f(x)]^2 \, dx - 2\int_0^{2L} f(x)\left(\frac{a_0}{2} + \sum_{k=1}^{n}\left(a_k \cos\frac{k\pi x}{L}\right.\right.$$

$$\left.\left. + b_k \sin\frac{k\pi x}{L}\right)\right) dx + \int_0^{2L}\left(\frac{a_0^2}{4} + \sum_{k=1}^{n}\left[a_k^2\left(\cos\frac{k\pi x}{L}\right)^2\right.\right.$$

$$\left. + b_k^2\left(\sin\frac{k\pi x}{L}\right)^2\right] + a_0\sum_{k=1}^{n}\left(a_k\cos\frac{k\pi x}{L} + b_k\sin\frac{k\pi x}{L}\right)$$

$$+ 2\sum_{i,j=1}^{n} a_i b_j \cos\frac{i\pi x}{L}\sin\frac{j\pi x}{L}$$

$$\left. + 2\sum_{i>j=1}^{n}\left(a_i a_j \cos\frac{i\pi x}{L}\cos\frac{j\pi x}{L} + b_i b_j \sin\frac{i\pi x}{L}\sin\frac{j\pi x}{L}\right)\right) dx$$

$$= \int_0^{2L} [f(x)]^2 \, dx - 2\left(\frac{a_0}{2}(a_0 L) + \sum_{k=1}^{n}[a_k(a_k L) + b_k(b_k L)]\right)$$

$$+ \frac{a_0^2}{4}(2L) + \sum_{k=1}^{n}[a_k^2(L) + b_k^2(L)].$$

Consequently, for any n,

$$\frac{a_0^2}{2} + \sum_{k=1}^{n}(a_k^2 + b_k^2) = \frac{1}{L}\left(\int_0^{2L}[f(x)]^2 \, dx - \int_0^{2L}[f(x) - S_n(x)]^2 \, dx\right).$$

Since the second integral on the right is nonnegative, it follows that for any n whatsoever,

$$\frac{a_0^2}{2} + \sum_{k=1}^{n}(a_k^2 + b_k^2) \le \frac{1}{L}\int_0^{2L}[f(x)]^2 \, dx. \qquad\blacksquare$$

By letting n become infinite, we can also state that

$$\frac{a_0^2}{2} + \sum_{n=1}^{\infty}(a_n^2 + b_n^2) \le \frac{1}{L}\int_0^{2L}[f(x)]^2 \, dx. \tag{24}$$

In Theorem 11 it is shown that inequality (24) may be replaced by an equality, the result being known as Parseval's theorem. Our proof of Parseval's theorem requires uniform convergence of the Fourier series of a function. Conditions that guarantee this are stated in the following theorem.

Theorem 10

If a $2L$-periodic function $f(x)$ is continuous and has a piecewise continuous first derivative, its Fourier series converges uniformly and absolutely to $f(x)$.

Proof: The conditions on $f(x)$ and $f'(x)$ ensure pointwise convergence of the Fourier series

$$f(x) = \frac{a_0}{2} + \sum_{n=1}^{\infty} \left(a_n \cos \frac{n\pi x}{L} + b_n \sin \frac{n\pi x}{L} \right)$$

of $f(x)$ to $f(x)$ for each x. Since each term in this series may be expressed in the form

$$a_n \cos \frac{n\pi x}{L} + b_n \sin \frac{n\pi x}{L} = \sqrt{a_n^2 + b_n^2} \sin \left(\frac{n\pi x}{L} + \phi_n \right),$$

it follows that the series of absolute values

$$\left| \frac{a_0}{2} \right| + \sum_{n=1}^{\infty} \left| a_n \cos \frac{n\pi x}{L} + b_n \sin \frac{n\pi x}{L} \right| \leq \frac{|a_0|}{2} + \sum_{n=1}^{\infty} \sqrt{a_n^2 + b_n^2}. \tag{25}$$

Uniform and absolute convergence of the Fourier series of $f(x)$ will be established once the series $\sum_{n=1}^{\infty} \sqrt{a_n^2 + b_n^2}$ is shown to be convergent. If

$$\frac{A_0}{2} + \sum_{n=1}^{\infty} \left(A_n \cos \frac{n\pi x}{L} + B_n \sin \frac{n\pi x}{L} \right)$$

is the Fourier series for $f'(x)$, its Fourier coefficients are related to those of $f(x)$ by the equations

$$A_n = \frac{n\pi}{L} b_n, \qquad B_n = \frac{-n\pi}{L} a_n$$

(see the proof of Theorem 3). Thus,

$$\sum_{n=1}^{m} \sqrt{a_n^2 + b_n^2} = \sum_{n=1}^{m} \frac{L}{n\pi} \sqrt{A_n^2 + B_n^2} = \frac{L}{\pi} \sum_{n=1}^{m} \frac{\sqrt{A_n^2 + B_n^2}}{n}. \tag{26}$$

To proceed further, we require a result called Schwarz's inequality. It states that for arbitrary finite sequences $\{c_n\}$ and $\{d_n\}$, $n = 1, \ldots, m$ of nonnegative numbers,

$$\sum_{n=1}^{m} c_n d_n \leq \left(\sum_{n=1}^{m} c_n^2 \right)^{1/2} \left(\sum_{n=1}^{m} d_n^2 \right)^{1/2}. \tag{27}$$

This result is verified in Exercise 1. When it is applied to the series $\sum_{n=1}^{m} \sqrt{A_n^2 + B_n^2}/n$ on the right side of equation (26), we obtain

$$\sum_{n=1}^{m} \sqrt{a_n^2 + b_n^2} \leq \frac{L}{\pi} \left(\sum_{n=1}^{m} \frac{1}{n^2} \right)^{1/2} \left(\sum_{n=1}^{m} (A_n^2 + B_n^2) \right)^{1/2}.$$

Since $\sum_{n=1}^{m} 1/n^2 < \sum_{n=1}^{\infty} 1/n^2 = \pi^2/6$ (see Example 2), it follows that

$$\sum_{n=1}^{m} \sqrt{a_n^2 + b_n^2} \leq \frac{L}{\sqrt{6}} \left(\sum_{n=1}^{m} (A_n^2 + B_n^2) \right)^{1/2}.$$

But Bessel's inequality (24) applied to the Fourier series for $f'(x)$ gives

$$\sum_{n=1}^{m} (A_n^2 + B_n^2) < \sum_{n=1}^{\infty} (A_n^2 + B_n^2) \leq \frac{1}{L} \int_0^{2L} [f'(x)]^2 \, dx - \frac{A_0^2}{2}.$$

Consequently,

$$\sum_{n=1}^{m} \sqrt{a_n^2 + b_n^2} \leq \frac{L}{\sqrt{6}} \left(\frac{1}{L} \int_0^{2L} [f'(x)]^2 \, dx - \frac{A_0^2}{2} \right)^{1/2}.$$

Because this inequality is valid for any m whatsoever, it follows that the series $\sum_{n=1}^{\infty} \sqrt{a_n^2 + b_n^2}$ converges. Inequality (25) then indicates that the Fourier series of $f(x)$ converges uniformly and absolutely. ∎

Continuity of $f(x)$ is indispensable to this theorem. A Fourier series cannot converge uniformly over an interval that contains a discontinuity because a uniformly convergent series of continuous functions always converges to a continuous function (Theorem 6). If $f(x)$ is defined only on the interval $0 \le x \le 2L$, continuity of its periodic extension requires that $f(2L) = f(0)$.

When $f(x)$ satisfies the conditions of Theorem 10, inequality (24) may be replaced by an equality. This result is contained in Theorem 11.

Theorem 11 (Parseval's Theorem)

If $f(x)$ is a $2L$-periodic function that is continuous and has a piecewise continuous first derivative, its Fourier coefficients satisfy

$$\boxed{\frac{a_0^2}{2} + \sum_{n=1}^{\infty} (a_n^2 + b_n^2) = \frac{1}{L} \int_0^{2L} [f(x)]^2 \, dx.}$$

(28)

Proof: With the conditions cited on $f(x)$, the Fourier series of $f(x)$,

$$f(x) = \frac{a_0}{2} + \sum_{n=1}^{\infty} \left(a_n \cos \frac{n\pi x}{L} + b_n \sin \frac{n\pi x}{L} \right),$$

is uniformly convergent (Theorem 10). It may therefore be multiplied by $f(x)$ and integrated term by term between 0 and $2L$ to yield

$$\int_0^{2L} [f(x)]^2 \, dx = \frac{a_0}{2} \int_0^{2L} f(x) \, dx$$

$$+ \sum_{n=1}^{\infty} \left(a_n \int_0^{2L} f(x) \cos \frac{n\pi x}{L} \, dx + b_n \int_0^{2L} f(x) \sin \frac{n\pi x}{L} \, dx \right)$$

$$= \frac{a_0}{2} (a_0 L) + \sum_{n=1}^{\infty} (a_n(La_n) + b_n(Lb_n)).$$

Thus,

$$\frac{a_0^2}{2} + \sum_{n=1}^{\infty} (a_n^2 + b_n^2) = \frac{1}{L} \int_0^{2L} [f(x)]^2 \, dx. \qquad ∎$$

This theorem can also be proved (albeit by different methods) when $f(x)$ is only piecewise smooth and $2L$-periodic.

When $f(x)$ is continuous with a piecewise continuous first derivative, its Fourier series converges uniformly. This guarantees that the series can be integrated term by term between any two limits, and the resulting series of constants converges to the definite integral of $f(x)$ between the same two limits. The following theorem indicates that term-by-term integration of Fourier series is possible even when $f(x)$ is not continuous (and therefore the Fourier series is not uniformly convergent).

Theorem 12

When a $2L$-periodic function $f(x)$ is piecewise continuous, its Fourier series may be integrated term by term between any finite limits, and the resulting series converges to the definite integral of $f(x)$ between the same limits.

Proof:

To prove the theorem, we must show that for any c and d,

$$\int_c^d f(x)\,dx = \frac{a_0}{2}\int_c^d dx + \sum_{n=1}^\infty \left(a_n \int_c^d \cos\frac{n\pi x}{L}\,dx + b_n \int_c^d \sin\frac{n\pi x}{L}\,dx \right)$$

$$= \frac{a_0}{2}(d-c) + \sum_{n=1}^\infty \left[\frac{La_n}{n\pi}\left(\sin\frac{n\pi d}{L} - \sin\frac{n\pi c}{L} \right) - \frac{Lb_n}{n\pi}\left(\cos\frac{n\pi d}{L} - \cos\frac{n\pi c}{L} \right) \right]$$

when a_0, a_n, and b_n are the coefficients in the Fourier series of $f(x)$.

Because $\int_c^d f(x)\,dx$ can always be expressed as the difference $\int_0^d f(x)\,dx - \int_0^c f(x)\,dx$, it suffices to show the result for integrals over the interval $(0, x)$, that is, to show that

$$\int_0^x f(t)\,dt = \frac{a_0 x}{2} + \frac{L}{\pi}\sum_{n=1}^\infty \frac{1}{n}\left[a_n \sin\frac{n\pi x}{L} - b_n\left(\cos\frac{n\pi x}{L} - 1 \right) \right].$$

To show this, we consider the function

$$F(x) = \int_0^x f(t)\,dt - \frac{a_0 x}{2}.$$

Since $f(x)$ is piecewise continuous, $F(x)$ is continuous and $F'(x)$ is piecewise continuous. Furthermore,

$$F(x + 2L) = \int_0^{x+2L} f(t)\,dt - \frac{a_0}{2}(x + 2L)$$

$$= \int_0^x f(t)\,dt + \int_x^{x+2L} f(t)\,dt - \frac{a_0 x}{2} - a_0 L$$

$$= F(x) + \int_0^{2L} f(t)\,dt - a_0 L$$

$$= F(x),$$

since $a_0 L = \int_0^{2L} f(t)\,dt$. Thus $F(x)$ is $2L$-periodic. It follows that the Fourier series of $F(x)$ converges to $F(x)$ for all x; that is,

$$F(x) = \frac{A_0}{2} + \sum_{n=1}^\infty \left(A_n \cos\frac{n\pi x}{L} + B_n \sin\frac{n\pi x}{L} \right)$$

where, for $n > 0$,

$$A_n = \frac{1}{L}\int_0^{2L} F(x)\cos\frac{n\pi x}{L}\,dx = \left\{ \frac{1}{n\pi} F(x)\sin\frac{n\pi x}{L} \right\}_0^{2L} - \frac{1}{n\pi}\int_0^{2L} F'(x)\sin\frac{n\pi x}{L}\,dx$$

$$= \frac{-1}{n\pi}\int_0^{2L}\left(f(x) - \frac{a_0}{2} \right)\sin\frac{n\pi x}{L}\,dx$$

$$= \frac{-1}{n\pi}\int_0^{2L} f(x)\sin\frac{n\pi x}{L}\,dx + \frac{a_0}{2n\pi}\left\{ \frac{-L}{n\pi}\cos\frac{n\pi x}{L} \right\}_0^{2L} = \frac{-L}{n\pi} b_n.$$

Similarly, $B_n = La_n/(n\pi)$. To obtain A_0, we evaluate the series for $F(x)$ at $x = 2L$:

$$\frac{A_0}{2} + \sum_{n=1}^{\infty} A_n = F(2L) = \int_0^{2L} f(t)\,dt - a_0 L = a_0 L - a_0 L = 0.$$

Thus,

$$A_0 = -2 \sum_{n=1}^{\infty} A_n = \frac{2L}{\pi} \sum_{n=1}^{\infty} \frac{b_n}{n}.$$

The Fourier series for $F(x)$ is therefore

$$F(x) = \frac{L}{\pi} \sum_{n=1}^{\infty} \frac{b_n}{n} + \sum_{n=1}^{\infty} \left(\frac{-Lb_n}{n\pi} \cos \frac{n\pi x}{L} + \frac{La_n}{n\pi} \sin \frac{n\pi x}{L} \right);$$

that is

$$\int_0^x f(t)\,dt = \frac{a_0 x}{2} + \frac{L}{\pi} \sum_{n=1}^{\infty} \left[\frac{a_n}{n} \sin \frac{n\pi x}{L} + \frac{b_n}{n} \left(1 - \cos \frac{n\pi x}{L} \right) \right]. \tag{29}$$

■

This theorem also provides the additional result that the antiderivative of a Fourier series is itself a Fourier series only when $a_0 = 0$.

Example 9: Illustrate that term-by-term integration of the Fourier series of the function $f(x)$ in Example 1 over the interval $0 \le x \le L$ gives the correct value for the integral of $f(x)$. You will need the fact that $\sum_{n=1}^{\infty} 1/(2n-1)^2 = \pi^2/8$.

Solution: The integral of $f(x)$ for $0 \le x \le L$ is

$$\int_0^L x\,dx = \frac{L^2}{2}.$$

On the other hand, term-by-term integration of the Fourier series of $f(x)$ (see Example 1) gives

$$L\left(\int_0^L dx - \frac{2}{\pi} \sum_{n=1}^{\infty} \frac{1}{n} \int_0^L \sin \frac{n\pi x}{L}\,dx \right) = L\left(L - \frac{2}{\pi} \sum_{n=1}^{\infty} \frac{1}{n} \left\{ \frac{-L}{n\pi} \cos \frac{n\pi x}{L} \right\}_0^L \right)$$

$$= L\left(L + \frac{2L}{\pi^2} \sum_{n=1}^{\infty} \frac{1}{n^2} [(-1)^n - 1] \right)$$

$$= L^2\left(1 + \frac{2}{\pi^2} \sum_{n=1}^{\infty} \frac{-2}{(2n-1)^2} \right)$$

$$= L^2\left(1 - \frac{4}{\pi^2} \sum_{n=1}^{\infty} \frac{1}{(2n-1)^2} \right)$$

$$= L^2\left[1 - \frac{4}{\pi^2} \left(\frac{\pi^2}{8} \right) \right] = \frac{L^2}{2}.$$

■

Exercises 2.3

1. In this exercise we verify Schwarz's inequality [(27)].

   (a) Show that (27) becomes an equality when terms in the sequences $\{c_n\}$ and $\{d_n\}$ are proportional, that is, when $d_n = \lambda c_n$ for all n ($\lambda > 0$).

(b) Now suppose that the sequences $\{c_n\}$ and $\{d_n\}$ are not proportional. Consider the finite series

$$\sum_{n=1}^{m} (c_n x + d_n)^2 = x^2 \sum_{n=1}^{m} c_n^2 + 2x \sum_{n=1}^{m} c_n d_n + \sum_{n=1}^{m} d_n^2.$$

Establish that the quadratic expression on the right has no zeros, and use this to verify (27).

2. (a) Prove that if a $2L$-periodic function is continuous with a piecewise continuous first derivative, its Fourier coefficients satisfy

$$\lim_{n \to \infty} na_n = 0 = \lim_{n \to \infty} nb_n.$$

(*Hint:* See Theorem 10.)

(b) Does the result in (a) hold if the function is only piecewise continuous?

3. Show that when $f(x)$ is a piecewise continuous function on $0 \le x \le L$,

(a)
$$\sum_{n=1}^{\infty} b_n^2 = \frac{2}{L} \int_0^L [f(x)]^2 \, dx$$

when the b_n are calculated according to (18b) and

(b)
$$\frac{a_0^2}{2} + \sum_{n=1}^{\infty} a_n^2 = \frac{2}{L} \int_0^L [f(x)]^2 \, dx$$

when the a_n are calculated according to (17b).

4. (a) A function $f(x)$ is continuous on the interval $0 \le x \le 2L$ and has a piecewise continuous first derivative. Does the Fourier series of the $2L$-periodic extension of $f(x)$ converge uniformly?

(b) A function $f(x)$ is continuous on the interval $0 \le x \le L$ and has a piecewise continuous first derivative. Does the Fourier sine series of the odd, $2L$-periodic extension of $f(x)$ converge uniformly?

(c) Is your conclusion in (b) the same for the Fourier cosine series of the even, $2L$-periodic extension of $f(x)$?

5. A sequence of functions $\{S_n(x)\}$ is said to *converge in the mean* to a function $f(x)$ on the interval $a \le x \le b$ if

$$\lim_{n \to \infty} \int_a^b [S_n(x) - f(x)]^2 \, dx = 0.$$

A series of functions $\sum_{n=1}^{\infty} u_n(x)$ is said to converge in the mean to a function $f(x)$ on the interval $a \le x \le b$ if its sequence of partial sums converges in the mean to $f(x)$.

Use Theorems 9 and 11 to show that the Fourier series of a piecewise continuous function of period $2L$ converges in the mean to the function.

6. A piecewise continuous, $2L$-periodic function $f(x)$ is to be approximated by a sum of the form

$$S_n(x) = \frac{\alpha_0}{2} + \sum_{k=1}^{n} \left(\alpha_k \cos \frac{k\pi x}{L} + \beta_k \sin \frac{k\pi x}{L} \right).$$

One measure of the accuracy of this approximation is the quantity

$$E_n = \int_0^{2L} [f(x) - S_n(x)]^2 \, dx,$$

called the *mean square error*. Suppose you are required to choose coefficients α_0, α_k, and β_k in such a way that E_n is as small as possible.

(a) Use the technique in Theorem 9 to show that E_n can be expressed in the form

$$E_n = \int_0^{2L} [f(x)]^2 \, dx + L\left(\frac{\alpha_0^2}{2} + \sum_{k=1}^{n} (\alpha_k^2 + \beta_k^2)\right)$$
$$- 2L\left(\frac{\alpha_0 a_0}{2} + \sum_{k=1}^{n} (\alpha_k a_k + \beta_k b_k)\right),$$

where a_0, a_k, and b_k are Fourier coefficients of $f(x)$.

(b) Regarding E_n as a function of $2n + 1$ variables α_0, α_j, and β_j, set its derivatives with respect to these variables equal to zero to find critical values of E_n. Show that the solution set is $\alpha_0 = a_0$, $\alpha_k = a_k$, and $\beta_k = b_k$. In other words, the partial sums of the Fourier series of a function approximate the function in the mean square sense better than any other trigonometric function of the same form.

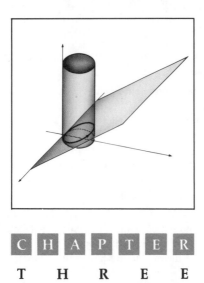

Separation of Variables

3.1 Linearity and Superposition

Separation of variables is one of the most fundamental techniques for solving PDEs. It is a method that can by itself yield solutions to many initial boundary value problems; in addition, it is the basis for more sophisticated techniques that must be used on more complicated problems. Separation of variables is applied to linear PDEs. A PDE is said to be *linear* if it is linear in the unknown function and all its derivatives (but not necessarily in the independent variables). For example, the most general linear second-order PDE for a function $u(x, y)$ of two independent variables is

$$a(x, y)\frac{\partial^2 u}{\partial x^2} + b(x, y)\frac{\partial^2 u}{\partial x \partial y} + c(x, y)\frac{\partial^2 u}{\partial y^2} + A(x, y)\frac{\partial u}{\partial x} + B(x, y)\frac{\partial u}{\partial y} + C(x, y)u = F(x, y);$$

(1)

it is a linear combination of u and its partial derivatives, the coefficients being functions of only the independent variables x and y. All linear PDEs may be represented symbolically in the form

$$Lu = F,$$

(2)

102

where L is a linear[†] differential operator. In particular, for PDE (1), $L = a\partial^2/\partial x^2 + b\partial^2/\partial x \partial y + c\partial^2/\partial y^2 + A\partial/\partial x + B\partial/\partial y + C$.

When $F(x, y) \equiv 0$ in (1), the PDE is said to be *homogeneous*; otherwise, it is said to be *nonhomogeneous*.

The study of linear ordinary differential equations is based on the idea of *superposition*—that when solutions to a linear, homogeneous ODE are added together, new solutions are obtained. These same principles are the basis for separation of variables in PDEs. We set them forth in the following two theorems.

Theorem 1 (Superposition Principle 1)

If u_j $(j = 1, \ldots, n)$ are solutions of the same linear, homogeneous PDE, then so also is any linear combination of the u_j,

$$u = \sum_{j=1}^{n} c_j u_j, \qquad c_j = \text{constants.}$$

Furthermore, if each u_j satisfies the same linear, homogeneous boundary and/or initial conditions, then so also does u.

For example, if $y_1(x, t)$ and $y_2(x, t)$ are solutions of the one-dimensional wave equation $y_{tt} = (\tau/\rho)y_{xx}$ and the boundary conditions $y(0, t) = 0$ and $y(L, t) = 0$, then for $y(x, t) = c_1 y_1 + c_2 y_2$,

$$\frac{\partial^2 y}{\partial t^2} = \frac{\partial^2}{\partial t^2}(c_1 y_1 + c_2 y_2) = c_1 \frac{\partial^2 y_1}{\partial t^2} + c_2 \frac{\partial^2 y_2}{\partial t^2}$$

$$= c_1 \frac{\tau}{\rho} \frac{\partial^2 y_1}{\partial x^2} + c_2 \frac{\tau}{\rho} \frac{\partial^2 y_2}{\partial x^2} = \frac{\tau}{\rho} \frac{\partial^2}{\partial x^2}(c_1 y_1 + c_2 y_2) = \frac{\tau}{\rho} \frac{\partial^2 y}{\partial x^2}$$

and

$$y(0, t) = c_1 y_1(0, t) + c_2 y_2(0, t) = 0,$$

$$y(L, t) = c_1 y_1(L, t) + c_2 y_2(L, t) = 0.$$

Thus $y(x, t)$ satisfies the same linear, homogeneous PDE and boundary conditions as y_1 and y_2.

In short, superposition principle 1 states that linear combinations of solutions to linear, homogeneous PDEs and linear, homogeneous subsidiary conditions are solutions of the same PDE and conditions. Superposition principle 2 addresses nonhomogeneous PDEs. It states that nonhomogeneous terms in a PDE may be handled individually, if it is desirable to do so.

Theorem 2 (Superposition Principle 2)

If u_j $(j = 1, \ldots, n)$ are, respectively, solutions of linear, nonhomogeneous PDEs $Lu = F_j$, then $u = \sum_{j=1}^{n} u_j$ is a solution of $Lu = \sum_{j=1}^{n} F_j$.

[†] An operator L is linear if for any two functions $u(x, y)$ and $v(x, y)$ and any constants C_1 and C_2,

$$L(C_1 u + C_2 v) = C_1(Lu) + C_2(Lv).$$

For example, if $U_1(x, y, t)$ and $U_2(x, y, t)$ satisfy the two-dimensional heat conduction equations

$$\frac{\partial U}{\partial t} = k\left(\frac{\partial^2 U}{\partial x^2} + \frac{\partial^2 U}{\partial y^2}\right) + \frac{k}{\kappa} g_1(x, y, t), \qquad \frac{\partial U}{\partial t} = k\left(\frac{\partial^2 U}{\partial x^2} + \frac{\partial^2 U}{\partial y^2}\right) + \frac{k}{\kappa} g_2(x, y, t),$$

respectively, then $U(x, y, t) = U_1(x, y, t) + U_2(x, y, t)$ satisfies

$$\frac{\partial U}{\partial t} = k\left(\frac{\partial^2 U}{\partial x^2} + \frac{\partial^2 U}{\partial y^2}\right) + \frac{k}{\kappa}[g_1(x, y, t) + g_2(x, y, t)].$$

This principle can also be extended to incorporate nonhomogeneous boundary conditions. To illustrate, consider the boundary value problem

$$\frac{\partial^2 V}{\partial x^2} + \frac{\partial^2 V}{\partial y^2} = F(x, y), \qquad 0 < x < L, \qquad 0 < y < L',$$

$$V(0, y) = g_1(y), \qquad 0 < y < L',$$
$$V(L, y) = g_2(y), \qquad 0 < y < L',$$
$$V(x, 0) = h_1(x), \qquad 0 < x < L,$$
$$V(x, L') = h_2(x), \qquad 0 < x < L,$$

for potential in the rectangle of Figure 3.1. The solution is the sum of the functions $V_1(x, y)$, $V_2(x, y)$, and $V_3(x, y)$, satisfying the PDEs in Figure 3.2 together with the

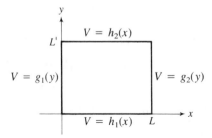

Figure 3.1

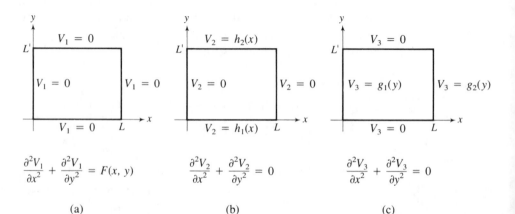

Figure 3.2   (a)   (b)   (c)

indicated boundary conditions. The problem in Figure 3.2(b) could be further subdivided into two problems, each of which contained only one nonhomogeneous boundary condition [as could the problem in Figure 3.2(c)]. In Section 3.2 we show that this is not necessary.

Exercises 3.1

In Exercises 1–10, determine whether the PDE is linear. Which of the linear equations are homogeneous and which are nonhomogeneous?

1. $\dfrac{\partial^2 y}{\partial x^2} = \dfrac{\partial^2 y}{\partial t^2} + \dfrac{\partial y}{\partial t} + y$

2. $\dfrac{\partial^2 U}{\partial x^2} = 3\dfrac{\partial U}{\partial t} + U^2 + t^2 x$

3. $\dfrac{\partial^2 y}{\partial x^2}\dfrac{\partial^2 y}{\partial t^2} = \dfrac{\partial y}{\partial t} + \dfrac{\partial y}{\partial x}$

4. $\dfrac{\partial^2 y}{\partial x^2} + \dfrac{\partial^2 y}{\partial t^2} = \dfrac{\partial y}{\partial t}\dfrac{\partial y}{\partial x}$

5. $\dfrac{\partial^2 V}{\partial x^2} + \dfrac{\partial^2 V}{\partial y^2} + \dfrac{\partial^2 V}{\partial z^2} = F(x, y, z)V$

6. $x^2\dfrac{\partial V}{\partial x} + x\dfrac{\partial^2 V}{\partial y^2} = xy$

7. $2\dfrac{\partial y}{\partial t} = xt\dfrac{\partial^2 y}{\partial x^2} + e^t\dfrac{\partial y}{\partial x} + t$

8. $\dfrac{\partial^2 U}{\partial t^2} + 2\dfrac{\partial^2 U}{\partial x \partial t} + \dfrac{\partial^2 U}{\partial x^2} = U\left(\dfrac{\partial U}{\partial x} + \dfrac{\partial U}{\partial t}\right)$

9. $\dfrac{\partial^2 U}{\partial x^2} - \dfrac{\partial^2 U}{\partial y^2} = 0$

10. $\dfrac{\partial^2 V}{\partial x^2} + \dfrac{\partial^2 V}{\partial y^2} + \dfrac{\partial V}{\partial x} - \dfrac{\partial V}{\partial y} = 3V$

11. Prove Theorem 1.

12. Prove Theorem 2.

13. Based on superposition principle 2, how would you subdivide the problem consisting of Poisson's equation $\nabla^2 V = F(x, y, z)$ inside the box $0 < x < L, 0 < y < L', 0 < z < L''$, subject to the following boundary conditions?

$$
\begin{aligned}
V(0, y, z) &= f_1(y, z), & 0 < y < L', && 0 < z < L'', \\
V(L, y, z) &= f_2(y, z), & 0 < y < L', && 0 < z < L'', \\
V(x, 0, z) &= g_1(x, z), & 0 < x < L, && 0 < z < L'', \\
V(x, L', z) &= g_2(x, z), & 0 < x < L, && 0 < z < L'', \\
V(x, y, 0) &= h_1(x, y), & 0 < x < L, && 0 < y < L', \\
V(x, y, L'') &= h_2(x, y), & 0 < x < L, && 0 < y < L'.
\end{aligned}
$$

14. (a) Show that $u_1(x, y) = e^{x+y}$ and $u_2(x, y) = e^{x-y}$ are solutions of the nonlinear PDE

$$
\left(\frac{\partial u}{\partial x}\right)^2 + \left(\frac{\partial u}{\partial y}\right)^2 = 2u^2.
$$

(b) Is $u_1 + u_2$ a solution?

3.2 Separation of Variables

Before considering specific initial boundary value problems, we illustrate the basic idea of separation of variables on the PDE

$$
\frac{\partial^2 y}{\partial x^2} = \frac{\partial y}{\partial t}. \tag{3}
$$

Separation of variables assumes that functions $y(x, t)$ satisfying (3) can be found that are functions $X(x)$ of x multiplied by functions $T(t)$ of t; that is, it assumes that there are functions satisfying (3) that are of the form

$$y(x, t) = X(x)T(t). \tag{4}$$

When this representation for $y(x, t)$ is substituted into the PDE,

$$\frac{d^2 X}{dx^2} T(t) = X(x)\frac{dT}{dt},$$

and division by $X(x)T(t)$ gives

$$\frac{1}{X(x)}\frac{d^2 X}{dx^2} = \frac{1}{T(t)}\frac{dT}{dt}. \tag{5}$$

The right side of this equation is a function of t only, and the left side is a function of x only. In other words, variables x and t have been *separated* from each other. Now, the only way this equation can hold for a range of values of x and t is for both sides to be equal to some constant, say α, which we take as real[†]; that is, we may write

$$\frac{1}{X}\frac{d^2 X}{dx^2} = \alpha = \frac{1}{T}\frac{dT}{dt}. \tag{6}$$

We call this the *separation principle*.[‡] Equation (6) gives rise to two ordinary differential equations for $X(x)$ and $T(t)$,

$$\frac{d^2 X}{dx^2} - \alpha X = 0 \quad \text{and} \quad \frac{dT}{dt} - \alpha T = 0. \tag{7}$$

Thus, by assuming that a function $y(x, t) = X(x)T(t)$ with variables separated satisfies (3), the PDE is replaced by the two ODEs (7). Boundary and/or initial conditions accompanying PDE (3) may give rise to subsidiary conditions to accompany ODEs (7). We shall see these in the examples to follow.

There is no reason to expect *a priori* that the solution to an initial boundary value problem should separate in form (4). In fact, separation of variables, by itself, seldom yields the solution to an initial boundary value problem. However, separated functions can often be combined to yield the solution to an initial boundary value problem. We illustrate these ideas with the initial boundary value problem for transverse vibrations of a taut string with fixed ends (Figure 3.3):

$$\frac{\partial^2 y}{\partial t^2} = c^2 \frac{\partial^2 y}{\partial x^2}, \qquad 0 < x < L, \qquad t > 0, \tag{8a}$$

$$y(0, t) = 0, \qquad t > 0, \tag{8b}$$

[†] That α must be real for the problems of this chapter is proved in Exercise 30. That α must always be real is verified in Chapter 4.
[‡] That the separation principle is valid can also be seen by differentiating (5) with respect to x. The result is

$$\frac{d}{dx}\left(\frac{1}{X}\frac{d^2 X}{dx^2}\right) = 0,$$

and this implies that $(1/X)d^2 X/dx^2$ must be equal to a numerical constant.

$$y(L, t) = 0, \qquad t > 0, \tag{8c}$$

$$y(x, 0) = f(x), \qquad 0 < x < L, \tag{8d}$$

$$y_t(x, 0) = 0, \qquad 0 < x < L, \tag{8e}$$

where $c^2 = \tau/\rho$. Conditions (8d, e) indicate an initial displacement defined by $f(x)$ and zero initial velocity. We solve this problem for three initial displacement functions:

$$\text{(a) } 3\sin\frac{\pi x}{L}, \qquad \text{(b) } 3\sin\frac{\pi x}{L} - \sin\frac{2\pi x}{L}, \qquad \text{(c) } x(L - x).$$

We begin by searching for separated functions that satisfy the (linear, homogeneous) PDE, the (linear) homogeneous boundary conditions (8b, c), and the (linear) homogeneous initial condition (8e). We do not consider initial condition (8d); it is non-homogeneous. As a general principle, then, separated functions are sought to satisfy only linear and homogeneous PDEs, boundary conditions, and initial conditions.

Figure 3.3

When we substitute a separated function $y(x, t) = X(x)T(t)$ into (8a),

$$XT'' = c^2 X''T \quad \text{or} \quad \frac{X''}{X} = \frac{T''}{c^2 T},$$

where the $''$ on X'' indicates derivatives with respect to x, whereas on T'', it represents derivatives with respect to t. By the separation principle, we may set each side of this equation equal to a constant, say α, which is independent of both x and t. This results in two ODEs for $X(x)$ and $T(t)$,

$$X'' - \alpha X = 0, \qquad T'' - \alpha c^2 T = 0. \tag{9}$$

Homogeneous boundary condition (8b) implies that

$$X(0)T(t) = 0, \qquad t > 0.$$

Because $T(t) \not\equiv 0$ (why not?), it follows that $X(0) = 0$. Similarly, homogeneous boundary condition (8c) and initial condition (8e) require that $X(L) = 0$ and $T'(0) = 0$. Thus, $X(x)$ and $T(t)$ must satisfy

$$X'' - \alpha X = 0, \quad 0 < x < L, \quad \textbf{(10a)} \qquad T'' - \alpha c^2 T = 0, \quad t > 0, \quad \textbf{(11a)}$$

$$X(0) = 0, \qquad\qquad\qquad \textbf{(10b)} \qquad\qquad\qquad T'(0) = 0. \qquad\qquad \textbf{(11b)}$$

$$X(L) = 0; \qquad\qquad\qquad \textbf{(10c)}$$

Notice once again that we do not consider nonhomogeneous condition (8d) at this time. For a separated function $y(x, t) = X(x)T(t)$, it would imply that $X(x)T(0) = f(x)$, but this would give no information about $X(x)$ and $T(t)$ separately. This is always the situation; nonhomogeneous boundary and/or initial conditions are never considered in conjunction with separation of the PDE.

Solutions of ODEs (10) and (11) depend on whether α is positive, zero, or negative. On purely physical grounds, a positive or zero value can be eliminated, for in these cases the time dependence of y is given by

$$T(t) = Ae^{c\sqrt{\alpha}t} + Be^{-c\sqrt{\alpha}t} \quad \text{and} \quad T(t) = At + B,$$

respectively, and these certainly do not yield oscillatory motions. Alternatively, for positive α and zero α, the general solution of (10a) is

$$X(x) = Ae^{\sqrt{\alpha}x} + Be^{-\sqrt{\alpha}x} \quad \text{and} \quad X(x) = Ax + B.$$

But boundary conditions (10b, c) imply that $A = B = 0$, and this in turn implies that $y(x, t) = 0$. Because α must therefore be negative, we set $\alpha = -\lambda^2$ $(\lambda > 0)$ and replace systems (10) and (11) with

$$X'' + \lambda^2 X = 0, \qquad 0 < x < L, \quad \textbf{(12a)} \qquad T'' + c^2\lambda^2 T = 0, \qquad t > 0, \quad \textbf{(13a)}$$

$$X(0) = 0, \qquad\qquad\qquad \textbf{(12b)} \qquad\qquad\qquad T'(0) = 0. \qquad\qquad \textbf{(13b)}$$

$$X(L) = 0; \qquad\qquad\qquad \textbf{(12c)}$$

Boundary conditions (12b, c) on the general solution

$$X(x) = A \cos \lambda x + B \sin \lambda x$$

of (12a) yield

$$0 = A, \qquad 0 = B \sin \lambda L.$$

Since we cannot set $B = 0$ [else $X(x) = 0$], we must therefore set $\sin \lambda L = 0$, and this implies that $\lambda L = n\pi$, n an integer. Thus,

$$X(x) = B \sin \frac{n\pi x}{L}.$$

Condition (13b) on the general solution

$$T(t) = F \cos \frac{n\pi c t}{L} + G \sin \frac{n\pi c t}{L}$$

of (13a) yields

$$0 = \frac{n\pi c}{L} G \quad \text{or} \quad G = 0.$$

We have now determined that the separated function

$$y(x, t) = X(x)T(t) = \left(B \sin \frac{n\pi x}{L} \right)\left(F \cos \frac{n\pi c t}{L} \right) = b \sin \frac{n\pi x}{L} \cos \frac{n\pi c t}{L} \qquad \textbf{(14)}$$

for an arbitrary constant b and any integer n is a solution of the one-dimensional wave equation (8a) and conditions (8b, c, e). The final condition (8d) requires b and n to satisfy

$$f(x) = b \sin \frac{n\pi x}{L}, \qquad 0 < x < L. \qquad \textbf{(15)}$$

We now consider the three cases for $f(x)$ following equation (8e), namely, $3\sin(\pi x/L)$, $3\sin(\pi x/L) - \sin(2\pi x/L)$, and $x(L-x)$.

(a) When $f(x) = 3\sin(\pi x/L)$, this condition becomes

$$3\sin\frac{\pi x}{L} = b\sin\frac{n\pi x}{L}, \qquad 0 < x < L.$$

Obviously, we should choose $b = 3$ and $n = 1$, in which case the solution of initial boundary value problem (8) is

$$y(x,t) = 3\sin\frac{\pi x}{L}\cos\frac{\pi ct}{L}.$$

This function is drawn for various values of t in Figure 3.4. The string oscillates back and forth between its initial position and the negative thereof, doing so once every $2L/c$ seconds.

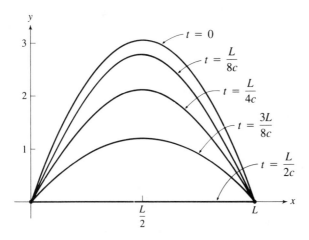

Figure 3.4

We have shown, then, that when the initial position of the string is $3\sin(\pi x/L)$, separation of variables leads to the solution of problem (8).

(b) When $f(x) = 3\sin(\pi x/L) - \sin(2\pi x/L)$, condition (15) is

$$3\sin\frac{\pi x}{L} - \sin\frac{2\pi x}{L} = b\sin\frac{n\pi x}{L}, \qquad 0 < x < L.$$

It is not possible to choose values for b and n to satisfy this equation. In other words, the solution of (8) is not separable when $f(x) = 3\sin(\pi x/L) - \sin(2\pi x/L)$. Does this mean that we must abandon separation? Fortunately, the answer is no. Because PDE (8a), boundary conditions (8b, c), and initial condition (8e) are all linear and homogeneous, superposition principle 1 states that linear combinations of solutions of (8a, b, c, e) are also solutions. In particular, the function

$$y(x,t) = b\sin\frac{n\pi x}{L}\cos\frac{n\pi ct}{L} + d\sin\frac{m\pi x}{L}\cos\frac{m\pi ct}{L}$$

satisfies (8a, b, c, e) for arbitrary integers n and m and any constants b and d. If we apply initial condition (8d) to this function, b, d, n, and m must satisfy

$$3 \sin \frac{\pi x}{L} - \sin \frac{2\pi x}{L} = b \sin \frac{n\pi x}{L} + d \sin \frac{m\pi x}{L}, \qquad 0 < x < L.$$

Clearly, we should choose $b = 3$, $d = -1$, $n = 1$, and $m = 2$, in which case the solution of (8) is

$$y(x,t) = 3 \sin \frac{\pi x}{L} \cos \frac{\pi ct}{L} - \sin \frac{2\pi x}{L} \cos \frac{2\pi ct}{L}.$$

This is not a separated solution; it is the sum of two separated functions. The motion of the string in this case has two terms, called *modes*. The first term, $3 \sin(\pi x/L) \times \cos(\pi ct/L)$, called the fundamental mode, is shown in Figure 3.4. The second mode, $-\sin(2\pi x/L)\cos(2\pi ct/L)$, is illustrated in Figure 3.5 for the same times. Oscillations of this mode occur twice as fast as those for the fundamental mode. The addition of these two modes gives the position of the string in Figure 3.6.

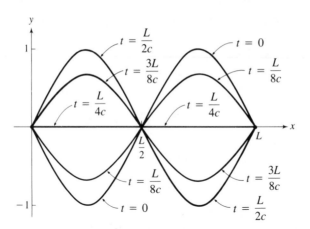

Figure 3.5

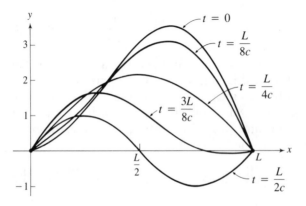

Figure 3.6

(c) Finally, we consider the case in which the initial displacement in the string is parabolic, $f(x) = x(L - x)$. It is definitely impossible to satisfy (15),

$$x(L - x) = b \sin \frac{n\pi x}{L}, \qquad 0 < x < L,$$

for any choice of b and n. Furthermore, for no finite linear combination of terms of the form $b \sin(n\pi x/L)$ can coefficients (b) and integers (n) be chosen to satisfy this condition. Does this mean the ultimate demise of separation of variables? Again, the answer is no. We superpose an infinity of separated functions in the form

$$y(x, t) = \sum_{n=1}^{\infty} b_n \sin \frac{n\pi x}{L} \cos \frac{n\pi ct}{L}, \tag{16}$$

where the constants b_n are arbitrary. No advantage is gained by including terms with negative values of n, for if we had a term in $-n$ (n positive), say

$$X_{-n}(x) = b_{-n} \sin \left(\frac{-n\pi x}{L} \right),$$

we could combine it with

$$X_n(x) = b_n \sin \frac{n\pi x}{L}$$

and write

$$X_n + X_{-n} = (b_n - b_{-n}) \sin \frac{n\pi x}{L} = B_n \sin \frac{n\pi x}{L},$$

which is of the same form as $X_n(x)$.

Initial condition (8d) requires the b_n in (16) to satisfy

$$x(L - x) = \sum_{n=1}^{\infty} b_n \sin \frac{n\pi x}{L}, \qquad 0 < x < L. \tag{17}$$

This equation is satisfied if the b_n are chosen as the coefficients in the Fourier sine series of the odd extension of $x(L - x)$ to a function of period $2L$. According to equation (18b) in Chapter 2,

$$b_n = \frac{2}{L} \int_0^L x(L - x) \sin \frac{n\pi x}{L} dx,$$

and integration by parts leads to

$$b_n = \frac{4L^2 [1 + (-1)^{n+1}]}{n^3 \pi^3}$$

(see Exercise 10 in Section 2.2). Substitution of these into (16) gives displacements of the string when the initial position is $f(x) = x(L - x)$:

$$\begin{aligned} y(x, t) &= \sum_{n=1}^{\infty} \frac{4L^2 [1 + (-1)^{n+1}]}{n^3 \pi^3} \sin \frac{n\pi x}{L} \cos \frac{n\pi ct}{L} \\ &= \frac{8L^2}{\pi^3} \sum_{n=1}^{\infty} \frac{1}{(2n-1)^3} \sin \frac{(2n-1)\pi x}{L} \cos \frac{(2n-1)\pi ct}{L}. \end{aligned} \tag{18}$$

Each term in this series is called a mode of vibration of the string. The position of the string is the sum of an infinite number of modes, lower modes contributing more significantly than higher ones. We shall have more to say about them in Section 5.2.

You would be wise in questioning whether (18) is really a solution of problem (8). Certainly it satisfies boundary conditions (8b, c), and, because $x(L - x)$ is continuously differentiable, our theory of Fourier series implies that initial condition (8d) must also be satisfied. Conditions (8a) and (8e) present difficulties, however. First of all, because (16) is the superposition of an infinity of separated functions, and superposition principle 1 discusses only finite combinations, an infinite combination must be suspect. Second, because (18) is an infinite series, there is a question of its convergence. Does it, for instance, converge for $0 < x < L$ and $t > 0$, and do its derivatives satisfy wave equation (8a) and initial condition (8e)? Each of these questions must be answered, and we shall do so, but not at this time. In this chapter, we wish to illustrate the technique of separation of variables and some of its adaptations to more difficult problems. Verification that the resulting series are truly solutions of initial boundary value problems is discussed in Sections 5.6–5.8. To remind us that these series have not yet been verified as solutions to their respective problems, we call them *formal* solutions.

The one-dimensional wave equation (8a) is a hyperbolic second-order equation (see Section 1.8). In the following two examples we show that separation of variables can be used on parabolic and elliptic equations as well.

Example 1: Solve the following initial boundary value problem for temperature in a homogeneous, isotropic rod with insulated sides and no internal heat generation (Figure 3.7):

$$\frac{\partial U}{\partial t} = k\frac{\partial^2 U}{\partial x^2}, \qquad 0 < x < L, \qquad t > 0, \tag{19a}$$

$$U_x(0, t) = 0, \qquad t > 0, \tag{19b}$$

$$U_x(L, t) = 0, \qquad t > 0, \tag{19c}$$

$$U(x, 0) = x, \qquad 0 < x < L. \tag{19d}$$

The ends of the rod are also insulated [conditions (19b, c)], and its initial temperature increases linearly from $U = 0$ at $x = 0$ to $U = L$ at $x = L$.

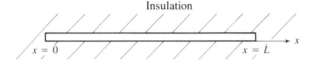

Insulation

$x = 0$ $x = L$

Figure 3.7

Solution: The assumption of a separated function $U(x, t) = X(x)T(t)$ satisfying (19a) leads to

$$XT' = kX''T \quad \text{or} \quad \frac{X''}{X} = \frac{T'}{kT}.$$

The separation principle implies that both sides of the last equation must be equal to a constant, say α, in which case

$$X'' - \alpha X = 0, \qquad T' - \alpha kT = 0.$$

Homogeneous boundary conditions (19b, c) imply that $X'(0) = 0 = X'(L)$, so that $X(x)$ and $T(t)$ must satisfy

$$X'' - \alpha X = 0, \qquad 0 < x < L, \quad \textbf{(20a)} \qquad T' - \alpha k T = 0. \qquad \textbf{(21)}$$

$$X'(0) = 0, \qquad\qquad\qquad \textbf{(20b)}$$

$$X'(L) = 0; \qquad\qquad\qquad \textbf{(20c)}$$

For positive α, the general solution of (20a) is

$$X(x) = Ae^{\sqrt{\alpha}x} + Be^{-\sqrt{\alpha}x},$$

and boundary conditions (20b, c) require that

$$0 = A - B, \qquad 0 = Ae^{\sqrt{\alpha}L} - Be^{-\sqrt{\alpha}L}.$$

From these, $A = B = 0$, and therefore α cannot be positive. For $\alpha = 0$, we obtain $X(x) = Ax + B$, and the boundary conditions imply that $A = 0$. Thus when $\alpha = 0$, solutions of (20) and (21) are

$$X(x) = B = \text{constant} \quad \text{and} \quad T(t) = D = \text{constant}.$$

What we have shown, then, is that $U(x, t) = X(x)T(t) = \text{constant}$ satisfies PDE (19a) and boundary conditions (19b, c).

When α is negative, for convenience we set $\alpha = -\lambda^2 \, (\lambda > 0)$, in which case (20) and (21) are replaced by

$$X'' + \lambda^2 X = 0, \qquad 0 < x < L, \quad \textbf{(22a)} \qquad T' + k\lambda^2 T = 0, \qquad t > 0. \qquad \textbf{(23)}$$

$$X'(0) = 0, \qquad\qquad\qquad \textbf{(22b)}$$

$$X'(L) = 0; \qquad\qquad\qquad \textbf{(22c)}$$

Boundary conditions (22b, c) on the general solution

$$X(x) = A \cos \lambda x + B \sin \lambda x$$

of (22a) require that

$$0 = B, \qquad 0 = \lambda A \sin \lambda L.$$

Since we cannot set $A = 0$ [else $X(x) = 0$], we must therefore set $\sin \lambda L = 0$, and this implies that $\lambda L = n\pi$, n an integer. Thus,

$$X(x) = A \cos \frac{n\pi x}{L}.$$

The general solution of (23) is

$$T(t) = De^{-n^2\pi^2 kt/L^2}.$$

Consequently, besides constant functions, we also have separated functions,

$$X(x)T(t) = \left(A \cos \frac{n\pi x}{L} \right)(De^{-n^2\pi^2 kt/L^2}) = ae^{-n^2\pi^2 kt/L^2} \cos \frac{n\pi x}{L},$$

which satisfy (19a–c) for integers $n > 0$ and arbitrary a. Notice that when $n = 0$, this function reduces to the constant function corresponding to $\alpha = 0$. In other words, all separated functions satisfying (19a–c) can be expressed in the form

$$ae^{-n^2\pi^2kt/L^2}\cos\frac{n\pi x}{L}, \qquad n \geq 0.$$

(It is not necessary to include $n < 0$, since a is arbitrary.) Initial condition (19d) would require a separated function to satisfy

$$x = a\cos\frac{n\pi x}{L}, \qquad 0 < x < L,$$

an impossibility. But because the heat equation and boundary conditions are linear and homogeneous, we superpose separated functions and take

$$U(x,t) = \frac{a_0}{2} + \sum_{n=1}^{\infty} a_n e^{-n^2\pi^2kt/L^2}\cos\frac{n\pi x}{L}$$

with arbitrary constants a_n. Initial condition (19d) requires the a_n to satisfy

$$x = \frac{a_0}{2} + \sum_{n=1}^{\infty} a_n\cos\frac{n\pi x}{L}, \qquad 0 < x < L.$$

This equation is satisfied if the a_n are chosen as the coefficients in the Fourier cosine series of the even extension of the function $f(x) = x$ to a function of period $2L$. According to equation (17b) in Chapter 2,

$$a_n = \frac{2}{L}\int_0^L x\cos\frac{n\pi x}{L}\,dx,$$

and integration gives

$$a_0 = L, \qquad a_n = \frac{2L[(-1)^n - 1]}{n^2\pi^2}, \qquad n > 0.$$

The formal solution of heat conduction problem (19) is therefore

$$U(x,t) = \frac{L}{2} + \sum_{n=1}^{\infty}\frac{2L[(-1)^n - 1]}{n^2\pi^2}e^{-n^2\pi^2kt/L^2}\cos\frac{n\pi x}{L}$$

$$= \frac{L}{2} - \frac{4L}{\pi^2}\sum_{n=1}^{\infty}\frac{1}{(2n-1)^2}e^{-(2n-1)^2\pi^2kt/L^2}\cos\frac{(2n-1)\pi x}{L}. \qquad (24)$$

An interesting feature of this solution is its limit as time t becomes very large:

$$\lim_{t\to\infty} U(x,t) = \frac{L}{2}.$$

In other words, for large times, the temperature of the rod becomes constant throughout. But this is exactly what we should expect. Because the rod is totally insulated after $t = 0$, the original amount of heat in the rod will redistribute itself until a steady-state situation is achieved, the steady-state temperature being a constant value equal to the average of the initial temperature distribution. Since initially the temperature varies linearly from $U = 0$ at one end to $U = L$ at the other, its average value is $L/2$, precisely that predicted by the above limit.   ∎

For a copper rod of length 1 m and diffusivity $k = 114 \times 10^{-6}$ m^2/s, (24) becomes

$$U(x,t) = \frac{1}{2} - \frac{4}{\pi^2} \sum_{n=1}^{\infty} \frac{1}{(2n-1)^2} e^{-114 \times 10^{-6}(2n-1)^2\pi^2 t} \cos(2n-1)\pi x.$$

This function is plotted in Figure 3.8 for various values of t to illustrate the transition from initial temperature $U(x,0) = x$ to final temperature 1/2. These curves indicate that $U(x,t)$ is always an increasing function of x, and therefore heat always flows from right to left. Notice also that each curve is horizontal at $x = 0$ and $x = 1$. This reflects boundary conditions (19b, c).

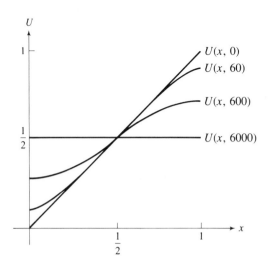

Figure 3.8

Example 2:   Solve the following boundary value problem for potential in the rectangular plate of Figure 3.9 when the sides are maintained at the potentials shown:

$$\frac{\partial^2 V}{\partial x^2} + \frac{\partial^2 V}{\partial y^2} = 0, \qquad 0 < x < L, \qquad 0 < y < L, \tag{25a}$$

$$V(0, y) = 0, \qquad 0 < y < L', \tag{25b}$$

$$V(L, y) = 0, \qquad 0 < y < L', \tag{25c}$$

$$V(x, L') = 0, \qquad 0 < x < L, \tag{25d}$$

$$V(x, 0) = 1, \qquad 0 < x < L. \tag{25e}$$

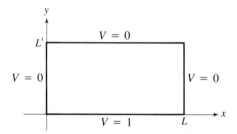

Figure 3.9

Solution: When we assume that a function with variables separated, $V(x, y) = X(x)Y(y)$, satisfies (25a),

$$X''Y + XY'' = 0 \quad \text{or} \quad \frac{X''}{X} = -\frac{Y''}{Y}.$$

The separation principle requires X''/X and $-Y''/Y$ both to equal a constant α, so that

$$X'' - \alpha X = 0, \qquad Y'' + \alpha Y = 0.$$

Homogeneous boundary conditions (25b–d) imply that $X(0) = X(L) = Y(L') = 0$, and therefore $X(x)$ and $Y(y)$ must satisfy

$$X'' - \alpha X = 0, \qquad 0 < x < L, \quad \textbf{(26a)} \qquad \qquad Y'' + \alpha Y = 0, \qquad 0 < y < L', \quad \textbf{(27a)}$$

$$X(0) = 0, \qquad\qquad\qquad\qquad \textbf{(26b)} \qquad\qquad\qquad Y(L') = 0. \qquad\qquad\qquad \textbf{(27b)}$$

$$X(L) = 0; \qquad\qquad\qquad\qquad \textbf{(26c)}$$

System (26) is identical to (10); nontrivial solutions exist only when α is negative. If we set $\alpha = -\lambda^2 \ (\lambda > 0)$, then $\lambda = n\pi/L$, and the solution of (26) is

$$X(x) = B \sin \frac{n\pi x}{L}$$

for arbitrary B and n an integer. With $\alpha = -\lambda^2 = -n^2\pi^2/L^2$, the general solution of (27a) is

$$Y(y) = D \cosh \frac{n\pi y}{L} + E \sinh \frac{n\pi y}{L},$$

and (27b) requires that

$$0 = D \cosh \frac{n\pi L'}{L} + E \sinh \frac{n\pi L'}{L}.$$

We solve this for E in terms of D, in which case

$$Y(y) = D \cosh \frac{n\pi y}{L} - D \frac{\cosh(n\pi L'/L)}{\sinh(n\pi L'/L)} \sinh \frac{n\pi y}{L}$$

$$= \frac{D}{\sinh(n\pi L'/L)} \left(\sinh \frac{n\pi L'}{L} \cosh \frac{n\pi y}{L} - \cosh \frac{n\pi L'}{L} \sinh \frac{n\pi y}{L} \right)$$

$$= F \sinh \frac{n\pi(L' - y)}{L}, \qquad F = \frac{D}{\sinh(n\pi L'/L)}.$$

We have now determined that separated functions

$$X(x)Y(y) = b \sin \frac{n\pi x}{L} \sinh \frac{n\pi(L' - y)}{L} \qquad (b = BF)$$

for any constant b and any integer n are solutions of Laplace's equation (25a) and boundary conditions (25b–d). Since these conditions and this PDE are linear and homogeneous, we superpose separated functions and take

$$V(x, y) = \sum_{n=1}^{\infty} b_n \sin \frac{n\pi x}{L} \sinh \frac{n\pi(L' - y)}{L} \tag{28}$$

with arbitrary constants b_n. Boundary condition (25e) requires the b_n to satisfy

$$1 = \sum_{n=1}^{\infty} b_n \sin \frac{n\pi x}{L} \sinh \frac{n\pi L'}{L} = \sum_{n=1}^{\infty} C_n \sin \frac{n\pi x}{L}, \qquad 0 < x < L,$$

where $C_n = b_n \sinh(n\pi L'/L)$. But this equation is satisfied if the numbers C_n are chosen as the coefficients in the Fourier sine series of the odd extension of the function $f(x) = 1$ to a function of period $2L$. Hence

$$C_n = b_n \sinh \frac{n\pi L'}{L} = \frac{2}{L} \int_0^L (1) \sin \frac{n\pi x}{L} \, dx = \frac{2[1 + (-1)^{n+1}]}{n\pi}.$$

Formal solution (28) of potential problem (25) is therefore

$$V(x, y) = \sum_{n=1}^{\infty} \frac{2[1 + (-1)^{n+1}]}{n\pi \sinh \dfrac{n\pi L'}{L}} \sin \frac{n\pi x}{L} \sinh \frac{n\pi(L' - y)}{L}$$

$$= \frac{4}{\pi} \sum_{n=1}^{\infty} \frac{1}{(2n-1)\sinh \dfrac{(2n-1)\pi L'}{L}} \sin \frac{(2n-1)\pi x}{L} \sinh \frac{(2n-1)\pi(L' - y)}{L}. \tag{29}$$

■

   These three examples have illustrated the essentials of the method of separation of variables and Fourier series for boundary value and initial boundary value problems. In each, functions with variables separated are found to satisfy the linear, homogeneous PDE and the linear, homogeneous boundary and/or initial conditions. These separated functions invariably involve an arbitrary multiplicative constant and an integer parameter. To satisfy the one nonhomogeneous boundary or initial condition, these functions are superposed into an infinite series.
   Our next example illustrates that separation of variables is not restricted to second-order PDEs.

Example 3:   Transverse vibrations of a uniform beam with simply supported ends (Figure 3.10) are described by the initial boundary value problem

$$\frac{\partial^2 y}{\partial t^2} + c^2 \frac{\partial^4 y}{\partial x^4} = 0, \qquad 0 < x < L, \qquad t > 0, \tag{30a}$$

$$y(0, t) = 0, \qquad t > 0, \tag{30b}$$

$$y(L, t) = 0, \qquad t > 0, \tag{30c}$$

$$y_{xx}(0, t) = 0, \qquad t > 0, \tag{30d}$$

$$y_{xx}(L, t) = 0, \qquad t > 0, \tag{30e}$$

$$y(x, 0) = x \sin \frac{\pi x}{L}, \qquad 0 < x < L, \tag{30f}$$

$$y_t(x, 0) = 0, \qquad 0 < x < L, \tag{30g}$$

where $c^2 = EI/\rho$. The force of gravity on the beam has been assumed negligible relative to internal forces (see Section 1.5). Conditions (30f, g) indicate an initial displacement $x \sin(\pi x/L)$ and zero initial velocity. Solve this problem.

Figure 3.10

Solution: Substitution of a function $y(x,t) = X(x)T(t)$ with variables separated into (30a) gives

$$XT'' + c^2X''''T = 0 \quad \text{or} \quad \frac{X''''}{X} = \frac{-T''}{c^2T}.$$

The separation principle implies that

$$X'''' - \alpha X = 0 \quad \text{and} \quad T'' + \alpha c^2 T = 0$$

for some constant α. When $\alpha < 0$ and $\alpha = 0$, general solutions for $T(t)$ are

$$T(t) = A \cosh c\sqrt{-\alpha}\,t + B \sinh c\sqrt{-\alpha}\,t \quad \text{and} \quad T(t) = At + B,$$

respectively. Because the motion of the beam must be oscillatory, and neither of these functions displays this characteristic, we conclude that α must be positive. [The same conclusion can be obtained from the ODE $X'''' - \alpha X = 0$ in conjunction with boundary conditions (30b–e), but not so easily.] When we set $\alpha = \lambda^4$ ($\lambda > 0$) and use separation on homogeneous boundary conditions (30b–e) and initial condition (30g), $X(x)$ and $T(t)$ must satisfy the systems

$$X'''' - \lambda^4 X = 0, \qquad 0 < x < L, \quad \textbf{(31a)} \qquad T'' + c^2\lambda^4 T = 0, \qquad t > 0, \quad \textbf{(32a)}$$
$$X(0) = 0, \qquad\qquad\qquad \textbf{(31b)} \qquad\qquad\qquad T'(0) = 0. \qquad\qquad \textbf{(32b)}$$
$$X(L) = 0, \qquad\qquad\qquad \textbf{(31c)}$$
$$X''(0) = 0, \qquad\qquad\qquad \textbf{(31d)}$$
$$X''(L) = 0; \qquad\qquad\qquad \textbf{(31e)}$$

Boundary conditions (31b–e) on the general solution

$$X(x) = A \cos \lambda x + B \sin \lambda x + C \cosh \lambda x + D \sinh \lambda x$$

of (31a) yield

$$0 = A + C,$$
$$0 = A \cos \lambda L + B \sin \lambda L + C \cosh \lambda L + D \sinh \lambda L,$$
$$0 = -\lambda^2 A + \lambda^2 C,$$
$$0 = -\lambda^2 A \cos \lambda L - \lambda^2 B \sin \lambda L + \lambda^2 C \cosh \lambda L + \lambda^2 D \sinh \lambda L.$$

The first and third of these imply that $A = C = 0$, while the second and fourth require that

$$B \sin \lambda L = 0, \qquad D \sinh \lambda L = 0.$$

Since $\lambda > 0$, we must set $D = 0$, in which case $B \neq 0$. It follows, then, that $\lambda L = n\pi$, n an integer, and

$$X(x) = B \sin \frac{n\pi x}{L}.$$

Condition (32b) on the general solution

$$T(t) = E \cos \frac{n^2 \pi^2 ct}{L^2} + F \sin \frac{n^2 \pi^2 ct}{L^2}$$

of (32a) yields

$$0 = \frac{n^2 \pi^2 c}{L^2} F,$$

from which $F = 0$. We have now determined that separated functions

$$X(x)T(t) = b \sin \frac{n\pi x}{L} \cos \frac{n^2 \pi^2 ct}{L^2}$$

for an arbitrary constant b and any integer n are solutions of PDE (30a), its boundary conditions (30b–e), and initial condition (30g). Since the PDE and these conditions are linear and homogeneous, we superpose separated functions and take

$$y(x, t) = \sum_{n=1}^{\infty} b_n \sin \frac{n\pi x}{L} \cos \frac{n^2 \pi^2 ct}{L^2}$$

with arbitrary constants b_n. Condition (30f) requires the b_n to satisfy

$$x \sin \frac{\pi x}{L} = \sum_{n=1}^{\infty} b_n \sin \frac{n\pi x}{L}, \qquad 0 < x < L.$$

The b_n are therefore the coefficients in the Fourier sine series of the odd extension of $x \sin(\pi x/L)$ to a function of period $2L$. Hence,

$$b_n = \frac{2}{L} \int_0^L x \sin \frac{\pi x}{L} \sin \frac{n\pi x}{L} \, dx,$$

and integration leads to

$$b_1 = \frac{L}{2}, \qquad b_n = \frac{-4nL[1 + (-1)^n]}{(n^2 - 1)^2 \pi^2}, \qquad n > 1.$$

Transverse vibrations of the beam are therefore described formally by

$$y(x, t) = \frac{L}{2} \sin \frac{\pi x}{L} \cos \frac{\pi^2 ct}{L^2} + \sum_{n=2}^{\infty} \frac{-4nL[1 + (-1)^n]}{(n^2 - 1)^2 \pi^2} \sin \frac{n\pi x}{L} \cos \frac{n^2 \pi^2 ct}{L^2}$$

$$= \frac{L}{2} \sin \frac{\pi x}{L} \cos \frac{\pi^2 ct}{L^2} - \frac{16L}{\pi^2} \sum_{n=1}^{\infty} \frac{n}{(4n^2 - 1)^2} \sin \frac{2n\pi x}{L} \cos \frac{4n^2 \pi^2 ct}{L^2}. \qquad (33)$$

∎

Exercises 3.2

Part A—Heat Conduction

1. Determine $U(x, t)$ in Example 1 if the initial temperature is constant throughout.

2. A cylindrical, homogeneous, isotropic rod with insulated sides has temperature $f(x), 0 \leq x \leq L$, at time $t = 0$. For time $t > 0$, its ends (at $x = 0$ and $x = L$) are held at temperature $0°C$. Find a formula for the temperature $U(x, t)$ in the rod for $0 < x < L$ and $t > 0$.

3. (a) Use the result in Exercise 2 to find $U(x, t)$ when

$$f(x) = \begin{cases} x & 0 \leq x \leq L/2 \\ L - x & L/2 \leq x \leq L \end{cases}.$$

   (b) The amount of heat per unit area per unit time flowing from left to right across the cross section of the rod at position x and time t is the x-component of the heat flux vector (this being the only component) $q(x, t) = -\kappa \partial U/\partial x$ (see Section 1.2). Find the heat flow rate for cross sections at positions $x = 0$, $x = L/2$, and $x = L$ by calculating

$$\lim_{x \to 0^+} q(x, t), \quad q\left(\frac{L}{2}, t\right), \quad \lim_{x \to L^-} q(x, t).$$

   (c) Calculate limits of the heat flows in (b) as $t \to 0^+$ and $t \to \infty$.

4. Repeat parts (a), (b), and (c) of Exercise 3 if $f(x) = 10, 0 \leq x \leq L$. In addition,

   (d) Calculate

$$\lim_{x \to 0^+} U(x, 0) \quad \text{and} \quad \lim_{t \to 0^+} U(0, t).$$

   (e) Sketch what you feel $U(x, t)$ would look like as a function of x for various fixed values of t.

5. (a) Find the rate of flow of heat across the cross section at position $x = L/2$ for the rod in Example 1.

   (b) What is the limit of your answer in (a) as $t \to 0^+$?

6. A cylindrical, homogeneous, isotropic rod with insulated sides has temperature $L - x$, $0 \leq x \leq L$, at time $t = 0$. For time $t > 0$, its right end, $x = L$, is held at temperature zero and its left end, $x = 0$, is insulated. Use the result of Exercise 22 in Section 2.2 to find the temperature $U(x, t)$ in the rod for $0 < x < L$ and $t > 0$.

Part B—Vibrations

7. A taut string has its ends fixed at $x = 0$ and $x = L$ on the x-axis. It is given an initial displacement

$$f(x) = \begin{cases} x/5 & 0 \leq x \leq L/2 \\ (L - x)/5 & L/2 \leq x \leq L \end{cases}$$

   at time $t = 0$, but no initial velocity. Find its displacement for $t > 0$ and $0 < x < L$.

8. A taut string has its ends fixed at $x = 0$ and $x = L$ on the x-axis. It is given an initial velocity $g(x) = x(L - x), 0 \leq x \leq L$ at time $t = 0$, but no initial displacement. Find its displacement for $t > 0$ and $0 < x < L$.

9. If the string in Exercises 7 and 8 is given both the initial displacement $f(x)$ and the initial velocity $g(x)$ at time $t = 0$, what is its displacement for $t > 0$ and $0 < x < L$?

10. A taut string has its ends fixed at $x = 0$ and $x = L$ on the x-axis. If it is given an initial displacement $f(x)$ and an initial velocity $g(x)$ at time $t = 0$, find a formula for its subsequent displacement in terms of integrals of $f(x)$ and $g(x)$.

11. Solve Exercise 10 if an external force (per unit x-length) $F = -ky$ ($k > 0$) acts at each point in the string.

12. Solve Exercise 11 if the external force $F = -ky$ is replaced by $F = -\beta \partial y / \partial t$. Assume that $\beta < 2\rho\pi c / L$.

13. A taut string is given an initial displacement (at time $t = 0$) of $f(x)$, $0 \le x \le L$ and initial velocity $g(x)$, $0 \le x \le L$. If the ends $x = 0$ and $x = L$ of the string are free to slide vertically without friction, find $y(x, t)$.

14. (a) What is the solution in Exercise 10 when $g(x) \equiv 0$?
    (b) Show that the series solution in (a) can be expressed in the form

$$y(x, t) = \frac{1}{2}[f(x + ct) + f(x - ct)],$$

    provided $f(x)$ is extended outside the interval $0 \le x \le L$ as an odd function of period $2L$. Is this the result predicted by d'Alembert's formula [(119)] in Section 1.7?

15. (a) What is the solution in Exercise 10 when $f(x) \equiv 0$?
    (b) Show that the solution in (a) can be expressed in the form

$$y(x, t) = \frac{1}{2c} \int_{x-ct}^{x+ct} g(\zeta) \, d\zeta,$$

    provided $g(x)$ is extended outside the interval $0 \le x \le L$ as an odd function of period $2L$. Is this the result predicted by d'Alembert's formula [(119)] in Section 1.7?

16. A circular bar of natural length L is clamped at both ends and stretched until its length is L^*. At time $t = 0$ the left end of the bar is at position $x = 0$ and the clamps are removed. If horizontal vibrations occur along a frictionless surface, find displacements of cross sections of the bar.

Part C—Potential, Steady-State Heat Conduction, Static Deflections of Membranes

17. A region A (in the xy-plane) is bounded by the lines $x = 0$, $y = 0$, $x = L$, and $y = L'$. If the edges $y = 0$, $y = L'$, and $x = L$ are held at potential zero, and $x = 0$ is at potential equal to 100, find the potential in A.

18. Solve Exercise 17 if edges $x = 0$ and $y = 0$ are at potential 100, while $x = L$ and $y = L'$ are at zero potential. (*Hint:* See the extension of superposition principle 2 in Figure 3.2.)

19. Solve Exercise 17 if edges $x = 0$ and $x = L$ are at potential 100 while $y = 0$ and $y = L'$ are at zero potential.

20. Solve Exercise 17 if the condition $V(0, y) = 100$ along $x = 0$ is replaced by $\partial V(0, y)/\partial x = 100$, $0 < y < L'$.

21. Solve Exercise 17 if the boundary conditions are

$$\frac{\partial V(0, y)}{\partial x} = 100, \qquad 0 < y < L',$$

$$\frac{\partial V(L, y)}{\partial x} = 100, \qquad 0 < y < L',$$

$$\frac{\partial V(x, 0)}{\partial y} = \frac{\partial V(x, L')}{\partial y} = 0, \qquad 0 < x < L.$$

Is the solution unique? What is the solution if $V(L/2, L'/2) = 0$?

22. Can Exercise 21 be solved if the condition along $x = L$ is $\partial V(L, y)/\partial x = -100$, $0 < y < L'$? Explain.

23. A thin rectangular plate occupies the region described by $0 \le x \le L$, $0 \le y \le L'$. Its top and bottom surfaces are insulated. If edges $x = 0$ and $x = L$ are held at temperature $0°C$, while $y = 0$ and $y = L'$ have temperatures $x(L - x)$ and $-x(L - x)$, respectively, what is the steady-state temperature of the plate?

24. Solve Exercise 23 if edges $x = 0$, $x = L$, and $y = L'$ are held at temperature $0°C$ while heat is added along the edge $y = 0$ at a constant rate q W/m^2.

25. Solve Exercise 24 if heat is added to both edges $y = 0$ and $y = L'$ at rate q W/m^2 while edges $x = 0$ and $x = L$ are held at temperature $10°C$.

26. A membrane is stretched tightly over the rectangle $0 \le x \le L$, $0 \le y \le L'$. Its edges are given deflections described by the following boundary conditions:

$$z(0, y) = kL(y - L')/L', \qquad 0 < y < L',$$
$$z(L, y) = 0, \qquad 0 < y < L',$$
$$z(x, 0) = k(x - L), \qquad 0 < x < L,$$
$$z(x, L') = 0, \qquad 0 < x < L$$

($k > 0$ a constant). Find static deflections of the membrane when all external forces are negligible compared with tensions in the membrane.

27. Find a formula for the solution of Laplace's equation inside the rectangle $0 \le x \le L$, $0 \le y \le L'$ of Figure 3.1 when

(a) $g_1(y) = g_2(y) = h_2(x) = 0$;   (b) $g_1(y) = g_2(y) = h_1(x) = 0$;

(c) $g_1(y) = g_2(y) = 0$;   (d) $h_1(x) = h_2(x) = 0$.

28. Solve Exercise 23 if edges $x = 0$ and $y = L'$ are insulated, $x = L$ is held at temperature $0°C$, and $y = 0$ has temperature $(L - x)^2$, $0 \le x \le L$. (*Hint:* Use Exercise 22 in Section 2.2.)

Part D—General Results

29. Prove that a second-order, linear, homogeneous PDE in two independent variables with constant coefficients is always separable. (A more general result is proved in Exercise 10 of Section 4.3.)

30. Verify that we cannot have a complex separation constant α for the two problems (10) and (20).

3.3 Nonhomogeneities and Eigenfunction Expansions

In Section 3.2 we stressed the fact that separation of variables is carried out on linear, *homogeneous* PDEs and linear, *homogeneous* boundary and/or initial conditions. Separated functions are then superposed in order to satisfy nonhomogeneous conditions. When nonhomogeneities are present in PDE, or in the boundary conditions of time-dependent problems, separation by itself fails. To illustrate, we reconsider vibration problem (8) for displacement of a taut string with fixed end points, but take gravity into account:

$$\frac{\partial^2 y}{\partial t^2} = c^2 \frac{\partial^2 y}{\partial x^2} + g, \qquad 0 < x < L, \qquad t > 0, \qquad (g = -9.81), \qquad \textbf{(34a)}$$

$$y(0,t) = 0, \qquad t > 0, \tag{34b}$$

$$y(L,t) = 0, \qquad t > 0, \tag{34c}$$

$$y(x,0) = f(x), \qquad 0 < x < L, \tag{34d}$$

$$y_t(x,0) = 0, \qquad 0 < x < L. \tag{34e}$$

Only the partial differential equation is affected; it becomes nonhomogeneous. The boundary conditions remain homogeneous. Substitution of a separated function $y(x,t) = X(x)T(t)$ into (34a) gives

$$XT'' = c^2 X''T + g.$$

Our usual procedure of dividing by $X(x)T(t)$ would not lead to a separated equation; in fact, this equation cannot be separated. Likewise, were (34b) not homogeneous, say $y(0,t) = f(t)$, in which case the left end of the string would be forced to undergo specific motion, substitution of $y(x,t) = X(x)T(t)$ would not lead to information about $X(x)$ and $T(t)$ separately.

In this section we illustrate two methods for handling nonhomogeneities. The first method uses steady-state solutions for heat conduction problems and static deflections for vibration problems. It applies, however, only to time-independent nonhomogeneities. The second method is called *eigenfunction expansion*; it applies to time-dependent as well as time-independent nonhomogeneities.

Time-Independent Nonhomogeneities

Partial differential equation (34a) has a time-independent nonhomogeneity (it is also independent of x, but that is immaterial). To solve this problem, we define a new dependent variable $z(x,t)$ according to

$$y(x,t) = z(x,t) + \psi(x), \tag{35}$$

where $\psi(x)$ is the solution of the corresponding static-deflection problem

$$0 = c^2 \frac{d^2\psi}{dx^2} + g, \qquad 0 < x < L, \tag{36a}$$

$$\psi(0) = 0, \qquad \psi(L) = 0. \tag{36b}$$

Differential equation (36a) implies that

$$\psi(x) = \frac{-g}{2c^2} x^2 + Ax + B,$$

and boundary conditions (36b) require that

$$0 = B, \qquad 0 = \frac{-g}{2c^2} L^2 + AL + B.$$

From these we obtain the position of the string were it to hang motionless under gravity:

$$\psi(x) = \frac{-g}{2c^2} x^2 + \frac{gL}{2c^2} x = \frac{gx}{2c^2}(L - x). \tag{37}$$

We expect that the string will vibrate about this position and that $z(x, t)$ represents displacements from this position. A PDE satisfied by $z(x, t)$ can be found by substituting (35) into (34a):

$$\frac{\partial^2}{\partial t^2}[z(x, t) + \psi(x)] = c^2 \frac{\partial^2}{\partial x^2}[z(x, t) + \psi(x)] + g.$$

This equation simplifies to the following homogeneous PDE when we note that $\psi(x)$ is only a function of x that satisfies (36a):

$$\frac{\partial^2 z}{\partial t^2} = c^2 \frac{\partial^2 z}{\partial x^2}, \qquad 0 < x < L, \qquad t > 0. \tag{38a}$$

Boundary conditions for $z(x, t)$ are obtained by setting $x = 0$ and $x = L$ in (35) and using (34b, c):

$$z(0, t) = y(0, t) - \psi(0) = 0, \qquad t > 0, \tag{38b}$$

$$z(L, t) = y(L, t) - \psi(L) = 0, \qquad t > 0. \tag{38c}$$

Finally, by setting $t = 0$ in (35) and its partial derivative with respect to t, and using (34d, e), we obtain initial conditions for $z(x, t)$:

$$z(x, 0) = y(x, 0) - \psi(x) = f(x) - \frac{gx}{2c^2}(L - x), \qquad 0 < x < L, \tag{38d}$$

$$z_t(x, 0) = y_t(x, 0) = 0, \qquad 0 < x < L. \tag{38e}$$

We have therefore replaced problem (34), which has a nonhomogeneous PDE, with (38), which has a homogeneous PDE. We have complicated one of the initial conditions, but this is a small price to pay. As for problem (8), if a function with variables separated is to satisfy PDE (38a), boundary conditions (38b, c), and initial condition (38e), it must be of the form

$$b \sin\frac{n\pi x}{L} \cos\frac{n\pi ct}{L},$$

for arbitrary b and n an integer. Because PDE (38a) and conditions (38b, c, e) are linear and homogeneous, we superpose these functions and take

$$z(x, t) = \sum_{n=1}^{\infty} b_n \sin\frac{n\pi x}{L} \cos\frac{n\pi ct}{L}. \tag{39}$$

Initial condition (38d) requires the constants b_n to satisfy

$$f(x) - \frac{gx}{2c^2}(L - x) = \sum_{n=1}^{\infty} b_n \sin\frac{n\pi x}{L}, \qquad 0 < x < L.$$

Consequently, the b_n are coefficients in the Fourier sine series of the odd extension of $f(x) - gx(L - x)/(2c^2)$ to a function of period $2L$; that is,

$$b_n = \frac{2}{L}\int_0^L \left(f(x) - \frac{gx}{2c^2}(L - x)\right)\sin\frac{n\pi x}{L}\,dx. \tag{40}$$

The formal solution of vibration problem (34) is therefore

$$y(x,t) = \frac{gx}{2c^2}(L-x) + \sum_{n=1}^{\infty} b_n \sin\frac{n\pi x}{L}\cos\frac{n\pi ct}{L}, \tag{41}$$

where the b_n are given by (40).

This technique of separating off static deflections can be applied to any non-homogeneity that is only a function of position, be it in the PDE or in a boundary condition. We illustrate nonhomogeneities in boundary conditions in the following example.

Example 4: Solve the initial boundary value problem for temperature in a homogeneous, isotropic rod with insulated sides when the ends of the rod are held at constant nonzero temperatures

$$\frac{\partial U}{\partial t} = k\frac{\partial^2 U}{\partial x^2}, \qquad 0 < x < L, \qquad t > 0, \tag{42a}$$

$$U(0,t) = U_0, \qquad t > 0, \tag{42b}$$

$$U(L,t) = U_L, \qquad t > 0, \tag{42c}$$

$$U(x,0) = f(x), \qquad 0 < x < L. \tag{42d}$$

Solution: We define a new dependent variable $V(x,t)$ by

$$U(x,t) = V(x,t) + \psi(x), \tag{43}$$

where $\psi(x)$ is the solution of the associated steady-state problem

$$0 = k\frac{d^2\psi}{dx^2}, \qquad 0 < x < L, \tag{44a}$$

$$\psi(0) = U_0, \tag{44b}$$

$$\psi(L) = U_L. \tag{44c}$$

Differential equation (44a) implies that

$$\psi(x) = Ax + B,$$

and boundary conditions (44b, c) require that

$$U_0 = B, \qquad U_L = AL + B.$$

From these, we obtain the steady-state solution

$$\psi(x) = U_0 + \frac{(U_L - U_0)x}{L} \tag{45}$$

(the temperature in the rod after a very long time). With this choice for $\psi(x)$, the PDE for $V(x,t)$ can be found by substituting (43) into (42a):

$$\frac{\partial}{\partial t}[V(x,t) + \psi(x)] = k\frac{\partial^2}{\partial x^2}[V(x,t) + \psi(x)].$$

Because $\psi(x)$ is only a function of x that has a vanishing second derivative, this equation simplifies to

$$\frac{\partial V}{\partial t} = k\frac{\partial^2 V}{\partial x^2}, \qquad 0 < x < L, \qquad t > 0. \tag{46a}$$

Boundary conditions for $V(x, t)$ are obtained from (43) and (42b, c):

$U = V + \psi$

$V = U - \psi$

$$V(0, t) = U(0, t) - \psi(0) = U_0 - U_0 = 0, \qquad t > 0, \tag{46b}$$

$$V(L, t) = U(L, t) - \psi(L) = U_L - U_L = 0, \qquad t > 0. \tag{46c}$$

Finally, $V(x, t)$ must satisfy the initial condition

$$V(x, 0) = U(x, 0) - \psi(x) = f(x) - U_0 - \frac{(U_L - U_0)x}{L}, \qquad 0 < x < L. \tag{46d}$$

Separation of variables $V(x, t) = X(x)\,T(t)$ on (46a–c) leads to the ordinary differential equations

$$X'' + \lambda^2 X = 0, \qquad 0 < x < L \quad \textbf{(47a)} \qquad T' + k\lambda^2 T = 0, \qquad t > 0. \quad \textbf{(48)}$$

$$X(0) = X(L) = 0; \qquad \textbf{(47b)}$$

These give separated functions

$$be^{-n^2\pi^2 kt/L^2}\sin\frac{n\pi x}{L}$$

for arbitrary b and n an integer. To satisfy the initial condition, we superpose separated functions and take

$$V(x, t) = \sum_{n=1}^{\infty} b_n e^{-n^2\pi^2 kt/L^2}\sin\frac{n\pi x}{L}. \tag{49}$$

Initial condition (46d) requires the constants b_n to satisfy

$$f(x) - U_0 - \frac{(U_L - U_0)x}{L} = \sum_{n=1}^{\infty} b_n \sin\frac{n\pi x}{L}, \qquad 0 < x < L.$$

Consequently, the b_n are the coefficients in the Fourier sine series of the odd extension of $f(x) - U_0 - (U_L - U_0)x/L$ to a function of period $2L$:

$$b_n = \frac{2}{L}\int_0^L \left(f(x) - U_0 - \frac{(U_L - U_0)x}{L} \right)\sin\frac{n\pi x}{L}\,dx. \tag{50}$$

The formal solution of (42) is therefore

$$U(x, t) = V(x, t) + U_0 + \frac{(U_L - U_0)x}{L}, \tag{51}$$

where $V(x, t)$ is given by (49) and b_n by (50). ∎

It is interesting and informative to analyze solution (51) further for two specific initial temperature distributions $f(x)$. First, suppose that the initial temperature of the rod is 0°C throughout; that is, $f(x) \equiv 0$. In this case, equations (49)–(51) yield, for the temperature in the rod,

$$U(x,t) = U_0 + \frac{(U_L - U_0)x}{L} + \sum_{n=1}^{\infty} b_n e^{-n^2\pi^2 kt/L^2} \sin\frac{n\pi x}{L},$$

where $b_n = \dfrac{2}{L} \displaystyle\int_0^L \left(-U_0 - (U_L - U_0)\frac{x}{L} \right) \sin\frac{n\pi x}{L}\,dx = \dfrac{-2}{n\pi}[U_0 + (-1)^{n+1}U_L].$

This function is plotted for various fixed values of t in Figure 3.11 (using a diffusivity of $k = 12.4 \times 10^{-6}\,\text{m}^2/\text{s}$). What is important to notice is the smooth transition from initial temperature 0°C to final (steady-state) temperature at every point in the rod except for its ends, $x = 0$ and $x = L$. Here the transition is instantaneous, as is dictated by problem (42) when $f(x)$ is chosen to vanish identically. Physically, this is an impossibility, but the mathematics required to describe a very quick but smooth change in temperature from 0°C at $x = 0$ and $x = L$ to U_0 and U_L would complicate the problem enormously. In practice, then, we are willing to live with the anomaly of the solution at time $t = 0$ for $x = 0$ and $x = L$ in order to avoid these added complications. This anomaly is manifested in the heat transfer across the ends of the rod at time $t = 0$. According to equation (13) in Section 1.2, the amount of heat flowing left to right through any cross section of the rod is

$$q(x,t) = -\kappa \frac{\partial U}{\partial x} = -\kappa \left(\frac{U_L - U_0}{L} + \frac{\pi}{L} \sum_{n=1}^{\infty} n b_n e^{-n^2\pi^2 kt/L^2} \cos\frac{n\pi x}{L} \right)$$

$$= \frac{\kappa}{L} \left(U_0 - U_L + 2 \sum_{n=1}^{\infty} [U_0 + (-1)^{n+1}U_L] e^{-n^2\pi^2 kt/L^2} \cos\frac{n\pi x}{L} \right).$$

The series in this expression diverges (to infinity) when $x = 0$ and $t = 0$. In other words, the instantaneous temperature change at time $t = 0$ from 0°C to U_0°C is predicated on an infinite heat flux at that time. A similar situation occurs at the end $x = L$.

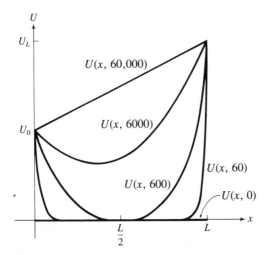

Figure 3.11

The second initial temperature function we consider is $f(x) = U_0(1 - x^2/L^2) + U_L x/L$, a distribution that does not give rise to abrupt temperature changes at time

$t = 0$ since $f(0) = U_0$ and $f(L) = U_L$. In this case, coefficients b_n in (50) are $b_n = 4U_0[1 + (-1)^{n+1}]/(n^3\pi^3)$, and

$$U(x,t) = U_0 + \frac{(U_L - U_0)x}{L} + \frac{8U_0}{\pi^3}\sum_{n=1}^{\infty}\frac{1}{(2n-1)^3}e^{-(2n-1)^2\pi^2kt/L^2}\sin\frac{(2n-1)\pi x}{L}.$$

As shown in Figure 3.12, the transition from initial to steady-state temperature is smooth for all $0 \le x \le L$. Supporting this is the heat flux vector

$$q(x,t) = \frac{\kappa}{L}\left(U_0 - U_L - \frac{8U_0}{\pi^2}\sum_{n=1}^{\infty}\frac{1}{(2n-1)^2}e^{-(2n-1)^2\pi^2kt/L^2}\cos\frac{(2n-1)\pi x}{L}\right).$$

The series herein converges uniformly for $0 \le x \le L$ and $t \ge 0$. If we take limits as $x \to 0^+$ and $t \to 0^+$, we find the initial heat flux across the end $x = 0$,

$$q(0+,0+) = \frac{\kappa}{L}\left(U_0 - U_L - \frac{8U_0}{\pi^2}\sum_{n=1}^{\infty}\frac{1}{(2n-1)^2}\right)$$

$$= \frac{\kappa}{L}\left[U_0 - U_L - \frac{8U_0}{\pi^2}\left(\frac{\pi^2}{8}\right)\right] = -\frac{\kappa U_L}{L}$$

[since $\sum_{n=1}^{\infty}1/(2n-1)^2 = \pi^2/8$]. Perhaps unexpectedly, we find that the direction of heat flow across $x = 0$ at time $t = 0$ is completely dictated by the sign of U_L. When $U_L < 0$, heat flows into the rod, and when $U_L > 0$, heat flows out. This is most easily seen by calculating the derivative of the initial temperature distribution in the rod at $x = 0$, $f'(0) = U_L/L$. If $U_L < 0$, points in the rod near $x = 0$ have temperature less than those in the end $x = 0$, and heat flows into the rod; if $U_L > 0$, points near $x = 0$ are at a higher temperature than those at $x = 0$, and heat flows out of the rod.

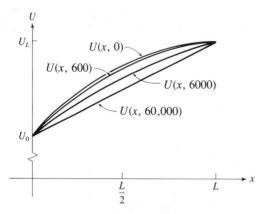

Figure 3.12

Time-Dependent Nonhomogeneities

When the nonhomogeneity in a PDE is time dependent, it is necessary to adopt a different approach. The technique used resembles the method of variation of parameters for ODEs. Because variation of parameters for ODEs is used in a form perhaps different from that which many readers might have seen, and because it leads into the method of eigenfunction expansion for PDEs, we digress to review the technique quickly. Consider the ODE

$$y'' + y = f(x), \tag{52a}$$

where $f(x)$ is as yet an unspecified function. The general solution of the associated homogeneous equation $y'' + y = 0$ is $y(x) = A \cos x + B \sin x$, to which must be added a particular solution of (52a). When $f(x)$ is a polynomial, an exponential, a sine, a cosine, or a combination of these, various techniques (such as undetermined coefficients, or operators) yield this particular solution. Variation of parameters also gives a particular solution in these cases, but it realizes its true potential when $f(x)$ is not one of these, or when a general solution is required for arbitrary $f(x)$. The method assumes that a general solution of (52a) can be found in the form $A \cos x + B \sin x$, but where A and B are functions of x; that is, it assumes that the general solution of the nonhomogeneous equation is $y(x) = A(x) \cos x + B(x) \sin x$. To obtain $A(x)$ and $B(x)$, this function is substituted into the differential equation. Because this imposes only one condition on two functions $A(x)$ and $B(x)$, the opportunity is taken to impose a second condition, and this condition is always taken as $A'(x) \cos x + B'(x) \sin x = 0$. The result is the following system of linear equations in $A'(x)$ and $B'(x)$:

$$A'(x) \cos x + B'(x) \sin x = 0, \tag{53a}$$

$$-A'(x) \sin x + B'(x) \cos x = f(x). \tag{53b}$$

These can be solved for

$$A'(x) = -f(x) \sin x \quad \text{and} \quad B'(x) = f(x) \cos x,$$

from which

$$A(x) = -\int f(x) \sin x \, dx + C_1 \quad \text{and} \quad B(x) = \int f(x) \cos x \, dx + C_2,$$

where C_1 and C_2 are constants of integration. The general solution of (52a) is therefore

$$y(x) = \left(C_1 - \int f(x) \sin x \, dx \right) \cos x + \left(C_2 + \int f(x) \cos x \, dx \right) \sin x. \tag{54}$$

(If C_1 and C_2 are omitted, this is a particular solution of the differential equation.) A simplified form results if we express the antiderivatives as definite integrals:

$$y(x) = C_1 \cos x + C_2 \sin x - \cos x \int_0^x f(t) \sin t \, dt + \sin x \int_0^x f(t) \cos t \, dt$$

$$= C_1 \cos x + C_2 \sin x + \int_0^x f(t) \sin(x - t) \, dt. \tag{55}$$

In this form, any initial conditions

$$y(0) = y_0 \quad \text{and} \quad y'(0) = y_0', \tag{52b}$$

that might accompany ODE (52a) are easily incorporated. They require that

$$y_0 = C_1 \qquad y_0' = C_2,$$

and therefore the final solution of differential equation (52a) subject to initial conditions (52b) is

$$y(x) = y_0 \cos x + y_0' \sin x + \int_0^x f(t) \sin(x - t) \, dt. \tag{56}$$

We now develop the analogous method for solving initial boundary value problems that have time-dependent nonhomogeneities in their PDEs. The one-dimensional vibration problem for displacements of a taut string with a time-dependent forcing function $F(x, t) = e^{-t}$ is a convenient vehicle:

$$\frac{\partial^2 y}{\partial t^2} = c^2 \frac{\partial^2 y}{\partial x^2} + \frac{e^{-t}}{\rho}, \qquad 0 < x < L, \qquad t > 0, \tag{57a}$$

$$y(0, t) = 0, \qquad t > 0, \tag{57b}$$

$$y(L, t) = 0, \qquad t > 0, \tag{57c}$$

$$y(x, 0) = f(x), \qquad 0 < x < L, \tag{57d}$$

$$y_t(x, 0) = 0, \qquad 0 < x < L. \tag{57e}$$

We have taken a forcing function that does not depend on x to simplify calculations, but the technique works when the forcing function is a function of x as well as t. If the forcing term were absent, the PDE would be homogeneous, and, according to our solution of problem (8), separation of variables on (57a, b, c, e) would lead to a superposed solution of the form

$$y(x, t) = \sum_{n=1}^{\infty} C_n \sin \frac{n\pi x}{L} \cos \frac{n\pi ct}{L},$$

where the C_n are arbitrary constants [see equation (16)]. To incorporate a nonzero forcing term, we use a method called eigenfunction expansion. (In Chapter 5, when we consider more general problems, we learn the significance of this name.) This method is much like variation of parameters for ODEs; we attempt to find a solution in this form, but where $C_n = C_n(t)$ are functions of t,

$$y(x, t) = \sum_{n=1}^{\infty} C_n(t) \sin \frac{n\pi x}{L} \cos \frac{n\pi ct}{L}. \tag{58}$$

Because at this point $C_n(t)$ is an unknown function, it is more convenient, and no less general, to group $C_n(t)$ and $\cos(n\pi ct/L)$ together as the unknown function, say $d_n(t) = C_n(t) \cos(n\pi ct/L)$. In other words, we replace (58) with

$$y(x, t) = \sum_{n=1}^{\infty} d_n(t) \sin \frac{n\pi x}{L}. \tag{59}$$

It is this series that is called an eigenfunction expansion. The $\sin(n\pi x/L)$ are the eigenfunctions, and $d_n(t)$ are coefficients in the expansion of $y(x, t)$ in terms of these eigenfunctions.

For any choice of $d_n(t)$ whatsoever, the representation in (59) satisfies boundary conditions (57b, c). To satisfy initial condition (57e), we must have

$$\sum_{n=1}^{\infty} d'_n(0) \sin \frac{n\pi x}{L} = 0, \qquad 0 < x < L.$$

This requires the unknown functions $d_n(t)$ to have vanishing first derivatives at $t = 0$, $d'_n(0) = 0$.

To determine whether a function of form (59) can satisfy (57a), we substitute (59) into (57a) and formally differentiate term by term:

$$\sum_{n=1}^{\infty} d_n''(t) \sin \frac{n\pi x}{L} = c^2 \sum_{n=1}^{\infty} -\frac{n^2\pi^2}{L^2} d_n(t) \sin \frac{n\pi x}{L} + \frac{e^{-t}}{\rho}. \tag{60}$$

In its present form, this equation is intractable, but the fact that two of the terms are series in $\sin(n\pi x/L)$ suggests that the function e^{-t}/ρ be expressed in this way also; that is, we should write

$$\frac{e^{-t}}{\rho} = \sum_{n=1}^{\infty} F_n \sin \frac{n\pi x}{L}. \tag{61a}$$

We have seen equations of this form before; they are Fourier sine series representations for the function on the left. However, should not the function on the left be a function of x, not t? Indeed it should, but e^{-t}/ρ is trivially a function of x, and in addition it is a function of t. In other words, it is not that e^{-t}/ρ is a function of the wrong variable; it is a function of both x and t, and we wish to express this function of x and t as a Fourier sine series in x for any given t. Clearly, this can happen only if coefficients are functions of t; that is, we really want to express e^{-t}/ρ in the form

$$\frac{e^{-t}}{\rho} = \sum_{n=1}^{\infty} F_n(t) \sin \frac{n\pi x}{L}. \tag{61b}$$

For each fixed t, (61b) is the Fourier sine series of the odd, $2L$-periodic extension of the constant function (of x) e^{-t}/ρ. According to equation (18b) in Section 2.2, then,

$$F_n(t) = \frac{2}{L} \int_0^L \frac{1}{\rho} e^{-t} \sin \frac{n\pi x}{L} dx = \frac{2e^{-t}[1 + (-1)^{n+1}]}{n\pi\rho},$$

and therefore

$$\frac{e^{-t}}{\rho} = \frac{2e^{-t}}{\rho\pi} \sum_{n=1}^{\infty} \frac{[1 + (-1)^{n+1}]}{n} \sin \frac{n\pi x}{L}. \tag{62}$$

If (62) is now substituted into (60), the result is

$$\sum_{n=1}^{\infty} d_n''(t) \sin \frac{n\pi x}{L} = \sum_{n=1}^{\infty} -\frac{n^2\pi^2 c^2}{L^2} d_n(t) \sin \frac{n\pi x}{L} + \frac{2e^{-t}}{\rho\pi} \sum_{n=1}^{\infty} \frac{[1 + (-1)^{n+1}]}{n} \sin \frac{n\pi x}{L}$$

or

$$\sum_{n=1}^{\infty} \left(d_n''(t) + \frac{n^2\pi^2 c^2}{L^2} d_n(t) - \frac{2e^{-t}[1 + (-1)^{n+1}]}{\rho\pi n} \right) \sin \frac{n\pi x}{L} = 0.$$

But for each fixed t, the series on the left of this equation is the Fourier sine series of the function on the right, the function that is identically zero. It follows that all coefficients must be zero; that is,

$$d_n''(t) + \frac{n^2\pi^2 c^2}{L^2} d_n(t) - \frac{2e^{-t}[1 + (-1)^{n+1}]}{n\pi\rho} = 0.$$

In other words, each unknown function $d_n(t)$ must satisfy the differential equation

$$\frac{d^2 d_n}{dt^2} + \frac{n^2\pi^2 c^2}{L^2} d_n = \frac{2[1 + (-1)^{n+1}]e^{-t}}{n\pi\rho}.$$

The general solution of this equation is

$$d_n(t) = b_n \cos\frac{n\pi ct}{L} + a_n \sin\frac{n\pi ct}{L} + \frac{2L^2[1 + (-1)^{n+1}e^{-t}]}{n\pi\rho(L^2 + n^2\pi^2 c^2)},$$

where a_n and b_n are constants. The condition $d_n'(0) = 0$ implies that

$$a_n = \frac{2L^3[1 + (-1)^{n+1}]}{n^2\pi^2\rho c(L^2 + n^2\pi^2 c^2)},$$

and therefore

$$d_n(t) = b_n \cos\frac{n\pi ct}{L} + \frac{2L^2[1 + (-1)^{n+1}]}{n^2\pi^2\rho c(L^2 + n^2\pi^2 c^2)}\left(n\pi ce^{-t} + L\sin\frac{n\pi ct}{L}\right).$$

Substitution of this expression into (59) gives

$$y(x, t) = \sum_{n=1}^{\infty}\left[b_n \cos\frac{n\pi ct}{L} + \frac{2L^2[1 + (-1)^{n+1}]}{n^2\pi^2\rho c(L^2 + n^2\pi^2 c^2)}\left(n\pi ce^{-t} + L\sin\frac{n\pi ct}{L}\right)\right]\sin\frac{n\pi x}{L}.$$

$$(63)$$

Initial condition (57d) requires that

$$f(x) = \sum_{n=1}^{\infty}\left(b_n + \frac{2L^2[1 + (-1)^{n+1}]}{n\pi\rho(L^2 + n^2\pi^2 c^2)}\right)\sin\frac{n\pi x}{L}, \qquad 0 < x < L,$$

from which

$$b_n + \frac{2L^2[1 + (-1)^{n+1}]}{n\pi\rho(L^2 + n^2\pi^2 c^2)} = \frac{2}{L}\int_0^L f(x)\sin\frac{n\pi x}{L}\,dx. \qquad (64)$$

The formal solution of (57) is now complete; it is (63) with the b_n defined by (64).

Perhaps a summary of the eigenfunction expansion technique would be valuable at this juncture. When a PDE has a nonhomogeneity, the method proceeds as follows:

(1) Find separated functions satisfying the homogeneous boundary conditions (and homogeneous initial conditions) and the corresponding *homogeneous* PDE. Suppose we denote the functions of x by $X_n(x)$. [$X_n(x) = \sin(n\pi x/L)$ in our previous problem.]

(2) Represent the unknown function in a series of the form

$$\sum_{n=1}^{\infty} d_n(t)X_n(x)$$

with unknown coefficients $d_n(t)$.

(3) Substitute the eigenfunction expansion of step (2) into the PDE, at the same time expanding the nonhomogeneity in terms of the functions $X_n(x)$.

(4) Obtain and solve ordinary differential equations for the $d_n(t)$.

(5) Use initial conditions on the PDE to determine any constants of integration in step (4).

When time-dependent nonhomogeneities are present in boundary conditions, they are transformed into nonhomogeneities in the PDE. They can then be handled by an eigenfunction expansion. This is illustrated in the following example.

Example 5:   Solve the following initial boundary value problem for temperature in a homogeneous, isotropic rod with insulated sides:

$$\frac{\partial U}{\partial t} = k\frac{\partial^2 U}{\partial x^2}, \qquad 0 < x < L, \qquad t > 0, \tag{65a}$$

$$U(0,t) = \phi_0(t), \qquad t > 0, \tag{65b}$$

$$U(L,t) = \phi_L(t), \qquad t > 0, \tag{65c}$$

$$U(x,0) = f(x), \qquad 0 < x < L. \tag{65d}$$

The rod is free of internal heat generation, and its ends are kept at prescribed temperatures.

Solution: We define a new dependent variable $V(x,t)$ according to

$$U(x,t) = V(x,t) + \psi(x,t), \tag{66}$$

where $\psi(x,t)$ is to be chosen so that $V(x,t)$ will satisfy homogeneous boundary conditions. Boundary conditions (65b, c) require that

$$V(0,t) = \phi_0(t) - \psi(0,t) \quad \text{and} \quad V(L,t) = \phi_L(t) - \psi(L,t).$$

Consequently, $V(x,t)$ will satisfy homogeneous boundary conditions

$$V(0,t) = 0, \qquad t > 0, \tag{67a}$$

$$V(L,t) = 0, \qquad t > 0 \tag{67b}$$

if $\psi(x,t)$ is chosen so that

$$\psi(0,t) = \phi_0(t), \qquad \psi(L,t) = \phi_L(t).$$

These are accommodated if $\psi(x,t)$ is chosen as

$$\psi(x,t) = \phi_0(t) + \frac{x}{L}[\phi_L(t) - \phi_0(t)]. \tag{68}$$

This is not the only choice for $\psi(x,t)$, but it is perhaps the simplest. With this choice,

$$U(x,t) = V(x,t) + \phi_0(t) + \frac{x}{L}[\phi_L(t) - \phi_0(t)]. \tag{69}$$

The PDE for $V(x,t)$ can be obtained by substituting (69) into (65a):

$$\frac{\partial}{\partial t}\left(V(x,t) + \phi_0(t) + \frac{x}{L}[\phi_L(t) - \phi_0(t)]\right) = k\frac{\partial^2}{\partial x^2}\left(V(x,t) + \phi_0(t) + \frac{x}{L}[\phi_L(t) - \phi_0(t)]\right)$$

or
$$\frac{\partial V}{\partial t} = k\frac{\partial^2 V}{\partial x^2} + G(x,t), \tag{67c}$$

where
$$G(x,t) = -\phi_0'(t) - \frac{x}{L}[\phi_L'(t) - \phi_0'(t)]. \tag{67d}$$

Initial condition (65d) yields the initial condition for $V(x, t)$,

$$V(x, 0) = f(x) - \phi_0(0) - \frac{x}{L}[\phi_L(0) - \phi_0(0)], \qquad 0 < x < L. \tag{67e}$$

Our problem now is to solve PDE (67c, d) subject to homogeneous boundary conditions (67a, b) and initial condition (67e); that is, $V(x, t)$ must satisfy

$$\frac{\partial V}{\partial t} = k\frac{\partial^2 V}{\partial x^2} + G(x, t), \qquad 0 < x < L, \qquad t > 0, \tag{70a}$$

$$V(0, t) = 0, \qquad t > 0, \tag{70b}$$

$$V(L, t) = 0, \qquad t > 0, \tag{70c}$$

$$V(x, 0) = f(x) - \phi_0(0) - \frac{x}{L}[\phi_L(0) - \phi_0(0)], \qquad 0 < x < L, \tag{70d}$$

where
$$G(x, t) = -\phi_0'(t) - \frac{x}{L}[\phi_L'(t) - \phi_0'(t)]. \tag{70e}$$

What we have done is transform the nonhomogeneities in boundary conditions (65b, c) into PDE (70a). But this presents no difficulty; eigenfunction expansions handle nonhomogeneous PDEs. Were $G(x, t)$ not present, separation of variables would lead to a solution in the form

$$V(x, t) = \sum_{n=1}^{\infty} C_n e^{-n^2\pi^2 kt/L^2} \sin\frac{n\pi x}{L}.$$

We therefore assume a solution for nonhomogeneous problem (70) in the form

$$V(x, t) = \sum_{n=1}^{\infty} C_n(t) \sin\frac{n\pi x}{L}, \tag{71}$$

where the exponential has been absorbed into the unknown function $C_n(t)$. This function satisfies boundary conditions (70b, c) and will satisfy PDE (70a) if

$$\sum_{n=1}^{\infty} C_n'(t) \sin\frac{n\pi x}{L} = k\sum_{n=1}^{\infty} -\frac{n^2\pi^2}{L^2} C_n(t) \sin\frac{n\pi x}{L} + G(x, t). \tag{72}$$

To simplify this equation, we extend $G(x, t)$ as an odd, $2L$-periodic function and expand it in a Fourier sine series

$$G(x, t) = \sum_{n=1}^{\infty} G_n(t) \sin\frac{n\pi x}{L}, \tag{73a}$$

where
$$G_n(t) = \frac{2}{L}\int_0^L G(x, t) \sin\frac{n\pi x}{L} dx. \tag{73b}$$

Substitution of this series into (72) gives

$$\sum_{n=1}^{\infty} \left(C_n'(t) + \frac{n^2\pi^2 k}{L^2} C_n(t) - G_n(t) \right) \sin\frac{n\pi x}{L} = 0.$$

But for each fixed t, the series on the left of this equation is the Fourier sine series of the function on the right, the function that is identically zero. It follows that all coefficients must vanish; that is,

$$C'_n(t) + \frac{n^2\pi^2 k}{L^2} C_n(t) = G_n(t).$$

The general solution of this linear, first-order ODE is

$$C_n(t) = b_n e^{-n^2\pi^2 kt/L^2} + \int_0^t G_n(u) e^{n^2\pi^2 k(u-t)/L^2}\, du,$$

where b_n is a constant. Substitution of this into (71) gives

$$V(x, t) = \sum_{n=1}^{\infty} \left(b_n e^{-n^2\pi^2 kt/L^2} + \int_0^t G_n(u) e^{n^2\pi^2 k(u-t)/L^2}\, du \right) \sin\frac{n\pi x}{L}. \tag{74}$$

To satisfy initial condition (70d), we must have

$$f(x) - \phi_0(0) - \frac{x}{L}[\phi_L(0) - \phi_0(0)] = \sum_{n=1}^{\infty} b_n \sin\frac{n\pi x}{L}, \qquad 0 < x < L,$$

and this implies that

$$b_n = \frac{2}{L} \int_0^L \left(f(x) - \phi_0(0) - \frac{x}{L}[\phi_L(0) - \phi_0(0)] \right) \sin\frac{n\pi x}{L}\, dx. \tag{75}$$

The formal solution of (65) is therefore

$$U(x, t) = V(x, t) + \phi_0(t) + \frac{x}{L}[\phi_L(t) - \phi_0(t)],$$

with $V(x, t)$ given by (74), (75), and (73b).   ∎

Let us summarize the techniques for handling nonhomogeneities.

(1) When nonhomogeneous boundary conditions are associated with Laplace's equation, all that is needed is superposition principle 2. The problem is divided into two or more subproblems, each of which can be solved by separation of variables, and the solutions of these subproblems are then added together. [For example, when $F(x, y) \equiv 0$ in the problem of Figure 3.1, $V(x, y)$ is the sum of $V_1(x, y)$ and $V_2(x, y)$.] Nonhomogeneities that turn Laplace's equation into Poisson's equation require eigenfunction expansions (see Exercise 20).

(2) When time-independent nonhomogeneities occur in initial boundary value problems (be they in the boundary conditions or in the PDE), it is advantageous to separate out steady-state or static solutions. The remaining part of the solution then satisfies a homogeneous PDE and homogeneous boundary conditions.

(3) When nonhomogeneities in boundary conditions of initial boundary value problems are time dependent, they can be transformed into time-dependent nonhomogeneities in the PDE. [See, for example, transformation (69) in Example 5.] Eigenfunction expansions then take care of time-dependent nonhomogeneities in PDEs.

Because time-independent nonhomogeneities [in technique (2)] are trivially functions of time, it is natural to ask whether technique (2) is necessary now that we have technique (3). To answer this question, we use technique (3) on problem (34). Separation of variables on (34a, b, c, e) in the absence of the nonhomogeneity leads to a superposition of separated functions in the form

$$y(x, t) = \sum_{n=1}^{\infty} C_n \sin \frac{n\pi x}{L} \cos \frac{n\pi ct}{L}.$$

Eigenfunction expansions suggest a solution of (34) (with g now present) in the form

$$y(x, t) = \sum_{n=1}^{\infty} d_n(t) \sin \frac{n\pi x}{L}.$$

When this solution is pursued, the result obtained is

$$y(x, t) = \sum_{n=1}^{\infty} \left[a_n \cos \frac{n\pi ct}{L} + \frac{2gL^2[1 + (-1)^{n+1}]}{n^3 \pi^3 c^2} \left(1 - \cos \frac{n\pi ct}{L} \right) \right] \sin \frac{n\pi x}{L}, \quad \textbf{(76a)}$$

where

$$a_n = \frac{2}{L} \int_0^L f(x) \sin \frac{n\pi x}{L} dx. \quad \textbf{(76b)}$$

This does not appear to be the same as solution (41) of (34),

$$y(x, t) = \frac{gx(L - x)}{2c^2} + \sum_{n=1}^{\infty} b_n \sin \frac{n\pi x}{L} \cos \frac{n\pi ct}{L}, \quad \textbf{(41)}$$

where

$$b_n = \frac{2}{L} \int_0^L \left(f(x) - \frac{gx(L - x)}{2c^2} \right) \sin \frac{n\pi x}{L} dx. \quad \textbf{(40)}$$

They do, however, represent the same function as we now show. Integration by parts gives

$$b_n = \frac{2}{L} \int_0^L f(x) \sin \frac{n\pi x}{L} dx - \frac{2}{L} \int_0^L \frac{gx(L - x)}{2c^2} \sin \frac{n\pi x}{L} dx$$

$$= a_n - \frac{2gL^2[1 + (-1)^{n+1}]}{n^3 \pi^3 c^2}$$

and therefore (41) may be expressed as

$$y(x, t) = \frac{gx(L - x)}{2c^2} + \sum_{n=1}^{\infty} \left(a_n - \frac{2gL^2[1 + (-1)^{n+1}]}{n^3 \pi^3 c^2} \right) \cos \frac{n\pi ct}{L} \sin \frac{n\pi x}{L}.$$

If we divide the summation in (76a) into two parts, this function may be written in the form

$$y(x, t) = \sum_{n=1}^{\infty} \frac{2gL^2[1 + (-1)^{n+1}]}{n^3 \pi^3 c^2} \sin \frac{n\pi x}{L}$$

$$+ \sum_{n=1}^{\infty} \left(a_n - \frac{2gL^2[1 + (-1)^{n+1}]}{n^3 \pi^3 c^2} \right) \cos \frac{n\pi ct}{L} \sin \frac{n\pi x}{L}.$$

These expressions are indeed identical, since the first series in the latter equation is the Fourier sine series of the odd, $2L$-periodic extension of $gx(L - x)/(2c^2)$,

$$\frac{gx(L - x)}{2c^2} = \sum_{n=1}^{\infty} \frac{2gL^2[1 + (-1)^{n+1}]}{n^3\pi^3c^2} \sin \frac{n\pi x}{L}, \qquad 0 \le x \le L.$$

Although this example illustrates that eigenfunction expansions can also be used to solve problems when nonhomogeneities are time independent, we would not suggest abandoning technique (2). There is a definite advantage to solution (41) over (76). Contained in (41) is a closed-form part, $gx(L - x)/(2c^2)$. This is also a part of (76a), but it is in the form of a Fourier sine series. This is the advantage of technique (2); it always separates out, in closed form, a steady-state or static part of the solution. Technique (3) does not; it delivers steady-state or static parts in series form. Given only the Fourier series for steady-state and static solutions, it could be very difficult to recognize their closed forms.

In Sections 3.2 and 3.3 we have shown how the method of separation of variables leads to the use of Fourier series in the solution of various initial boundary value problems. We have considered problems with one and more than one nonhomogeneous condition, many second-order equations, and one fourth-order equation. All equations contained two independent variables in order that the method not be obscured by overly complicated calculations. Certainly, however, the method can, and will, be used for problems in several independent variables.

We do not yet know whether we have solved any of the initial boundary value problems in these sections; we have found only what we call *formal* solutions. They are formal because of the questionable validity of superposing an infinity of separated functions. Each formal solution must therefore be verified as a valid solution to its initial boundary value problem. We do this in Sections 5.6–5.8 when we take up detailed analyses of convergence properties of formal solutions.

In problems (8), (25), (34), (42), (57), and (65), separation of variables led to the system

$$X'' + \lambda^2 X = 0, \qquad 0 < x < L,$$
$$X(0) = 0 = X(L)$$

and in problem (19) to the system

$$X'' + \lambda^2 X = 0, \qquad 0 < x < L,$$
$$X'(0) = 0 = X'(L).$$

Each of these problems is a special case of a general mathematical system called a *Sturm-Liouville system*. It consists of an ordinary differential equation

$$\frac{d}{dx}\left(r(x)\frac{dy}{dx}\right) + \{\lambda p(x) - q(x)\}y = 0 \tag{77a}$$

on some interval $a < x < b$, together with two boundary conditions

$$-l_1 y'(a) + h_1 y(a) = 0, \tag{77b}$$
$$l_2 y'(b) + h_2 y(b) = 0, \tag{77c}$$

where λ is a parameter and h_1, h_2, l_1, and l_2 are constants.

In Chapter 4 we discuss Sturm-Liouville systems in a general context and obtain properties of solutions of such systems. These systems lead to *generalized Fourier series* containing not only trigonometric functions but many other types of functions, such as Bessel functions and Legendre functions.

Finally, it is obvious that the steps in the solutions of boundary value and initial boundary value problems in Sections 3.2 and 3.3, and even the wording of the steps, are almost identical. Surely, then, we should be able to devise a method that would eliminate the tedious repetition of these steps in every problem. Indeed, *finite Fourier transforms* associated with Sturm-Liouville systems can be used for this purpose. They are discussed in Chapter 6.

Exercises 3.3

Part A—Heat Conduction

1. A cylindrical, homogeneous, isotropic rod with insulated sides has temperature 20°C throughout $(0 \leq x \leq L)$ at time $t = 0$. For $t > 0$, a constant electric current I is passed along the length of the rod, creating heat generation $g(x, t) = I^2/(A^2\sigma)$, where σ is the electrical conductivity of the rod and A is its cross-sectional area (see Exercise 32 in Section 1.2). If the ends of the rod are held at temperature zero for $t > 0$, find the temperature in the rod for $t > 0$ and $0 < x < L$.

2. Repeat Exercise 1 if the ends of the rod are held at temperature 100°C for $t > 0$.

3. Repeat Exercise 1 if the ends $x = 0$ and $x = L$ are held at constant temperatures U_0 and U_L, respectively, for $t > 0$.

4. Repeat Exercise 1 if the electric current is a function of time $I = e^{-\alpha t}$.

5. A cylindrical, homogeneous, isotropic rod with insulated sides has temperature 100°C throughout $(0 \leq x \leq L)$ at time $t = 0$. For $t > 0$, its left end $(x = 0)$ is held at temperature zero and its right end has temperature $100e^{-t}$. Find the temperature in the rod for $t > 0$ and $0 < x < L$. Assume that $k \neq L^2/(n^2\pi^2)$ for any integer n.

6. Repeat Exercise 1 if the ends of the rod are insulated for $t > 0$.

7. Repeat Exercise 1 if the ends of the rod are insulated and $I = e^{-\alpha t}$.

8. A cylindrical, homogeneous, isotropic rod with insulated sides is initially at temperature zero throughout $(0 \leq x \leq L)$. For time $t > 0$, its ends $x = 0$ and $x = L$ continue to be held at temperature zero, and heat generation at each point of the rod is described by $g(x, t) = e^{-\alpha t}\sin(m\pi x/L)$, where $\alpha > 0$ and m is a positive integer. Find the temperature in the rod as a function of x and t.

9. Repeat Exercise 8 if $g(x, t) = e^{-\alpha t}$, $\alpha > 0$, and the initial temperature in the rod is 10°C throughout. Assume that $\alpha \neq n^2\pi^2 k/L^2$ for any integer n.

10. The general one-dimensional heat conduction problem for a homogeneous, isotropic rod with insulated sides is

$$\frac{\partial U}{\partial t} = k\frac{\partial^2 U}{\partial x^2} + \frac{k}{\kappa}g(x, t), \qquad 0 < x < L, \qquad t > 0,$$

$$-l_1\frac{\partial U}{\partial x} + h_1 U = f_1(t), \qquad x = 0, \qquad t > 0,$$

$$l_2 \frac{\partial U}{\partial x} + h_2 U = f_2(t), \qquad x = L, \qquad t > 0,$$

$$U(x, 0) = f(x), \qquad 0 < x < L.$$

Show that when the nonhomogeneities $g(x, t)$, $f_1(t)$, and $f_2(t)$ are independent of time, the change of dependent variable $U(x, t) = V(x, t) + \psi(x)$, where $\psi(x)$ is the solution of the corresponding steady-state problem, leads to an initial boundary value problem in $V(x, t)$ that has a homogeneous PDE and homogeneous boundary conditions.

11. Explain how to solve Exercise 1 if the current is turned on for only $100\,\text{s}$ beginning at time $t = 0$. Do not solve the problem; just explain the steps you would take to solve it.

12. Suppose that heat generation in the thin wire of Exercise 31 in Section 1.2 is caused by an electric current I. When the temperature of the material surrounding the wire is a constant $0°\text{C}$ and σ is the electrical conductivity of the material in the wire, temperature at points in the wire must satisfy the PDE

$$\frac{\partial U}{\partial t} = k \frac{\partial^2 U}{\partial x^2} - hU + \frac{kI^2}{\kappa \sigma A^2}, \qquad 0 < x < L, \qquad t > 0$$

(see Exercise 32 in Section 1.2).

(a) Assuming that the ends of the wire are held at temperature $0°\text{C}$ and the initial temperature in the wire at time $t = 0$ is also $0°\text{C}$, show that when $U(x, t)$ is separated into steady-state and transient parts, $U(x, t) = V(x, t) + \psi(x)$:

$$\psi(x) = \frac{kI^2}{\kappa h \sigma A^2} \left(1 - \frac{\sinh\sqrt{h/k}\,x + \sinh\sqrt{h/k}(L - x)}{\sinh\sqrt{h/k}\,L} \right).$$

(b) Find $V(x, t)$ and hence $U(x, t)$.

Part B—Vibrations

13. A taut string has its ends fixed at $x = 0$ and $x = L$ on the x-axis. It is given an initial displacement at time $t = 0$ of $f(x)$, $0 \le x \le L$, and an initial velocity $g(x)$, $0 \le x \le L$. If an external force per unit length of constant magnitude acts vertically downward at every point on the string, find displacements in the string for $t > 0$ and $0 < x < L$.

14. A taut string has an end at $x = 0$ fixed on the x-axis, but the end at $x = L$ is removed a small amount y_L away from the x-axis and kept at this position. If it has initial position $f(x)$ and velocity $g(x)$ (at time $t = 0$), find displacements for $t > 0$ and $0 < x < L$.

15. A horizontal cylindrical bar is originally at rest and unstrained along the x-axis between $x = 0$ and $x = L$. For time $t > 0$, the left end is fixed and the right end is subjected to a constant elongating force per unit area F parallel to the bar. Displacements $y(x, t)$ of cross sections then satisfy the initial boundary value problem

$$\frac{\partial^2 y}{\partial t^2} = c^2 \frac{\partial^2 y}{\partial x^2}, \qquad 0 < x < L, \qquad t > 0,$$

$$y(0, t) = 0, \qquad t > 0,$$

$$E \frac{\partial y(L, t)}{\partial x} = F, \qquad t > 0,$$

$$y(x, 0) = y_t(x, 0) = 0, \qquad 0 < x < L.$$

(a) Can this problem be solved by separation $[y(x,t) = X(x)T(t)]$ and superposition? It has only one nonhomogeneous condition.

(b) Replace this initial boundary value problem by one in $z(x,t)$ in which $y(x,t) = z(x,t) + \psi(x)$ and $\psi(x)$ is the solution of the associated static deflection problem.

(c) If separation of variables and superposition are used on the problem for $z(x,t)$, what form does the series take? Finish the problem using the result of Exercise 21 in Section 2.2.

16. A beam of uniform cross section and length L has its ends simply supported at $x = 0$ and $x = L$. The beam has constant density ρ (in kilograms per meter) and is subjected to an additional uniform loading of k kg/m. If the beam is released from rest at a horizontal position at time $t = 0$, find subsequent displacements.

17. Repeat Exercise 16 if the beam is at rest at time $t = 0$ with displacement $f(x)$, $0 \le x \le L$.

18. Repeat Exercise 10 for the general one-dimensional vibration problem

$$\frac{\partial^2 y}{\partial t^2} = c^2 \frac{\partial^2 y}{\partial x^2} + \frac{F(x,t)}{\rho}, \qquad 0 < x < L, \qquad t > 0,$$

$$-l_1 \frac{\partial y}{\partial x} + h_1 y = f_1(t), \qquad x = 0, \qquad t > 0,$$

$$l_2 \frac{\partial y}{\partial x} + h_2 y = f_2(t), \qquad x = L, \qquad t > 0,$$

$$y(x,0) = f(x), \qquad 0 < x < L,$$

$$y_t(x,0) = g(x), \qquad 0 < x < L.$$

Part C—Potential, Steady-State Heat Conduction, Static Deflections of Membranes

19. Find a formula for the solution of Laplace's equation inside the rectangle $0 \le x \le L, 0 \le y \le L'$ when the boundary conditions are as indicated in Figure 3.1.

20. Nonhomogeneities in Laplace's equation $\nabla^2 V = 0$ convert it into Poisson's equation. For example, suppose a charge distribution with density $\sigma(x,y)$ coulombs per cubic meter occupies the volume R in space bounded by the planes $x = 0$, $y = 0$, $x = L$, and $y = L'$.

(a) If the bounding planes are maintained at zero potential, what is the boundary value problem for potential in R?

(b) Use eigenfunction expansions to solve the boundary value problem in (a) when σ is constant. Find two series, one in terms of $\sin(n\pi x/L)$ and the other is terms of $\sin(n\pi y/L')$. Is either series preferred?

(c) Solve the problem in (a) when σ is constant by setting $V(x,y) = U(x,y) + \psi(x)$, where $\psi(x)$ satisfies

$$\frac{d^2 \psi}{dx^2} = \frac{-\sigma}{\varepsilon_0}, \qquad 0 < x < L,$$

$$\psi(0) = \psi(L) = 0.$$

Is this the same solution as in (b)?

(d) If $\sigma = \sigma(x)$ is a function of x only, which type of expansion in (b) is preferred? Find the potential in this case.

(e) Find the potential when $\sigma = xy$.

21. Solve Exercise 28 in Section 3.2 if heat is generated at a constant rate at every point in the plate.

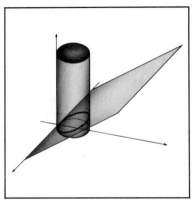

CHAPTER

F O U R

Sturm-Liouville Systems

4.1 Eigenvalues and Eigenfunctions

In Chapter 3, separation of variables on linear (initial) boundary value problems led to what are called Sturm-Liouville systems. In particular, we obtained two Sturm-Liouville systems,

$$\frac{d^2X}{dx^2} + \lambda^2 X = 0, \qquad 0 < x < L, \tag{1a}$$

$$X(0) = 0, \tag{1b}$$

$$X(L) = 0; \tag{1c}$$

and

$$\frac{d^2X}{dx^2} + \lambda^2 X = 0, \qquad 0 < x < L, \tag{2a}$$

$$X'(0) = 0, \tag{2b}$$

$$X'(L) = 0. \tag{2c}$$

In this chapter we undertake a general study of Sturm-Liouville systems. The results obtained are then applied to Sturm-Liouville systems that arise from more difficult problems associated with the (initial) boundary value problems of Chapter 1.

141

Nontrivial solutions of Sturm-Liouville systems (1) and (2) do not exist for arbitrary λ. On the contrary, only for specific values of λ, namely $\lambda = n\pi/L$, do nontrivial solutions exist, and to each such value there corresponds a solution (unique to a multiplicative constant). Because the solution depends on the value of λ chosen, it is customary to indicate this dependence by writing $X(\lambda, x)$ instead of $X(x)$. For system (1), the solution is $X(\lambda, x) = C \sin \lambda x$, and for system (2), it is $X(\lambda, x) = C \cos \lambda x$, C an arbitrary constant.

In general, a Sturm-Liouville system consists of a second-order, homogeneous differential equation of the following form, together with two linear, homogeneous boundary conditions for an unknown function $y(\lambda, x)$:

$$\frac{d}{dx}\left(r(x)\frac{dy(\lambda, x)}{dx}\right) + \{\lambda p(x) - q(x)\}y(\lambda, x) = 0, \qquad a < x < b, \tag{3a}$$

$$-l_1 y'(\lambda, a) + h_1 y(\lambda, a) = 0, \tag{3b}$$

$$l_2 y'(\lambda, b) + h_2 y(\lambda, b) = 0. \tag{3c}$$

The constants $h_1, h_2, l_1,$ and l_2 are real and independent of the parameter λ. When the functions $p, q, r,$ and r' are real and continuous for $a \leq x \leq b$, and $p > 0$ and $r > 0$ for $a \leq x \leq b$, the Sturm-Liouville system is said to be *regular*. The negative signs in (3a, b) are chosen simply as a matter of convenience for applications.

No matter what the value of λ, the trivial function $y(\lambda, x) \equiv 0$ always satisfies (3), but for certain values of λ, called *eigenvalues*, the system has nontrivial solutions. We shall see that there is always a countable (but infinite) number of such eigenvalues, which we denote by $\lambda_n (n = 1, 2, \ldots)$. A solution of (3) corresponding to an eigenvalue λ_n is called an *eigenfunction* and is denoted by

$$y_n(x) = y(\lambda_n, x). \tag{4}$$

Eigenfunctions are to satisfy the usual conditions for solutions of second-order differential equations, namely that y_n and dy_n/dx be continuous for $a \leq x \leq b$.

When $\lambda = 0$ is an eigenvalue of a Sturm-Liouville system, it is customary to denote it by $\lambda_0 = 0$. Such is the case for system (2).

The eigenfunctions $\sin(n\pi x/L)$ of system (1) form the basis for Fourier sine series, and in Chapter 2 we saw that they were orthogonal on the interval $0 \leq x \leq L$. The eigenfunctions $\cos(n\pi x/L)$ of system (2) are also orthogonal on this interval. This is not coincidence; the following theorem verifies orthogonality for eigenfunctions of every regular Sturm-Liouville system.

Theorem 1

All eigenvalues of a regular Sturm-Liouville system are real, and eigenfunctions corresponding to distinct eigenvalues are orthogonal with respect to the weight function $p(x)$,

$$\int_a^b p(x)y_n(x)y_m(x)\,dx = 0. \tag{5}$$

[See equation (6) in Section 2.1 for the definition of orthogonality of a sequence of functions.]

Proof: If $[\lambda_n, y_n(x)]$ and $[\lambda_m, y_m(x)]$ are eigenpairs of Sturm-Liouville system (3), where $\lambda_n \neq \lambda_m$, then

$$(ry_n')' = -(\lambda_n p - q)y_n, \qquad (ry_m')' = -(\lambda_m p - q)y_m.$$

Multiplication of the first by y_m and of the second by y_n, and subtraction of the two equations, eliminates q:

$$y_m(ry_n')' - y_n(ry_m')' = -\lambda_n p y_n y_m + \lambda_m p y_m y_n$$

or

$$(\lambda_n - \lambda_m)p y_n y_m = (ry_m')'y_n - (ry_n')'y_m.$$

The expression on the right can be expressed as a total derivative if we simultaneously add and subtract the term $ry_m'y_n'$:

$$(\lambda_n - \lambda_m)p y_n y_m = [(ry_m')'y_n + (ry_m')y_n'] - [(ry_n')'y_m + (ry_n')y_m']$$

$$= (ry_m'y_n)' - (ry_n'y_m)'$$

$$= (ry_m'y_n - ry_n'y_m)'.$$

Integration of this equation with respect to x from $x = a$ to $x = b$ gives

$$\int_a^b (\lambda_n - \lambda_m)p y_n y_m \, dx = \int_a^b \frac{d}{dx}(ry_m'y_n - ry_n'y_m)\, dx = \{ry_m'y_n - ry_n'y_m\}_a^b.$$

The right side of this result may be expressed as the difference in the values of two determinants:

$$(\lambda_n - \lambda_m)\int_a^b p y_n y_m \, dx = r(b)\begin{vmatrix} y_n(b) & y_m(b) \\ y_n'(b) & y_m'(b) \end{vmatrix} - r(a)\begin{vmatrix} y_n(a) & y_m(a) \\ y_n'(a) & y_m'(a) \end{vmatrix}.$$

Since $y_n(x)$ and $y_m(x)$ both satisfy boundary condition (3b),

$$-l_1 y_n'(a) + h_1 y_n(a) = 0,$$
$$-l_1 y_m'(a) + h_1 y_m(a) = 0.$$

Because at least one of h_1 and l_1 is not zero, these equations (regarded as homogeneous, linear equations in l_1 and h_1) must have nontrivial solutions. Consequently, the determinant of their coefficients must vanish:

$$\begin{vmatrix} y_n'(a) & y_n(a) \\ y_m'(a) & y_m(a) \end{vmatrix} = 0.$$

A similar discussion with boundary condition (3c) indicates that

$$\begin{vmatrix} y_n'(b) & y_n(b) \\ y_m'(b) & y_m(b) \end{vmatrix} = 0.$$

It follows now that

$$(\lambda_n - \lambda_m)\int_a^b p(x)y_n(x)y_m(x)\, dx = 0,$$

and, because $\lambda_n \neq \lambda_m$, (5) has been established.

   To prove that eigenvalues are real, we assume that $\lambda = \alpha + i\beta$ $(\beta \neq 0)$ is a complex eigenvalue with eigenfunction $y(\lambda, x)$. This eigenfunction could be complex, but if it is, it is a complex-valued function of the real variable x. If we divide $y(\lambda, x)$ into real and imaginary parts,

$y(\lambda, x) = u(\lambda, x) + iv(\lambda, x)$, the complex conjugate of dy/dx is

$$\overline{\frac{dy}{dx}} = \overline{\frac{d}{dx}(u + iv)} = \overline{\frac{du}{dx} + i\frac{dv}{dx}} = \frac{du}{dx} - i\frac{dv}{dx} = \frac{d}{dx}(u - iv) = \frac{d\bar{y}}{dx}.$$

With this result, it is straightforward to take complex conjugates of (3). Because the functions $r(x)$, $p(x)$, and $q(x)$ are all real, as are the constants h_1, h_2, l_1, and l_2, we find that $\bar{\lambda}$ and $\overline{y(\lambda, x)}$ must satisfy

$$(r\bar{y}')' + (\bar{\lambda}p - q)\bar{y} = 0,$$
$$-l_1\overline{y(\lambda, a)}' + h_1\overline{y(\lambda, a)} = 0, \qquad l_2\overline{y(\lambda, b)}' + h_2\overline{y(\lambda, b)} = 0.$$

These imply that $\overline{y(\lambda, x)}$ is an eigenfunction of (3) corresponding to the eigenvalue $\bar{\lambda}$. Since $\lambda \neq \bar{\lambda}$, $y(x, \lambda)$ and $\overline{y(x, \lambda)}$ must therefore be orthogonal; that is,

$$\int_a^b p(x)\overline{y(\lambda, x)}y(\lambda, x)\,dx = 0.$$

But this is impossible because $p(x) > 0$ for $a < x < b$, and $\overline{y(\lambda, x)}y(\lambda, x) = |y(\lambda, x)|^2 \geq 0$. Consequently, λ cannot be complex. ∎

It is evident from the above proof that Theorem 1 is also valid under the circumstances in the following corollary.

Corollary

The results of Theorem 1 are valid when

(1) $r(a) = 0$ [boundary condition (3b) then being unnecessary];
(2) $r(b) = 0$ [boundary condition (3c) then being unnecessary];
(3) $r(a) = r(b)$ if boundary conditions (3b, c) are replaced by the periodic conditions

$$y(a) = y(b), \qquad y'(a) = y'(b). \tag{6}$$

A Sturm-Liouville system is said to be *singular* if either or both of its boundary conditions is absent; it is said to be *periodic* if $r(a) = r(b)$ and boundary conditions (3b, c) are replaced by periodic conditions (6). Theorem 1 and its corollary state that eigenfunctions of regular and periodic Sturm-Liouville systems are always orthogonal. They are also orthogonal for singular systems when boundary conditions (3b) or (3c) or both are absent, provided either $r(a) = 0$ or $r(b) = 0$, or both, respectively. We consider only regular and periodic Sturm-Liouville systems in this chapter; singular systems are discussed in Chapter 8.

Example 1:   Find eigenvalues and eigenfunctions of the Sturm-Liouville system

$$X'' + \lambda X = 0, \qquad 0 < x < L,$$
$$X(0) = 0 = X'(L).$$

Solution: When $\lambda < 0$, the general solution of the differential equation is

$$X(x) = Ae^{\sqrt{-\lambda}x} + Be^{-\sqrt{-\lambda}x}.$$

The boundary conditions require that

$$0 = X(0) = A + B, \qquad 0 = X'(L) = A\sqrt{-\lambda}\,e^{\sqrt{-\lambda}L} - B\sqrt{-\lambda}\,e^{-\sqrt{-\lambda}L},$$

the only solution of which is $A = B = 0$.

When $\lambda = 0$, $X(x) = Ax + B$, and the boundary conditions once again imply that $A = B = 0$.

Thus, eigenvalues of the Sturm-Liouville system must be positive, and when $\lambda > 0$, the boundary conditions require constants A and B in the general solution $X(x) = A\cos\sqrt{\lambda}x + B\sin\sqrt{\lambda}x$ of the differential equation to satisfy

$$0 = X(0) = A, \qquad 0 = X'(L) = -A\sqrt{\lambda}\sin\sqrt{\lambda}L + B\sqrt{\lambda}\cos\sqrt{\lambda}L.$$

With A vanishing, the second condition reduces to $B\sqrt{\lambda}\cos\sqrt{\lambda}L = 0$. Since neither B nor λ can vanish, $\cos\sqrt{\lambda}L$ must be zero. Hence, $\sqrt{\lambda}L$ must be equal to $-\pi/2$ plus an integer multiple of π; that is, permissible values of λ are λ_n where $\sqrt{\lambda_n}L = n\pi - \pi/2$, n an integer. Corresponding functions are

$$X_n(x) = B\sin\sqrt{\lambda_n}x = B\sin\frac{(2n-1)\pi x}{2L}.$$

But the set of functions for $n \le 0$ is identical to that for $n > 0$. In other words, eigenvalues of the Sturm-Liouville system are $\lambda_n = (2n-1)^2\pi^2/(4L^2)$, $n \ge 1$, with corresponding eigenfunctions $X_n(x) = B\sin[(2n-1)\pi x/(2L)]$. ∎

Example 2: Discuss the periodic Sturm-Liouville system

$$y'' + \lambda y = 0, \qquad -L < x < L, \tag{7a}$$

$$y(-L) = y(L), \tag{7b}$$

$$y'(-L) = y'(L). \tag{7c}$$

Solution: If $\lambda > 0$, the general solution of (7a) is

$$y(\lambda, x) = A\cos\sqrt{\lambda}x + B\sin\sqrt{\lambda}x.$$

Conditions (7b, c) require that

$$A\cos\sqrt{\lambda}L - B\sin\sqrt{\lambda}L = A\cos\sqrt{\lambda}L + B\sin\sqrt{\lambda}L,$$

$$\sqrt{\lambda}A\sin\sqrt{\lambda}L + \sqrt{\lambda}B\cos\sqrt{\lambda}L = -\sqrt{\lambda}A\sin\sqrt{\lambda}L + \sqrt{\lambda}B\cos\sqrt{\lambda}L.$$

These equations require that $\sin\sqrt{\lambda}L = 0$, and this implies that $\sqrt{\lambda}L = n\pi$. In other words, eigenvalues of the Sturm-Liouville system are $\lambda_n = n^2\pi^2/L^2$, where n is an integer that we take as positive. Corresponding to these eigenvalues are the eigenfunctions

$$y_n(x) = y(\lambda_n, x) = A\cos\frac{n\pi x}{L} + B\sin\frac{n\pi x}{L}.$$

When $\lambda = 0$, $y(0, x) = A + Bx$, and the boundary conditions require that $B = 0$. Thus, corresponding to the eigenvalue $\lambda_0 = 0$, we have the eigenfunction $y_0(x) = A$. The only solution of (7) when $\lambda < 0$ is the trivial solution.

Theorem 1 guarantees that for nonnegative integers m and n $(m \neq n)$, the eigenfunctions

$$y_n(x) = A \cos \frac{n\pi x}{L} + B \sin \frac{n\pi x}{L} \quad \text{and} \quad y_m(x) = C \cos \frac{m\pi x}{L} + D \sin \frac{m\pi x}{L}$$

are orthogonal over the interval $-L \le x \le L$. It is true, however, that all functions in the set

$$\left\{ 1, \cos \frac{n\pi x}{L}, \sin \frac{n\pi x}{L} \right\}$$

are orthogonal. These are precisely the "eigenfunctions" found in the Fourier series expansion of a function of period $2L$. We shall return to this point in Section 4.2. ■

Because differential equation (3a) and boundary conditions (3b, c) are homogeneous, if $[\lambda_n, y_n(x)]$ is an eigenpair for a Sturm-Liouville system, then so also is $[\lambda_n, cy_n(x)]$ for any constant $c \neq 0$. In other words, eigenfunctions are not unique; if $y_n(x)$ is an eigenfunction corresponding to an eigenvalue λ_n, then any constant times $y_n(x)$ is also an eigenfunction corresponding to the same λ_n. This fact is reflected in Example 1, where eigenfunctions were determined only to multiplicative constants. In this example, there is, except for the multiplicative constant, only one eigenfunction, $\sin[(2n - 1)\pi x/(2L)]$, corresponding to each eigenvalue. This is not the case in Example 2. Corresponding to each positive eigenvalue in Example 2 there are two linearly independent eigenfunctions, $\sin(n\pi x/L)$ and $\cos(n\pi x/L)$. The difference is that in Example 1 the Sturm-Liouville system is regular, but in Example 2 it is periodic. It can be shown (see Exercise 12) that in a regular Sturm-Liouville system, there cannot be two linearly independent eigenfunctions corresponding to the same eigenvalue.

In regular Sturm-Liouville systems, it is customary to single out one of the eigenfunctions $y_n(x)$ corresponding to an eigenvalue as special and refer all other eigenfunctions to it. The one that is chosen is an eigenfunction with "length" unity, that is, an eigenfunction $y_n(x)$ satisfying

$$\|y_n(x)\| = \sqrt{\int_a^b p(x)[y_n(x)]^2 \, dx} = 1.$$

Normalized eigenfunctions can always be found by dividing nonnormalized eigenfunctions by their lengths. Consider, for example, Sturm-Liouville system (1). Since $\sin(n\pi x/L)$ is an eigenfunction of this system corresponding to the eigenvalue $\lambda_n^2 = n^2\pi^2/L^2$, so also is $c \sin(n\pi x/L)$ for any constant $c \neq 0$. The normalized eigenfunction corresponding to this eigenvalue is

$$\frac{\sin(n\pi x/L)}{\|\sin(n\pi x/L)\|},$$

where

$$\left\| \sin \frac{n\pi x}{L} \right\|^2 = \int_0^L \sin^2 \frac{n\pi x}{L} \, dx = \frac{L}{2}.$$

Thus, with each eigenvalue $\lambda_n^2 = n^2\pi^2/L^2$ of the Sturm-Liouville system, we associate the normalized eigenfunction

$$X_n(x) = \sqrt{\frac{2}{L}} \sin\frac{n\pi x}{L}.$$

All other eigenfunctions for λ_n^2 are then $cX_n(x)$.

Similarly, normalized eigenfunctions for Sturm-Liouville system (2) are

$$X_0(x) = \frac{1}{\sqrt{L}} \quad \text{corresponding to } \lambda_0^2 = 0$$

and $\qquad X_n(x) = \sqrt{\frac{2}{L}} \cos\frac{n\pi x}{L} \quad$ corresponding to $\lambda_n^2 = n^2\pi^2/L^2, \qquad n > 0.$

In general, if $y_n(x)$ is an eigenfunction of Sturm-Liouville system (3), we replace it by the normalized eigenfunction

$$\frac{1}{N} y_n(x) \tag{8a}$$

where $\qquad N^2 = \|y_n(x)\|^2 = \int_a^b p(x)[y_n(x)]^2\, dx. \tag{8b}$

The complete set of normalized eigenfunctions, one for each eigenvalue, then constitutes a set of orthonormal eigenfunctions for the Sturm-Liouville system. Unless otherwise stated, we shall always regard $y_n(x)$ as normalized eigenfunctions of a Sturm-Liouville system. Notice that any number of the $y_n(x)$ could be replaced by $-y_n(x)$, and the new set would also be orthonormal. In other words, orthonormal eigenfunctions are determined only to a factor of ± 1.

Example 3: Find eigenvalues and normalized eigenfunctions of the Sturm-Liouville system

$$\frac{d^2y}{dx^2} + \frac{dy}{dx} + \lambda y = 0, \qquad 0 < x < 1,$$

$$y(0) = 0 = y(1).$$

Solution: Roots of the auxiliary equation $m^2 + m + \lambda = 0$ associated with the differential equation are $m = (-1 \pm \sqrt{1-4\lambda})/2$. When $\lambda < 1/4$, these roots are real; denote them by $\omega_1 = (-1 + \sqrt{1-4\lambda})/2$ and $\omega_2 = (-1 - \sqrt{1-4\lambda})/2$. The general solution of the differential equation in this case is $y(x) = Ae^{\omega_1 x} + Be^{\omega_2 x}$, and the boundary conditions require that

$$0 = A + B, \qquad 0 = Ae^{\omega_1} + Be^{\omega_2}.$$

The only solution of these equations is $A = B = 0$, leading to the trivial solution $y(x) \equiv 0$.

When $\lambda = 1/4$, the auxiliary equation has equal roots, and $y(x) = (A + Bx)e^{-x/2}$. Once again, the boundary conditions require that $A = B = 0$.

Consequently, λ must be greater than 1/4, in which case we set $m = -1/2 \pm i\omega$, where $\omega = \sqrt{4\lambda - 1}/2$. The boundary conditions require constants A and B in the general solution $y(x) = e^{-x/2}(A \cos \omega x + B \sin \omega x)$ to satisfy

$$0 = A, \qquad 0 = e^{-1/2}(A \cos \omega + B \sin \omega).$$

With vanishing A, the second condition requires that $\sin \omega = 0$, that is, that $\omega = n\pi$, n an integer. In other words, eigenvalues of the Sturm-Liouville system are given by $\sqrt{4\lambda_n - 1}/2 = n\pi$, or

$$\lambda_n = \frac{1}{4} + n^2 \pi^2.$$

Except for the multiplicative constant B, corresponding eigenfunctions are $e^{-x/2} \sin n\pi x$. Clearly, we need only take $n > 0$. To normalize these functions, we express the differential equation in standard Sturm-Liouville form (3a). This can be done by multiplying by e^x (see Exercise 1):

$$0 = e^x \frac{d^2 y}{dx^2} + e^x \frac{dy}{dx} + \lambda e^x y = \frac{d}{dx}\left(e^x \frac{dy}{dx}\right) + \lambda e^x y.$$

With the weight function now identified as $p(x) = e^x$, we calculate lengths of the eigenfunctions:

$$\|e^{-x/2} \sin n\pi x\|^2 = \int_0^1 e^x (e^{-x/2} \sin n\pi x)^2 \, dx = \int_0^1 \sin^2 n\pi x \, dx = \frac{1}{2}.$$

Normalized eigenfunctions are therefore

$$y_n(x) = \sqrt{2}\, e^{-x/2} \sin n\pi x. \qquad \blacksquare$$

Exercises 4.1

1. (a) Show that when the differential equation

$$\alpha(x) \frac{d^2 y}{dx^2} + \beta(x) \frac{dy}{dx} + [\gamma(x) + \lambda \delta(x)] y = 0, \qquad a < x < b,$$

is multiplied by the "integrating factor"

$$r(x) = e^{\int \beta(x)/\alpha(x)\, dx},$$

it can immediately be expressed in standard Sturm-Liouville form (3a). Notice that $\alpha(x)$ must not vanish for $a \le x \le b$.

(b) In view of Example 3, what is the importance of this result?

In Exercises 2–9 find eigenvalues and orthonormal eigenfunctions for the given Sturm-Liouville system.

2. $\dfrac{d^2 y}{dx^2} + \lambda y = 0, \quad 0 < x < 3, \quad y(0) = 0 = y(3)$

3. $\dfrac{d^2y}{dx^2} + \lambda y = 0, \quad 0 < x < 4, \quad y'(0) = 0 = y'(4)$

4. $\dfrac{d^2y}{dx^2} + \lambda y = 0, \quad 0 < x < 9, \quad y(0) = 0 = y'(9)$

5. $\dfrac{d^2y}{dx^2} + \lambda y = 0, \quad 0 < x < 1, \quad y'(0) = 0 = y(1)$

6. $\dfrac{d^2y}{dx^2} + \lambda y = 0, \quad 0 < x < L, \quad y'(0) = 0 = y(L)$

7. $\dfrac{d^2y}{dx^2} + \lambda y = 0, \quad 1 < x < 10, \quad y(1) = 0 = y(10)$

    (Do this directly and also by making the change of independent variable $z = x - 1$.)

8. $\dfrac{d^2y}{dx^2} - \dfrac{dy}{dx} + \lambda y = 0, \quad 0 < x < 1, \quad y(0) = 0 = y(1)$

9. $\dfrac{d^2y}{dx^2} + \dfrac{dy}{dx} + \lambda y = 0, \quad 1 < x < 5, \quad y'(1) = 0 = y'(5)$

    (*Hint:* Use the change of variable $z = x - 1$.)

10. Find eigenvalues and eigenfunctions of the periodic Sturm-Liouville system

    $$y'' + \lambda y = 0, \qquad 0 < x < 2L,$$
    $$y(0) = y(2L),$$
    $$y'(0) = y'(2L).$$

11. Consider the Sturm-Liouville system

    $$\dfrac{d^2y}{dx^2} + 4\lambda y = 0, \qquad 0 < x < L,$$
    $$y(0) = 0 = y(L).$$

    We could regard this system as one with eigenvalues λ and weight function $p(x) = 4$, or, alternatively, as one with eigenvalues 4λ and weight function $p(x) = 1$. Is there a difference as far as normalized eigenfunctions are concerned?

12. In this exercise we prove that a regular Sturm-Liouville system cannot have two linearly independent eigenfunctions corresponding to the same eigenvalue.

    (a) Suppose that $y(x)$ and $z(x)$ are eigenfunctions of (3) corresponding to the same eigenvalue λ. Show that $w(x) \equiv y'(a)z(x) - z'(a)y(x)$ satisfies (3a) and that $w(a) = w'(a) = 0$. This implies that $w(x) \equiv 0$ [and therefore that $y(x)$ and $z(x)$ are linearly dependent] unless $y'(a) = z'(a) = 0$.

    (b) If $y'(a) = z'(a) = 0$, then $h_1 = 0$. Define $w(x) = y(a)z(x) - z(a)y(x)$ to show once again that $w(x) \equiv 0$.

13. Use the result of Exercise 12 to show that up to a multiplicative constant, eigenfunctions of regular Sturm-Liouville systems are real.

14. In Exercises 7 and 9 we suggested the change of variable $z = x - 1$ in order to find eigenfunctions of the Sturm-Liouville system. Does it make any difference whether normalization is carried out in the z-variable or in the x-variable?

4.2 Eigenfunction Expansions

In Chapters 2 and 3 we learned how to express functions $f(x)$, which are piecewise smooth on the interval $0 \leq x \leq L$, in the form of Fourier sine series

$$f(x) = \sum_{n=1}^{\infty} b_n \sin \frac{n\pi x}{L}, \tag{9a}$$

where
$$b_n = \frac{2}{L} \int_0^L f(x) \sin \frac{n\pi x}{L}\, dx. \tag{9b}$$

We regard the Fourier coefficients b_n as the components of the function $f(x)$ with respect to the basis functions $\{\sin(n\pi x/L)\}$. In Section 4.1 we discovered that the $\sin(n\pi x/L)$ are eigenfunctions of Sturm-Liouville system (1), and it has become our practice to replace eigenfunctions with normalized eigenfunctions, namely $\sqrt{2/L}\sin(n\pi x/L)$. Representation (9) can easily be replaced by an equivalent expression in terms of these normalized eigenfunctions:

$$f(x) = \sum_{n=1}^{\infty} c_n \left(\sqrt{\frac{2}{L}} \sin \frac{n\pi x}{L} \right), \tag{10a}$$

where
$$c_n = \int_0^L f(x) \left(\sqrt{\frac{2}{L}} \sin \frac{n\pi x}{L} \right) dx. \tag{10b}$$

Coefficients c_n are components of $f(x)$ with respect to the orthonormal basis $\{\sqrt{2/L}\sin(n\pi x/L)\}$. Equation (9) should be compared with equation (3) in Section 2.1, together with the fact that the length of $\sin(n\pi x/L)$ is $\sqrt{L/2}$. Equation (10) is analogous to equation (1) in Section 2.1.

The same function $f(x)$ can be represented by a Fourier cosine series in terms of normalized eigenfunctions of system (2):

$$f(x) = \frac{c_0}{\sqrt{L}} + \sum_{n=1}^{\infty} c_n \left(\sqrt{\frac{2}{L}} \cos \frac{n\pi x}{L} \right) \tag{11a}$$

where

$$c_0 = \int_0^L f(x) \left(\frac{1}{\sqrt{L}} \right) dx \quad \text{and} \quad c_n = \int_0^L f(x) \left(\sqrt{\frac{2}{L}} \cos \frac{n\pi x}{L} \right) dx, \qquad n > 0. \tag{11b}$$

A natural question to ask now is the following: Given a function $f(x)$, defined on the interval $a \leq x \leq b$, and given a Sturm-Liouville system on the same interval, is it always possible to express $f(x)$ in terms of the orthonormal eigenfunctions of the Sturm-Liouville system? It is still not clear that every Sturm-Liouville system has an infinity of eigenfunctions, but, as we shall see, this is indeed the case. We wish then to investigate the possibility of finding coefficients c_n such that on $a \leq x \leq b$

$$f(x) = \sum_{n=1}^{\infty} c_n y_n(x), \tag{12}$$

where $y_n(x)$ are the orthonormal eigenfunctions of Sturm-Liouville system (3). If we formally multiply equation (12) by $p(x)y_m(x)$, and integrate term by term between $x = a$

and $x = b$,

$$\int_a^b p(x)f(x)y_m(x)\,dx = \sum_{n=1}^\infty c_n \int_a^b p(x)y_n(x)y_m(x)\,dx.$$

Because of the orthogonality of eigenfunctions, only the mth term in the series does not vanish, and therefore

$$\int_a^b p(x)f(x)y_m(x)\,dx = c_m. \tag{13}$$

This has been strictly a formal procedure. It has illustrated that *if* $f(x)$ can be represented in form (12), and *if* the series is suitably convergent, coefficients c_n must be calculated according to (13). What we must answer is the converse question: if coefficients c_n are calculated according to (13), where $y_n(x)$ are orthonormal eigenfunctions of a Sturm-Liouville system, does series (12) converge to $f(x)$? This question is answered in the following theorem.

Theorem 2

Let p, q, r, r', and $(pr)''$ be real and continuous functions of x for $a \le x \le b$, and let $p > 0$ and $r > 0$ for $a \le x \le b$. Let l_1, l_2, h_1, and h_2 be real constants independent of λ. Then Sturm-Liouville system (3) has a countable infinity of eigenvalues $\lambda_1 < \lambda_2 < \lambda_3 < \cdots$ (all real), not more than a finite number of which are negative, and $\lim_{n\to\infty} \lambda_n = \infty$. Corresponding orthonormal eigenfunctions $y_n(x)$ are such that $y_n(x)$ and $y_n'(x)$ are continuous and $|y_n(x)|$ and $|\lambda_n^{-1/2} y_n'(x)|$ are uniformly bounded with respect to x and n. If $f(x)$ is piecewise smooth on $a \le x \le b$, then for any x in $a < x < b$,

$$\frac{f(x+) + f(x-)}{2} = \sum_{n=1}^\infty c_n y_n(x), \tag{14a}$$

where

$$c_n = \int_a^b p(x)f(x)y_n(x)\,dx. \tag{14b}$$

■

Series (14a) is called the *generalized Fourier series* for $f(x)$ with respect to the eigenfunctions $y_n(x)$, and the c_n are the *generalized Fourier coefficients*. They are the components of $f(x)$ with respect to the orthonormal basis of eigenfunctions $\{y_n(x)\}$. Notice the similarity between this theorem and Theorem 2 in Section 2.1 for Fourier series. Both guarantee pointwise convergence of Fourier series for a piecewise smooth function to the value of the function at a point of continuity of the function, and to average values of right- and left-hand limits at a point of discontinuity. Because the eigenfunctions in Theorem 2 of Section 2.1 are periodic, convergence is also assured at the end points of the interval $0 \le x \le 2L$. This is not the case in Theorem 2 above. Eigenfunctions are not generally periodic, and convergence at $x = a$ and $x = b$ is not guaranteed. It should be clear, however, that when $l_1 = 0$ [in which case $y_n(a) = 0$] convergence of (14a) at $x = a$ can be expected only if $f(a) = 0$ also. A similar statement can be made at $x = b$.

When a regular Sturm-Liouville system satisfies the conditions of this theorem as well as the conditions that $q(x) \ge 0$, $a \le x \le b$, and $l_1 h_1 \ge 0$, $l_2 h_2 \ge 0$, it is said to be a *proper Sturm-Liouville system.* For such a system we shall take l_1, l_2, h_1, and h_2 all nonnegative, in which case we can prove the following corollary.

Corollary

All eigenvalues of a proper Sturm-Liouville system are nonnegative. Furthermore, zero is an eigenvalue of a proper Sturm-Liouville system only when $q(x) \equiv 0$ and $h_1 = h_2 = 0$.

Proof: Let λ and $y(\lambda, x)$ be an eigenpair of a regular Sturm-Liouville system. Multiplication of (3a) by $y(\lambda, x)$ and integration from $x = a$ to $x = b$ gives

$$\lambda \int_a^b p(x) y^2(\lambda, x)\, dx = \int_a^b q(x) y^2(\lambda, x)\, dx - \int_a^b y(\lambda, x)[r(x) y'(\lambda, x)]'\, dx$$

$$= \int_a^b q(x) y^2(\lambda, x)\, dx - \{ r(x) y(\lambda, x) y'(\lambda, x) \}_a^b$$

$$+ \int_a^b r(x)[y'(\lambda, x)]^2\, dx.$$

When we solve boundary conditions (3b, c) for $y'(\lambda, b)$ and $y'(\lambda, a)$ and substitute into the second term on the right, we obtain

$$\lambda \int_a^b p(x) y^2(\lambda, x)\, dx = \int_a^b q(x) y^2(\lambda, x)\, dx + \int_a^b r(x)[y'(\lambda, x)]^2\, dx$$

$$+ \frac{h_2}{l_2} r(b) y^2(\lambda, b) + \frac{h_1}{l_1} r(a) y^2(\lambda, a).$$

When the Sturm-Liouville system is proper, every term on the right is nonnegative, as is the integral on the left, and therefore $\lambda \geq 0$. (If either $l_1 = 0$ or $l_2 = 0$, the corresponding terms in the above equation are absent and the result is the same.)

Furthermore, if $\lambda = 0$ is an eigenvalue, then each of the four terms on the right side of the above equation must vanish separately. The first requires that $q(x) \equiv 0$ and the second that $y'(\lambda, x) = 0$. But the fact that $y(\lambda, x)$ is constant implies that the last two terms can vanish only if $h_1 = h_2 = 0$.   ∎

Since eigenvalues of a proper Sturm-Liouville system must be nonnegative, we may replace λ by λ^2 in differential equation (3a) whenever it is convenient to do so:

$$\frac{d}{dx}\left(r(x) \frac{dy}{dx} \right) + [\lambda^2 p(x) - q(x)] y = 0, \qquad a < x < b.$$

This often has the advantage of eliminating unnecessary square roots in calculations.

Example 4:   Expand the function $f(x) = L - x$ in terms of normalized eigenfunctions of the Sturm-Liouville system of Example 1.

Solution: According to Example 1, eigenfunctions of this system are $\sin[(2n - 1)\pi x/(2L)]$. Because

$$\left\| \sin \frac{(2n - 1)\pi x}{2L} \right\|^2 = \int_0^L \left(\sin \frac{(2n - 1)\pi x}{2L} \right)^2 dx = \frac{L}{2},$$

normalized eigenfunctions are $X_n(x) = \sqrt{2/L}\,\sin[(2n-1)\pi x/(2L)]$. The generalized Fourier series for $f(x) = L - x$ in terms of these eigenfunctions is

$$L - x = \sum_{n=1}^{\infty} c_n X_n(x),$$

where $\quad c_n = \int_0^L (L-x)\sqrt{\frac{2}{L}}\,\sin\frac{(2n-1)\pi x}{2L}\,dx = \frac{2\sqrt{2}\,L^{3/2}}{\pi^2}\left(\frac{\pi}{2n-1} + \frac{2(-1)^n}{(2n-1)^2}\right).$

Thus, $\quad L - x = \dfrac{2\sqrt{2}\,L^{3/2}}{\pi^2}\sum_{n=1}^{\infty}\left(\dfrac{\pi}{2n-1} + \dfrac{2(-1)^n}{(2n-1)^2}\right)\sqrt{\dfrac{2}{L}}\,\sin\dfrac{(2n-1)\pi x}{2L}.$

Theorem 2 guarantees convergence of the series to $L - x$ for $0 < x < L$. It obviously does not converge to $L - x$ at $x = 0$, but it does converge to $L - x$ at $x = L$. This follows from the facts that

$$\sum_{n=1}^{\infty} \frac{(-1)^{n+1}}{2n-1} = \frac{\pi}{4} \quad \text{and} \quad \sum_{n=1}^{\infty} \frac{1}{(2n-1)^2} = \frac{\pi^2}{8}. \qquad \blacksquare$$

In Chapter 3, when separation of variables was applied to (initial) boundary value problems, all boundary conditions in a given problem were either of Dirichlet type or of Neumann type. These led to Fourier sine and cosine series, series that we now know are eigenfunction expansions in terms of eigenfunctions of Sturm-Liouville systems (1) and (2). We did not consider problems with Robin conditions, nor did we mix Dirichlet and Neumann conditions. That would have led to series expansions for which we would have had no backup theory. With our results on Sturm-Liouville systems, we are now well prepared to tackle these expansions. A proper Sturm-Liouville system that arises repeatedly in our discussions is

$$\frac{d^2X}{dx^2} + \lambda^2 X = 0, \qquad 0 < x < L, \tag{15a}$$

$$-l_1 X' + h_1 X = 0, \qquad x = 0, \tag{15b}$$

$$l_2 X' + h_2 X = 0, \qquad x = L. \tag{15c}$$

[Systems (1) and (2) are special cases of (15) when $l_1 = l_2 = 0$ and $h_1 = h_2 = 0$, respectively. Examples 1 and 4 contain the special case of $l_1 = h_2 = 0$ and $l_2 = h_1 = 1$.] We consider here the most general case, in which $h_1 h_2 l_1 l_2 \neq 0$; special cases in which one or two of h_1, h_2, l_1, and l_2 vanish are tabulated later. In the general case when $h_1 h_2 l_1 l_2 \neq 0$, we could divide (15b) by either l_1 or h_1. This would lead to a boundary condition with only one arbitrary constant (h_1/l_1 or l_1/h_1). Likewise, we could divide (15c) by l_2 or h_2 and express this boundary condition in terms of the ratio h_2/l_2 or the ratio l_2/h_2. However, when this is done, it is not quite so transparent how to specialize the results we obtain here in the cases in which one or two of h_1, h_2, l_1, and l_2 vanish. For this reason, we prefer to leave (15b, c) in their present forms.

We are justified in representing the eigenvalues of system (15) by λ^2 rather than λ, because all eigenvalues of a proper Sturm-Liouville system are nonnegative. The general solution of differential equation (15a) is

$$X(\lambda, x) = A\cos\lambda x + B\sin\lambda x, \tag{16}$$

and when we impose boundary conditions (15b, c),

$$-l_1 \lambda B + h_1 A = 0, \tag{17a}$$

$$l_2(-A\lambda \sin \lambda L + B\lambda \cos \lambda L) + h_2(A \cos \lambda L + B \sin \lambda L) = 0. \tag{17b}$$

We solve (17a) for $B = h_1 A/(l_1 \lambda)$ and substitute into (17b). After rearrangement, we obtain

$$\tan \lambda L = \frac{\lambda\left(\dfrac{h_1}{l_1} + \dfrac{h_2}{l_2}\right)}{\lambda^2 - \dfrac{h_1 h_2}{l_1 l_2}}, \tag{18}$$

the equation that must be satisfied by λ. We denote by λ_n ($n = 1, \ldots$) the eigenvalues of this transcendental equation, although, in fact, λ_n^2 *are the eigenvalues of the Sturm-Liouville system.* Corresponding to these eigenvalues are the orthonormal eigenfunctions

$$X_n(x) = X(\lambda_n, x) = \frac{1}{N}\left(\cos \lambda_n x + \frac{h_1}{\lambda_n l_1} \sin \lambda_n x\right), \tag{19a}$$

where

$$N^2 = \int_0^L \left(\cos \lambda_n x + \frac{h_1}{\lambda_n l_1} \sin \lambda_n x\right)^2 dx. \tag{19b}$$

In Exercise 1, integration is shown to lead to

$$2N^2 = \left[1 + \left(\frac{h_1}{\lambda_n l_1}\right)^2\right]\left[L + \frac{h_2/l_2}{\lambda_n^2 + (h_2/l_2)^2}\right] + \frac{h_1/l_1}{\lambda_n^2}. \tag{19c}$$

Of the nine possible combinations of boundary conditions at $x = 0$ and $x = L$, we have considered only one, the most general in which none of h_1, h_2, l_1, and l_2 vanishes. Results for the remaining eight cases can be obtained from (18) and (19), or by similar analyses; they are tabulated in Table 4.1.

Each eigenvalue equation in Table 4.1 is unchanged if λ is replaced by $-\lambda$, so that for every positive solution λ of the equation, $-\lambda$ is also a solution. Since NX_n is invariant (up to a sign change) by the substitution of $-\lambda_n$ for λ_n, it is necessary only to consider the nonnegative solutions of the eigenvalue equations. This agrees with the fact that the eigenvalues of the Sturm-Liouville system are λ_n^2 and that there cannot be two linearly independent eigenfunctions corresponding to the same eigenvalue. Table 4.1 gives the eigenvalues explicitly in only four of the nine cases. The eigenvalues in the remaining five cases are illustrated geometrically below and on the following pages.

If $h_1 h_2 l_1 l_2 \neq 0$, eigenvalues are illustrated graphically in Figure 4.1 as points of intersection of the curves

$$y = \tan \lambda L, \qquad y = \frac{\lambda(h_1/l_1 + h_2/l_2)}{\lambda^2 - [(h_1 h_2)/(l_1 l_2)]}.$$

It might appear that $\lambda = 0$ is an eigenvalue in this case. However, the corollary to Theorem 2 indicates that zero is an eigenvalue only when $h_1 = h_2 = 0$. This can also be verified using conditions (17), which led to the eigenvalue equation (see Exercise 3).

Table 4.1   *Eigenpairs for the Sturm-Liouville System $X'' + \lambda^2 X = 0$, $0 < x < L$,*
$-l_1 X'(0) + h_1 X(0) = 0$, $l_2 X'(L) + h_2 X(L) = 0$.

Condition at $x = 0$	Condition at $x = L$	Eigenvalue Equation	$N X_n$	$2N^2$
$h_1 l_1 \neq 0$	$h_2 l_2 \neq 0$	$\tan \lambda L = \dfrac{\lambda\left(\dfrac{h_1}{l_1} + \dfrac{h_2}{l_2}\right)}{\lambda^2 - \dfrac{h_1 h_2}{l_1 l_2}}$	$\cos \lambda_n x$ $+ \dfrac{h_1}{\lambda_n l_1} \sin \lambda_n x$	$\dfrac{h_1/l_1}{\lambda_n^2} + \left[1 + \left(\dfrac{h_1}{\lambda_n l_1}\right)^2\right]$ $\times \left[L + \dfrac{h_2/l_2}{\lambda_n^2 + \left(\dfrac{h_2}{l_2}\right)^2}\right]$
$h_1 l_1 \neq 0$	$h_2 = 0$ $(l_2 = 1)$	$\tan \lambda L = \dfrac{h_1}{\lambda l_1}$	$\dfrac{\cos \lambda_n (L - x)}{\cos \lambda_n L}$	$L\left[1 + \left(\dfrac{h_1}{\lambda_n l_1}\right)^2\right] + \dfrac{h_1/l_1}{\lambda_n^2}$
$h_1 l_1 \neq 0$	$l_2 = 0$ $(h_2 = 1)$	$\cot \lambda L = -\dfrac{h_1}{\lambda l_1}$	$\dfrac{\sin \lambda_n (L - x)}{\sin \lambda_n L}$	$L\left[1 + \left(\dfrac{h_1}{\lambda_n l_1}\right)^2\right] + \dfrac{h_1/l_1}{\lambda_n^2}$
$h_1 = 0$ $(l_1 = 1)$	$h_2 l_2 \neq 0$	$\tan \lambda L = \dfrac{h_2}{\lambda l_2}$	$\cos \lambda_n x$	$L + \dfrac{h_2/l_2}{\lambda_n^2 + (h_2/l_2)^2}$
$h_1 = 0$ $(l_1 = 1)$	$h_2 = 0$ $(l_2 = 1)$	$\sin \lambda L = 0$ $\lambda_n = \dfrac{n\pi}{L}$, $n = 0, 1, 2, \ldots$	$\cos \lambda_n x$	$L\ (n \neq 0)$ $2L\ (n = 0)$
$h_1 = 0$ $(l_1 = 1)$	$l_2 = 0$ $(h_2 = 1)$	$\cos \lambda L = 0$ $\lambda_n = \left(\dfrac{2n - 1}{2}\right)\dfrac{\pi}{L}$, $n = 1, 2, \ldots$	$\cos \lambda_n x$	L
$l_1 = 0$ $(h_1 = 1)$	$h_2 l_2 \neq 0$	$\cot \lambda L = -\dfrac{h_2}{\lambda l_2}$	$\sin \lambda_n x$	$L + \dfrac{h_2/l_2}{\lambda_n^2 + (h_2/l_2)^2}$
$l_1 = 0$ $(h_1 = 1)$	$h_2 = 0$ $(l_2 = 1)$	$\cos \lambda L = 0$ $\lambda_n = \left(\dfrac{2n - 1}{2}\right)\dfrac{\pi}{L}$, $n = 1, 2, \ldots$	$\sin \lambda_n x$	L
$l_1 = 0$ $(h_1 = 1)$	$l_2 = 0$ $(h_2 = 1)$	$\sin \lambda L = 0$ $\lambda_n = \dfrac{n\pi}{L}$, $n = 1, 2, \ldots$	$\sin \lambda_n x$	L

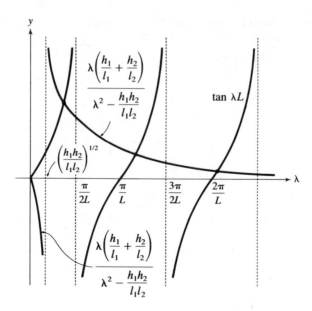

Figure 4.1

If $h_1 l_1 \neq 0$ and $h_2 = 0$ (in which case we set $l_2 = 1$), eigenvalues are illustrated graphically (Figure 4.2) as points of intersection of the curves

$$y = \tan \lambda L \quad \text{and} \quad y = \frac{h_1}{\lambda l_1}.$$

A similar situation arises when $h_2 l_2 \neq 0$ and $h_1 = 0$.

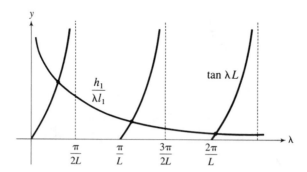

Figure 4.2

If $h_1 l_1 \neq 0$ and $l_2 = 0$ (in which case we set $h_2 = 1$), eigenvalues are illustrated graphically (Figure 4.3) as points of intersection of

$$y = \cot \lambda L \quad \text{and} \quad y = -\frac{h_1}{\lambda l_1}.$$

A similar situation arises when $h_2 l_2 \neq 0$ and $l_1 = 0$.

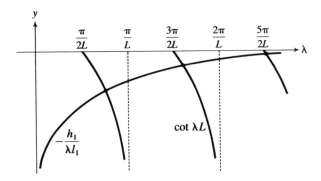

Figure 4.3

Theorem 2 states that when a function $f(x)$ is piecewise smooth on the interval $0 \leq x \leq L$, we may write for $0 < x < L$

$$f(x) = \sum_{n=1}^{\infty} c_n X_n(x) \tag{20a}$$

where

$$c_n = \int_0^L f(x) X_n(x)\, dx. \tag{20b}$$

Example 5:   Expand the function $f(x) = 2x - 1,\ 0 \leq x \leq 4$ in terms of the orthonormal eigenfunctions of the Sturm-Liouville system

$$X'' + \lambda^2 X = 0, \qquad 0 < x < 4,$$
$$X'(0) = 0 = X(4).$$

Solution: When we set $L = 4$ in line 6 of Table 4.1, normalized eigenfunctions of the Sturm-Liouville system are

$$X_n(x) = \frac{1}{\sqrt{2}} \cos \frac{(2n-1)\pi x}{8}, \qquad n = 1, 2, \ldots.$$

For $0 < x < 4$, we may write

$$2x - 1 = \sum_{n=1}^{\infty} c_n X_n(x),$$

where $c_n = \displaystyle\int_0^4 (2x - 1) X_n(x)\, dx$

$$= \frac{1}{\sqrt{2}} \left\{ \frac{8(2x-1)}{(2n-1)\pi} \sin \frac{(2n-1)\pi x}{8} + \frac{128}{(2n-1)^2\pi^2} \cos \frac{(2n-1)\pi x}{8} \right\}_0^4$$

$$= \frac{-8[16 + 7\,(-1)^n(2n-1)\pi]}{\sqrt{2}\,(2n-1)^2\pi^2}.$$

Thus, $2x - 1 = \displaystyle\sum_{n=1}^{\infty} \frac{-8[16 + 7\,(-1)^n(2n-1)\pi]}{\sqrt{2}\,(2n-1)^2\pi^2} \frac{1}{\sqrt{2}} \cos \frac{(2n-1)\pi x}{8}$

$$= -\frac{4\sqrt{2}}{\pi^2} \sum_{n=1}^{\infty} \frac{16 + 7\,(-1)^n(2n-1)\pi}{(2n-1)^2} \frac{1}{\sqrt{2}} \cos \frac{(2n-1)\pi x}{8},$$

$$0 < x < 4. \qquad\blacksquare$$

Periodic Sturm-Liouville systems do not come under the purview of Theorem 2. In particular, this theorem does not guarantee expansions in terms of normalized eigenfunctions of periodic Sturm-Liouville systems. For instance, eigenvalues for the periodic Sturm-Liouville system of Example 2 are $\lambda_n = n^2\pi^2/L^2$ $(n = 0, 1, \ldots)$, with corresponding eigenfunctions

$$\lambda_0 \leftrightarrow 1, \qquad \lambda_n \leftrightarrow \sin\frac{n\pi x}{L}, \qquad \cos\frac{n\pi x}{L} \qquad (n > 0).$$

Normalized eigenfunctions are

$$\lambda_0 \leftrightarrow \frac{1}{\sqrt{2L}}, \qquad \lambda_n \leftrightarrow \frac{1}{\sqrt{L}}\sin\frac{n\pi x}{L}, \qquad \frac{1}{\sqrt{L}}\cos\frac{n\pi x}{L} \qquad (n > 0).$$

Theorem 2 does not ensure the expansion of a function $f(x)$ in terms of these eigenfunctions, but our theory of ordinary Fourier series does. These are precisely the basis functions for ordinary Fourier series, except for normalizing factors, so we may write

$$f(x) = \frac{a_0}{\sqrt{2L}} + \sum_{n=1}^{\infty}\left(a_n\frac{1}{\sqrt{L}}\cos\frac{n\pi x}{L} + b_n\frac{1}{\sqrt{L}}\sin\frac{n\pi x}{L}\right), \qquad \text{(21a)}$$

where

$$a_0 = \int_{-L}^{L} f(x)\left(\frac{1}{\sqrt{2L}}\right)dx, \qquad a_n = \int_{-L}^{L} f(x)\left(\frac{1}{\sqrt{L}}\cos\frac{n\pi x}{L}\right)dx, \qquad \text{(21b)}$$

$$b_n = \int_{-L}^{L} f(x)\left(\frac{1}{\sqrt{L}}\sin\frac{n\pi x}{L}\right)dx. \qquad \text{(21c)}$$

Exercises 4.2

1. Obtain expression (19c) for $2N^2$ by direct integration of (19b). *Hint:* Show that

$$\sin\lambda_n L = \frac{(-1)^{n+1}\lambda_n\left(\dfrac{h_1}{l_1} + \dfrac{h_2}{l_2}\right)}{\left[\left(\lambda_n^2 + \dfrac{h_1^2}{l_1^2}\right)\left(\lambda_n^2 + \dfrac{h_2^2}{l_2^2}\right)\right]^{1/2}}$$

and

$$\cos\lambda_n L = \frac{(-1)^{n+1}\left(\lambda_n^2 - \dfrac{h_1 h_2}{l_1 l_2}\right)}{\left[\left(\lambda_n^2 + \dfrac{h_1^2}{l_1^2}\right)\left(\lambda_n^2 + \dfrac{h_2^2}{l_2^2}\right)\right]^{1/2}}.$$

2. For each Sturm-Liouville system in Table 4.1, find expressions for $\sin\lambda_n L$ and $\cos\lambda_n L$ that involve only h_1, h_2, l_1, l_2, and/or λ_n. These should be tabulated and attached to Table 4.1 for future reference.

3. Use equations (17) to verify that $\lambda = 0$ is an eigenvalue of Sturm-Liouville system (15) only when $h_1 = h_2 = 0$.

In Exercises 4–9, express the function $f(x) = x$, $0 \le x \le L$, in terms of orthonormal eigenfunctions of the Sturm-Liouville system.

4. $X'' + \lambda^2 X = 0$, $X(0) = X(L) = 0$ 5. $X'' + \lambda^2 X = 0$, $X'(0) = X'(L) = 0$

6. $X'' + \lambda^2 X = 0$, $X(0) = X'(L) = 0$ 7. $X'' + \lambda^2 X = 0$, $X'0) = X(L) = 0$

8. $X'' + \lambda^2 X = 0$, $X'(0) = 0$, $l_2 X'(L) + h_2 X(L) = 0$

9. $X'' + \lambda^2 X = 0$, $X(0) = 0$, $l_2 X'(L) + h_2 X(L) = 0$

10. Express the function $f(x) = x^2$, $0 \le x \le L$, in terms of orthonormal eigenfunctions of the Sturm-Liouville system

$$X'' + \lambda^2 X = 0, \qquad 0 < x < L,$$
$$X(0) = 0 = X'(L).$$

In Exercises 11–13, find eigenvalues and orthonormal eigenfunctions of the proper Sturm-Liouville system.

11. $\dfrac{d^2 y}{dx^2} + 2\dfrac{dy}{dx} + \lambda^2 y = 0$, $0 < x < L$, $y'(0) = 0 = y'(L)$

12. $\dfrac{d^2 y}{dx^2} + \beta\dfrac{dy}{dx} + \lambda^2 y = 0$, $0 < x < L$ ($\beta \ne 0$ a given constant), $y(0) = 0 = y(L)$

13. $\dfrac{d^2 y}{dx^2} + \beta\dfrac{dy}{dx} + \lambda^2 y = 0$, $0 < x < L$ ($\beta \ne 0$ a given constant), $y'(0) = 0 = y'(L)$

14. **(a)** Find eigenvalues and (nonnormalized) eigenfunctions for the proper Sturm-Liouville system

$$y'' + \lambda^2 y = 0, \qquad -L < x < L,$$
$$y'(-L) = 0 = y'(L).$$

     (b) Show that the eigenfunctions in (a) can be expressed in the compact form
$\cos[n\pi(x + L)/(2L)]$, $n = 0, 1, 2, \ldots$.

     (c) Normalize the eigenfunctions.

15. **(a)** Show that the transformation $x = e^z$ replaces the Sturm-Liouville system

$$x^2 \dfrac{d^2 y}{dx^2} + x\dfrac{dy}{dx} + \lambda^2 y = 0, \qquad 1 < x < L,$$
$$y(1) = 0 = y(L)$$

     in $y(x)$ with the system

$$\dfrac{d^2 y}{dz^2} + \lambda^2 y = 0, \qquad 0 < z < \ln L,$$
$$y(0) = 0 = y(\ln L)$$

     in $y(z)$. If we use Table 4.1, what are the normalized eigenfunctions $y_n(z)$? Replace z by $\ln x$ to obtain eigenfunctions $y_n(x)$.

     (b) Repeat (a) with the transformation $x = L^z$.

16. Find eigenvalues and orthonormal eigenfunctions of the Sturm-Liouville system

$$\frac{d}{dx}\left(x\frac{dy}{dx}\right) + \frac{\lambda^2}{x}y = 0, \qquad 1 < x < b,$$

$$y(b) = 0 = y'(1).$$

In Exercises 17–19, find approximations for the four smallest eigenvalues of the Sturm-Liouville system.

17. $X'' + \lambda^2 X = 0, \quad 0 < x < 1, \quad -200X'(0) + 400{,}000X(0) = 0, \quad X'(1) = 0$

18. $X'' + \lambda^2 X = 0, \quad 0 < x < 1, \quad X(0) = 0, \quad 150X'(1) + 100{,}000X(1) = 0$

19. $X'' + \lambda^2 X = 0, \quad 0 < x < 1, \quad -200X'(0) + 400X(0) = 0, \quad 200X'(1) + 100X(1) = 0$

20. (a) Expand the function

$$f(x) = \begin{cases} 1 & 0 < x < L/2 \\ -1 & L/2 < x < L \end{cases}$$

in terms of the normalized eigenfunctions of Sturm-Liouville system (2).

(b) What does the series converge to at $x = L/2$? Is this to be expected?

(c) What does the series converge to at $x = 0$ and $x = L$? Are these to be expected?

21. Repeat Exercise 20 with the eigenfunctions of Sturm-Liouville system (1).

22. In Exercise 11 of Section 4.1, we suggested two ways of interpreting the 4 in the differential equation. Does it make a difference as far as eigenfunction expansions are concerned?

23. The initial boundary value problem for transverse vibrations $y(x, t)$ of a beam simply supported at one end ($x = L$) and horizontally built in at the other end ($x = 0$) when gravity is negligible compared with internal forces is

$$\frac{\partial^2 y}{\partial t^2} + c^2 \frac{\partial^4 y}{\partial x^4} = 0, \qquad 0 < x < L, \qquad t > 0,$$

$$y(0, t) = y_x(0, t) = 0, \qquad t > 0,$$

$$y(L, t) = y_{xx}(L, t) = 0, \qquad t > 0,$$

$$y(x, 0) = f(x) \qquad 0 < x < L,$$

$$y_t(x, 0) = g(x), \qquad 0 < x < L.$$

(a) Show that by assuming that $y(x, t) = X(x)T(t)$, eigenfunctions

$$X_n(x) = \frac{1}{\cos \lambda_n L} \sin \lambda_n (L - x) - \frac{1}{\cosh \lambda_n L} \sinh \lambda_n (L - x)$$

are obtained, where eigenvalues λ_n must satisfy

$$\tan \lambda L = \tanh \lambda L.$$

(b) Prove that these eigenfunctions are orthogonal on the interval $0 \leq x \leq L$ with respect to the weight function $p(x) = 1$. [*Hint:* Use the differential equation defining $X_n(x)$ and a construction like that in Theorem 1.]

24. Does the Sturm-Liouville system in line 6 of Table 4.1 give rise to the expansion in Exercise 22 of Section 2.2 for even and odd-harmonic functions?

25. Does the Sturm-Liouville system in line 8 of Table 4.1 give rise to the expansion in Exercise 21 of Section 2.2 for odd and odd-harmonic functions?

26. Show that the Sturm-Liouville system

$$\frac{d^2X}{dx^2} + \lambda X = 0, \qquad 0 < x < L,$$

$$X'(0) = 0,$$

$$l_2 X'(L) - h_2 X(L) = 0, \qquad (l_2 > 0, h_2 > 0)$$

has exactly one negative eigenvalue. What is the corresponding eigenfunction?

4.3 Further Properties of Sturm-Liouville Systems

When $f(x)$ is a piecewise smooth function, its Fourier series converges to $[f(x+) + f(x-)]/2$. When $f(x)$ is continuous, the Fourier series converges absolutely and uniformly (see Theorem 10 in Section 2.3). The counterpart of the latter result for generalized Fourier series is contained in the following theorem.

Theorem 3
───

Suppose that $f(x)$ is continuous and $f'(x)$ is piecewise continuous on $a \le x \le b$. If $f(x)$ satisfies the boundary conditions of a proper Sturm-Liouville system on $a \le x \le b$, then the generalized Fourier series (14) for $f(x)$ converges uniformly to $f(x)$ for $a \le x \le b$.

───

For example, when the function $x(L - x)$ is expanded in terms of the eigenfunctions of Sturm-Liouville system (1), the result is

$$x(L - x) = \frac{2\sqrt{2}L^{5/2}}{\pi^3} \sum_{n=1}^{\infty} \frac{1 + (-1)^{n+1}}{n^3} \sqrt{\frac{2}{L}} \sin\frac{n\pi x}{L}$$

$$= \frac{8L^2}{\pi^3} \sum_{n=1}^{\infty} \frac{1}{(2n-1)^3} \sin\frac{(2n-1)\pi x}{L}, \qquad 0 \le x \le L.$$

Because $x(L - x)$ satisfies conditions (1b, c), convergence is uniform. This could also be verified with the Weierstrass M-test (see Section 2.3).

Exercise 4 in Section 2.3 contains special cases of this result.

Expansions of functions as generalized Fourier series are very different from power series expansions. A function can be represented in a Taylor series on an interval only if the function and all of its derivatives are continuous throughout the interval, and even these conditions may not be sufficient to guarantee convergence of the series to the function. Eigenfunction expansions, however, are valid even though a function and its first derivative may each possess a finite number of finite discontinuities.

On the other hand, whereas Taylor series expansions may be differentiated term by term inside the interval of convergence of the series, such may not be the case for generalized Fourier series. The following result is analogous to Theorem 3 in Section 2.1.

Theorem 4

Suppose that $f(x)$ is continuous and $f'(x)$ and $f''(x)$ are piecewise continuous on $a \leq x \leq b$. If $f(x)$ satisfies the boundary conditions of a proper Sturm-Liouville system, then for any x in $a < x < b$, series (14) may be differentiated term by term with the resulting series converging to $[f'(x+) + f'(x-)]/2$.

We now prove the Sturm comparison theorem, a result that has implications when we study singular Sturm-Liouville systems in Chapter 8.

Theorem 5 (Sturm Comparison Theorem)

Let $r(x)$ be a function that is positive on the interval $a < x < b$ and has a continuous first derivative for $a \leq x \leq b$. Suppose that $s_1(x)$ and $s_2(x)$ are continuous functions for $a < x < b$ such that $s_2(x) > s_1(x)$ thereon. If $y_1(x)$ and $y_2(x)$ satisfy

$$\frac{d}{dx}\left(r(x)\frac{dy_1}{dx}\right) + s_1(x)y_1 = 0 \tag{22a}$$

and
$$\frac{d}{dx}\left(r(x)\frac{dy_2}{dx}\right) + s_2(x)y_2 = 0 \tag{22b}$$

there is at least one zero of $y_2(x)$ between every consecutive pair of zeros of $y_1(x)$ in $a < x < b$.

Proof: Let α and β be any two consecutive zeros of $y_1(x)$ in $a < x < b$, and suppose that $y_2(x)$ has no zero between α and β. We assume, without loss in generality, that $y_1(x) > 0$ and $y_2(x) > 0$ on $\alpha < x < \beta$. [If this were not true, we would work with $-y_1(x)$ and $-y_2(x)$.] When (22a) and (22b) are multiplied by y_2 and y_1, respectively, and the results are subtracted,

$$0 = y_1\left[\frac{d}{dx}\left(r\frac{dy_2}{dx}\right) + s_2 y_2\right] - y_2\left[\frac{d}{dx}\left(r\frac{dy_1}{dx}\right) + s_1 y_1\right].$$

Integration of this equation from α to β gives

$$\int_\alpha^\beta (s_2 - s_1)y_1 y_2\, dx = \int_\alpha^\beta [(ry_1')'y_2 - (ry_2')'y_1]\, dx$$

$$= \int_\alpha^\beta (ry_1' y_2 - ry_2' y_1)'\, dx$$

$$= \{r(y_2 y_1' - y_1 y_2')\}_\alpha^\beta$$

$$= r(\beta)[y_2(\beta)y_1'(\beta) - y_1(\beta)y_2'(\beta)] - r(\alpha)[y_2(\alpha)y_1'(\alpha) - y_1(\alpha)y_2'(\alpha)]$$

$$= r(\beta)y_2(\beta)y_1'(\beta) - r(\alpha)y_2(\alpha)y_1'(\alpha),$$

since $y_1(\alpha) = y_1(\beta) = 0$. Because $y_1(x) > 0$ for $\alpha < x < \beta$, it follows that $y_1'(\alpha) \geq 0$ and $y_1'(\beta) \leq 0$. Furthermore, because $r(\alpha)$, $r(\beta)$, $y_2(\alpha)$, and $y_2(\beta)$ are all positive, we must have

$$r(\beta)y_2(\beta)y_1'(\beta) - r(\alpha)y_2(\alpha)y_1'(\alpha) \leq 0.$$

But this contradicts the fact that

$$\int_\alpha^\beta [s_2(x) - s_1(x)]y_2(x)y_1(x)\,dx > 0,$$

since $s_2 > s_1$ on $\alpha \le x \le \beta$. Consequently, $y_2(x)$ must have a zero between α and β. ∎

To see the implication of this theorem in Sturm-Liouville theory, we set $s_1(x) = \lambda_1 p(x) - q(x)$ and $s_2(x) = \lambda_2 p(x) - q(x)$, where $\lambda_2 > \lambda_1$ are eigenvalues of system (3). It then follows that between every pair of zeros of the eigenfunction $y_1(x)$ corresponding to λ_1, there is at least one zero of the eigenfunction $y_2(x)$ associated with λ_2. Figure 4.4 illustrates the situation for eigenfunction $X_3(x)$ and $X_4(x)$ of Sturm-Liouville system (1).

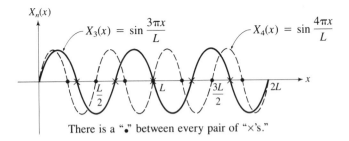

Figure 4.4

There is a "•" between every pair of "×'s."

As a final consideration in this chapter, we show that the Sturm-Liouville systems in Table 4.1 arise when separation of variables is applied to (initial) boundary value problems having second-order PDEs expressed in Cartesian coordinates. To illustrate this, we apply separation of variables to the rather general second-order PDE

$$\nabla^2 V = p\frac{\partial^2 V}{\partial t^2} + q\frac{\partial V}{\partial t} + sV, \tag{23}$$

where p, q, and s are constants and t is time. We consider this PDE because it includes as special cases many of those in Chapter 1. In particular,

(1) if $V = V(\mathbf{r}, t)$, $p = s = 0$, and $q = k^{-1}$, then (23) is the one-, two-, or three-dimensional heat conduction equation;

(2) if $V = V(\mathbf{r}, t)$, and $p = \rho/\tau$ (or ρ/E), then (23) is the one-, two-, or three-dimensional wave equation;

(3) if $V = V(\mathbf{r})$, $p = q = s = 0$, then (23) is the one-, two-, or three-dimensional Laplace equation.

Thus, the results obtained here are valid for heat conduction, vibration, and potential problems.

When (23) is to be solved in some finite region, boundary conditions and possibly initial conditions are associated with the PDE. If this region is a rectangular parallelopiped (box) in space, Cartesian coordinates can be chosen to specify the region in the form $0 \le x \le L, 0 \le y \le L', 0 \le z \le L''$ (Figure 4.5). Boundary conditions must then be specified on the six faces $x = 0$, $y = 0$, $z = 0$, $x = L$, $y = L'$, and $z = L''$. Suppose, for example, that the following homogeneous Dirichlet, Neumann, and Robin conditions accompany (23):

$$\nabla^2 V = p\frac{\partial^2 V}{\partial t^2} + q\frac{\partial V}{\partial t} + sV,$$

$$0 < x < L, \qquad 0 < y < L', \qquad 0 < z < L'', \qquad t > 0, \tag{24a}$$

$$V = 0, \qquad x = 0, \qquad 0 < y < L', \qquad 0 < z < L'', \qquad t > 0, \tag{24b}$$

$$\frac{\partial V}{\partial x} = 0, \qquad x = L, \qquad 0 < y < L', \qquad 0 < z < L'', \qquad t > 0, \tag{24c}$$

$$-l_3\frac{\partial V}{\partial y} + h_3 V = 0, \qquad y = 0, \qquad 0 < x < L, \qquad 0 < z < L'', \qquad t > 0, \tag{24d}$$

$$V = 0, \qquad y = L', \qquad 0 < x < L, \qquad 0 < z < L'', \qquad t > 0, \tag{24e}$$

$$\frac{\partial V}{\partial z} = 0, \qquad z = 0, \qquad 0 < x < L, \qquad 0 < y < L', \qquad t > 0, \tag{24f}$$

$$l_6\frac{\partial V}{\partial z} + h_6 V = 0, \qquad z = L'', \qquad 0 < x < L, \qquad 0 < y < L', \qquad t > 0, \tag{24g}$$

Initial conditions, if applicable. $\tag{24h}$

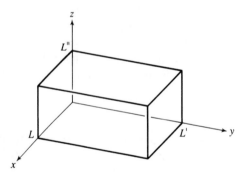

Figure 4.5

If we assume that a function with variables separated, $V(x, y, z, t) = X(x)Y(y)Z(z)T(t)$, satisfies (24a),

$$X''YZT + XY''ZT + XYZ''T = pXYZT'' + qXYZT' + sXYZT.$$

Division by $XYZT$ gives

$$\frac{X''}{X} + \frac{Y''}{Y} + \frac{Z''}{Z} = \frac{pT'' + qT' + sT}{T}$$

or

$$-\frac{X''}{X} = \frac{Y''}{Y} + \frac{Z''}{Z} - \frac{pT'' + qT' + sT}{T}.$$

The separation principle (see Section 3.1) implies that each side of this equation must be equal to a constant, say α:

$$-\frac{X''}{X} = \alpha = \frac{Y''}{Y} + \frac{Z''}{Z} - \frac{pT'' + qT' + sT}{T}. \tag{25}$$

Thus $X(x)$ must satisfy the ODE $X'' + \alpha X = 0$, $0 < x < L$. When the separated function is substituted into boundary conditions (24b, c), there results

$$X(0)Y(y)Z(z)T(t) = 0, \qquad X'(L)Y(y)Z(z)T(t) = 0.$$

From these, $X(0) = 0 = X'(L)$, and hence $X(x)$ must satisfy

$$X'' + \alpha X = 0, \qquad 0 < x < L, \tag{26a}$$

$$X(0) = 0 = X'(L). \tag{26b}$$

This is proper Sturm-Liouville system (15) with $l_1 = h_2 = 0$ and $h_1 = l_2 = 1$. When we set $\alpha = \lambda^2$, eigenvalues λ_n^2 and orthonormal eigenfunctions $X_n(x)$ are then as given in line 8 of Table 4.1:

$$\lambda_n^2 = \frac{(2n-1)^2 \pi^2}{4L^2}, \qquad X_n(x) = \sqrt{\frac{2}{L}} \sin \frac{(2n-1)\pi x}{2L}.$$

Further separation of (25) gives

$$-\frac{Y''}{Y} = \beta = \frac{Z''}{Z} - \frac{pT'' + qT' + sT}{T} - \lambda_n^2. \tag{27}$$

where β is a constant. Boundary conditions (24d, e) imply that $Y(y)$ must satisfy

$$Y'' + \beta Y = 0, \qquad 0 < y < L', \tag{28a}$$

$$-l_3 Y'(0) + h_3 Y(0) = 0, \tag{28b}$$

$$Y(L') = 0. \tag{28c}$$

This is Sturm-Liouville system (15) with y's replacing x's, with h_3, l_3, and L replacing h_1, l_1, and L, and with $l_2 = 0, h_2 = 1$. When we set $\beta = \mu^2$, the eigenvalue equation and orthonormal eigenfunctions are as found in line 3 of Table 4.1:

$$\cot \mu L' = -\frac{h_3}{\mu l_3}, \qquad N Y_m(y) = \frac{1}{\sin \mu_m L'} \sin \mu_m (L' - y),$$

where

$$2N^2 = L'\left[1 + \left(\frac{h_3}{\mu_m l_3}\right)^2\right] + \frac{h_3/l_3}{\mu_m^2}.$$

Continued separation of (27) yields

$$-\frac{Z''}{Z} = \gamma = -\frac{pT'' + qT' + sT}{T} - \lambda_n^2 - \mu_m^2, \tag{29}$$

where γ is a constant. When this is combined with boundary conditions (24f, g), $Z(z)$ must satisfy the Sturm-Liouville system

$$Z'' + \gamma Z = 0, \qquad 0 < z < L'', \tag{30a}$$

$$Z'(0) = 0, \tag{30b}$$

$$l_6 Z'(L'') + h_6 Z(L'') = 0. \tag{30c}$$

With changes in notation, this is the Sturm-Liouville system in line 4 of Table 4.1. Eigenvalues $\gamma = v^2$ are defined by

$$\tan vL'' = \frac{h_6}{vl_6},$$

with orthonormal eigenfunctions $N^{-1} \cos v_j z$ where

$$2N^2 = L'' + \frac{h_6/l_6}{v_j^2 + (h_6/l_6)^2}.$$

The time-dependent part $T(t)$ of $V(x, y, z, t)$ is obtained by solving the ODE

$$pT'' + qT' + sT = -(\lambda_n^2 + \mu_m^2 + v_j^2)T. \tag{31}$$

In summary, separation of variables on (initial) boundary value problem (24) has led to the Sturm-Liouville systems in lines 3, 4, and 8 of Table 4.1. Other choices for boundary conditions led to the remaining five Sturm-Liouville systems in Table 4.1 (see Exercises 7–9).

Exercises 4.3

1. Theorem 4 indicates that generalized Fourier series from proper Sturm-Liouville systems may be differentiated term by term when $f(x)$ is continuous, $f'(x)$ and $f''(x)$ are piecewise continuous, and $f(x)$ satisfies the boundary conditions of the system. We illustrate with two examples.

(a) Find the eigenfunction expansion for

$$f(x) = \begin{cases} x & 0 \le x \le L/2 \\ L - x & L/2 \le x \le L \end{cases}$$

in terms of the normalized eigenfunctions of Sturm-Liouville system (1). Show graphically that $f(x)$ is continuous, and $f'(x)$ and $f''(x)$ are piecewise continuous, on $0 \le x \le L$. Since $f(0) = f(L) = 0$, Theorem 4 guarantees that term-by-term differentiation of the eigenfunction expansion for $f(x)$ yields a series that converges to $[f'(x+) + f'(x-)]/2$ for $0 < x < L$. Verify that this is indeed true, but do so without using Theorem 4.

(b) Find the eigenfunction expansion for $g(x) = 1, 0 \le x \le L$, in terms of the eigenfunctions of (1). Show that term-by-term differentiation of this series gives a series that converges only for $x = L/2$. Which of the conditions in Theorem 4 are violated by $g(x)$?

2. Prove Bessel's inequality for eigenfunction expansions: If $f(x)$ is a piecewise continuous function on $a \le x \le b$, and $y_n(x)$ are the eigenfunctions of a proper Sturm-Liouville system, the generalized Fourier coefficients of $f(x)$ satisfy the inequality

$$\sum_{n=1}^{\infty} c_n^2 \le \int_a^b p(x)[f(x)]^2 \, dx.$$

This result is extended to an equality in Exercise 3.

3. Parseval's theorem states that when $f(x)$ is a piecewise continuous function on $a \le x \le b$, and $y_n(x)$ are the eigenfunctions of a proper Sturm-Liouville system, the generalized Fourier

coefficients of $f(x)$ satisfy the equality

$$\sum_{n=1}^{\infty} c_n^2 = \int_a^b p(x)[f(x)]^2 \, dx.$$

Verify this in the case that $f(x)$ is continuous, has a piecewise continuous first derivative, and satisfies the boundary conditions of the Sturm-Liouville system.

4. In Exercise 6 of Section 2.3, it was shown that the partial sums of the Fourier series of a function $f(x)$ are the best trigonometric approximation of the function in the mean square sense. In this exercise we show that generalized Fourier series are also best approximations in the mean square sense. A piecewise continuous function $f(x)$ is to be approximated by a sum of the form

$$S_n(x) = \sum_{k=1}^{n} \alpha_k y_k(x),$$

where α_k are constants and $y_k(x)$ are normalized eigenfunctions of Sturm-Liouville system (3). One measure of the accuracy of this approximation is the quantity

$$E_n = \int_a^b p(x)[f(x) - S_n(x)]^2 \, dx,$$

called the mean square error with respect to the weight function $p(x)$.

(a) Show that E_n can be expressed in the form

$$E_n = \int_a^b p(x)[f(x)]^2 \, dx + \sum_{k=1}^{n} \alpha_k^2 - 2 \sum_{k=1}^{n} \alpha_k c_k,$$

where c_k are the generalized Fourier coefficients of $f(x)$.

(b) Regarding E_n as a function of n variables $\alpha_1, \ldots, \alpha_n$, show that E_n is minimized when the α_k are chosen as c_k.

5. The generalized Fourier series of $f(x)$ in terms of the eigenfunctions of Sturm-Liouville system (3) is said to converge in the mean to $f(x)$ on $a \le x \le b$ if

$$\lim_{n \to \infty} \int_a^b p(x)[S_n(x) - f(x)]^2 \, dx = 0,$$

where $S_n(x)$ is the nth partial sum

$$S_n(x) = \sum_{k=1}^{n} c_k y_k(x)$$

and

$$c_k = \int_a^b p(x) f(x) y_k(x) \, dx.$$

Use the results of Exercises 3 and 4 to show that this is indeed the case when $f(x)$ is continuous and $f'(x)$ is piecewise continuous.

6. (a) Show that an eigenvalue λ_n of a regular Sturm-Liouville system can be expressed in terms of its corresponding normalized eigenfunction $y_n(x)$ according to

$$\lambda_n = \int_a^b \left(r(x)[y_n'(x)]^2 + q(x)[y_n(x)]^2 \right) dx - \{r(x)y_n(x)y_n'(x)\}_a^b.$$

(b) What form does the expression in (a) take when both boundary conditions are Dirichlet? When both are Neumann?

In Exercises 7–9, determine all Sturm-Liouville systems that result when separation of variables is used to solve the problem. Do not solve the problem; simply find the Sturm-Liouville systems. Find eigenvalues (or eigenvalue equations) for each Sturm-Liouville system and orthonormal eigenfunctions. Give a physical interpretation of each problem.

7. $\dfrac{\partial^2 U}{\partial x^2} + \dfrac{\partial^2 U}{\partial y^2} = k^{-1}\dfrac{\partial U}{\partial t}$, $\quad 0 < x < L, \quad 0 < y < L', \quad t > 0; \quad U(0, y, t) = 0, \quad 0 < y < L', \quad t > 0;$

$\partial U(L, y, t)/\partial x + 200 U(L, y, t) = 0, \quad 0 < y < L', \quad t > 0; \quad \partial U(x, 0, t)/\partial y = 0, \quad 0 < x < L,$
$t > 0; \quad \partial U(x, L', t)/\partial y = 0, \quad 0 < x < L, \quad t > 0; \quad U(x, y, 0) = f(x, y), \quad 0 < x < L,$
$0 < y < L'$

8. $\dfrac{\partial^2 y}{\partial t^2} = c^2\dfrac{\partial^2 y}{\partial x^2} - \beta\dfrac{\partial y}{\partial t}$, $\quad 0 < x < L, \quad t > 0; \quad -\tau\partial y(0, t)/\partial x + ky(0, t) = 0, \quad t > 0; \quad y(L, t) = 0,$

$t > 0; \quad y(x, 0) = f(x), \quad 0 < x < L; \quad y_t(x, 0) = 0, \quad 0 < x < L$

9. $\dfrac{\partial^2 V}{\partial x^2} + \dfrac{\partial^2 V}{\partial y^2} + \dfrac{\partial^2 V}{\partial z^2} = 0, \quad 0 < x < L, \quad 0 < y < L', \quad 0 < z < L''; \quad V(0, y, z) = 0, \quad 0 < y < L',$

$0 < z < L''; \quad \partial V(L, y, z)/\partial x = 0, \quad 0 < y < L, \quad 0 < z < L''; \quad V(x, 0, z) = 0, \quad 0 < x < L,$
$0 < z < L''; \quad V(x, L', z) = 0, \quad 0 < x < L, \quad 0 < z < L''; \quad V(x, y, 0) = f(x, y), \quad 0 < x < L,$
$0 < y < L'; \quad V(x, y, L'') = 0, \quad 0 < x < L, \quad 0 < y < L'$

10. (a) Show that the homogeneous PDE

$$a(x, y)\frac{\partial^2 u}{\partial x^2} + b(x, y)\frac{\partial^2 u}{\partial x \partial y} + c(x, y)\frac{\partial^2 u}{\partial y^2} + d(x, y)\frac{\partial u}{\partial x} + e(x, y)\frac{\partial u}{\partial y} + f(x, y)u = 0$$

is separable if $a(x, y) = a(x)$, $b(x, y) = $ constant, $c(x, y) = c(y)$, $d(x, y) = d(x)$, $e(x, y) = e(y)$, and $f(x, y) = f_1(x) + f_2(y)$.

(b) Are the conditions in (a) necessary for separability?

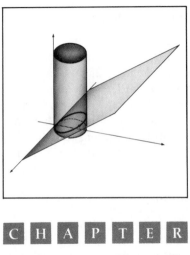

C H A P T E R
F I V E

Solution of Homogeneous Problems
by Separation of Variables

5.1 Introduction

In Chapter 1 we developed boundary value and initial boundary value problems to describe physical phenomena such as heat conduction, vibrations, and electrostatic potentials. In Chapter 2 we introduced ordinary Fourier series, which we then used in Chapter 3, in conjunction with separation of variables, to solve very simple problems. These straightforward examples led to consideration of Sturm-Liouville systems in Chapter 4. We are now ready to apply these results in more complex homogeneous problems. In Chapter 6 we introduce finite Fourier transforms to solve nonhomogeneous problems.

A great variety of homogeneous problems could be considered—heat conduction, vibration, or potential; one-, two-, or three-dimensional; time dependent or steady-state. Because we cannot hope to consider all of these problems, we select a few straightforward examples to illustrate the technique; this puts us in a position to consider quite general PDEs, such as

$$\nabla^2 V = p\frac{\partial^2 V}{\partial t^2} + q\frac{\partial V}{\partial t} + sV, \tag{1}$$

where p, q, and s are constants. We pointed out in Section 4.3 that this PDE contains many of the PDEs in Chapter 1 [see equation (23) in Chapter 4]. It follows that initial boundary value problems associated with PDE (1) contain as special cases many of the (initial) boundary value problems of Chapter 1. In fact, when we solve (1) subject to Robin boundary conditions, we obtain general formulas that may be specialized to give solutions to many problems. We begin in Sections 5.2 and 5.3 with problems in two independent variables. In Section 5.4 we generalize to problems in higher dimensions.

5.2 Homogeneous Initial Boundary Value Problems in Two Variables

We begin this section by using separation of variables to solve two initial boundary value problems, one in heat conduction and the other in vibrations. What we learn from these examples will prepare us for separation of variables in more general problems. The heat conduction problem is

$$\frac{\partial U}{\partial t} = k\frac{\partial^2 U}{\partial x^2}, \qquad 0 < x < L, \qquad t > 0, \tag{2a}$$

$$U_x(0, t) = 0, \qquad t > 0, \tag{2b}$$

$$\kappa\frac{\partial U(L, t)}{\partial x} + \mu U(L, t) = 0, \qquad t > 0, \tag{2c}$$

$$U(x, 0) = f(x), \qquad 0 < x < L. \tag{2d}$$

Physically described is a rod of uniform cross section and insulated sides that at time $t = 0$ has temperature $f(x)$ (Figure 5.1). For time $t > 0$, the end $x = 0$ is also insulated, and heat is exchanged at the other end with an environment at temperature $0°C$. The problem is said to be homogeneous because PDE (2a) and boundary conditions (2b, c) are homogeneous.

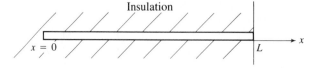

Insulation

$x = 0$ L → x

Figure 5.1

If we assume that a function $U(x, t)$, separated in the form $U(x, t) = X(x)T(t)$, satisfies PDE (2a), then

$$XT' = kX''T,$$

or

$$\frac{X''}{X} = \frac{T'}{kT} = \alpha = \text{constant}.$$

When this is combined with boundary conditions (2b, c), $X(x)$ must satisfy the system

$$X'' - \alpha X = 0, \qquad 0 < x < L, \tag{3a}$$

$$X'(0) = 0, \tag{3b}$$

$$\kappa X'(L) + \mu X(L) = 0 \tag{3c}$$

and $T(t)$ must satisfy the ODE

$$T' - \alpha k T = 0, \qquad t > 0. \tag{4}$$

System (3) is a special case of proper Sturm-Liouville system (15) in Section 4.2. Since eigenvalues $(-\alpha)$ must be positive, we set $-\alpha = \lambda^2$, in which case line 4 in Table 4.1 defines eigenvalues as solutions of the equation

$$\tan \lambda L = \frac{\mu}{\kappa \lambda}$$

and orthonormal eigenfunctions as $X_n(x) = N^{-1} \cos \lambda_n x$, where the normalizing factor N^{-1} is given by

$$2N^2 = L + \frac{\mu/\kappa}{\lambda_n^2 + (\mu/\kappa)^2}.$$

For these eigenvalues, the general solution of (4) is $T(t) = ce^{-k\lambda_n^2 t}$, where c is an arbitrary constant. It follows that separated functions

$$ce^{-k\lambda_n^2 t} X_n(x)$$

for any constant c and any eigenvalue λ_n satisfy PDE (2a) and boundary conditions (2b, c). To satisfy initial condition (2d), we superpose separated functions (the PDE and boundary conditions being linear and homogeneous) and take

$$U(x,t) = \sum_{n=1}^{\infty} c_n e^{-k\lambda_n^2 t} X_n(x), \tag{5}$$

where the c_n are constants. Condition (2d) now implies that

$$f(x) = \sum_{n=1}^{\infty} c_n X_n(x), \qquad 0 < x < L. \tag{6}$$

But this equation states that the c_n are the Fourier coefficients in the generalized Fourier series of $f(x)$ in terms of $X_n(x)$ and are defined according to equation (20b) in Section 4.2 by

$$c_n = \int_0^L f(x) X_n(x)\, dx = \frac{1}{N} \int_0^L f(x) \cos \lambda_n x\, dx. \tag{7a}$$

The final formal solution of problem (2) is therefore

$$U(x,t) = \sum_{n=1}^{\infty} c_n e^{-k\lambda_n^2 t} N^{-1} \cos \lambda_n x, \tag{7b}$$

where the c_n are defined in (7a). To see how the boundary conditions affect temperature in the rod, we consider a specific initial temperature distribution. Suppose, for example, that the rod is 1 m long and that $f(x) = 100(1 - x)$. Furthermore, suppose that the conductivity κ and diffusivity k of the material in the rod are 48 W/mK and 12×10^{-6} m²/s and that the heat transfer coefficient at $x = L$ is $\mu = 96$ W/m²K. With these physical attributes, eigenvalues are defined by

$$\tan \lambda = \frac{2}{\lambda}$$

and normalizing factors are

$$2N^2 = 1 + \frac{2}{\lambda_n^2 + 4}.$$

Coefficients c_n are given by (7a):

$$c_n = \frac{1}{N} \int_0^1 100(1-x)\cos\lambda_n x \, dx = \frac{100}{N\lambda_n^2}(1 - \cos\lambda_n).$$

Thus,

$$U(x,t) = \sum_{n=1}^{\infty} \frac{100}{N\lambda_n^2}(1 - \cos\lambda_n)e^{-12 \times 10^{-6}\lambda_n^2 t}N^{-1}\cos\lambda_n x$$

$$= \sum_{n=1}^{\infty} \frac{200(\lambda_n^2 + 4)(1 - \cos\lambda_n)}{\lambda_n^2(\lambda_n^2 + 6)}e^{-12 \times 10^{-6}\lambda_n^2 t}\cos\lambda_n x.$$

When this series is approximated by its first four terms, sketches for various values of t are as shown in Figure 5.2. (The four smallest positive solutions of $\tan\lambda = 2/\lambda$ are 1.076874, 3.643597, 6.578334, and 9.629560.)

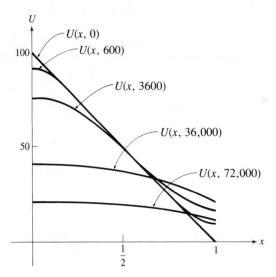

Figure 5.2

In Figure 5.3 we show temperature in the rod for the same times when boundary condition (2c) is replaced by $U(L,t) = 0$. What this means is that the heat transfer coefficient μ in (2c) has become very large and there is essentially no resistance to heat transfer across the boundary $x = L$. The solution in this case is

$$U(x,t) = \frac{800}{\pi^2}\sum_{n=1}^{\infty} \frac{1}{(2n-1)^2}e^{-12 \times 10^{-6}(2n-1)^2\pi^2 t/4}\cos\frac{(2n-1)\pi x}{2}.$$

Ultimately, the solution approaches the situation in which temperature in the rod is identically zero, as it does in problem (2), but it does so more quickly.

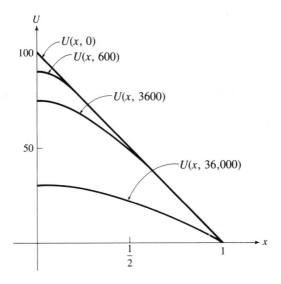

Figure 5.3

Our second illustrative example is concerned with displacements of the taut string in Figure 5.4. The end at $x = L$ is fixed on the x-axis, while the end at $x = 0$ is looped around a vertical support and can move thereon without friction. If the position of the string is initially parabolic, $x(L - x)$, and it is motionless, subsequent displacements are described by the homogeneous initial boundary value problem

$$\frac{\partial^2 y}{\partial t^2} = c^2 \frac{\partial^2 y}{\partial x^2}, \qquad 0 < x < L, \qquad t > 0, \tag{8a}$$

$$y_x(0, t) = 0, \qquad t > 0, \tag{8b}$$

$$y(L, t) = 0, \qquad t > 0, \tag{8c}$$

$$y(x, 0) = x(L - x), \qquad 0 < x < L, \tag{8d}$$

$$y_t(x, 0) = 0, \qquad 0 < x < L. \tag{8e}$$

Figure 5.4

When a separated function $y(x, t) = X(x)T(t)$ is substituted into PDE (8a), boundary conditions (8b, c), and initial condition (8e), a Sturm-Liouville system in $X(x)$ results

$$X'' + \lambda^2 X = 0, \qquad 0 < x < L, \tag{9a}$$

$$X'(0) = 0 = X(L), \tag{9b}$$

and an ODE in $T(t)$,

$$T'' + c^2\lambda^2 T = 0, \qquad t > 0, \tag{10a}$$

$$T'(0) = 0. \tag{10b}$$

According to line 6 in Table 4.1, eigenvalues of the Sturm-Liouville system are $\lambda_n^2 = (2n-1)^2\pi^2/(4L^2)$ $(n \geq 1)$, with orthonormal eigenfunctions $X_n(x) = \sqrt{2/L}\cos\lambda_n x$. For these eigenvalues, the solution of (10) is $T(t) = A\cos c\lambda_n t$, where A is an arbitrary constant. We have shown, therefore, that separated functions $A\cos c\lambda_n t\, X_n(x)$ for any constant A and any eigenvalues λ_n satisfy PDE (8a), boundary conditions (8b, c), and initial condition (8e). To satisfy initial condition (8d), we superpose separated functions and take

$$y(x, t) = \sum_{n=1}^{\infty} A_n \cos c\lambda_n t\, X_n(x), \tag{11}$$

where the A_n are constants. Condition (8d) now requires that

$$x(L - x) = \sum_{n=1}^{\infty} A_n X_n(x), \qquad 0 < x < L. \tag{12}$$

Consequently, the A_n are Fourier coefficients in the generalized Fourier series of $x(L - x)$; that is,

$$A_n = \int_0^L x(L - x)X_n(x)\,dx = \int_0^L x(L - x)\sqrt{\frac{2}{L}}\cos\frac{(2n-1)\pi x}{2L}\,dx$$

$$= \frac{16\sqrt{2}\,L^{5/2}(-1)^{n+1}}{(2n-1)^3\pi^3} - \frac{4\sqrt{2}\,L^{5/2}}{(2n-1)^2\pi^2}.$$

When these are substituted into (11), the formal solution is

$$y(x, t) = \frac{-8L^2}{\pi^3}\sum_{n=1}^{\infty}\frac{(2n-1)\pi + 4(-1)^n}{(2n-1)^3}\cos\frac{(2n-1)\pi ct}{2L}\cos\frac{(2n-1)\pi x}{2L}. \tag{13}$$

Each term in (13) is called a *normal mode of vibration* of the string. The first term, let us denote it by

$$H_1(x, t) = \frac{-8L^2(\pi - 4)}{\pi^3}\cos\frac{\pi ct}{2L}\cos\frac{\pi x}{2L} = 0.22L^2\cos\frac{\pi ct}{2L}\cos\frac{\pi x}{2L},$$

is called the *fundamental mode* or *first harmonic*. As a separated function, $H_1(x, t)$ satisfies (8a, b, c, e); at time $t = 0$, it reduces to $0.22L^2\cos[\pi x/(2L)]$. In other words, $H_1(x, t)$ describes displacements of a string identical to that in problem (8), except that the initial displacement is $0.22L^2\cos[\pi x/(2L)]$ instead of $x(L - x)$. Positions of this string for various values of t are shown in Figure 5.5. The string vibrates back and forth between the enveloping curves $\pm 0.22L^2\cos[\pi x/(2L)]$, always maintaining the shape of a cosine.

The second harmonic is the second term in (13),

$$H_2(x, t) = -0.13L^2\cos\frac{3\pi ct}{2L}\cos\frac{3\pi x}{2L};$$

it represents displacements of the same string were the initial displacement $-0.13L^2 \cos[3\pi x/(2L)]$. Positions of this string for various values of t are shown in Figure 5.6. The point at $x = L/3$ in the string remains motionless; it is called a *node* of $H_2(x, t)$.

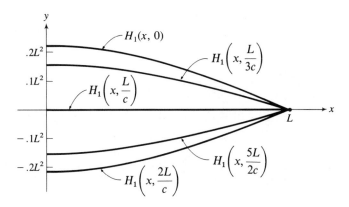

Figure 5.5

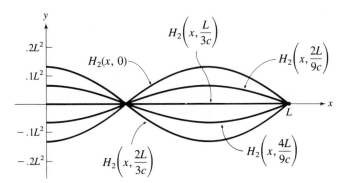

Figure 5.6

The third harmonic,

$$H_3(x, t) = -0.024L^2 \cos\frac{5\pi ct}{2L} \cos\frac{5\pi x}{2L},$$

is shown in Figure 5.7. It has two nodes, one at $x = L/5$ and the other at $x = 3L/5$.

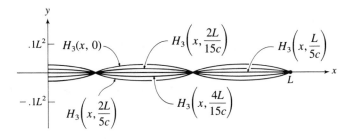

Figure 5.7

Solution (13) of problem (8) is the sum of all its harmonics. Because A_n decreases rapidly with increasing n, lower harmonics are more significant than higher ones.

We are now in a position to consider the general homogeneous initial boundary value problem

$$\frac{\partial^2 V}{\partial x^2} = p\frac{\partial^2 V}{\partial t^2} + q\frac{\partial V}{\partial t} + sV, \qquad 0 < x < L, \qquad t > 0, \qquad \text{(14a)}$$

$$-l_1\frac{\partial V}{\partial x} + h_1 V = 0, \qquad x = 0, \qquad t > 0, \qquad \text{(14b)}$$

$$l_2\frac{\partial V}{\partial x} + h_2 V = 0, \qquad x = L, \qquad t > 0, \qquad \text{(14c)}$$

$$V(x,0) = f(x), \qquad 0 < x < L, \qquad \text{(14d)}$$

$$V_t(x,0) = g(x), \qquad 0 < x < L. \qquad \text{(14e)}$$

It is said to be homogeneous because the PDE and boundary conditions are homogeneous. Problem (14) includes as special cases the following problems from Chapter 1:

(1) If $V(x,t) = U(x,t)$, $p = s = 0$, and $q = k^{-1}$, then (14) is the one-dimensional heat conduction problem with no internal heat generation but with heat transfer at ends $x = 0$ and $x = L$ into or from media at temperature zero. In this case, initial condition (14e) would be absent.

(2) If $V(x,t) = y(x,t)$, $p = \rho\tau^{-1}$ (or ρE^{-1}), $q = \beta\tau^{-1}$, and $s = k\tau^{-1}$, then (14) is the one-dimensional vibration problem with a damping force proportional to velocity and a restoring force proportional to displacement.

When a function separated in the form $V(x,t) = X(x)T(t)$ is substituted into (14a),

$$X''T = pXT'' + qXT' + sXT$$

or $\qquad \dfrac{X''}{X} = \dfrac{pT'' + qT' + sT}{T} = \alpha = \text{constant independent of } x \text{ and } t.$

This separation, together with boundary conditions (14b, c), leads to a Sturm-Liouville system in $X(x)$,

$$X'' - \alpha X = 0, \qquad 0 < x < L, \qquad \text{(15a)}$$

$$-l_1 X' + h_1 X = 0, \qquad x = 0, \qquad \text{(15b)}$$

$$l_2 X' + h_2 X = 0, \qquad x = L, \qquad \text{(15c)}$$

and an ODE in $T(t)$,

$$pT'' + qT' + (s - \alpha)T = 0, \qquad t > 0. \qquad \text{(16)}$$

System (15) is precisely Sturm-Liouville system (15) in Chapter 4. When we set $\alpha = -\lambda^2$ ($\lambda \geq 0$) (since eigenvalues of a proper Sturm-Liouville system must be nonnegative), eigenvalues λ_n and orthonormal eigenfunctions $X_n(x) = X(\lambda_n, x)$ are as listed in Table 4.1.

When $p = 0$, ODE (16) has general solution

$$T(t) = ce^{-(s + \lambda_n^2)t/q}, \tag{17}$$

where c is a constant. We have shown, therefore, that separated functions

$$V(x, t) = X(t)T(t) = ce^{-(s + \lambda_n^2)t/q} X_n(x),$$

for any constant c, and any eigenvalue λ_n are solutions of PDE (14a) and boundary conditions (14b, c). There is but one initial condition when $p = 0$, namely (14d), and to satisfy it, we superpose separated functions (the PDE and boundary conditions being linear and homogeneous) and take

$$V(x, t) = \sum_{n=1}^{\infty} c_n X_n(x) e^{-(s + \lambda_n^2)t/q}, \tag{18}$$

where the c_n are constants. Initial condition (14d) now implies that the c_n must satisfy

$$f(x) = \sum_{n=1}^{\infty} c_n X_n(x), \qquad 0 < x < L. \tag{19}$$

The constants c_n are therefore Fourier coefficients in the generalized Fourier series of $f(x)$,

$$c_n = \int_0^L f(x) X_n(x) \, dx. \tag{20}$$

The formal solution of (14) for $p = 0$ is therefore (18) with the c_n defined by (20).

When $p \neq 0$, ODE (16) has general solution

$$T(t) = c\phi_1(t) + d\phi_2(t), \tag{21}$$

where $\phi_1(t)$ and $\phi_2(t)$ are independent solutions of (16) and c and d are arbitrary constants. In this case, separated functions

$$V(x, t) = X(x)T(t) = X_n(x)\{c\phi_1(t) + d\phi_2(t)\},$$

for any constants c and d and any eigenvalue λ_n, are solutions of PDE (14a) and boundary conditions (14b, c). To satisfy the initial conditions, we superpose separated functions and take

$$V(x, t) = \sum_{n=1}^{\infty} X_n(x)\{c_n \phi_1(t) + d_n \phi_2(t)\}, \tag{22}$$

where c_n and d_n are constants. Initial conditions (14d, e) now imply that the c_n and d_n must satisfy

$$f(x) = \sum_{n=1}^{\infty} X_n(x)\{c_n \phi_1(0) + d_n \phi_2(0)\}, \qquad 0 < x < L \tag{23a}$$

and

$$g(x) = \sum_{n=1}^{\infty} X_n(x)\{c_n \phi_1'(0) + d_n \phi_2'(0)\}, \qquad 0 < x < L. \tag{23b}$$

If we multiply (23a) by $\phi_2'(0)$, multiply (23b) by $\phi_2(0)$, and subtract,

$$\phi_2'(0)f(x) - \phi_2(0)g(x) = \sum_{n=1}^{\infty} c_n\{\phi_1(0)\phi_2'(0) - \phi_1'(0)\phi_2(0)\} X_n(x). \tag{24}$$

This equation implies that $c_n\{\phi_1(0)\phi_2'(0) - \phi_1'(0)\phi_2(0)\}$ must be the Fourier coefficients in the generalized Fourier series of $\phi_2'(0)f(x) - \phi_2(0)g(x)$ in terms of $X_n(x)$ and are therefore defined by equation (20b) of Chapter 4:

$$c_n\{\phi_1(0)\phi_2'(0) - \phi_1'(0)\phi_2(0)\} = \int_0^L \{\phi_2'(0)f(x) - \phi_2(0)g(x)\}X_n(x)\,dx. \tag{25}$$

[Equation (25) can also be obtained by multiplying (24) by $X_m(x)$ and integrating with respect to x from $x = 0$ to $x = L$.] Thus,

$$c_n = \frac{1}{\phi_1(0)\phi_2'(0) - \phi_1'(0)\phi_2(0)} \int_0^L \{\phi_2'(0)f(x) - \phi_2(0)g(x)\}X_n(x)\,dx. \tag{26}$$

Similarly, it can be shown that

$$d_n = \frac{1}{\phi_1'(0)\phi_2(0) - \phi_1(0)\phi_2'(0)} \int_0^L \{\phi_1'(0)f(x) - \phi_1(0)g(x)\}X_n(x)\,dx. \tag{27}$$

The formal solution of (14) for $p \neq 0$ is therefore (22), where c_n and d_n are defined by (26) and (27).

We have demonstrated that separation of variables can be used to solve initial boundary value problems of form (14) and therefore, as special cases, problems (1) and (2) following (14). In fact, (18) and (22) represent formulas for solutions of many of these problems. For example, to solve heat conduction problem (19) in Section 3.2, we could set $p = s = h_1 = h_2 = 0, l_1 = l_2 = 1$, and $q = k^{-1}$ in (14), delete initial condition (14e), and set $f(x) = x$. According to (18), the solution is

$$U(x, t) = \sum_{n=1}^{\infty} c_n e^{-k\lambda_n^2 t} X_n(x),$$

where
$$c_n = \int_0^L f(x)X_n(x)\,dx.$$

Eigenpairs are found in line 5 of Table 4.1:

$$\lambda_0 = 0 \leftrightarrow X_0(x) = \frac{1}{\sqrt{L}}, \qquad \lambda_n = \frac{n\pi}{L} \leftrightarrow \sqrt{\frac{2}{L}}\cos\frac{n\pi x}{L}.$$

With these,

$$c_0 = \int_0^L x\frac{1}{\sqrt{L}}\,dx = \frac{L^{3/2}}{2}, \qquad c_n = \int_0^L x\sqrt{\frac{2}{L}}\cos\frac{n\pi x}{L}\,dx = \frac{\sqrt{2}\,L^{3/2}[(-1)^n - 1]}{n^2\pi^2},$$

and therefore

$$U(x, t) = \frac{L^{3/2}}{2}\left(\frac{1}{\sqrt{L}}\right) + \sum_{n=1}^{\infty} \frac{\sqrt{2}\,L^{3/2}[(-1)^n - 1]}{n^2\pi^2} e^{-n^2\pi^2 kt/L^2}\sqrt{\frac{2}{L}}\cos\frac{n\pi x}{L}$$

$$= \frac{L}{2} - \frac{4L}{\pi^2}\sum_{n=1}^{\infty} \frac{1}{(2n-1)^2} e^{-(2n-1)^2\pi^2 kt/L^2}\cos\frac{(2n-1)\pi x}{L}.$$

This is solution (24) of problem (19) in Section 3.2.

We are not in the habit of recommending that you use results such as (18) and (22) as formulas. Formulas are fine for those who have mastered fundamentals and are now looking for shortcuts in solving large classes of problems. We prefer to regard our analysis of equation (14) as an illustration of the fact that any problem of this form can be solved by separation of variables. The procedure leading from problem (14) to either solution (18) or solution (22) should be used as a guideline for solving other problems—separate variables, obtain the appropriate Sturm-Liouville system, solve the system (perhaps by quoting Table 4.1), solve the ODE in $T(t)$, superpose separated functions, and apply the nonhomogeneous initial condition(s).

Exercises 5.2

Part A—Heat Conduction

1. (a) A homogeneous, isotropic rod with insulated sides has temperature $f(x) = L - x$, $0 \le x \le L$, at time $t = 0$. If, for time $t > 0$, the end $x = 0$ is insulated and the end $x = L$ is held at temperature $0°C$, find the temperature in the rod.

   (b) Find an expression (in series form) for the amount of heat leaving the end $x = L$ of the rod as a function of time t.

   (c) Sketch a graph of the function in (b) if $\kappa = 48$ W/mK, $k = 12 \times 10^{-6}$ m²/s, and $L = 1$ m.

2. What is the solution to Exercise 1(a) for an arbitrary initial temperature $f(x)$?

3. Let $U(x, t)$ denote temperature in the thin-wire problem (see Exercise 31 in Section 1.2) of a thin wire of length L lying along the x-axis. When the temperature of the surrounding medium is zero and there is no heat generation, $U(x, t)$ must satisfy the PDE

$$\frac{\partial U}{\partial t} = k\frac{\partial^2 U}{\partial x^2} - hU, \qquad 0 < x < L, \qquad t > 0,$$

   where $h > 0$ is a constant.

   (a) If the ends of the wire are insulated and the initial temperature distribution is denoted by some function $f(x)$, find and solve the initial boundary value problem for $U(x, t)$.

   (b) Compare the solution in (a) with that obtained when the lateral sides are also insulated.

4. Exercise 3 suggests the following result. The general homogeneous thin-wire problem (see Exercise 31 in Section 1.2) is

$$\frac{\partial U}{\partial t} = k\frac{\partial^2 U}{\partial x^2} - hU, \qquad 0 < x < L, \qquad t > 0,$$

$$-l_1\frac{\partial U}{\partial x} + h_1 U = 0, \qquad x = 0, \qquad t > 0,$$

$$l_2\frac{\partial U}{\partial x} + h_2 U = 0, \qquad x = L, \qquad t > 0,$$

$$U(x, 0) = f(x), \qquad 0 < x < L.$$

(Homogeneity requires an environmental temperature identically zero. Nonzero environmental temperatures and other nonhomogeneities are considered in the exercises in Section 6.2.) Show that the solution of this problem is always e^{-ht} times that of the corresponding problem when no heat transfer takes place over the surface of the wire.

Part B—Vibrations

5. (a) A taut string is given an initial displacement (at time $t = 0$) of $f(x)$, $0 \leq x \leq L$, and initial velocity $g(x)$, $0 \leq x \leq L$. If the ends $x = 0$ and $x = L$ of the string are fixed on the x-axis, find displacements of points in the string thereafter.

   (b) As functions of time, what are the amplitudes of the first, second, and third harmonics? Sketch graphs of these harmonics for various fixed values of t. Are frequencies of higher harmonics integer multiples of the frequency of the fundamental mode?

   (c) The nodes of a normal mode of vibration are those points that remain motionless for that mode. What are the nodes for the first three harmonics?

6. (a) A taut string is given an initial displacement (at time $t = 0$) of $f(x)$, $0 \leq x \leq L$, and initial velocity $g(x)$, $0 \leq x \leq L$. The end $x = 0$ is fixed on the x-axis, while the end $x = L$ is looped around a vertical support and can move thereon without friction. Find displacements in the string for $0 < x \leq L$ and $t > 0$.

   (b) Specialize the result in (a) when

$$f(x) = \begin{cases} x/10 & 0 \leq x \leq L/2 \\ (L - x)/10 & L/2 \leq x \leq L \end{cases}, \qquad g(x) \equiv 0.$$

   (c) Repeat (b) for $f(x) \equiv 0$ and $g(x) = x(L - x)$.

7. (a) Repeat Exercise 5(a) if an external force (per unit x-length) $F = -ky$ ($k > 0$) acts at each point in the string.

   (b) Compare the normal modes of vibration with those in Exercise 5.

8. Repeat Exercise 5(a) if an external force (per unit x-length) $F = -\beta \partial y / \partial t$ ($0 < \beta < 2\pi\rho c/L$) acts at every point on the string.

9. A taut string is given a displacement bx, b a constant, $0 \leq x \leq L$, and zero initial velocity. The end $x = 0$ is fixed on the x-axis, and the right end moves vertically but is restrained by a spring (constant k) that is unstretched on the x-axis (Figure 5.8).

Figure 5.8

   (a) Show that subsequent displacements of points on the string can be expressed in the form

$$y(x, t) = \frac{2b(kL + \tau)}{\tau} \sum_{n=1}^{\infty} \frac{(\tau^2 \lambda_n^2 + k^2) \sin \lambda_n L}{\lambda_n^2 [L(\tau^2 \lambda_n^2 + k^2) + k\tau]} \cos c\lambda_n t \sin \lambda_n x,$$

   where λ_n are the positive solutions of the equation

$$\cot \lambda L = \frac{-k}{\tau\lambda},$$

   τ is the constant tension in the string, and $c^2 = \tau/\rho$, where ρ is the constant density of the string.

(b) Reduce the expression in (a) to

$$y(x, t) = 2b(kL + \tau) \sum_{n=1}^{\infty} \frac{(-1)^{n+1}\sqrt{k^2 + \tau^2\lambda_n^2}}{\lambda_n[L(k^2 + \tau^2\lambda_n^2) + k\tau]} \cos c\lambda_n t \sin \lambda_n x.$$

10. A bar of uniform cross section and length L lies along the x-axis. Its left end is fixed at $x = 0$, and its right end is attached to a spring with constant k that is unstretched when the bar is unstrained (Figure 5.9). If at time $t = 0$ the bar is pulled to the right so that cross sections are displaced according to $f(x) = x/100$, then released from rest at this position, find subsequent displacements of cross sections.

Figure 5.9

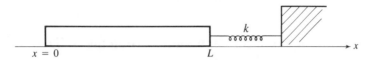

$x = 0$ $\qquad$ k $\qquad$ L $\qquad$ x

Equations (14a–e) describe displacements of a taut string when $p \neq 0$. Separation leads to a solution in form (22) with coefficients c_n and d_n given by (26) and (27). The normal modes of this solution are

$$H_n(x, t) = X_n(x)[c_n\phi_1(t) + d_n\phi_2(t)],$$

where $X_n(x)$ are the eigenfunctions in Table 4.1. Nodes of $H_n(x, t)$ are points that remain motionless for all t. They are the zeros of $X_n(x)$. In Exercises 11–16, we show that the number of nodes of the nth mode is exactly $n - 1$ (except when both ends of the string are looped around vertical supports and move freely without friction).

11. Show that when both ends are fixed on the x-axis, the distance between successive nodes is L/n, and hence there are $n - 1$ equally spaced nodes between $x = 0$ and $x = L$.

12. Show that when the end $x = 0$ is fixed on the x-axis and the end $x = L$ is looped around a vertical support and moves without friction thereon (a free end), there are $n - 1$ nodes between $x = 0$ and $x = L$. A similar result holds when the left end is free and the right end is fixed.

13. Verify that when both ends are free, the nth mode has n nodes.

14. (a) Verify that when the end $x = 0$ is fixed on the x-axis and the end $x = L$ satisfies a homogeneous Robin condition, nodes of the nth mode occur for $x_m = m\pi/\lambda_n$, $m > 0$ an integer.

    (b) Use Figure 4.3 to establish that eigenvalues λ_n satisfy

    $$\frac{(n-1)\pi}{L} < \lambda_n < \frac{n\pi}{L}.$$

    Use this to verify the existence of exactly $n - 1$ nodes. A similar result holds when the right end is fixed and the left end satisfies a homogeneous Robin condition.

15. (a) Verify that when end $x = 0$ is free and end $x = L$ satisfies a homogeneous Robin condition, nodes of the nth mode occur for $x_m = (2m - 1)\pi/(2\lambda_n)$, $m > 0$ an integer.

    (b) Establish the inequality

    $$\frac{(n-1)\pi}{L} < \lambda_n < \frac{(2n-1)\pi}{2L}$$

    for this case, and use it to verify that there are exactly $n - 1$ nodes. A similar result holds when the right end is free and the left end satisfies a homogeneous Robin condition.

16. The final case is when both ends of the string satisfy homogeneous Robin conditions, in which case $X_n(x)$ is given in line 1 of Table 4.1.

(a) Show that zeros of $X_n(x)$ occur for

$$x_m = \frac{m\pi}{\lambda_n} - \phi_n, \qquad m \text{ an integer},$$

where $\phi_n = \lambda_n^{-1} \operatorname{Tan}^{-1}(\lambda_n l_1/h_1)$.

(b) Establish the inequality in Exercise 15(b) and the fact that the difference between successive nodes is π/λ_n.

(c) Use the results in (b) to verify that there are exactly $n - 1$ nodes between $x = 0$ and $x = L$.

5.3 Homogeneous Boundary Value Problems in Two Variables

The Helmholtz equation on a rectangle $0 \le x \le L, 0 \le y \le L'$ takes the form

$$\frac{\partial^2 V}{\partial x^2} + \frac{\partial^2 V}{\partial y^2} - sV = 0, \qquad 0 < x < L, \qquad 0 < y < L' \tag{28a}$$

where s is some given constant. When $s = 0$, we obtain the extremely important special case of Laplace's equation. A boundary value problem accompanying either of these equations is said to be homogeneous if the boundary conditions on a pair of parallel sides are homogeneous. For example, the following conditions on $x = 0$ and $x = L$ yield a homogeneous problem:

$$V(0, y) = 0, \qquad 0 < y < L', \tag{28b}$$

$$\frac{\partial V(L, y)}{\partial x} = 0, \qquad 0 < y < L', \tag{28c}$$

$$V(x, 0) = f(x), \qquad 0 < x < L, \tag{28d}$$

$$V(x, L') = g(x), \qquad 0 < x < L. \tag{28e}$$

No real difficulty is encountered in the solution of problem (28) if (28b, c) are not homogeneous, if say,

$$V(0, y) = h(y), \qquad 0 < y < L', \tag{28f}$$

$$\frac{\partial V(L, y)}{\partial x} = k(y), \qquad 0 < y < L'. \tag{28g}$$

We simply use superposition to write $V(x, y) = V_1(x, y) + V_2(x, y)$, where V_1 and V_2 both satisfy PDE (28a) and the following boundary conditions:

$$V_1(0, y) = 0, \qquad 0 < y < L', \qquad V_2(0, y) = h(y), \qquad 0 < y < L',$$

$$\frac{\partial V_1(L, y)}{\partial x} = 0, \qquad 0 < y < L', \qquad \frac{\partial V_2(L, y)}{\partial x} = k(y), \qquad 0 < y < L',$$

$$V_1(x, 0) = f(x), \qquad 0 < x < L, \qquad V_2(x, 0) = 0, \qquad 0 < x < L,$$

$$V_1(x, L') = g(x), \qquad 0 < x < L; \qquad V_2(x, L') = 0, \qquad 0 < x < L.$$

In other words, the nonhomogeneous boundary value problem (28a, d, e, f, g) can be divided into two homogeneous problems. It follows, then, that separation of variables as illustrated here in problem (28a–e) is typical for all boundary value problems on rectangles (provided the PDE is homogeneous).

Substitution of a separated function $V(x, y) = X(x)Y(y)$ into (28a, b, c) leads to a Sturm-Liouville system in $X(x)$,

$$X'' + \lambda^2 X = 0, \qquad 0 < x < L,$$
$$X(0) = 0 = X'(L),$$

and an ODE in $Y(y)$,

$$Y'' - (s + \lambda^2)Y = 0, \qquad 0 < y < L'.$$

Eigenpairs of the Sturm-Liouville system are $\lambda_n^2 = (2n - 1)^2 \pi^2 / (4L^2)$ and $X_n(x) = \sqrt{2/L} \sin \lambda_n x$. Corresponding solutions for $Y(y)$ are $Y(y) = A \cosh \sqrt{s + \lambda_n^2}\, y + B \sinh \sqrt{s + \lambda_n^2}\, y$. We superpose separated functions and take

$$V(x, y) = \sum_{n=1}^{\infty} [A_n \cosh \sqrt{s + \lambda_n^2}\, y + B_n \sinh \sqrt{s + \lambda_n^2}\, y] X_n(x). \qquad \text{(29a)}$$

Boundary conditions (28d, e) require that

$$f(x) = \sum_{n=1}^{\infty} A_n X_n(x), \qquad 0 < x < L$$

and $\quad g(x) = \sum_{n=1}^{\infty} [A_n \cosh \sqrt{s + \lambda_n^2}\, L' + B_n \sinh \sqrt{s + \lambda_n^2}\, L'] X_n(x), \qquad 0 < x < L.$

These imply that

$$A_n = \int_0^L f(x) X_n(x)\, dx \qquad \text{(29b)}$$

and $\qquad A_n \cosh \sqrt{s + \lambda_n^2}\, L' + B_n \sinh \sqrt{s + \lambda_n^2}\, L' = \int_0^L g(x) X_n(x)\, dx \qquad \text{(29c)}$

or $\qquad B_n = \dfrac{1}{\sinh \sqrt{s + \lambda_n^2}\, L'} \left(\int_0^L g(x) X_n(x)\, dx - A_n \cosh \sqrt{s + \lambda_n^2}\, L' \right). \qquad \text{(29d)}$

The formal solution of (28a–e) is therefore

$$V(x, y) = \sqrt{\frac{2}{L}} \sum_{n=1}^{\infty} [A_n \cosh \sqrt{s + \lambda_n^2}\, y + B_n \sinh \sqrt{s + \lambda_n^2}\, y] \sin \lambda_n x, \qquad \text{(30)}$$

where A_n and B_n are calculated in (29b, d).

As a specific example, suppose $s = 0$, so that (28a) becomes Laplace's equation, and suppose that $f(x) = 0$ and $g(x) = x$. One possible interpretation of problem (28) would be that for determining steady-state temperature in a rectangle in which sides $x = 0$ and $y = 0$ are held at temperature $0°C$, side $x = L$ is insulated, and $y = L'$ has temperature x. The solution to this problem is

$$V(x, y) = \sqrt{\frac{2}{L}} \sum_{n=1}^{\infty} B_n \sinh \lambda_n y \sin \frac{(2n - 1)\pi x}{2L},$$

where $\quad B_n = \dfrac{1}{\sinh \lambda_n L'} \int_0^L x \sqrt{\dfrac{2}{L}} \sin \dfrac{(2n - 1)\pi x}{2L}\, dx = \dfrac{4\sqrt{2}\, L^{3/2}(-1)^{n+1}}{(2n - 1)^2 \pi^2 \sinh \lambda_n L'}.$

Thus,

$$V(x, y) = \sqrt{\frac{2}{L}} \sum_{n=1}^{\infty} \frac{4\sqrt{2}\,L^{3/2}(-1)^{n+1}}{(2n-1)^2 \pi^2 \sinh \lambda_n L'} \sinh \lambda_n y \sin \frac{(2n-1)\pi x}{2L}$$

$$= \frac{8L}{\pi^2} \sum_{n=1}^{\infty} \frac{(-1)^{n+1}}{(2n-1)^2 \sinh\left[(2n-1)\pi L'/(2L)\right]} \sinh \frac{(2n-1)\pi y}{2L} \sin \frac{(2n-1)\pi x}{2L}.$$

We now consider Laplace's equation in a circle of radius a with a Dirichlet boundary condition (Figure 5.10):

$$\frac{\partial^2 V}{\partial r^2} + \frac{1}{r}\frac{\partial V}{\partial r} + \frac{1}{r^2}\frac{\partial^2 V}{\partial \theta^2} = 0, \qquad 0 < r < a, \qquad -\pi < \theta \le \pi, \tag{31a}$$

$$V(a, \theta) = f(\theta), \qquad -\pi < \theta \le \pi. \tag{31b}$$

The solution of this problem describes a number of physical phenomena. It represents (axially symmetric) electrostatic potential in a source-free cylinder $r \le a$, with potential prescribed on the surface of the cylinder $r = a$ as $f(\theta)$. Also described is steady-state temperature in a thin circular plate, insulated at top and bottom, with circumferential temperature $f(\theta)$. Finally, $V(r, \theta)$ represents static deflections of a circular membrane subjected to no external forces but with edge deflections $f(\theta)$.

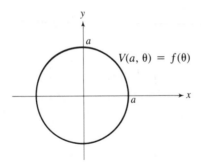

Figure 5.10

When we substitute a separated function $V(r, \theta) = R(r)\Theta(\theta)$ into (31a) and multiply by $r^2/V(r, \theta)$, separation results:

$$\frac{r^2 R''}{R} + \frac{rR'}{R} = -\frac{\Theta''}{\Theta} = \lambda = \text{constant.}$$

Thus, $R(r)$ and $\Theta(\theta)$ must satisfy the ODEs

$$r^2 R'' + rR' - \lambda R = 0, \qquad \Theta'' + \lambda\Theta = 0.$$

Now, $V(r, \theta)$ must be 2π-periodic in θ, as must its first derivative with respect to θ; that is,

$$V(r, \theta + 2\pi) = V(r, \theta),$$

$$\frac{\partial V(r, \theta + 2\pi)}{\partial \theta} = \frac{\partial V(r, \theta)}{\partial \theta}.$$

These imply that $\Theta(\theta)$ and $\Theta'(\theta)$ must also be periodic. It follows that $\Theta(\theta)$ must satisfy the periodic Sturm-Liouville system

$$\Theta'' + \lambda\Theta = 0, \qquad -\pi < \theta < \pi,$$

$$\Theta(-\pi) = \Theta(\pi),$$

$$\Theta'(-\pi) = \Theta'(\pi).$$

According to Example 2 in Section 4.1, eigenvalues of this system are $\lambda_n = n^2$ ($n \geq 0$), with a single eigenfunction, $1/\sqrt{2\pi}$, corresponding to $\lambda_0 = 0$ and a pair of eigenfunctions, $(1/\sqrt{\pi})\cos n\theta$ and $(1/\sqrt{\pi})\sin n\theta$ corresponding to $\lambda_n = n^2$ ($n > 0$).

The differential equation in $R(r)$ is a Cauchy-Euler equation, which can be solved (in the case in which $n > 0$) by setting $R(r) = r^m$, m an unknown constant. This results in the general solution

$$R(r) = \begin{cases} A + B\ln r & n = 0 \\ Ar^n + Br^{-n} & n \geq 1 \end{cases}. \tag{32}$$

For these solutions to remain bounded near $r = 0$, we must set $B = 0$. Separated functions have now been determined to be $A/\sqrt{2\pi}$, corresponding to $\lambda_0 = 0$, and $(Ar^n/\sqrt{\pi})\cos n\theta$ and $(Ar^n/\sqrt{\pi})\sin n\theta$, corresponding to $\lambda_n = n^2$ ($n > 0$). To satisfy boundary condition (31b), we superpose separated functions and take

$$V(r, \theta) = \frac{A_0}{\sqrt{2\pi}} + \sum_{n=1}^{\infty} r^n \left(A_n \frac{\cos n\theta}{\sqrt{\pi}} + B_n \frac{\sin n\theta}{\sqrt{\pi}} \right). \tag{33a}$$

The boundary condition requires that

$$f(\theta) = \frac{A_0}{\sqrt{2\pi}} + \sum_{n=1}^{\infty} a^n \left(A_n \frac{\cos n\theta}{\sqrt{\pi}} + B_n \frac{\sin n\theta}{\sqrt{\pi}} \right), \qquad -\pi < \theta \leq \pi,$$

from which

$$A_0 = \int_{-\pi}^{\pi} f(\theta) \frac{1}{\sqrt{2\pi}} \, d\theta, \qquad A_n = \frac{1}{a^n} \int_{-\pi}^{\pi} f(\theta) \frac{\cos n\theta}{\sqrt{\pi}} \, d\theta,$$

$$B_n = \frac{1}{a^n} \int_{-\pi}^{\pi} f(\theta) \frac{\sin n\theta}{\sqrt{\pi}} \, d\theta \tag{33b}$$

[see equations (21) in Section 4.2, with $L = \pi$ and x replaced by θ]. The formal solution of problem (31) is now complete; it is (33a) with coefficients defined in (33b). An integral expression for the solution can be obtained by substituting coefficients A_n and B_n into (33a). In order to keep variable θ in (33a) distinct from the variable of integration in (33b), we replace θ by u in (33b):

$$V(r, \theta) = \frac{1}{2\pi} \int_{-\pi}^{\pi} f(u) \, du$$

$$+ \sum_{n=1}^{\infty} \frac{1}{\pi} \left(\frac{r}{a} \right)^n \left(\cos n\theta \int_{-\pi}^{\pi} f(u) \cos nu \, du + \sin n\theta \int_{-\pi}^{\pi} f(u) \sin nu \, du \right)$$

$$= \frac{1}{\pi} \left(\frac{1}{2} \int_{-\pi}^{\pi} f(u) \, du + \sum_{n=1}^{\infty} \left(\frac{r}{a} \right)^n \int_{-\pi}^{\pi} f(u) \cos n(\theta - u) \, du \right). \tag{34}$$

If we interchange the order of integration and summation,

$$V(r, \theta) = \frac{1}{\pi} \int_{-\pi}^{\pi} \left[\frac{1}{2} + \sum_{n=1}^{\infty} \left(\frac{r}{a} \right)^n \cos n(\theta - u) \right] f(u) \, du.$$

The series can be summed in closed form by noting that $\cos n(\theta - u)$ is the real part of a complex exponential, $\cos n(\theta - u) = \mathrm{Re}(e^{in(\theta - u)})$,

$$\sum_{n=1}^{\infty} \left(\frac{r}{a} \right)^n \cos n(\theta - u) = \sum_{n=1}^{\infty} \left(\frac{r}{a} \right)^n \mathrm{Re}[e^{in(\theta - u)}] = \mathrm{Re}\left[\sum_{n=1}^{\infty} \left(\frac{r}{a} e^{i(\theta - u)} \right)^n \right].$$

Since the right side is a geometric series with common ratio $(r/a)e^{i(\theta - u)}$, converging therefore when $r < a$, we may write

$$\sum_{n=1}^{\infty} \left(\frac{r}{a} \right)^n \cos n(\theta - u) = \mathrm{Re}\left(\frac{(r/a)e^{i(\theta - u)}}{1 - (r/a)e^{i(\theta - u)}} \right) = \mathrm{Re}\left(\frac{r[\cos(\theta - u) + i\sin(\theta - u)]}{a - r[\cos(\theta - u) + i\sin(\theta - u)]} \right)$$

$$= \frac{ar \cos(\theta - u) - r^2}{a^2 + r^2 - 2ar \cos(\theta - u)}. \tag{35}$$

Consequently,

$$V(r, \theta) = \frac{1}{\pi} \int_{-\pi}^{\pi} \left(\frac{1}{2} + \frac{ar \cos(\theta - u) - r^2}{a^2 + r^2 - 2ar \cos(\theta - u)} \right) f(u) \, du$$

$$= \frac{a^2 - r^2}{2\pi} \int_{-\pi}^{\pi} \frac{f(u)}{a^2 + r^2 - 2ar \cos(\theta - u)} \, du. \tag{36}$$

This result is called *Poisson's integral formula*. It expresses the solution to Laplace's equation inside the circle $r \le a$ in terms of its values on the circle. Immediate consequences of the Poisson integral formula are the following two results.

Theorem 1

When $V(r, \theta)$ is the solution to Dirichlet's problem for Laplace's equation in a circle $r \le a$, the value $V(0, \theta)$ at the center of the circle is the average of its values on $r = a$.

Proof: According to (36), the value of $V(r, \theta)$ at $r = 0$ is

$$V(0, \theta) = \frac{a^2}{2\pi} \int_{-\pi}^{\pi} \frac{f(u)}{a^2} \, du = \frac{1}{2\pi a} \int_{-\pi}^{\pi} f(\theta) a \, d\theta,$$

the average value of $f(\theta)$ on $r = a$.   ∎

Corollary

When $V(r, \theta)$ is the solution to Dirichlet's problem for Laplace's equation in a circle $r \le a$, the average value of $V(r, \theta)$ around every circle centered at $r = 0$ is $V(0, \theta)$.

Exercises 5.3

1. (a) Solve Exercise 17 from Section 3.2.
   (b) Find an approximate value for the potential at the center of the plate if the plate is square.

2. (a) Find the steady-state temperature $U(x, y)$ inside a plate $0 \le x, y \le L$ if the sides $x = 0$, $y = 0$, and $x = L$ are all insulated and the boundary condition on $y = L$ is $\partial U(x, L)/\partial y = f(x)$. Can $f(x)$ be specified arbitrarily?

   (b) What is the solution when $f(x) = (L - 2x)/2$ and the temperature at the center of the plate is $50°C$?

   (c) What is the solution when $f(x) = x(L - x)$?

3. (a) Find the steady-state temperature $U(x, y)$ inside a rectangular plate $0 \le x \le L, 0 \le y \le L'$ if the sides $y = 0$ and $y = L'$ are insulated; the temperature along $x = L$ is prescribed by the function $f_2(y)$, $0 < y < L'$; and the boundary condition along $x = 0$ is $\partial U(0, y)/\partial x = f_1(y)$, $0 < y < L'$.

   (b) Simplify the solution in (a) when $f_1(y)$ and $f_2(y)$ are constants.

4. A membrane is stretched tightly over the rectangle $0 \le x \le L, 0 \le y \le L'$. Its edges are given deflections that are described by the following boundary conditions:

$$z(0, y) = f_1(y), \qquad 0 < y < L',$$
$$z(L, y) = f_2(y), \qquad 0 < y < L',$$
$$z(x, 0) = g_1(x), \qquad 0 < x < L,$$
$$z(x, L') = g_2(x), \qquad 0 < x < L.$$

Find static deflections of the membrane when all external forces are negligible compared with tensions in the membrane.

5. Solve Laplace's equation in the rectangle $0 \le x \le L, 0 \le y \le L'$ subject to the following boundary conditions:

$$V(0, y) = f_1(y), \qquad 0 < y < L',$$
$$V_x(L, y) = f_2(y), \qquad 0 < y < L',$$
$$V_y(x, 0) = 0, \qquad 0 < x < L,$$
$$V(x, L') = g(x), \qquad 0 < x < L.$$

6. (a) Solve Laplace's equation in a semicircle $r \le a, 0 \le \theta \le \pi$ when the unknown function is zero on the diameter and $f(\theta)$ on the semicircle.

   (b) Simplify the solution when $f(\theta) \equiv 1$. Evaluate this solution along the y-axis.

7. (a) Along the circle $r = a$, a solution $V(r, \theta)$ of Laplace's equation must take on the value 1 for $0 < \theta < \pi$ and 0 for $-\pi < \theta < 0$. Show that the series solution for $V(r, \theta)$ is

$$V(r, \theta) = \frac{1}{2} + \frac{2}{\pi} \sum_{n=1}^{\infty} \frac{(r/a)^{2n-1}}{2n-1} \sin(2n-1)\theta.$$

A closed-form solution of this problem is found in Exercise 19.

   (b) What is the value of $V(r, \theta)$ along the x-axis?

8. Find the steady-state temperature inside the quarter-circle $r \le a, 0 \le \theta \le \pi/2$ if its straight edges are insulated and the temperature along the curved edge is $\sin \theta$.

9. (a) Solve boundary value problem (31) when boundary condition (31b) is of Neumann type:

$$\frac{\partial V(a, \theta)}{\partial r} = f(\theta), \qquad -\pi < \theta \le \pi.$$

(b) Show that the solution can be expressed in the form

$$V(r, \theta) = C - \frac{a}{2\pi} \int_{-\pi}^{\pi} f(u) \ln[a^2 + r^2 - 2ar\cos(\theta - u)] \, du,$$

where C is an arbitrary constant. This result is called Dini's integral.

10. (a) Solve boundary value problem (31) when boundary condition (31b) is of Robin type:

$$l\frac{\partial V}{\partial r} + hV = f(\theta), \qquad r = a, \qquad -\pi < \theta \le \pi.$$

11. What is the solution to boundary value problem (31) in the exterior region $r > a$ if

(a) $V(r, \theta)$ is required to be bounded at infinity [i.e., $V(r, \theta)$ must be bounded for large r]?

(b) $V(r, \theta)$ must vanish at infinity?

12. Solve the boundary value problem of Exercise 11 when the boundary condition is of Neumann type:

$$-\frac{\partial V(a, \theta)}{\partial r} = f(\theta), \qquad -\pi < \theta \le \pi.$$

13. Solve the boundary value problem of Exercise 11 when the boundary condition is of Robin type:

$$-l\frac{\partial V}{\partial r} + hV = f(\theta), \qquad r = a, \qquad -\pi < \theta \le \pi.$$

14. Solve Laplace's equation inside a circular annulus $a < r < R$ with Dirichlet boundary conditions

$$V(a, \theta) = f_1(\theta), \qquad V(R, \theta) = f_2(\theta), \qquad -\pi < \theta \le \pi.$$

15. Solve Exercise 14 when the boundary conditions are Neumann:

$$-\frac{\partial V(a, \theta)}{\partial r} = f_1(\theta), \qquad \frac{\partial V(R, \theta)}{\partial r} = f_2(\theta), \qquad -\pi < \theta \le \pi.$$

16. Solve Exercise 14 when the boundary conditions are Robin:

$$-l_1\frac{\partial V(a, \theta)}{\partial r} + h_1 V(a, \theta) = f_1(\theta), \qquad -\pi < \theta \le \pi,$$

$$l_2\frac{\partial V(R, \theta)}{\partial r} + h_2 V(R, \theta) = f_2(\theta), \qquad -\pi < \theta \le \pi.$$

17. (a) A circular membrane of radius R is in a steady-state position with radial lines $\theta = 0$ and $\theta = \alpha$ clamped on the xy-plane. If the displacement of the edge $r = R$ is $f(\theta)$ for $0 < \theta < \alpha$, find the displacement in the sector $0 < \theta < \alpha$.

(b) Take the limit of your answer in (a) as $\alpha \to 2\pi$. What does this function represent physically?

(c) What is the answer in (b) if $f(\theta) = \sin(\theta/2)$?

When $f(\theta)$ in the boundary condition for Dirichlet problem (31) is piecewise constant, Poisson's integral can be evaluated analytically. We illustrate this in Exercises 18–20.

18. Show that

$$\int \frac{1}{a^2 + r^2 - 2ar\cos(\theta - u)} \, du = \frac{-2}{a^2 - r^2} \text{Tan}^{-1}\left[\frac{a + r}{a - r}\tan\left(\frac{\theta - u}{2}\right)\right] + C,$$

provided $u \ne \theta \pm \pi$.

19. (a) When

$$f(\theta) = \begin{cases} 0 & -\pi < \theta < 0 \\ 1 & 0 < \theta < \pi \end{cases},$$

use the result of Exercise 18 to obtain the following solution for problem (31):

$$V(r,\theta) = \begin{cases} \dfrac{1}{\pi}\mathrm{Tan}^{-1}\left[\dfrac{a+r}{a-r}\tan\left(\dfrac{\theta}{2}\right)\right] + \dfrac{1}{\pi}\mathrm{Tan}^{-1}\left[\dfrac{a+r}{a-r}\cot\left(\dfrac{\theta}{2}\right)\right] & 0 < \theta < \pi \\[4mm] 1 + \dfrac{1}{\pi}\mathrm{Tan}^{-1}\left[\dfrac{a+r}{a-r}\tan\left(\dfrac{\theta}{2}\right)\right] + \dfrac{1}{\pi}\mathrm{Tan}^{-1}\left[\dfrac{a+r}{a-r}\cot\left(\dfrac{\theta}{2}\right)\right] & -\pi < \theta < 0. \end{cases}$$

(b) For $\theta = 0$ and $\theta = \pi$, the solution in (a) must be regarded in the sense of limits as $\theta \to 0^+$ and $\theta \to \pi^-$. What are $V(r,0)$ and $V(r,\pi)$?

(c) Use trigonometry to combine the description for $V(r,\theta)$ in (a) into the single expression

$$V(r,\theta) = \frac{1}{2} + \frac{1}{\pi}\mathrm{Tan}^{-1}\left(\frac{2ar\sin\theta}{a^2 - r^2}\right).$$

(d) Solve the expression in (c) for r in terms of V and θ, and use the result to plot equipotential curves for $V = 1/8, 1/4, 3/8, 5/8, 3/4$, and $7/8$.

20. Use the result of Exercise 19 to solve problem (31) when

$$f(\theta) = \begin{cases} V_2 & -\pi < \theta < 0 \\ V_1 & 0 < \theta < \pi \end{cases}.$$

21. Find expressions similar to those in Exercise 19(a) when the boundary condition is

$$f(\theta) = \begin{cases} 0, & -\pi < \theta < 0 \\ 1, & 0 < \theta < \pi/2. \\ 0, & \pi/2 < \theta \le \pi \end{cases}$$

5.4 Homogeneous Problems in Three and Four Variables (Cartesian Coordinates Only)

In this section we extend the technique of separation of variables to homogeneous problems in two and three space variables, but confine our discussions to rectangles $0 \le x \le L, 0 \le y \le L'$ in the xy-plane and boxes $0 \le x \le L, 0 \le y \le L', 0 \le z \le L''$ in space. In other words, boundaries of the region under consideration must be coordinate curves $x = $ constant and $y = $ constant in the xy-plane and coordinate surfaces $x = $ constant, $y = $ constant, and $z = $ constant in space. This is an inherent restriction on the method of separation of variables for any problem whatsoever, be it initial boundary value or boundary value; be it two- or three-dimensional; be it in Cartesian, polar, cylindrical, or spherical coordinates. Separation of variables requires a region bounded by coordinate curves or surfaces; then and only then will separation of variables lead to Sturm-Liouville systems in space variables.

First consider the homogeneous initial boundary value problem

$$\frac{\partial^2 z}{\partial t^2} = c^2 \left(\frac{\partial^2 z}{\partial x^2} + \frac{\partial^2 z}{\partial y^2} \right), \qquad 0 < x < L, \qquad 0 < y < L', \qquad t > 0, \qquad \text{(37a)}$$

$$z(0, y, t) = 0, \qquad 0 < y < L', \qquad t > 0, \tag{37b}$$

$$z(L, y, t) = 0, \qquad 0 < y < L', \qquad t > 0, \tag{37c}$$

$$z(x, 0, t) = 0, \qquad 0 < x < L, \qquad t > 0, \tag{37d}$$

$$z(x, L', t) = 0, \qquad 0 < x < L, \qquad t > 0, \tag{37e}$$

$$z(x, y, 0) = f(x, y), \qquad 0 < x < L, \qquad 0 < y < L', \tag{37f}$$

$$z_t(x, y, 0) = 0, \qquad 0 < x < L, \qquad 0 < y < L'. \tag{37g}$$

Physically described are the vertical oscillations of a rectangular membrane that is released from rest at time $t = 0$ with displacement described by $f(x, y)$. Its edges are fixed on the xy-plane for all time, and no external forces act on the membrane.

If a function separated in the form $z(x, y, t) = X(x)Y(y)T(t)$ is substituted into (37a), the x-dependence can be separated from the y- and t-dependence:

$$\frac{X''}{X} = -\frac{Y''}{Y} + \frac{T''}{c^2 T} = \alpha = \text{constant independent of } x, y, \text{ and } t.$$

When this is combined with boundary conditions (37b, c), the Sturm-Liouville system

$$X'' - \alpha X = 0, \qquad 0 < x < L, \tag{38a}$$

$$X(0) = X(L) = 0 \tag{38b}$$

is obtained. Since eigenvalues of a proper Sturm-Liouville system must be nonnegative, we set $\alpha = -\lambda^2$ ($\lambda \geq 0$), in which case eigenvalues are $\lambda_n^2 = n^2 \pi^2 / L^2$, with normalized eigenfunctions $X_n(x) = \sqrt{2/L} \sin(n\pi x/L)$.

We continue to separate the equation in $Y(y)$ and $T(t)$:

$$\frac{Y''}{Y} = \frac{T''}{c^2 T} + \lambda_n^2 = \beta = \text{constant independent of } y \text{ and } t.$$

Combine this with boundary conditions (38d, e), and the system

$$Y'' - \beta Y = 0, \qquad 0 < y < L', \tag{39a}$$

$$Y(0) = Y(L') = 0 \tag{39b}$$

results. With $\beta = -\mu^2$, the eigenvalues of this proper Sturm-Liouville system are $\mu_m^2 = m^2 \pi^2 / L'^2$, with orthonormal eigenfunctions $Y_m(y) = \sqrt{2/L'} \sin(m\pi y/L')$.

The ordinary differential equation

$$T'' + c^2 (\lambda_n^2 + \mu_m^2) T = 0$$

has general solution $A \cos c\sqrt{\lambda_n^2 + \mu_m^2}\, t + B \sin c\sqrt{\lambda_n^2 + \mu_m^2}\, t$. But initial condition (37g) requires that $B = 0$, and therefore

$$T(t) = A \cos c\sqrt{\lambda_n^2 + \mu_m^2}\, t.$$

We have determined that separated functions

$$X_n(x)\,Y_m(y)\,T(t) = A\sqrt{\frac{2}{L}}\sin\frac{n\pi x}{L}\sqrt{\frac{2}{L'}}\sin\frac{m\pi y}{L'}\cos c\sqrt{\lambda_n^2 + \mu_m^2}\,t$$

for any positive integers m and n and any constant A, satisfy PDE (37a), boundary conditions (37b–e), and initial condition (37g). Since these conditions are all linear and homogeneous, we superpose separated functions in an attempt to satisfy the initial displacement condition,

$$z(x, y, t) = \sum_{m=1}^{\infty}\sum_{n=1}^{\infty} A_{mn}\sqrt{\frac{2}{L}}\sin\frac{n\pi x}{L}\sqrt{\frac{2}{L'}}\sin\frac{m\pi y}{L'}\cos c\sqrt{\lambda_n^2 + \mu_m^2}\,t, \qquad \textbf{(40a)}$$

where A_{mn} are constants. Condition (37f) requires that

$$f(x, y) = \sum_{m=1}^{\infty}\sum_{n=1}^{\infty} A_{mn}\sqrt{\frac{2}{L}}\sin\frac{n\pi x}{L}\sqrt{\frac{2}{L'}}\sin\frac{m\pi y}{L'}, \qquad 0 < x < L, \qquad 0 < y < L'.$$

If we multiply this equation by $\sqrt{2/L}\sin(k\pi x/L)$, integrate with respect to x from $x = 0$ to $x = L$, and interchange orders of summation and integration on the right, orthogonality of the eigenfunctions $\sqrt{2/L}\sin(n\pi x/L)$ leads to

$$\int_0^L f(x, y)\sqrt{\frac{2}{L}}\sin\frac{k\pi x}{L}\,dx = \sum_{m=1}^{\infty} A_{mk}\sqrt{\frac{2}{L'}}\sin\frac{m\pi y}{L'}, \qquad 0 < y < L'.$$

Multiplication by $\sqrt{2/L'}\sin(j\pi y/L')$ and integration with respect to y from $y = 0$ to $y = L'$ gives, similarly,

$$\int_0^{L'}\left(\int_0^L f(x, y)\sqrt{\frac{2}{L}}\sin\frac{k\pi x}{L}\,dx\right)\sqrt{\frac{2}{L'}}\sin\frac{j\pi y}{L'}\,dy = A_{jk}.$$

Thus, coefficients A_{mn} in (40a) are given by

$$A_{mn} = \int_0^{L'}\int_0^L f(x, y)\sqrt{\frac{2}{L}}\sin\frac{n\pi x}{L}\sqrt{\frac{2}{L'}}\sin\frac{m\pi y}{L'}\,dx\,dy, \qquad \textbf{(40b)}$$

and the formal solution is complete.

As a special case, suppose $f(x, y) = xy(L - x)(L' - y)$ so that cross sections of the initial displacement parallel to the xz- and yz-planes are parabolic. Integration by parts in (40b) yields

$$A_{mn} = \frac{8(LL')^{5/2}[1 + (-1)^{n+1}][1 + (-1)^{m+1}]}{n^3 m^3 \pi^6},$$

and hence

$$z(x, y, t) = \sum_{m=1}^{\infty}\sum_{n=1}^{\infty}\frac{8(LL')^{5/2}[1 + (-1)^{n+1}][1 + (-1)^{m+1}]}{n^3 m^3 \pi^6}\sqrt{\frac{2}{L}}\sin\frac{n\pi x}{L}$$

$$\times\sqrt{\frac{2}{L'}}\sin\frac{m\pi y}{L'}\cos c\sqrt{\frac{n^2\pi^2}{L^2} + \frac{m^2\pi^2}{L'^2}}\,t.$$

Since terms are nonzero only when both m and n are odd integers, we may write

$$z(x, y, t) = \frac{64(LL')^2}{\pi^6} \sum_{m=1}^{\infty} \sum_{n=1}^{\infty} \frac{1}{(2n-1)^3(2m-1)^3} \sin\frac{(2n-1)\pi x}{L}$$
$$\times \sin\frac{(2m-1)\pi y}{L'} \cos \pi c \sqrt{\frac{(2n-1)^2}{L^2} + \frac{(2m-1)^2}{L'^2}}\, t. \tag{41}$$

The terms in this series are called the *normal modes of vibration* for the membrane (similar to the normal modes of a vibrating string in Section 5.2). The first term corresponding to $n = 1$ and $m = 1$,

$$H_{1,1}(x, y, t) = \frac{64(LL')^2}{\pi^6} \sin\frac{\pi x}{L} \sin\frac{\pi y}{L'} \cos \pi c \sqrt{\frac{1}{L^2} + \frac{1}{L'^2}}\, t,$$

is called the *fundamental mode of vibration*. It represents displacements of a membrane identical to that in problem (37), except that the initial displacement is $[64(LL')^2/\pi^6]\sin(\pi x/L)\sin(\pi y/L')$. For such an initial displacement, the membrane oscillates back and forth between the enveloping surfaces $\pm[64(LL')^2/\pi^6]\sin(\pi x/L)\sin(\pi y/L')$; the shape of the membrane is always the same, the cosine factor describing the time dependence of the oscillations.

The $n = 1$ and $m = 2$ term in (41) is

$$H_{2,1}(x, y, t) = \frac{64(LL')^2}{27\pi^6} \sin\frac{\pi x}{L} \sin\frac{3\pi y}{L'} \cos \pi c \sqrt{\frac{1}{L^2} + \frac{9}{L'^2}}\, t.$$

It represents vibrations of the same membrane with an initial displacement $[64(LL')^2/(27\pi^6)]\sin(\pi x/L)\sin(3\pi y/L')$. The membrane oscillates back and forth between this surface and its negative. The lines $y = L'/3$ and $y = 2L'/3$, which always remain motionless, are called *nodal curves* for this mode of vibration.

The mode

$$H_{1,2}(x, y, t) = \frac{64(LL')^2}{27\pi^6} \sin\frac{3\pi x}{L} \sin\frac{\pi y}{L'} \cos \pi c \sqrt{\frac{9}{L^2} + \frac{1}{L'^2}}\, t$$

is similar with nodal curves $x = L/3$ and $x = 2L/3$.

Solution (41) is the sum of an infinity of modes of vibration, the modes of lower orders contributing more significantly than higher-order ones.

We now consider a three-dimensional boundary value problem,

$$\frac{\partial^2 U}{\partial x^2} + \frac{\partial^2 U}{\partial y^2} + \frac{\partial^2 U}{\partial z^2} = 0, \qquad 0 < x < L, \qquad 0 < y < L', \qquad 0 < z < L'', \tag{42a}$$

$$\frac{\partial U(0, y, z)}{\partial x} = 0, \qquad 0 < y < L', \qquad 0 < z < L'', \tag{42b}$$

$$U(L, y, z) = 0, \qquad 0 < y < L', \qquad 0 < z < L'', \tag{42c}$$

$$U(x, 0, z) = 0, \qquad 0 < x < L, \qquad 0 < z < L'', \tag{42d}$$

$$\frac{\partial U(x, L', z)}{\partial y} = 0, \qquad 0 < x < L, \qquad 0 < z < L'', \tag{42e}$$

$$U(x, y, 0) = f(x, y), \qquad 0 < x < L, \qquad 0 < y < L', \qquad \text{(42f)}$$

$$U(x, y, L'') = g(x, y), \qquad 0 < x < L, \qquad 0 < y < L'. \qquad \text{(42g)}$$

The problem describes steady-state temperature $U(x, y, z)$ in the box of Figure 5.11, where two faces ($x = 0$ and $y = L'$) are insulated, two faces ($x = L$ and $y = 0$) are held at temperature zero, and the remaining faces have prescribed nonzero temperatures $f(x, y)$ and $g(x, y)$. The problem is said to be homogeneous because the PDE is homogeneous, and all boundary conditions are homogeneous except those on a single pair of opposite faces.

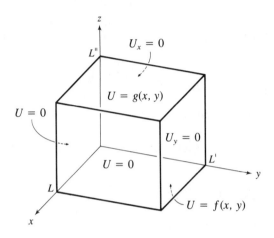

Figure 5.11

When a function with variables separated, $U(x, y, z) = X(x)Y(y)Z(z)$, is substituted into (42a), separation gives

$$-\frac{X''}{X} = \frac{Y''}{Y} + \frac{Z''}{Z} = \lambda^2 = \text{constant independent of } x, y, \text{ and } z.$$

Combined with boundary conditions (42b, c), this yields

$$X'' + \lambda^2 X = 0, \qquad 0 < x < L,$$

$$X'(0) = X(L) = 0.$$

Eigenvalues of this Sturm-Liouville system are $\lambda_n^2 = (2n - 1)^2 \pi^2 / (4L^2)$, with eigenfunctions $X_n(x) = \sqrt{2/L} \cos \lambda_n x$ (see Table 4.1).

Further separation of the equation in Y and Z leads to

$$-\frac{Y''}{Y} = \frac{Z''}{Z} - \lambda_n^2 = \mu^2 = \text{constant independent of } y \text{ and } z.$$

This equation, along with boundary conditions (42d, e), gives

$$Y'' + \mu^2 Y = 0, \qquad 0 < y < L',$$

$$Y(0) = Y'(L') = 0.$$

Eigenpairs of this Sturm-Liouville system are $\mu_m^2 = (2m-1)^2\pi^2/(4L'^2)$ and $Y_m(y) = \sqrt{2/L'}\sin\mu_m y$.

Finally, the ODE

$$Z'' - (\lambda_n^2 + \mu_m^2)Z = 0$$

has general solution

$$Z(z) = A\cosh\sqrt{\lambda_n^2 + \mu_m^2}\,z + B\sinh\sqrt{\lambda_n^2 + \mu_m^2}\,z.$$

We have now determined that separated functions

$$X_n(x)Y_m(y)Z(z) = X_n(x)Y_m(y)[A\cosh\sqrt{\lambda_n^2 + \mu_m^2}\,z + B\sinh\sqrt{\lambda_n^2 + \mu_m^2}\,z]$$

for positive integers n and m and arbitrary constants A and B satisfy PDE (42a) and boundary conditions (42b–e). To accommodate boundary conditions (42f, g), we superpose separated functions and take

$$U(x,y,z) = \sum_{m=1}^{\infty}\sum_{n=1}^{\infty} X_n(x)Y_m(y)[A_{mn}\cosh\sqrt{\lambda_n^2 + \mu_m^2}\,z + B_{mn}\sinh\sqrt{\lambda_n^2 + \mu_m^2}\,z], \quad \textbf{(43a)}$$

in which case (42f, g) require that

$$f(x,y) = \sum_{m=1}^{\infty}\sum_{n=1}^{\infty} A_{mn}X_n(x)Y_m(y), \qquad 0 < x < L, \qquad 0 < y < L'$$

and

$$g(x,y) = \sum_{m=1}^{\infty}\sum_{n=1}^{\infty} X_n(x)Y_m(y)[A_{mn}\cosh\sqrt{\lambda_n^2 + \mu_m^2}\,L'' + B_{mn}\sinh\sqrt{\lambda_n^2 + \mu_m^2}\,L''],$$

$$0 < x < L, \qquad 0 < y < L'.$$

Successive multiplications of these equations by eigenfunctions in x and y and integrations with respect to x and y lead to the following expressions for A_{mn} and B_{mn}:

$$A_{mn} = \int_0^{L'}\int_0^{L} f(x,y)X_n(x)Y_m(y)\,dx\,dy \qquad \textbf{(43b)}$$

and

$$B_{mn} = \frac{1}{\sinh\sqrt{\lambda_n^2 + \mu_m^2}\,L''}$$
$$\times\left[\int_0^{L'}\int_0^{L} g(x,y)X_n(x)Y_m(y)\,dx\,dy - A_{mn}\cosh\sqrt{\lambda_n^2 + \mu_m^2}\,L''\right]. \qquad \textbf{(43c)}$$

In Section 5.5, solutions like (40) and (43) are approached from a different point of view.

Exercises 5.4

Part A—Heat Condition

1. A thin rectangle occupying the region $0 \le x \le L$, $0 \le y \le L'$ has its top and bottom faces insulated. At time $t = 0$, its temperature is described by the function $f(x,y)$. Find its temperature for $t > 0$ if all four edges, $x = 0$, $y = 0$, $x = L$, and $y = L'$, are maintained at 0°C.

2. Repeat Exercise 1 if edges $x = 0$ and $y = L'$ are insulated.

3. (a) Repeat Exercise 1 if edges $y = 0$ and $y = L'$ are insulated.

   (b) Simplify the solution if the initial temperature is a function only of x.

4. Repeat Exercise 1 if heat is transferred to an environment at temperature $0°C$ along the edge $x = L$ (according to Newton's law of cooling).

5. A block of metal occupies the region $0 \le x \le L$, $0 \le y \le L'$, $0 \le z \le L''$. The surfaces $y = 0$, $y = L'$, and $z = L''$ are insulated, and faces $x = 0$, $x = L$, and $z = 0$ are held at temperature $0°C$. If the temperature of the block is initially a constant U_0 throughout, find the temperature in the block thereafter.

6. Repeat Exercise 5 if heat is transferred to the surrounding medium, at temperature zero, according to Newton's law of cooling on the face $z = L''$.

7. Repeat Exercise 5 if face $z = 0$ is insulated.

8. Repeat Exercise 5 if face $y = L'$ is held at temperature $0°C$.

9. In this exercise we prove a result for homogeneous heat conduction problems in two or three space variables that uses solutions of one-dimensional problems provided the initial temperature distribution is the product of one-dimensional functions. In particular, show that the solution of the two-dimensional problem

$$\frac{\partial U}{\partial t} = k\left(\frac{\partial^2 U}{\partial x^2} + \frac{\partial^2 U}{\partial y^2}\right), \qquad 0 < x < L, \qquad 0 < y < L', \qquad t > 0,$$

$$-l_1\frac{\partial U}{\partial x} + h_1 U = 0, \qquad x = 0, \qquad 0 < y < L', \qquad t > 0,$$

$$l_2\frac{\partial U}{\partial x} + h_2 U = 0, \qquad x = L, \qquad 0 < y < L', \qquad t > 0,$$

$$-l_3\frac{\partial U}{\partial y} + h_3 U = 0, \qquad y = 0, \qquad 0 < x < L, \qquad t > 0,$$

$$l_4\frac{\partial U}{\partial y} + h_4 U = 0, \qquad y = L', \qquad 0 < x < L, \qquad t > 0,$$

$$U(x, y, 0) = f(x)g(y), \qquad 0 < x < L, \qquad 0 < y < L'$$

is the product of the solutions of the one-dimensional problems

$$\frac{\partial U}{\partial t} = k\frac{\partial^2 U}{\partial x^2}, \quad 0 < x < L, \quad t > 0, \qquad\qquad \frac{\partial U}{\partial t} = k\frac{\partial^2 U}{\partial y^2}, \quad 0 < y < L', \quad t > 0,$$

$$-l_1\frac{\partial U}{\partial x} + h_1 U = 0, \quad x = 0, \quad t > 0, \qquad\qquad -l_3\frac{\partial U}{\partial y} + h_3 U = 0, \quad y = 0, \quad t > 0,$$

$$l_2\frac{\partial U}{\partial x} + h_2 U = 0, \quad x = L, \quad t > 0, \qquad\qquad l_4\frac{\partial U}{\partial y} + h_4 U = 0, \quad y = L', \quad t > 0,$$

$$U(x, 0) = f(x), \quad 0 < x < L; \qquad\qquad U(y, 0) = g(y), \quad 0 < y < L'.$$

This result is easily extended to heat conduction problems in x, y, z, and t. In addition, it can sometimes be generalized to other coordinate systems (see Exercise 15 in Section 9.1).

10. (a) Use the result of Exercise 9 in this section, together with those of Exercise 1 in Section 5.2 and

Example 1 in Section 3.2, to solve the following heat conduction problem:

$$\frac{\partial U}{\partial t} = k\left(\frac{\partial^2 U}{\partial x^2} + \frac{\partial^2 U}{\partial y^2}\right), \qquad 0 < x < L, \qquad 0 < y < L', \qquad t > 0,$$

$$U_x(0, y, t) = 0, \qquad 0 < y < L', \qquad t > 0,$$
$$U_x(L, y, t) = 0, \qquad 0 < y < L', \qquad t > 0,$$
$$U_y(x, 0, t) = 0, \qquad 0 < x < L, \qquad t > 0,$$
$$U(x, L', t) = 0, \qquad 0 < x < L, \qquad t > 0,$$
$$U(x, y, 0) = x(L' - y), \qquad 0 < x < L, \qquad 0 < y < L'.$$

(b) Solve the problem in (a) by separation of variables. Are the solutions identical?

Part B—Vibrations

11. (a) A membrane is stretched tightly over the square $0 \le x, y \le L$. If all four edges are clamped on the xy-plane and the membrane is released from rest at an initial displacement $f(x, y)$, find its subsequent displacements.

    (b) Simplify the solution when

    $$f(x, y) = \frac{(L - 2|x - L/2|)(L - 2|y - L/2|)}{32L}.$$

12. (a) A membrane is stretched tightly over the rectangle $0 \le x \le L, 0 \le y \le L'$. Edges $x = 0$ and $x = L$ are clamped on the xy-plane, but $y = 0$ and $y = L'$ are free to move vertically. If the membrane is released from rest at time $t = 0$ from a position described by $f(x, y)$, determine subsequent displacements of the membrane.

    (b) Simplify the solution when $f(x, y) = (L - 2|x - L/2|)/(32L)$.

13. Equation (40) describes displacements of a rectangular membrane with edges fixed on the xy-plane when oscillations are initiated by releasing the membrane from rest at a prescribed displacement. Find nodal curves for the mode $2A_{mn}/\sqrt{LL'} \sin(n\pi x/L) \sin(m\pi y/L') \times \cos c\sqrt{n^2/L^2 + m^2/L'^2}\,\pi t$.

14. Is there a result analogous to that in Exercise 9 for the vibration problem of displacements in a membrane?

Part C—Potential, Steady-State Heat Conduction

15. Find the potential inside the rectangular parallelopiped $0 \le x \le L, 0 \le y \le L', 0 \le z \le L''$ if faces $x = 0, y = 0, x = L$, and $y = L'$ are all held at potential zero while faces $z = 0$ and $z = L''$ are maintained at potentials $f(x, y)$ and $g(x, y)$, respectively.

16. Repeat Exercise 15 if faces $x = 0$ and $x = L$ are held at potentials $h(y, z)$ and $k(y, z)$, the other four faces remaining unchanged.

17. Find the steady-state temperature distribution inside a cube $0 \le x \le L, 0 \le y \le L, 0 \le z \le L$ if faces $x = 0$ and $z = L$ are insulated, faces $y = 0$ and $y = L$ are held at temperature zero, and heat is added to faces $x = L$ and $z = 0$ at constant rates q and Q W/m^2, respectively.

5.5 The Multidimensional Eigenvalue Problem

In Section 5.4 we demonstrated that successively separating off Cartesian variables in homogeneous problems leads to the Sturm-Liouville systems of Section 4.2. When the problem is an initial boundary value one, as opposed to a boundary value problem, there remains an ODE for the time dependence of the unknown function. An alternative procedure is first to separate off the time dependence, leaving what is called the multidimensional eigenvalue problem. To illustrate, suppose that the unknown function V in the homogeneous PDE

$$\nabla^2 V = p\frac{\partial^2 V}{\partial t^2} + q\frac{\partial V}{\partial t} + sV \tag{44}$$

is separated into a spatial part, which we designate by W, and a time-dependent part, $T(t)$, $V = WT(t)$. (We have purposely not expressed W as a function of coordinates because what we are about to do is independent of the particular choice of coordinate system.) When this product representation for V is substituted into (44), the time dependence contained in T may be separated from the spatial dependence in W:

$$\frac{\nabla^2 W}{W} = \frac{pT'' + qT' + sT}{T} = -k = \text{constant independent of all variables.}$$

It follows that $T(t)$ must satisfy the ODE

$$pT'' + qT' + (s + k)T = 0$$

and W must satisfy the Helmholtz equation

$$\nabla^2 W + kW = 0.$$

When PDE (44) is accompanied by homogeneous boundary conditions on V, these become homogeneous boundary conditions for W. If we set $k = \lambda^2$, the problem

$$\nabla^2 W + \lambda^2 W = 0, \tag{45a}$$

$$\text{Homogeneous boundary conditions} \tag{45b}$$

is called the *multidimensional eigenvalue problem*. For certain eigenvalues λ^2, there exist nontrivial solutions of (45) called *eigenfunctions*. Properties of eigenvalues and eigenfunctions of this eigenvalue problem parallel those of Sturm-Liouville systems in Chapter 4, but important differences do exist. We consider one example here and give general discussions and further examples in the exercises.

When boundary conditions (45b) are of Dirichlet type on the edges of a rectangle $0 \le x \le L, 0 \le y \le L'$, (45) takes the form

$$\frac{\partial^2 W}{\partial x^2} + \frac{\partial^2 W}{\partial y^2} + \lambda^2 W = 0, \qquad 0 < x < L, \qquad 0 < y < L', \tag{46a}$$

$$W(0, y) = 0, \qquad 0 < y < L', \tag{46b}$$

$$W(L, y) = 0, \qquad 0 < y < L', \tag{46c}$$

$$W(x, 0) = 0, \qquad 0 < x < L, \tag{46d}$$

$$W(x, L') = 0, \qquad 0 < x < L. \tag{46e}$$

To solve this problem, we separate $W(x, y) = X(x)Y(y)$. This results in the SL-systems

$$X'' + \mu^2 X = 0, \qquad 0 < x < L, \qquad Y'' + (\lambda^2 - \mu^2)Y = 0, \qquad 0 < y < L',$$
$$X(0) = X(L) = 0; \qquad\qquad\qquad Y(0) = Y(L') = 0,$$

solutions of which are

$$X_n(x) = \sqrt{\frac{2}{L}} \sin \frac{n\pi x}{L} \quad \text{corresponding to eigenvalues } \mu_n^2 = n^2\pi^2/L^2,$$

and $\quad Y_m(y) = \sqrt{\frac{2}{L'}} \sin \frac{m\pi y}{L'} \quad \text{corresponding to eigenvalues } \lambda^2 - \mu_n^2 = m^2\pi^2/L'^2.$

In other words, eigenvalues of (46) are $\lambda_{mn}^2 = n^2\pi^2/L^2 + m^2\pi^2/L'^2$, with corresponding eigenfunctions

$$W_{mn}(x, y) = \frac{2}{\sqrt{LL'}} \sin \frac{n\pi x}{L} \sin \frac{m\pi y}{L'}. \tag{47}$$

It is straightforward to show that these functions are orthonormal on the rectangle with respect to the weight function $p(x, y) = 1$; that is,

$$\int_0^L \int_0^{L'} W_{mn}(x, y) W_{kl}(x, y)\, dy\, dx = \begin{cases} 1 & \text{if } m = k \text{ and } n = l \\ 0 & \text{otherwise} \end{cases} \tag{48}$$

Furthermore, suppose we are given a function $f(x, y)$ that is, along with its first partial derivatives, piecewise continuous on the rectangle $0 \le x \le L, 0 \le y \le L'$. For fixed y, $f(x, y)$ and $\partial f(x, y)/\partial x$ are piecewise continuous functions of x, and we may therefore express $f(x, y)$ in terms of $X_n(x)$; that is, the eigenfunction expansion of $f(x, y)$ as a function of x is

$$\frac{f(x+, y) + f(x-, y)}{2} = \sum_{n=1}^{\infty} d_n(y) \sqrt{\frac{2}{L}} \sin \frac{n\pi x}{L}, \tag{49a}$$

where the functions $d_n(y)$ are defined by

$$d_n(y) = \int_0^L f(x, y) \sqrt{\frac{2}{L}} \sin \frac{n\pi x}{L}\, dx. \tag{49b}$$

Equations (49) are valid provided $f(x, y)$ is continuous in y at the chosen value of y. When this is not the case, these equations must be replaced by appropriate limiting expressions. Because $d_n(y)$ is itself piecewise continuous, with a piecewise continuous first derivative, it may be expanded in terms of $Y_m(y)$:

$$\frac{d_n(y+) + d_n(y-)}{2} = \sum_{m=1}^{\infty} c_{mn} \sqrt{\frac{2}{L'}} \sin \frac{m\pi y}{L'} \tag{50a}$$

where

$$c_{mn} = \int_0^{L'} d_n(y) \sqrt{\frac{2}{L'}} \sin \frac{m\pi y}{L'}\, dy. \tag{50b}$$

We combine these expressions to write

$$\left(\frac{f(x+,y+)+f(x-,y+)}{2}\right) + \left(\frac{f(x+,y-)+f(x-,y-)}{2}\right)$$

$$= \sum_{n=1}^{\infty} d_n(y+)\sqrt{\frac{2}{L}}\sin\frac{n\pi x}{L} + \sum_{n=1}^{\infty} d_n(y-)\sqrt{\frac{2}{L}}\sin\frac{n\pi x}{L}$$

$$= \sum_{n=1}^{\infty} [d_n(y+)+d_n(y-)]\sqrt{\frac{2}{L}}\sin\frac{n\pi x}{L}$$

$$= \sum_{n=1}^{\infty}\left(2\sum_{m=1}^{\infty} C_{mn}\sqrt{\frac{2}{L'}}\sin\frac{m\pi y}{L'}\right)\sqrt{\frac{2}{L}}\sin\frac{n\pi x}{L}$$

$$= 2\sum_{n=1}^{\infty}\sum_{m=1}^{\infty} C_{mn}\frac{2}{\sqrt{LL'}}\sin\frac{n\pi x}{L}\sin\frac{m\pi y}{L'}.$$

In other words, the function $f(x, y)$ has been expanded in terms of the orthonormal eigenfunctions of eigenvalue problem (46),

$$\frac{f(x+,y+)+f(x+,y-)+f(x-,y+)+f(x-,y-)}{4}$$

$$= \sum_{n=1}^{\infty}\sum_{m=1}^{\infty} C_{mn}W_{mn}(x, y) = \sum_{n=1}^{\infty}\sum_{m=1}^{\infty} C_{mn}\frac{2}{\sqrt{LL'}}\sin\frac{n\pi x}{L}\sin\frac{m\pi y}{L'}, \qquad \text{(51a)}$$

where

$$C_{mn} = \int_0^L\int_0^{L'} f(x, y)W_{mn}(x, y)\,dy\,dx$$

$$= \int_0^L\int_0^{L'} f(x, y)\frac{2}{\sqrt{LL'}}\sin\frac{n\pi x}{L}\sin\frac{m\pi y}{L'}\,dy\,dx, \qquad \text{(51b)}$$

and this result is valid for $0 < x < L, 0 < y < L'$.

We have illustrated with this example that for the multidimensional eigenvalue problem we should expect multisubscripted eigenvalues, orthogonal eigenfunctions, and multidimensional eigenfunction expansions. This is illustrated further in the exercises.

When solving homogeneous initial boundary value problems by separation of variables, there is always the choice of separating off the time dependence first or last. The solution will ultimately be the same for either approach, but the steps differ in arriving at this solution. Let us illustrate with the heat conduction problem

$$\frac{\partial U}{\partial t} = k\left(\frac{\partial^2 U}{\partial x^2}+\frac{\partial^2 U}{\partial y^2}\right), \qquad 0 < x < L, \qquad 0 < y < L', \qquad t > 0, \quad \text{(52a)}$$

$$U(0, y, t) = 0, \qquad 0 < y < L', \qquad t > 0, \tag{52b}$$

$$U(L, y, t) = 0, \qquad 0 < y < L', \qquad t > 0, \tag{52c}$$

$$U(x, 0, t) = 0, \qquad 0 < x < L, \qquad t > 0, \tag{52d}$$

$$U(x, L', t) = 0, \qquad 0 < x < L, \qquad t > 0, \tag{52e}$$

$$U(x, y, 0) = f(x, y), \qquad 0 < x < L, \qquad 0 < y < L'. \tag{52f}$$

If the x- and y-dependences of a separated function $U(x, y, t) = X(x)Y(y)T(t)$ are separated off first (as was done in Section 5.4), Sturm-Liouville systems in $X(x)$ and $Y(y)$ are obtained:

$$X'' + \lambda^2 X = 0, \qquad 0 < x < L, \qquad Y'' + \mu^2 Y = 0, \qquad 0 < y < L',$$
$$X(0) = 0 = X(L); \qquad\qquad\qquad Y(0) = 0 = Y(L').$$

Eigenpairs of these systems are

$$\lambda_n^2 = \frac{n^2\pi^2}{L^2}, \qquad X_n(x) = \sqrt{\frac{2}{L}}\sin\frac{n\pi x}{L},$$

$$\mu_m^2 = \frac{m^2\pi^2}{L'^2}, \qquad Y_m(y) = \sqrt{\frac{2}{L'}}\sin\frac{m\pi y}{L'}.$$

What remains is an ODE in $T(t)$, namely,

$$T' + k(\lambda_n^2 + \mu_m^2)T = 0, \qquad t > 0,$$

with general solution

$$T(t) = Ae^{-k(\lambda_n^2 + \mu_m^2)t}.$$

To satisfy the initial condition, separated functions are superposed in the form

$$U(x, y, t) = \sum_{n=1}^{\infty}\sum_{m=1}^{\infty} A_{mn} e^{-k(\lambda_n^2 + \mu_m^2)t} \sqrt{\frac{2}{L}}\sin\frac{n\pi x}{L}\sqrt{\frac{2}{L'}}\sin\frac{m\pi y}{L'}, \qquad (53a)$$

and the initial temperature $f(x, y)$ at $t = 0$ then requires that

$$f(x, y) = \sum_{n=1}^{\infty}\sum_{m=1}^{\infty} A_{mn}\sqrt{\frac{2}{L}}\sin\frac{n\pi x}{L}\sqrt{\frac{2}{L'}}\sin\frac{m\pi y}{L'}, \qquad 0 < x < L, \qquad 0 < y < L'. \quad (54a)$$

To find expressions for the A_{mn}, we multiply successively by $\sqrt{2/L}\sin(k\pi x/L)$ and $\sqrt{2/L'}\sin(j\pi y/L')$, integrate with respect to x and y, and use orthogonality. The result is

$$A_{mn} = \int_0^{L'}\int_0^{L} f(x, y)\sqrt{\frac{2}{L}}\sin\frac{n\pi x}{L}\sqrt{\frac{2}{L'}}\sin\frac{m\pi y}{L'}\,dx\,dy. \qquad (53b)$$

Alternatively, if time is the first variable separated off by setting $U(x, y, t) = W(x, y)T(t)$, the ODE

$$T' + k\lambda^2 T = 0$$

is obtained along with eigenvalue problem (46). With the eigenpairs $\lambda_{mn}^2 = n^2\pi^2/L^2 + m^2\pi^2/L'^2$ and $W_{mn}(x, y) = (2/\sqrt{LL'})\sin(n\pi x/L)\sin(m\pi y/L')$, the solution for $T(t)$ is

$$T(t) = Ae^{-k\lambda_{mn}^2 t}.$$

Superposition of separated functions gives

$$U(x, y, t) = \sum_{n=1}^{\infty}\sum_{m=1}^{\infty} A_{mn} e^{-k\lambda_{mn}^2 t} W_{mn}(x, y), \qquad (55a)$$

and the initial condition (52f) requires that

$$f(x, y) = \sum_{n=1}^{\infty} \sum_{m=1}^{\infty} A_{mn} W_{mn}(x, y), \qquad 0 < x < L, \qquad 0 < y < L'. \tag{54b}$$

But then, A_{mn} are the Fourier coefficients in the eigenfunction expansion of $f(x, y)$ in terms of the $W_{mn}(x, y)$,

$$A_{mn} = \int_0^{L'} \int_0^L f(x, y) W_{mn}(x, y) \, dx \, dy. \tag{55b}$$

Solutions (53) and (55) are identical; it is only the way in which we regard equations (54a, b) that differs in our arriving at the solution.

Exercises 5.5

In Exercises 1–3 we prove some general results concerning eigenvalue problem (45) in the xy-plane. Results in three space variables are analogous.

1. Prove the following result corresponding to Theorem 1 in Chapter 4. All eigenvalues of the multidimensional eigenvalue problem

$$\nabla^2 W + \lambda^2 W = 0, \qquad (x, y) \text{ in } A, \tag{56a}$$

$$l \frac{\partial W}{\partial n} + h W = 0, \qquad (x, y) \text{ on } \beta(A), \qquad h > 0, \qquad l > 0, \tag{56b}$$

are real, and eigenfunctions corresponding to different eigenvalues are orthogonal with respect to the unit weight function.

2. Use eigenvalue problem (46) (with $L' = 2L$) to illustrate that a multidimensional eigenvalue problem can have linearly independent eigenfunctions corresponding to the same eigenvalue. (Contrast this with Exercise 12 in Section 4.1 for Sturm-Liouville systems.)

3. Show that all eigenvalues of (56) are nonnegative and that $\lambda = 0$ is an eigenvalue only when the boundary condition is Neumann. In this case, what is the eigenfunction corresponding to $\lambda = 0$?

In Exercises 4–8, find eigenvalues and orthonormal eigenfunctions of eigenproblem (45) on the rectangle $A: 0 \le x \le L, 0 \le y \le L'$ for the given boundary conditions.

4. $W(0, y) = 0, \quad 0 < y < L'; \quad W_x(L, y) = 0, \quad 0 < y < L'; \quad W(x, 0) = 0, \quad 0 < x < L;$
   $W(x, L') = 0, \quad 0 < x < L$

5. $W(0, y) = 0, \quad 0 < y < L'; \quad W(L, y) = 0, \quad 0 < y < L'; \quad \partial W(x, 0)/\partial y = 0, \quad 0 < x < L;$
   $\partial W(x, L')/\partial y = 0, \quad 0 < x < L$

6. $\partial W(0, y)/\partial x = 0, \quad 0 < y < L'; \quad W(L, y) = 0, \quad 0 < y < L'; \quad W(x, 0) = 0, \quad 0 < x < L;$
   $\partial W(x, L')/\partial y = 0, \quad 0 < x < L$

7. $W(0, y) = 0, \quad 0 < y < L'; \quad W(L, y) = 0, \quad 0 < y < L'; \quad \partial W(x, 0)/\partial y = 0, \quad 0 < x < L;$
   $l\partial W(x, L')/\partial y + h W(x, L') = 0, \quad 0 < x < L$

8. $-l_1 \partial W/\partial x + h_1 W = 0, \quad x = 0, \quad 0 < y < L'; \quad l_2 \partial W/\partial x + h_2 W = 0, \quad x = L, \quad 0 < y < L';$
   $-l_3 \partial W/\partial y + h_3 W = 0, \quad y = 0, \quad 0 < x < L; \quad l_4 \partial W/\partial y + h_4 W = 0, \quad y = L', \quad 0 < x < L$

In Exercises 9–11, use the multidimensional eigenvalue problem approach to solve the initial boundary value problem.

9. Exercise 11(a) in Section 5.4.   10. Exercise 12(a) in Section 5.4.

11. Exercise 5 in Section 5.4.

5.6 Properties of Parabolic Partial Differential Equations

We now return to a difficulty posed in Chapter 3. In what sense are the series obtained in Chapters 3 and 5 "solutions" of their respective problems? In arriving at each series solution, we superposed an infinity of functions satisfying a linear, homogeneous PDE and linear, homogeneous boundary and/or initial conditions. Because of the questionable validity of this step (superposition principle 1 in Section 3.1 endorses only finite linear combinations), we have called each series a formal solution. It is now incumbent on us to verify that each formal solution is indeed a valid solution of its (initial) boundary value problem. Unfortunately, it is not possible to prove general results that encompass all problems solved by means of separation of variables and generalized Fourier series; on the other hand, the situation is not so bad that every problem is its own special case. Techniques exist that verify formal solutions for large classes of problems. In this section and Sections 5.7 and 5.8, we illustrate techniques that work when separation of variables leads to the Sturm-Liouville systems in Table 4.1. At the same time, we take the opportunity to develop properties of solutions of parabolic, hyperbolic, and elliptic PDEs. Time-dependent heat conduction problems are manifested in parabolic equations; vibrations invariably involve hyperbolic equations; and potential problems give rise to elliptic equations.

We choose to illustrate the situation for parabolic PDEs with the heat conduction problem in equation (2) of Section 5.2:

$$\frac{\partial U}{\partial t} = k\frac{\partial^2 U}{\partial x^2}, \qquad 0 < x < L, \qquad t > 0, \tag{57a}$$

$$\frac{\partial U(0,t)}{\partial x} = 0, \qquad t > 0, \tag{57b}$$

$$\kappa\frac{\partial U(L,t)}{\partial x} + \mu U(L,t) = 0, \qquad t > 0, \tag{57c}$$

$$U(x,0) = f(x), \qquad 0 < x < L. \tag{57d}$$

The formal solution of this problem is

$$U(x,t) = \sum_{n=1}^{\infty} c_n e^{-k\lambda_n^2 t} X_n(x) \tag{58a}$$

where

$$c_n = \int_0^L f(x) X_n(x)\, dx. \tag{58b}$$

Eigenfunctions are $X_n(x) = N^{-1}\cos\lambda_n x$, where normalizing factors are $2N^2 = L + (\mu/\kappa)/[\lambda_n^2 + (\mu/\kappa)^2]$, and eigenvalues are defined by the equation $\tan\lambda L = \mu/(\kappa\lambda)$.

We shall show by direct substitution that the function $U(x,t)$ defined by series (58) does indeed satisfy PDE (57a), its boundary conditions (57b, c), and its initial condition (57d).

When coefficients c_n are calculated according to (58b), the series $\sum_{n=1}^{\infty} c_n X_n(x)$ converges to $f(x)$ for $0 < x < L$ [provided $f(x)$ is piecewise smooth for $0 \le x \le L$]. Since this series is $U(x,0)$, it follows that initial condition (57d) is satisfied if $f(x)$ is piecewise smooth on $0 \le x \le L$, provided at any point of discontinuity of $f(x)$, $f(x)$ is defined by $f(x) = [f(x+) + f(x-)]/2$.

To verify (57a–c) is not quite so simple. We first show that series (58a) converges for all $0 \leq x \leq L$ and $t > 0$ and can be differentiated with respect to either x or t. Because eigenfunctions $X_n(x)$ are uniformly bounded (see Theorem 2 of Chapter 4), there exists a constant M such that for all $n \geq 1$ and $0 \leq x \leq L$, $|X_n(x)| \leq N^{-1} \leq M$. Further, since $f(x)$ is piecewise continuous on $0 \leq x \leq L$, it is also bounded thereon: $|f(x)| \leq K$. These two results imply that the coefficients c_n defined by (58b) are bounded by

$$|c_n| \leq \int_0^L |f(x)||X_n(x)|\, dx \leq KML. \tag{59}$$

It follows that for any x in $0 \leq x \leq L$, and any $t \geq t_0 > 0$.

$$\sum_{n=1}^{\infty} |c_n X_n(x) e^{-k\lambda_n^2 t}| \leq KM^2 L \sum_{n=1}^{\infty} (e^{-kt_0})^{\lambda_n^2}.$$

Figure 4.2 indicates that the nth eigenvalue $\lambda_n \geq (n-1)\pi/L$. Combine this with the fact that $e^{-kt_0} < 1$, and we may write, for $0 \leq x \leq L$ and $t \geq t_0 > 0$,

$$\sum_{n=1}^{\infty} |c_n X_n(x) e^{-k\lambda_n^2 t}| \leq KM^2 L \sum_{n=1}^{\infty} (e^{-kt_0})^{(n-1)^2 \pi^2/L^2}$$

$$\leq KM^2 L \sum_{n=1}^{\infty} [(e^{-kt_0})^{\pi^2/L^2}]^{n-1} = KM^2 L \sum_{n=1}^{\infty} r^{n-1}, \tag{60}$$

and the geometric series on the right converges, since $r = e^{-kt_0 \pi^2/L^2} < 1$. According to the Weierstrass M-test (Theorem 4 in Section 2.3), series (58a) converges absolutely and uniformly with respect to x and t for $0 \leq x \leq L$ and $t \geq t_0 > 0$. Because $t_0 > 0$ is arbitrary, it also follows that series (58a) converges absolutely for $0 \leq x \leq L$ and $t > 0$.

Term-by-term differentiation of series (58a) with respect to t gives

$$\sum_{n=1}^{\infty} -k\lambda_n^2 c_n X_n(x) e^{-k\lambda_n^2 t}. \tag{61}$$

Since $\lambda_n \leq n\pi/L$ (see, once again, Figure 4.2), it follows that for all $0 \leq x \leq L$ and $t \geq t_0 > 0$,

$$\sum_{n=1}^{\infty} |-k\lambda_n^2 c_n X_n(x) e^{-k\lambda_n^2 t}| \leq \frac{kKM^2\pi^2}{L} \sum_{n=1}^{\infty} n^2 r^{n-1}. \tag{62}$$

Because the series $\sum_{n=1}^{\infty} n^2 r^{n-1}$ converges, we conclude that series (61) converges absolutely and uniformly with respect to x and t for $0 \leq x \leq L$ and $t \geq t_0 > 0$. As a result, series (61) represents $\partial U/\partial t$ for $0 \leq x \leq L$ and $t \geq t_0 > 0$ (Theorem 8 in Section 2.3). But, once again, the fact that t_0 is arbitrary implies that we may write

$$\frac{\partial U}{\partial t} = \sum_{n=1}^{\infty} -k\lambda_n^2 c_n X_n(x) e^{-k\lambda_n^2 t} \tag{63}$$

for $0 \leq x \leq L$ and $t > 0$.

Term-by-term differentiation of series (58a) with respect to x gives

$$\sum_{n=1}^{\infty} c_n X_n'(x) e^{-k\lambda_n^2 t} = \sum_{n=1}^{\infty} c_n (-\lambda_n) N^{-1} \sin \lambda_n x\, e^{-k\lambda_n^2 t}. \tag{64}$$

Since $N^{-1} \le M$, we have, for $0 \le x \le L$ and $t \ge t_0 > 0$,

$$\sum_{n=1}^{\infty} |c_n X_n'(x) e^{-k\lambda_n^2 t}| \le \sum_{n=1}^{\infty} (KML)(\lambda_n M) e^{-k\lambda_n^2 t_0}$$

$$\le KM^2 L \sum_{n=1}^{\infty} \left(\frac{n\pi}{L}\right) r^{n-1} = KM^2 \pi \sum_{n=1}^{\infty} n r^{n-1}. \qquad (65)$$

Because the series $\sum_{n-1}^{\infty} n r^{n-1}$ converges, series (64) likewise converges absolutely and uniformly. Consequently, series (58a) may be differentiated term by term to yield, for $0 \le x \le L$ and $t > 0$.

$$\frac{\partial U}{\partial x} = \sum_{n=1}^{\infty} c_n X_n'(x) e^{-k\lambda_n^2 t}. \qquad (66)$$

A similar analysis shows that for $0 \le x \le L$ and $t > 0$,

$$\frac{\partial^2 U}{\partial x^2} = \sum_{n=1}^{\infty} c_n X_n''(x) e^{-k\lambda_n^2 t} = \sum_{n=1}^{\infty} c_n [-\lambda_n^2 X_n(x)] e^{-k\lambda_n^2 t}. \qquad (67)$$

Expressions (63) and (67) for $\partial U/\partial t$ and $\partial^2 U/\partial x^2$ clearly indicate that $U(x, t)$ satisfies PDE (57a). Finally, expressions (66) and (58a) for $\partial U/\partial x$ and $U(x, t)$ indicate that

$$\frac{\partial U(0, t)}{\partial x} = \sum_{n=1}^{\infty} c_n X_n'(0) e^{-k\lambda_n^2 t} = 0$$

and $$\kappa \frac{\partial U(L, t)}{\partial x} + \mu U(L, t) = \kappa \sum_{n=1}^{\infty} c_n X_n'(L) e^{-k\lambda_n^2 t} + \mu \sum_{n=1}^{\infty} c_n X_n(L) e^{-k\lambda_n^2 t}$$

$$= \sum_{n=1}^{\infty} c_n [\kappa X_n'(L) + \mu X_n(L)] e^{-k\lambda_n^2 t} = 0$$

[since $X_n(x)$ satisfies $\kappa X_n'(L) + \mu X_n(L) = 0$].

We have now verified that the formal solution $U(x, t)$ defined by series (58) satisfies equations (57a–d). Clearly demonstrated was the dependence of our verification on properties of the Sturm-Liouville system associated with (57). Indeed, indispensable were the facts that eigenvalues satisfied the inequalities $(n - 1)\pi/L \le \lambda_n \le n\pi/L$ and that eigenfunctions were uniformly bounded. Without a knowledge of these properties, verification of the formal solution would have been impossible. Although (58) satisfies (57), verification of (58) as the solution of the heat conduction problem described by (57) is not complete. To illustrate why, consider the function defined by

$$U(x, t) = \begin{cases} \sum_{n=1}^{\infty} b_n e^{-k\lambda_n^2 t} X_n(x) & 0 \le x \le L, \quad t > 0 \\ f(x) & 0 \le x \le L, \quad t = 0 \end{cases}, \qquad (68)$$

where $\{b_n\}$ is a completely arbitrary, but bounded, sequence and $X_n(x)$ are the eigenfunctions in (58a). The above procedure can once again be used to verify that function (68) also satisfies (57a–c); in addition, it satisfies (57d). This means that, as stated, problem (57) is not well posed; it does not have a unique solution. It cannot therefore be an·adequate description of the physical problem following equation (2) in

Section 5.2—temperature in a rod of uniform cross section and insulated sides that at time $t = 0$ has temperature $f(x)$. For time $t > 0$, the end $x = 0$ is also insulated and heat is exchanged at the other end with an environment at temperature $0°C$. In actual fact, (57) does have a unique solution, provided we demand that the solution satisfy certain continuity conditions. Our immediate objective, then, is to discover what these conditions are; once we find them, we can then verify that (58) is the one and only solution of (57).

Continuity conditions for $U(x, t)$ depend on the class of functions permitted for $f(x)$. To simplify discussions, suppose we permit only functions $f(x)$ that are continuous for $0 \le x \le L$ and have piecewise continuous first derivatives. Physically this is realistic; continuity of $f(x)$ implies that the initial temperature distribution in the rod must be continuous. Because $f'(x)$ is proportional to heat flux across cross sections of the rod, piecewise continuity of $f'(x)$ implies that initially there can be no infinite surges of heat.

With $f(x)$ continuous, it is reasonable, physically, to demand that $U(x, t)$ be continuous for $0 \le x \le L$ and $t \ge 0$. [Were $f(x)$ assumed only piecewise continuous, continuity of $U(x, t)$ for $t = 0$ would not be appropriate.] The fact that $U(x, t)$ must satisfy PDE (57a) suggests that we demand that $\partial U/\partial t$, $\partial U/\partial x$, and $\partial^2 U/\partial x^2$ all be continuous for $0 < x < L$ and $t > 0$. Boundary conditions (57b, c) suggest that we require continuity of $\partial U/\partial x$ for $x = 0, t > 0$ and for $x = L, t > 0$ also. Because there are no heat sources (or sinks) at the ends of the rod, it follows that $\partial U/\partial t$ should be continuous at $x = 0$ and $x = L$ for $t > 0$. For a similar reason, $\partial^2 U/\partial x^2$ should also be continuous at $x = 0$ and $x = L$ for $t > 0$. We now show that these conditions guarantee a unique solution of (57); that is, we show that [when $f(x)$ is continuous and $f'(x)$ is piecewise continuous for $0 \le x \le L$] there is one and only one solution $U(x, t)$ of (57a–d) that also satisfies

$$U(x, t) \quad \text{continuous for } 0 \le x \le L \text{ and } t \ge 0; \tag{57e}$$

$$\frac{\partial U}{\partial x}, \quad \frac{\partial U}{\partial t}, \quad \text{and} \quad \frac{\partial^2 U}{\partial x^2} \quad \text{continuous for } 0 \le x \le L \text{ and } t > 0. \tag{57f}$$

Suppose, to the contrary, that there exist two solutions $U_1(x, t)$ and $U_2(x, t)$ satisfying (57a–f). The difference $U(x, t) = U_1(x, t) - U_2(x, t)$ must also satisfy (57a, b, c, e, f), but initial condition (57d) is replaced by the homogeneous condition $U(x, 0) = 0, 0 < x < L$. To show that $U_1(x, t) \equiv U_2(x, t)$, we show that $U(x, t) \equiv 0$. To do this, we multiply (57a) by $U(x, t)$ and integrate with respect to x from $x = 0$ to $x = L$:

$$\int_0^L \frac{\partial U}{\partial t} U(x, t)\, dx = k \int_0^L \frac{\partial^2 U}{\partial x^2} U(x, t)\, dx, \qquad t > 0.$$

Integration by parts on the right gives, for $t > 0$,

$$0 = \int_0^L \frac{1}{2} \frac{\partial [U(x, t)]^2}{\partial t}\, dx - k\left\{ U(x, t)\frac{\partial U}{\partial x}\right\}_0^L + k \int_0^L \left(\frac{\partial U}{\partial x}\right)^2 dx$$

$$= \frac{1}{2}\int_0^L \frac{\partial (U^2)}{\partial t}\, dx - kU(L, t)\frac{\partial U(L, t)}{\partial x} + kU(0, t)\frac{\partial U(0, t)}{\partial x} + k \int_0^L \left(\frac{\partial U}{\partial x}\right)^2 dx. \tag{69}$$

Substitutions from boundary conditions (57b, c) yield

$$0 = \frac{1}{2} \int_0^L \frac{\partial (U^2)}{\partial t} \, dx + k \int_0^L \left(\frac{\partial U}{\partial x} \right)^2 \, dx + \frac{k\mu [U(L,t)]^2}{\kappa}, \qquad t > 0. \qquad (70)$$

Because the last two terms are clearly nonnegative we must have

$$\int_0^L \frac{\partial (U^2)}{\partial t} \, dx = \frac{\partial}{\partial t} \int_0^L [U(x,t)]^2 \, dx \le 0, \qquad t > 0;$$

that is, the definite integral of $[U(x,t)]^2$ must be a decreasing function of t. But, because $U(x,t)$ satisfies the condition $U(x,0) = 0, 0 < x < L$, the definite integral of $[U(x,t)]^2$ at $t = 0$ has value zero:

$$\int_0^L [U(x,0)]^2 \, dx = 0.$$

In other words, as a function of t, for $t \ge 0$, the definite integral of $[U(x,t)]^2$ is non-negative, is decreasing, and has value zero at $t = 0$. It must therefore be identically equal to zero:

$$\int_0^L [U(x,t)]^2 \, dx \equiv 0, \qquad t \ge 0.$$

Because the integrand is continuous and nonnegative, we conclude that $U(x,t) \equiv 0$ for $0 \le x \le L$ and $t \ge 0$, that is, $U_1(x,t) \equiv U_2(x,t)$.

We have shown, then, that for the class of initial temperature distributions $f(x)$ that are continuous and have piecewise continuous first derivatives, conditions (57e, f) attached to equations (57a–d) yield a problem with a unique solution; there is one and only one solution satisfying (57a–f). To establish that (58) is the one and only solution of problem (57), we must verify that it satisfies (57e, f). In verifying (58) as a solution of (57a–d), we proved that series (63), (66), and (67) converge uniformly for $0 \le x \le L$ and $t \ge t_0 > 0$ for arbitrary t_0. This implies that $\partial U / \partial t$, $\partial U / \partial x$, and $\partial^2 U / \partial x^2$ are all continuous functions for $0 \le x \le L$ and $t > 0$ (see Theorem 6 in Section 2.3). This establishes (57f). To verify (57e), we assume, for simplicity, that $f(x)$ satisfies the boundary conditions of the Sturm-Liouville system associated with the problem, namely $f'(0) = 0$ and $\kappa f'(L) + \mu f(L) = 0$. In this case, Theorem 3 in Section 4.3 indicates that the generalized Fourier series $\sum_{n=1}^{\infty} c_n X_n(x)$ of $f(x)$ converges uniformly to $f(x)$ for $0 \le x \le L$. Because the functions $e^{-k\lambda_n^2 t}$ are uniformly bounded for $t \ge 0$ and for each such t the sequence $\{ e^{-k\lambda_n^2 t} \}$ is nonincreasing, it follows by Abel's test (Theorem 5 in Section 2.3) that series (58a) converges uniformly for $0 \le x \le L$ and $t \ge 0$. The temperature function $U(x,t)$ as defined by (58a) must therefore be continuous for $0 \le x \le L$ and $t \ge 0$.

Verification of (58) as the solution to the heat conduction problem described by (57) is now complete.

An important point to notice here is that even though the initial temperature distribution may have discontinuities in its first derivative $f'(x)$, the solution of problem (57) has continuous first derivatives for $0 \le x \le L$ and $t > 0$. In fact, it has continuous derivatives of all orders for $0 \le x \le L$ and $t > 0$. This means that the heat equation immediately smooths out discontinuities of $f'(x)$ and its derivatives. Even if

$f(x)$ itself were piecewise continuous, discontinuities would immediately be smoothed out by the heat equation. We shall see that this is also true for elliptic equations, but not for hyperbolic ones.

The method used to verify that problem (57a–f) has a unique solution is applicable to much more general problems. Consider, for example, the three-dimensional heat conduction problem

$$\frac{\partial U}{\partial t} = k\nabla^2 U + \frac{kg(x, y, z, t)}{\kappa}, \qquad (x, y, z) \text{ in } V, \qquad t > 0, \qquad \text{(71a)}$$

$$U(x, y, z, t) = F(x, y, z, t), \qquad (x, y, z) \text{ on } \beta(V), \qquad t > 0, \qquad \text{(71b)}$$

$$U(x, y, z, 0) = f(x, y, z), \qquad (x, y, z) \text{ in } \bar{V}, \qquad \text{(71c)}$$

where $\bar{V}$ is the closed region consisting of V and its boundary $\beta(V)$. In Exercise 2 it is proved that there cannot be more than one solution $U(x, y, z, t)$ that satisfies the conditions

$$U(x, y, z, t) \quad \text{continuous for } (x, y, z) \text{ in } \bar{V} \text{ and } t \geq 0, \qquad \text{(71d)}$$

First partial derivatives of $U(x, y, z)$ with respect to x, y, z, and t
and second partial derivatives with respect to x, y, and z continuous for
(x, y, z) in $\bar{V}$ and $t > 0$. $\qquad \text{(71e)}$

Heat conduction problems satisfy what are called maximum and minimum principles. We state and prove the one-dimensional situation here; three-dimensional principles are proved in Exercise 5. Temperature in a rod with insulated sides, when there is no internal heat generation and when the initial temperature distribution is $f(x)$, must satisfy the one-dimensional heat equation

$$\frac{\partial U}{\partial t} = k\frac{\partial^2 U}{\partial x^2}, \qquad 0 < x < L, \qquad t > 0 \qquad \text{(72a)}$$

and the initial condition

$$U(x, 0) = f(x), \qquad 0 \leq x \leq L. \qquad \text{(72b)}$$

By taking a closed interval in (72b), we are assuming compatibility between the initial temperature distribution $f(x)$ at $x = 0$ and $x = L$ and the boundary temperatures when $t = 0$. Boundary conditions have not been enunciated because maximum and minimum principles are independent of boundary conditions being Dirichlet, Neumann, or Robin. Let U_M be the largest of the following three numbers:

$$U_1 = \text{maximum value of } f(x) \text{ for } 0 \leq x \leq L,$$
$$U_2 = \text{maximum value of } U(0, t) \text{ for } 0 \leq t \leq T,$$
$$U_3 = \text{maximum value of } U(L, t) \text{ for } 0 \leq t \leq T,$$

where T is some given value of t. In other words, U_M is the maximum of the initial temperature of the rod and that found (or applied) at the ends of the rod up to time T. The *maximum principle* states that $U(x, t) \leq U_M$ for all $0 \leq x \leq L$ and $0 \leq t \leq T$; that is, at no point in the rod during the time interval $0 \leq t \leq T$ can the temperature ever exceed U_M. To prove this result, we define a function $V(x, t) = U(x, t) + \varepsilon x^2, 0 \leq x \leq L,$

$0 \le t \le T$, where $\varepsilon > 0$ is a very small number. Because U satisfies (72a), we can say that for $0 < x < L$ and $0 < t < T$,

$$\frac{\partial V}{\partial t} - k\frac{\partial^2 V}{\partial x^2} = \frac{\partial U}{\partial t} - k\left(\frac{\partial^2 U}{\partial x^2} + 2\varepsilon\right) = -2k\varepsilon < 0. \tag{73}$$

Assuming that $U(x, t)$ is continuous, so also is $V(x, t)$, and therefore $V(x, t)$ must take on a maximum in the closed rectangle $\bar{A}$ of Figure 5.12. This value must occur either on the edge of the rectangle or at an interior point (x^*, t^*). In the latter case, $V(x, t)$ must necessarily have a relative maximum at (x^*, t^*), and therefore $\partial V/\partial t = \partial V/\partial x = 0$ and $\partial^2 V/\partial x^2 \le 0$ at (x^*, t^*). But then $\partial V/\partial t - k\partial^2 V/\partial x^2 \ge 0$ at (x^*, t^*), contradicting (73). Hence, the maximum value of V must occur on the boundary of $\bar{A}$. It cannot occur along $t = T$, for, in this case, $\partial V/\partial t \ge 0$ at the point and $\partial^2 V/\partial x^2$ would still be nonpositive. Once again, (73) would be violated. Consequently, the maximum value of V on $\bar{A}$ must occur on one of the three boundaries $t = 0, x = 0,$ or $x = L$. Since $U \le U_M$ on these three lines, it follows that $V \le U_M + \varepsilon L^2$ on these lines and therefore in $\bar{A}$. But because $U(x, t) \le V(x, t)$, we can state that, in $\bar{A}$, $U(x, t) \le U_M + \varepsilon L^2$. Since ε can be made arbitrarily small, it follows that U_M must be the maximum value of U for $0 \le x \le L$ and $0 \le t \le T$.

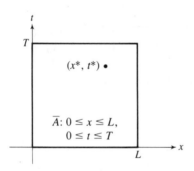

Figure 5.12

When this result is applied to $-U$, the *minimum principle* is obtained—at no point in the rod during the time interval $0 \le t \le T$ can the temperature ever be less than the minimum of the initial temperature of the rod and that found (or applied) at the ends of the rod up to time T.

We mention one final property of heat conduction problems, which, unfortunately, is not demonstrable with the series solutions of Chapters 3 and 5. [It is illustrated for infinite rods in Case 2 of solution (47b) in Section 7.4 and for finite rods in solution (44) of Section 10.4.] When heat is added to any part of an object, its effect is instantaneously felt throughout the whole object. For instance, suppose that the initial temperature $f(x)$ of the rod in problem (57) is identically equal to zero, and at $t = 0$ a small amount of heat is added to either end of the rod or over some cross section of the rod. Instantaneously, the temperature of every point of the rod rises. The increase may be extremely small, but, nonetheless, every point in the rod has a positive temperature for arbitrarily small $t > 0$, and this is true for arbitrarily large L. In other words, heat has been propagated infinitely fast from the source point to all other points in the rod. This apparent paradox is a result of the macroscopic derivation of the heat equation in Section 1.2. On a microscopic level, it would be necessary to take into account the moment of inertia of the molecules transmitting heat, and this would lead to a finite speed for propagation of heat.

Exercises 5.6

1. (a) What is the formal series solution of the one-dimensional heat conduction problem

$$\frac{\partial U}{\partial t} = k\frac{\partial^2 U}{\partial x^2}, \qquad 0 < x < L, \qquad t > 0,$$

$$-l_1\frac{\partial U}{\partial x} + h_1 U = 0, \qquad x = 0, \qquad t > 0,$$

$$l_2\frac{\partial U}{\partial x} + h_2 U = 0, \qquad x = L, \qquad t > 0,$$

$$U(x, 0) = f(x), \qquad 0 < x < L?$$

   (b) Use a technique similar to verification of formal solution (58) for problem (57) to verify that the formal solution in (a) satisfies the four equations in (a) when $f(x)$ is piecewise smooth on $0 \le x \le L$.

   (c) Assuming further that $f(x)$ is continuous on $0 \le x \le L$, show that there is one and only one solution of the problem in (a) that also satisfies continuity conditions (57e, f).

   (d) Verify that the formal solution in (a) satisfies (57e, f) when $f(x)$ satisfies the boundary conditions of the associated Sturm-Liouville system.

2. Use Green's first identity (see Appendix C) to verify that there cannot be more than one solution to problem (71).

3. Repeat Exercise 2 if the boundary condition on $\beta(V)$ is of Robin type.

4. Can you repeat Exercise 2 if the boundary condition on $\beta(V)$ is of Neumann type?

5. In this exercise we prove three-dimensional maximum and minimum principles. Let $U(x, y, z, t)$ be the continuous solution of the homogeneous three-dimensional heat conduction equation in some open region V,

$$\frac{\partial U}{\partial t} = k\nabla^2 U, \qquad (x, y, z) \text{ in } V, \qquad t > 0,$$

which also satisfies the initial condition

$$U(x, y, z, 0) = f(x, y, z), \qquad (x, y, z) \text{ in } \bar{V},$$

where $\bar{V}$ is the closed region consisting of V and its boundary $\beta(V)$. Let U_M be the maximum value of $f(x, y, z)$ and the value of U on $\beta(V)$ for $0 \le t \le T$, T some given time.

   (a) Define a function

$$W(x, y, z, t) = U(x, y, z, t) + \varepsilon(x^2 + y^2 + z^2),$$

where $\varepsilon > 0$ is a very small number. Show that

$$\frac{\partial W}{\partial t} - k\nabla^2 W < 0$$

for (x, y, z) in V and $0 < t < T$, and use this fact to verify that W cannot have a relative maximum for a point (x, y, z) in V and a time $0 < t < T$.

(b) Prove the maximum principle that $U(x, y, z, t) \leq U_M$ for (x, y, z) in $\bar{V}$ and $0 \leq t \leq T$.

(c) What is the minimum principle for this situation?

5.7 Properties of Elliptic Partial Differential Equations

Verifications that formal solutions of boundary value problems do indeed satisfy the elliptic PDEs and boundary conditions from which they were derived are similar to those for parabolic (heat) problems. We illustrate with the following Dirichlet problem for Laplace's equation

$$\frac{\partial^2 V}{\partial x^2} + \frac{\partial^2 V}{\partial y^2} = 0, \qquad 0 < x < L, \qquad 0 < y < L', \tag{74a}$$

$$V(0, y) = 0, \qquad 0 < y < L', \tag{74b}$$

$$V(L, y) = 0, \qquad 0 < y < L', \tag{74c}$$

$$V(x, 0) = 0, \qquad 0 < x < L, \tag{74d}$$

$$V(x, L') = f(x), \qquad 0 < x < L. \tag{74e}$$

Separation leads to the formal solution

$$V(x, y) = \sum_{n=1}^{\infty} A_n \sinh\frac{n\pi y}{L} X_n(x), \tag{75a}$$

where

$$A_n = \frac{1}{\sinh(n\pi L'/L)} \int_0^L f(x)X_n(x)\,dx \tag{75b}$$

and $X_n(x) = \sqrt{2/L} \, \sin(n\pi x/L)$.

Theorem 2 of Chapter 4 guarantees that boundary condition (74e) is satisfied when $f(x)$ is piecewise smooth on $0 \leq x \leq L$ [provided $f(x)$ is defined as the average of right- and left-hand limits at any point of discontinuity]. Boundary conditions (74b–d) are clearly satisfied by (75a). To verify that $V(x, y)$ as defined by (75a) satisfies PDE (74a), we first note that when $f(x)$ is piecewise continuous, it is necessarily bounded [$|f(x)| \leq K$]. Combine this with the fact that $|X_n(x)| \leq \sqrt{2/L}$, and we obtain

$$|A_n| \leq \frac{1}{|\sinh(n\pi L'/L)|} \int_0^L |f(x)||X_n(x)|\,dx$$

$$\leq \frac{K\sqrt{2/L}\,(L)}{\sinh(n\pi L'/L)} = \frac{\sqrt{2L}\,K}{\sinh(n\pi L'/L)}. \tag{76}$$

With this result, we may write, for any x in $0 \le x \le L$ and any y in $0 \le y \le y_0 < L'$,

$$\sum_{n=1}^{\infty} \left| A_n \sinh \frac{n\pi y}{L} X_n(x) \right| \le \sum_{n=1}^{\infty} \frac{\sqrt{2L}\,K}{\sinh(n\pi L'/L)} \sinh \frac{n\pi y}{L} \sqrt{\frac{2}{L}}$$

$$= 2K \sum_{n=1}^{\infty} \frac{\sinh(n\pi y/L)}{\sinh(n\pi L'/L)} \le 2K \sum_{n=1}^{\infty} e^{-n\pi(L'-y)/L}$$

$$\le 2K \sum_{n=1}^{\infty} e^{-n\pi(L'-y_0)/L} = 2K \sum_{n=1}^{\infty} \left(e^{-\pi(L'-y_0)/L} \right)^n$$

$$= 2K \sum_{n=1}^{\infty} r^n, \tag{77}$$

a convergent geometric series since $r = e^{-\pi(L'-y_0)/L} < 1$. Consequently, according to the Weierstrass M-test, series (75a) converges absolutely and uniformly with respect to x and y for $0 \le x \le L$ and $0 \le y \le y_0 < L'$. Because y_0 is arbitrary, series (75a) converges absolutely for $0 \le x \le L$ and $0 \le y < L'$. In addition, series (75a) represents a continuous function for $0 \le x \le L$ and $0 \le y < L'$. Thus, even though $f(x)$ may have discontinuities, the solution of Laplace's equation must be a continuous function. In other words, Laplace's equation smooths out discontinuities in boundary data.

Term-by-term differentiation of series (75a) with respect to x gives

$$\sum_{n=1}^{\infty} A_n \sinh \frac{n\pi y}{L} X_n'(x), \tag{78}$$

where $X_n'(x) = (n\pi/L)\sqrt{2/L}\,\cos(n\pi x/L)$. It follows that, for $0 \le x \le L$ and $0 \le y \le y_0 < L'$,

$$\sum_{n=1}^{\infty} \left| A_n \sinh \frac{n\pi y}{L} X_n'(x) \right| \le \frac{2K\pi}{L} \sum_{n=1}^{\infty} n r^n. \tag{79}$$

Because $\sum_{n=1}^{\infty} n r^n$ converges, series (78) converges absolutely and uniformly. Thus, series (75a) may be differentiated term by term to yield, for $0 \le x \le L$ and $0 \le y < L'$,

$$\frac{\partial V}{\partial x} = \sum_{n=1}^{\infty} A_n \sinh \frac{n\pi y}{L} X_n'(x). \tag{80}$$

Similarly, for $0 \le x \le L$ and $0 \le y < L'$,

$$\frac{\partial^2 V}{\partial x^2} = \sum_{n=1}^{\infty} A_n \sinh \frac{n\pi y}{L} X_n''(x). \tag{81}$$

Term-by-term differentiation of (75a) with respect to y gives

$$\frac{\pi}{L} \sum_{n=1}^{\infty} n A_n \cosh \frac{n\pi y}{L} X_n(x). \tag{82}$$

Using inequality (76) and the fact that $|X_n(x)| \le \sqrt{2/L}$, we may write

$$\frac{\pi}{L} \sum_{n=1}^{\infty} \left| n A_n \cosh \frac{n\pi y}{L} X_n(x) \right| \le \frac{2K\pi}{L} \sum_{n=1}^{\infty} \frac{n \cosh(n\pi y/L)}{\sinh(n\pi L'/L)}. \tag{83}$$

Now N can always be chosen sufficiently large that $\sinh(n\pi L'/L) \geq (1/4)e^{n\pi L'/L}$, whenever $n \geq N$. For such N,

$$
\frac{\pi}{L} \sum_{n=N}^{\infty} \left| nA_n \cosh\frac{n\pi y}{L} X_n(x) \right| \leq \frac{2K\pi}{L} \sum_{n=N}^{\infty} \frac{ne^{n\pi y/L}}{(1/4)e^{n\pi L'/L}}
$$

$$
= \frac{8K\pi}{L} \sum_{n=N}^{\infty} ne^{-n\pi(L'-y)/L} \leq \frac{8K\pi}{L} \sum_{n=N}^{\infty} ne^{-n\pi(L'-y_0)/L}
$$

$$
= \frac{8K\pi}{L} \sum_{n=N}^{\infty} nr^n, \tag{84}
$$

where $r = e^{-\pi(L'-y_0)/L}$, provided also that $0 \leq x \leq L$ and $0 \leq y \leq y_0 < L'$. Since the series $\sum_{n=1}^{\infty} nr^n$ converges, it follows that series (82) converges uniformly and absolutely for $0 \leq x \leq L$ and $0 \leq y \leq y_0 < L'$. Thus, series (75a) may be differentiated term by term with respect to y to yield, for $0 \leq x \leq L$ and $0 \leq y < L'$,

$$
\frac{\partial V}{\partial y} = \frac{\pi}{L} \sum_{n=1}^{\infty} nA_n \cosh\frac{n\pi y}{L} X_n(x). \tag{85}
$$

For the same values of x and y, we also obtain

$$
\frac{\partial^2 V}{\partial y^2} = \frac{\pi^2}{L^2} \sum_{n=1}^{\infty} n^2 A_n \sinh\frac{n\pi y}{L} X_n(x). \tag{86}
$$

Because $X_n''(x) = (-n^2\pi^2/L^2)X_n(x)$, expressions (81) and (86) clearly indicate that $V(x, y)$ satisfies Laplace's equation (74a). We have shown, therefore, that series solution (75) satisfies problem (74).

In order to guarantee a unique solution of (74), continuity conditions must also accompany the problem. We show that when $f(x)$ is a continuous function with a continuous first derivative $f'(x)$ and a piecewise continuous second derivative $f''(x)$, for which $f(0) = f(L) = 0$, appropriate conditions are

$$
V, \quad \frac{\partial V}{\partial x}, \quad \text{and} \quad \frac{\partial V}{\partial y} \quad \text{continuous for } 0 \leq x \leq L \text{ and } 0 \leq y \leq L'; \tag{74f}
$$

second partial derivatives of $V(x, y)$ continuous for

$$
0 < x < L, 0 < y < L'. \tag{74g}
$$

Suppose, to the contrary, that there exist two solutions, $V_1(x, y)$ and $V_2(x, y)$, satisfying (74). The difference $V(x, y) = V_1(x, y) - V_2(x, y)$ must also satisfy (74), but with (74e) replaced by the homogeneous condition $V(x, L') = 0, 0 < x < L$. If we multiply (74a) by $V(x, y)$, integrate over the rectangle $R: 0 < x < L, 0 < y < L'$, and use Green's first identity (Appendix C), we obtain

$$
0 = \iint_R V\nabla^2 V \, dA = \oint_{\beta(R)} V\frac{\partial V}{\partial n} \, ds - \iint_R |\nabla V|^2 \, dA, \tag{87}
$$

where $\partial V/\partial n$ is the directional derivative of V outwardly normal to $\beta(R)$. Since $V \equiv 0$ on $\beta(R)$,

$$
0 = -\iint_R |\nabla V|^2 \, dA.
$$

But this result requires that $\nabla V \equiv 0$ in R, and therefore $V(x, y)$ must be constant in R. Because V is constant in R, vanishes on $\beta(R)$, and is continuous for $0 \le x \le L$, $0 \le y \le L'$, it follows that $V(x, y) \equiv 0$. In other words, conditions (74f, g) guarantee a unique solution of problem (74).

Once again, we point out that Laplace's equation, like the heat equation, smooths out discontinuities. Even when the boundary data function $f(x)$ has discontinuities in its second derivative, (74g) demands that second derivatives of $V(x, y)$ be continuous for $0 < x < L$ and $0 < y < L'$.

We now establish that solution (75) of problem (74a–e) also satisfies conditions (74f, g). The facts that series (81) and (86) converge uniformly for $0 \le x \le L$ and $0 \le y \le y_0 < L'$ and y_0 is arbitrary imply that $\partial^2 V/\partial x^2$ and $\partial^2 V/\partial y^2$ are continuous for $0 \le x \le L$ and $0 \le y < L'$. To verify (74f), we use Theorem 5 in Section 2.3. First, note that with continuity of $f(x)$ and $f(0) = f(L) = 0$, the Fourier series of $f(x)$,

$$f(x) = \sum_{n=1}^{\infty} A_n \sinh \frac{n\pi L'}{L} X_n(x), \tag{88}$$

converges uniformly to $f(x)$ on $0 \le x \le L$ (see Theorem 3 in Section 4.3). Series (75a) can be obtained from series (88) by multiplying the nth term of (88) by

$$Y_n(y) = \frac{\sinh(n\pi y/L)}{\sinh(n\pi L'/L)}.$$

These functions are uniformly bounded for $0 \le y \le L'$. For fixed y in $0 \le y \le L'$, the derivative of $Y_n(y)$ as a function of a continuous variable n is

$$\frac{\partial Y_n}{\partial n} = \frac{(\pi y/L)\sinh(n\pi L'/L)\cosh(n\pi y/L) - (\pi L'/L)\sinh(n\pi y/L)\cosh(n\pi L'/L)}{\sinh^2(n\pi L'/L)}.$$

Thus,

$$\frac{L}{\pi}\sinh^2\left(\frac{n\pi L'}{L}\right)\frac{\partial Y_n}{\partial n} = y\sinh\frac{n\pi L'}{L}\cosh\frac{n\pi y}{L} - L'\sinh\frac{n\pi y}{L}\cosh\frac{n\pi L'}{L}$$

$$= \frac{y}{2}\left(\sinh\frac{n\pi(L'+y)}{L} + \sinh\frac{n\pi(L'-y)}{L}\right) - \frac{L'}{2}\left(\sinh\frac{n\pi(y+L')}{L} + \sinh\frac{n\pi(y-L')}{L}\right)$$

$$= \frac{L'+y}{2}\sinh\frac{n\pi(L'-y)}{L} - \frac{L'-y}{2}\sinh\frac{n\pi(L'+y)}{L}$$

$$= \frac{L'+y}{2}\sum_{m=0}^{\infty}\frac{1}{(2m+1)!}\left(\frac{n\pi(L'-y)}{L}\right)^{2m+1} - \frac{L'-y}{2}\sum_{m=0}^{\infty}\frac{1}{(2m+1)!}\left(\frac{n\pi(L'+y)}{L}\right)^{2m+1}$$

$$= \frac{(L'+y)(L'-y)}{2}\sum_{m=0}^{\infty}\frac{1}{(2m+1)!}\left((L'-y)^{2m} - (L'+y)^{2m}\right)\left(\frac{n\pi}{L}\right)^{2m+1},$$

which is clearly nonpositive. Thus, for each fixed y in $0 \le y \le L'$, the sequence $\{Y_n(y)\}$ is nonincreasing, and by Theorem 5 in Section 2.3, series (75a) converges uniformly for $0 \le x \le L$ and $0 \le y \le L'$. This series therefore defines a continuous function $V(x, y)$ on $0 \le x \le L$, $0 \le y \le L'$.

Because $f'(x)$ is continuous [and $f''(x)$ is piecewise continuous], the Fourier (cosine) series

$$f'(x) = \sum_{n=1}^{\infty} A_n \sinh \frac{n\pi L'}{L} X'_n(x) = \frac{\sqrt{2}\,\pi}{L^{3/2}} \sum_{n=1}^{\infty} nA_n \sinh \frac{n\pi L'}{L} \cos \frac{n\pi x}{L}$$

converges uniformly to $f'(x)$ for $0 \leq x \leq L$ [see Exercise 4(c) in Section 2.3]. Since series (80) for $\partial V/\partial x$ can be obtained from this series by multiplying the nth term by $Y_n(y)$, it follows that series (80) converges uniformly to $\partial V/\partial x$ for $0 \leq x \leq L$ and $0 \leq y \leq L'$ and that $\partial V/\partial x$ is continuous thereon.

Finally, we must show that $\partial V/\partial y$ as defined by series (85) is continuous. Because the above series for $f'(x)$ is uniformly convergent for $0 \leq x \leq L$, it follows (by setting $x = 0$) that the series

$$\sum_{n=1}^{\infty} \left| nA_n \sinh \frac{n\pi L'}{L} \right|$$

is convergent. Consequently, the series

$$\sum_{n=1}^{\infty} nA_n \sinh \frac{n\pi L'}{L} X_n(x)$$

converges absolutely and uniformly for $0 \leq x \leq L$. Series (85) for $\partial V/\partial y$ can be obtained from this series by multiplying the nth term by

$$Z_n(y) = \frac{\cosh(n\pi y/L)}{\sinh(n\pi L'/L)}.$$

These functions are uniformly bounded for $0 \leq y \leq L'$, and, furthermore,

$$[Z_n(y)]^2 = \frac{\cosh^2(n\pi y/L)}{\sinh^2(n\pi L'/L)} = \frac{1}{\sinh^2(n\pi L'/L)} + \left(\frac{\sinh(n\pi y/L)}{\sinh(n\pi L'/L)} \right)^2$$

$$= \frac{1}{\sinh^2(n\pi L'/L)} + [Y_n(y)]^2.$$

For fixed y in $0 \leq y \leq L'$, the sequence $\{Y_n(y)\}$ is nonincreasing, as is the sequence $\{1/\sinh^2(n\pi L'/L)\}$. Consequently, the same can be said for $\{Z_n(y)\}$, and it follows by Theorem 5 in Section 2.3 that series (85) converges uniformly for $0 \leq x \leq L$ and $0 \leq y \leq L'$. Thus, $\partial V/\partial y$ must be continuous thereon, and this completes the proof that solution (75) satisfies conditions (74f, g).

The method used to verify that problem (74a–g) has a unique solution is applicable to much more general problems. Consider, for example, the three-dimensional boundary value problem

$$\nabla^2 U = F(x, y, z), \qquad (x, y, z) \text{ in } V, \tag{89a}$$

$$l\frac{\partial U}{\partial n} + hU = f(x, y, z), \qquad (x, y, z) \text{ on } \beta(V), \tag{89b}$$

$$U \text{ and its first derivatives continuous in } \bar{V}, \tag{89c}$$

$$\text{Second derivatives of } U \text{ continuous in } V, \tag{89d}$$

where $\bar{V}$ is the closed region consisting of V and its boundary and $l \geq 0$ and $h \geq 0$ are constants. In Exercise 2 it is shown that when $h \neq 0$, there cannot be more than one solution of this problem, and when $h = 0$, the solution is unique to an additive constant (i.e., if U is a solution, then all solutions are of the form $U + C$, $C = $ constant). Uniqueness also results when different parts of $\beta(V)$ are subjected to different types of boundary conditions. For U not to be unique, the boundary condition must be Neumann on all of $\beta(V)$.

Maximum and minimum principles for elliptic problems are important theoretically and practically. We verify three-dimensional principles here. The maximum principle for Poisson's equation is as follows:

> If $U(x, y, z)$ is a continuous solution of (89a), and $F(x, y, z) \geq 0$ in V, then at no point in V can the value of $U(x, y, z)$ exceed the maximum value of U on $\beta(V)$.

To prove this result, we let U_M be the maximum value of U on $\beta(V)$ and define a function $W(x, y, z) = U(x, y, z) + \varepsilon(x^2 + y^2 + z^2)$ in $\bar{V}$, where $\varepsilon > 0$ is a very small number. Because U satisfies (89a), we can say that in V,

$$\nabla^2 W = \nabla^2 U + 6\varepsilon = F(x, y, z) + 6\varepsilon > 0. \tag{90}$$

Because W is continuous in $\bar{V}$, it must attain an absolute maximum therein. Suppose this maximum occurs at a point (x^*, y^*, z^*) in the interior V (which therefore must be a relative maximum). It follows, then, that

$$\frac{\partial W}{\partial x} = \frac{\partial W}{\partial y} = \frac{\partial W}{\partial z} = 0 \quad \text{and} \quad \frac{\partial^2 W}{\partial x^2} \leq 0, \quad \frac{\partial^2 W}{\partial y^2} \leq 0, \quad \frac{\partial^2 W}{\partial z^2} \leq 0,$$

all at (x^*, y^*, z^*). Because the last three inequalities contradict (90), the maximum of W must occur on $\beta(V)$.

Since $U \leq U_M$ on $\beta(V)$, $W \leq U_M + \varepsilon R^2$ on $\beta(V)$, where R is the radius of a sphere centered at the origin that contains V (such a sphere must exist when V is bounded). Since the maximum value of W must occur on $\beta(V)$, we can state further that $W \leq U_M + \varepsilon R^2$ for all (x, y, z) in $\bar{V}$. But because $U(x, y, z) \leq W(x, y, z)$ in $\bar{V}$, it follows that in $\bar{V}$, $U(x, y, z) \leq U_M + \varepsilon R^2$. Since ε can be made arbitrarily small, we conclude that $U(x, y, z) \leq U_M$ in $\bar{V}$, and the proof is complete.

When $U(x, y, z)$ is a solution of Laplace's equation, the above maximum principle still holds. In addition, the principle may also be applied to $-U$, resulting in a minimum principle. In other words, we have the following maximum-minimum principle for Laplace's equation:

> If a continuous solution of Laplace's equation $\nabla^2 U = 0$ in V satisfies the condition that $U_m \leq U \leq U_M$ on $\beta(V)$, then $U_m \leq U \leq U_M$ in V also.

This principle provides an alternative, and very simple, proof for uniqueness of solutions to problem (89) when the boundary condition is Dirichlet. If U_1 and U_2 are solutions of Poisson's equation (89a) and a Dirichlet condition $U = f(x, y, z)$ on $\beta(V)$, then $U = U_1 - U_2$ is a solution of Laplace's equation $\nabla^2 U = 0$ subject to $U = 0$ on $\beta(V)$. But, according to the maximum-minimum principle for Laplace's equation, U must then be identically equal to zero in V; that is, $U_1 \equiv U_2$.

These principles seem natural and evident in physical settings. For example, the boundary value problem

$$\frac{\partial^2 z}{\partial x^2} + \frac{\partial^2 z}{\partial y^2} = -\frac{F(x, y)}{\tau}, \qquad (x, y) \text{ in } A,$$

$$l\frac{\partial z}{\partial n} + hz = f(x, y), \qquad (x, y) \text{ on } \beta(A)$$

describes static deflections of a membrane subjected to a force per unit area with vertical component $F(x, y)$. The two-dimensional maximum principle for Poisson's equation states that if the vertical force is always negative (or zero), then at no point can the membrane have a deflection that exceeds the maximum value on its edge. Furthermore, if there is no external force on the membrane, the maximum-minimum principle for Laplace's equation states that deflections at all points of the membrane must be between maximum and minimum boundary deflections.

When $-F(x, y)/\tau$ is replaced by $-g(x, y)/\kappa$, the problem describes steady-state temperature in a plate insulated top and bottom with internal heat sources (or sinks) described by $g(x, y)$. Poisson's principle implies that when $g(x, y) \leq 0$, so that heat is being extracted at every point, *then* at no point in the plate can the temperature exceed its maximum value on the boundary. In addition, if $g(x, y) \equiv 0$, maximum and minimum temperatures must occur on the boundary. If this were not the case, heat would flow away from the point of maximum temperature in all directions and a steady-state situation would not exist.

Exercises 5.7

1. **(a)** What is the formal series solution of the two-dimensional potential problem

$$\frac{\partial^2 V}{\partial x^2} + \frac{\partial^2 V}{\partial y^2} = 0, \qquad 0 < x < L, \qquad 0 < y < L',$$

$$-l_1 \frac{\partial V}{\partial x} + h_1 V = 0, \qquad x = 0, \qquad 0 < y < L',$$

$$l_2 \frac{\partial V}{\partial x} + h_2 V = 0, \qquad x = L, \qquad 0 < y < L',$$

$$V(x, 0) = 0, \qquad 0 < x < L,$$

$$V(x, L') = f(x), \qquad 0 < x < L?$$

(b) Use a technique similar to verification of formal solution (75) for problem (74) to verify that the formal solution in (a) satisfies the five equations in (a) when $f(x)$ is piecewise smooth on $0 \leq x \leq L$.

(c) Assuming further that $f(x)$ and $f'(x)$ are continuous and that $f''(x)$ is piecewise continuous on $0 \leq x \leq L$, show that there is one and only one solution of the problem in (a) that also satisfies continuity conditions (74f, g).

(d) Verify that the formal solution in (a) satisfies (74f, g) when $f(x)$ satisfies the boundary conditions of the associated Sturm-Liouville system. Omit a proof of continuity of $\partial V/\partial x$ and $\partial V/\partial y$.

2. Use Green's first identity (see Appendix C) to verify that there cannot be more than one solution to problem (89) except when $h = 0$, in which case the solution is unique to an additive constant.

3. Verify that a solution of Laplace's equation in a volume V of space cannot have a relative maximum or minimum in V.

5.8 Properties of Hyperbolic Partial Differential Equations

Verification of formal solutions of initial boundary value problems involving hyperbolic PDEs requires a different approach from that used for parabolic and elliptic equations in the previous two sections. To see why, consider the initial boundary value problem for displacements of a string with fixed ends, released from rest at some given initial position $f(x)$:

$$\frac{\partial^2 y}{\partial t^2} = c^2 \frac{\partial^2 y}{\partial x^2}, \qquad 0 < x < L, \qquad t > 0, \tag{91a}$$

$$y(0, t) = 0, \qquad t > 0, \tag{91b}$$

$$y(L, t) = 0, \qquad t > 0, \tag{91c}$$

$$y(x, 0) = f(x), \qquad 0 < x < L, \tag{91d}$$

$$y_t(x, 0) = 0, \qquad 0 < x < L. \tag{91e}$$

If we assume that $f(x)$ is continuous and $f'(x)$ is piecewise continuous for $0 \le x \le L$, and that $f(0) = f(L) = 0$, the formal solution is

$$y(x, t) = \sum_{n=1}^{\infty} c_n X_n(x) \cos \frac{n\pi c t}{L} \tag{92a}$$

where

$$c_n = \int_0^L f(x) X_n(x)\, dx \tag{92b}$$

and $X_n(x) = \sqrt{2/L} \sin(n\pi x/L)$. A function $f(x)$ satisfying these requirements was considered in Figure 1.30(a) of Section 1.7. Figure 1.30(b)–(o) illustrate that the discontinuity in $f'(x)$ is propagated in both directions along the string at speed c. In other words, the solution $y(x, t)$ could not possibly satisfy PDE (91a). Likewise, discontinuities in the second derivative of $f(x)$ are also propagated at speed c. In order, therefore, for solution (92) to satisfy problem (91a) pointwise for $0 < x < L$ and $t > 0$, it is necessary to place very stringent conditions on $f(x)$. Suppose, for the moment, that we assume that $f(x)$, $f'(x)$, and $f''(x)$ are all continuous for $0 \le x \le L$ and that $f(0) = f(L) = 0$.

Now, verification of formal solution (58) to heat conduction problem (57) involved a detailed analysis of convergence of (58a) and its term-by-term derivatives with respect to x and t. A similar analysis ensued for potential problem (74). This type of analysis is inappropriate for problem (91). For instance, how do we show that (92a) converges for $0 \le x \le L$ and $t > 0$, knowing only that the c_n are bounded? To circumvent this difficulty, we use d'Alembert's representation of (92),

$$
\begin{aligned}
y(x, t) &= \sum_{n=1}^{\infty} c_n \sqrt{\frac{2}{L}} \sin \frac{n\pi x}{L} \cos \frac{n\pi c t}{L} \\
&= \frac{1}{2} \sum_{n=1}^{\infty} c_n \sqrt{\frac{2}{L}} \left(\sin \frac{n\pi(x + ct)}{L} + \sin \frac{n\pi(x - ct)}{L} \right) \\
&= \frac{1}{2} [f(x + ct) + f(x - ct)].
\end{aligned}
\tag{93}
$$

For this solution to define $y(x, t)$ for $0 \le x \le L$ and $t \ge 0$, $f(x)$ is extended as an odd, $2L$-periodic function. This extension immediately implies that (93) satisfies boundary conditions (91b, c) and initial condition (91e). Initial condition (91d) is clearly satisfied. With continuity of $f''(x)$, it is a straightforward application of chain rules to verify (91a).

We now show that problem (91) has a unique solution when $y(x, t)$ is also required to satisfy the condition that

$$
\begin{aligned}
&y(x, t) \text{ and its first and second partial derivatives} \\
&\text{be continuous for } 0 \le x \le L \text{ and } t \ge 0.
\end{aligned}
\tag{91f}
$$

Suppose, to the contrary, that $y_1(x, t)$ and $y_2(x, t)$ are two solutions of (91a–f). Their difference, $y(x, t) = y_1(x, t) - y_2(x, t)$, must then satisfy (91a, b, c, e, f), but (91d) is replaced by the homogeneous initial condition $y(x, 0) = 0$, $0 < x < L$. If we multiply (91a) by $\partial y / \partial t$ and integrate with respect to x from $x = 0$ to $x = L$,

$$
\int_0^L \frac{\partial^2 y}{\partial t^2} \frac{\partial y}{\partial t} dx = \int_0^L c^2 \frac{\partial^2 y}{\partial x^2} \frac{\partial y}{\partial t} dx, \qquad t > 0.
$$

Integration by parts on the right gives

$$
\begin{aligned}
\frac{1}{2} \int_0^L \frac{\partial}{\partial t} \left(\frac{\partial y}{\partial t} \right)^2 dx &= c^2 \left\{ \frac{\partial y}{\partial t} \frac{\partial y}{\partial x} \right\}_0^L - c^2 \int_0^L \frac{\partial y}{\partial x} \frac{\partial^2 y}{\partial x \, \partial t} dx \\
&= c_2 \left\{ \frac{\partial y}{\partial t} \frac{\partial y}{\partial x} \right\}_0^L - c^2 \int_0^L \frac{1}{2} \frac{\partial}{\partial t} \left(\frac{\partial y}{\partial x} \right)^2 dx, \qquad t > 0.
\end{aligned}
\tag{94}
$$

Because the ends of the string are fixed on the x-axis, it follows that $\partial y(0, t)/\partial t = \partial y(L, t)/\partial t = 0$, and therefore (94) reduces to

$$
0 = \frac{1}{2} \int_0^L \left[\frac{\partial}{\partial t} \left(\frac{\partial y}{\partial t} \right)^2 + c^2 \frac{\partial}{\partial t} \left(\frac{\partial y}{\partial x} \right)^2 \right] dx, \qquad t > 0.
\tag{95}
$$

When this equation is antidifferentiated with respect to time, the result is

$$
\frac{1}{2} \int_0^L \left[\left(\frac{\partial y}{\partial t} \right)^2 + c^2 \left(\frac{\partial y}{\partial x} \right)^2 \right] dx = K, \qquad t > 0,
\tag{96}
$$

where K is a constant. To evaluate K, we take the limit of each term in this equation as $t \to 0^+$. Because $\partial y / \partial t$ and $\partial y / \partial x$ are assumed continuous [condition (91f)],

$$\lim_{t \to 0^+} \frac{\partial y(x,t)}{\partial t} = \frac{\partial y(x,0)}{\partial t} = 0, \qquad 0 < x < L$$

[initial condition (91e)]. Furthermore, because $y(x,0) = y_1(x,0) - y_2(x,0) = 0$, we find that

$$\lim_{t \to 0^+} \frac{\partial y(x,t)}{\partial x} = \frac{\partial y(x,0)}{\partial x} = 0, \qquad 0 < x < L.$$

With these results, limits as $t \to 0^+$ in equation (96) show that $K = 0$, and, therefore, for $t \geq 0$ we may write

$$\int_0^L \left[\left(\frac{\partial y}{\partial t} \right)^2 + c^2 \left(\frac{\partial y}{\partial x} \right)^2 \right] dx = 0. \tag{97}$$

Since each term in this equation is continuous and nonnegative, it follows that each must vanish separately; that is, we must have $\partial y / \partial x = \partial y / \partial t = 0$ for $0 \leq x \leq L, t \geq 0$. These imply that $y(x,t)$ is constant for $0 \leq x \leq L$ and $t \geq 0$, and this constant must be zero since $y(x,0) = 0$. Thus, $y(x,t) \equiv 0$, and the solution of (91) is unique.

That (93) satisfies continuity condition (91f) is an immediate consequence of the assumption that $f''(x)$ is continuous for $0 \leq x \leq L$.

In Section 5.6 we saw that discontinuities in the initial temperature function were smoothed out by the heat equation. Likewise, discontinuities in boundary data were smoothed out by Laplace's equation. This is not the case for hyperbolic equations; a distinguishing property of hyperbolic equations is that discontinuities in initial data are propagated by the solution. We have already seen this with the discontinuity in $f'(x)$ for $f(x)$ in Figure 1.30(a). The discontinuity in $f'(x)$ is propagated in both directions along the string at speed c; it is not smoothed out. For a small time t (before the disturbance reaches the ends of the string), the discontinuity is found at positions $x = L/2 \pm ct$, that is, at points given by $x \pm ct = L/2$. But these are equations of characteristic curves for the one-dimensional wave equation (see Example 6 in Section 1.8). We have illustrated, therefore, that discontinuities in derivatives of initial data are propagated along characteristic curves of hyperbolic equations. These characteristics are shown in Figure 5.13. At time $t = L/(2c)$, the discontinuities reach the ends of the string for the first time, whereupon they are reflected to travel once again along the string. By drawing a horizontal line, say $t = t_0$, to intersect the broken lines in this figure, we obtain the positions of the discontinuities at time t_0. Intersections with a vertical line $x = x_0$ give the times at which the discontinuities pass through the point x_0 on the string.

The formal solution of problem (91) when $f(x)$ is as shown in Figure 1.30(a) is still defined by (92) or, more compactly, by (93). It is not, however, a function that satisfies (91a) for all $0 < x < L$ and $t > 0$. It satisfies (91a) at all points (x,t) in Figure 5.13 that are not on the characteristics $x = L/2 \pm ct$ and their reflections.

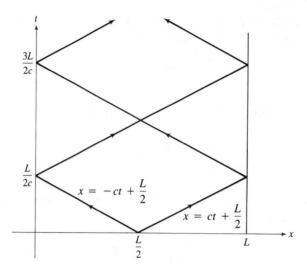

Figure 5.13

Exercises 5.8

1. (a) What is the formal series solution of the vibration problem

$$\frac{\partial^2 y}{\partial t^2} = c^2 \frac{\partial^2 y}{\partial x^2}, \qquad 0 < x < L, \qquad t > 0,$$

$$y_x(0, t) = 0, \qquad t > 0,$$

$$y_x(L, t) = 0, \qquad t > 0,$$

$$y(x, 0) = f(x), \qquad 0 < x < L,$$

$$y_t(x, 0) = 0, \qquad 0 < x < L?$$

Express this solution in closed form.

(b) Verify that the formal solution in (a) satisfies the five equations in (a) when $f(x)$, $f'(x)$, and $f''(x)$ are continuous on $0 \le x \le L$ and $f'(0) = f'(L) = 0$.

(c) Show that there is a unique solution to the problem in (a) that also satisfies continuity condition (91f).

(d) Verify that the formal solution in (a) satisfies (91f).

2. (a) What is the formal series solution of vibration problem (91) if initial conditions (91d, e) are replaced by

$$y(x, 0) = 0, \qquad y_t(x, 0) = g(x), \qquad 0 < x < L?$$

Express the formal solution in closed form when $g(x)$ and $g'(x)$ are continuous for $0 \le x \le L$ and $g(0) = g(L) = 0$.

(b) Verify that the formal solution in (a) satisfies (91a–c) and the initial conditions in (a).

(c) Show that there is a unique solution to the problem in (a) that also satisfies continuity condition (91f).

(d) Verify that the formal solution in (a) satisfies (91f).

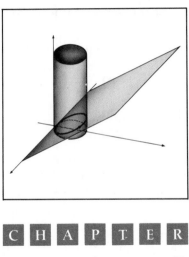

Finite Fourier Transforms and Nonhomogeneous Problems

6.1 Finite Fourier Transforms

In Section 3.3 we used transformations and eigenfunction expansions to solve nonhomogeneous (initial) boundary value problems. These problems were relatively straightforward, principally because they contained only one spatial variable. When nonhomogeneities were time independent, the solution was represented as the sum of steady-state and transient parts. The steady-state portion was determined by an ODE, and the transient portion satisfied a homogeneous problem. (In problems with two or three spatial variables, the steady-state part will satisfy two- or three-dimensional boundary value problems.) When nonhomogeneities were time dependent, the method of eigenfunction expansions had to be used. The corresponding homogeneous problem was solved, and arbitrary constants were then replaced by functions of time.

In this chapter we present an alternative technique for solving nonhomogeneous (initial) boundary value problems, namely, finite Fourier transforms. They handle time-dependent and time-independent nonhomogeneities in exactly the same way and adapt to problems in higher dimensions very easily.

221

Theorem 2 of Chapter 4 states that every Sturm-Liouville system

$$\frac{d}{dx}\left(r(x)\frac{dy}{dx}\right) + \{\lambda p(x) - q(x)\}y = 0, \qquad a < x < b, \tag{1a}$$

$$-l_1 y'(\lambda, a) + h_1 y(\lambda, a) = 0, \tag{1b}$$

$$l_2 y'(\lambda, b) + h_2 y(\lambda, b) = 0 \tag{1c}$$

has an infinity of eigenvalues λ_n $(n = 1, 2, \ldots)$ and corresponding orthonormal eigenfunctions $y_n(x) = y(\lambda_n, x)$. Furthermore, if $f(x)$ is a piecewise smooth function on the interval $a \le x \le b$, then on the open interval $a < x < b$, $f(x)$ can be expressed in a (generalized) Fourier series

$$f(x) = \sum_{n=1}^{\infty} c_n y_n(x), \tag{2a}$$

where c_n, the Fourier coefficients, are defined by

$$c_n = \int_a^b p(x)f(x)y_n(x)\,dx. \tag{2b}$$

Equality holds in (2a) only if $f(x)$ is defined as $[f(x+) + f(x-)]/2$ at points of discontinuity of $f(x)$.

We say that Sturm-Liouville system (1) defines an "integral transform" that associates with a function $f(x)$ a sequence of constants $\{c_n\}$ defined by the integral in (2b). This sequence of constants is called the (generalized) *finite Fourier transform of* $f(x)$ and is given the notation $\{\tilde{f}(\lambda_n)\}$, where, therefore,

$$\tilde{f}(\lambda_n) = \int_a^b p(x)f(x)y_n(x)\,dx. \tag{3a}$$

We often speak somewhat loosely of $\tilde{f}(\lambda_n)$ being the transform of $f(x)$ rather than the sequence $\{\tilde{f}(\lambda_n)\}$ of the $\tilde{f}(\lambda_n)$. If $f(x)$ is piecewise smooth on $a \le x \le b$, then (for $a < x < b$) (2a) becomes

$$f(x) = \sum_{n=1}^{\infty} \tilde{f}(\lambda_n)y_n(x). \tag{3b}$$

The series on the right is called the *inverse transform* corresponding to (3a); it defines a function $f(x)$ that has $\{\tilde{f}(\lambda_n)\}$ as its finite Fourier transform.

The finite Fourier transform of a given function $f(x)$ is unique; that is, integral (3a) defines a unique sequence of constants $\{\tilde{f}(\lambda_n)\}$ for each function $f(x)$. On the other hand, many functions have the same transform. For example, the functions $f_1(x)$ and $f_2(x)$ in Figure 6.1, which differ only in their values at $x = 1$, 2, and 3, have the same transform. Of all functions with the same transform, inverse transform (3b) associates in the first instance that one which is continous at each x; failing this, (3b) associates that function which has only finite jump discontinuities. In the latter case, the value of the function at any discontinuity is the average of its left- and right-hand limits.

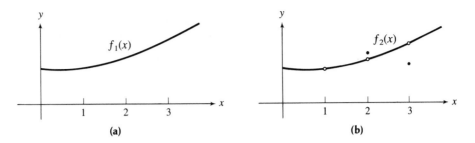

Figure 6.1   (a)   (b)

For example, the eigenvalues and orthonormal eigenfunctions of the Sturm-Liouville system

$$X'' + \lambda^2 X = 0, \qquad 0 < x < L,$$
$$X(0) = 0 = X(L)$$

are $\lambda_n^2 = n^2\pi^2/L^2$ $(n = 1, 2, \ldots)$ and $X_n(x) = \sqrt{2/L}\,\sin(n\pi x/L)$. The finite Fourier transform of a function $f(x)$ defined on $0 \le x \le L$ is $\{\tilde{f}(\lambda_n)\}$, where

$$\tilde{f}(\lambda_n) = \int_0^L f(x)\sqrt{\frac{2}{L}}\,\sin\frac{n\pi x}{L}\,dx.$$

In particular, if $f(x) = x$, then integration by parts gives

$$\tilde{f}(\lambda_n) = \frac{\sqrt{2L^3}}{n\pi}(-1)^{n+1}.$$

On the interval $0 < x < L$, we may therefore express $f(x) = x$ in the form

$$x = \sum_{n=1}^{\infty} \tilde{f}(\lambda_n)X_n(x) = \sum_{n=1}^{\infty} \frac{\sqrt{2L^3}}{n\pi}(-1)^{n+1}\sqrt{\frac{2}{L}}\,\sin\frac{n\pi x}{L}$$
$$= \frac{2L}{\pi}\sum_{n=1}^{\infty}\frac{(-1)^{n+1}}{n}\,\sin\frac{n\pi x}{L}.$$

Because the series also converges to $f(x) = x$ at $x = 0$, but not at $x = L$, we write

$$x = \frac{2L}{\pi}\sum_{n=1}^{\infty}\frac{(-1)^{n+1}}{n}\,\sin\frac{n\pi x}{L}, \qquad 0 \le x < L.$$

With respect to the same Sturm-Liouville system, the finite Fourier transform for the function $g(x)$ in Figure 6.2(a) is

$$\tilde{g}(\lambda_n) = \int_0^L g(x)X_n(x)\,dx = \int_0^{L/2}\sqrt{\frac{2}{L}}\,\sin\frac{n\pi x}{L}\,dx = \frac{\sqrt{2L}}{n\pi}\left(1 - \cos\frac{n\pi}{2}\right).$$

On the interval $0 < x < L$, the inverse transform (3b) defines a function

$$h(x) = \sum_{n=1}^{\infty}\tilde{g}(\lambda_n)X_n(x) = \sum_{n=1}^{\infty}\frac{\sqrt{2L}}{n\pi}\left(1 - \cos\frac{n\pi}{2}\right)\sqrt{\frac{2}{L}}\,\sin\frac{n\pi x}{L}$$
$$= \frac{2}{\pi}\sum_{n=1}^{\infty}\frac{1 - \cos(n\pi/2)}{n}\,\sin\frac{n\pi x}{L}.$$

This function is identical to $g(x)$ except at $x = L/2$, where its value is $1/2$. In addition, because the series converges to zero at $x = 0$ and $x = L$, we may write

$$h(x) = \frac{2}{\pi} \sum_{n=1}^{\infty} \frac{1 - \cos(n\pi/2)}{n} \sin \frac{n\pi x}{L}, \qquad 0 \le x \le L,$$

where $h(x)$ is the function in Figure 6.2(b).

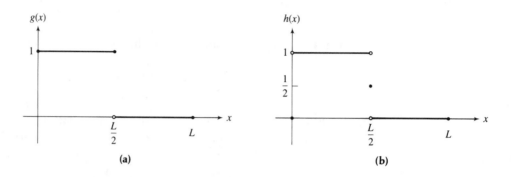

Figure 6.2

(a)   (b)

When solving (initial) boundary value problems by finite Fourier transforms, it is often necessary to answer questions like that posed in the following example.

Example 1:   Given that the finite Fourier transform of a function $f(x)$ with respect to the Sturm-Liouville system

$$X'' + \lambda^2 X = 0, \qquad 0 < x < L,$$
$$X(0) = 0 = X(L)$$

is $$\tilde{f}(\lambda_n) = \frac{\sqrt{2L}\,[1 + (-1)^{n+1}] + (2L)^{3/2}(-1)^{n+1}}{n\pi},$$

find $f(x)$.

Solution: Eigenvalues of the Sturm-Liouville system are $\lambda_n^2 = n^2\pi^2/L^2$, with corresponding normalized eigenfunctions $X_n(x) = \sqrt{2/L}\,\sin(n\pi x/L)$. When $g(x) = x$,

$$\tilde{g}(\lambda_n) = \int_0^L x \sqrt{\frac{2}{L}} \sin \frac{n\pi x}{L}\, dx = \sqrt{\frac{2}{L}} \left\{ \frac{-Lx}{n\pi} \cos \frac{n\pi x}{L} + \frac{L^2}{n^2\pi^2} \sin \frac{n\pi x}{L} \right\}_0^L$$

$$= \frac{\sqrt{2L^3}}{n\pi} (-1)^{n+1}.$$

In addition, if $h(x) = 1$,

$$\tilde{h}(\lambda_n) = \int_0^L \sqrt{\frac{2}{L}} \sin \frac{n\pi x}{L}\, dx = \sqrt{\frac{2}{L}} \left\{ \frac{-L}{n\pi} \cos \frac{n\pi x}{L} \right\}_0^L = \frac{\sqrt{2L}}{n\pi} [1 + (-1)^{n+1}].$$

Since $\tilde{f}(\lambda_n) = 2\tilde{g}(\lambda_n) + \tilde{h}(\lambda_n)$, it follows that $f(x) = 2g(x) + h(x) = 2x + 1$.   ∎

Exercises 6.1

In Exercises 1–10, find the finite Fourier transform of the function $f(x)$, defined on the interval $0 \leq x \leq L$, with respect to the given Sturm-Liouville system.

1. $f(x) = x^2 - 2x; \quad X'' + \lambda^2 X = 0, \quad X(0) = X'(L) = 0$

2. $f(x) = 5; \quad X'' + \lambda^2 X = 0, \quad X(0) = X(L) = 0$

3. $f(x) = 5; \quad X'' + \lambda^2 X = 0, \quad X'(0) = X'(L) = 0$

4. $f(x) = x; \quad X'' + \lambda^2 X = 0, \quad X(0) = 0, \quad l_2 X'(L) + h_2 X(L) = 0$

5. $f(x) = L - x; \quad X'' + \lambda^2 X = 0, \quad X'(0) = 0, \quad l_2 X'(L) + h_2 X(L) = 0$

6. $f(x) = \sin x; \quad X'' + \lambda^2 X = 0, \quad X'(0) = X(L) = 0$

7. $f(x) = e^x; \quad X'' + \lambda^2 X = 0, \quad X'(0) = X'(L) = 0$

8. $f(x) = \begin{cases} x^2 & 0 \leq x \leq L/2 \\ 0 & L/2 < x \leq L \end{cases}; \quad X'' + \lambda^2 X = 0, \quad X(0) = X'(L) = 0$

9. $f(x) = \sin(\pi x/L)\cos(\pi x/L); \quad X'' + \lambda^2 X = 0, \quad X(0) = X(L) = 0$

10. $f(x) = 1; \quad X'' + 2X' + \lambda^2 X = 0, \quad X'(0) = X'(L) = 0$

In Exercises 11–14, find, in closed form, the inverse finite Fourier transform for $\tilde{f}(\lambda_n)$ with respect to the given Sturm-Liouville system.

11. $\tilde{f}(\lambda_n) = (-1)^{n+1}(2L)^{3/2}/(n\pi); \quad X'' + \lambda^2 X = 0, \quad X(0) = X(L) = 0$

12. $\tilde{f}(\lambda_n) = \dfrac{3\sqrt{2}L^{5/2}(-1)^n}{n\pi} + \dfrac{6\sqrt{2}L^{5/2}[1 + (-1)^{n+1}]}{n^3\pi^3}; \quad X'' + \lambda^2 X = 0, \quad X(0) = X(L) = 0$

13. $\tilde{f}(\lambda_n) = \begin{cases} 2\sqrt{2L} & n = 0 \\ 0 & n > 0 \end{cases}; \quad X'' + \lambda^2 X = 0, \quad X'(0) = X'(L) = 0$

14. $\tilde{f}(\lambda_n) = \dfrac{(2L-1)\sqrt{2/L}(-1)^{n+1}}{\lambda_n} - \dfrac{2\sqrt{2/L}}{\lambda_n^2}; \quad X'' + \lambda^2 X = 0, \quad X'(0) = X(L) = 0$

6.2 Nonhomogeneous Problems in Two Variables

We now show how finite Fourier transforms can be used to solve (initial) boundary value problems. Every initial boundary value problem that we have solved by separation of variables can also be solved using transforms. There is little advantage, however, in using transforms for homogeneous problems; their power is realized when the PDE and/or the boundary conditions are nonhomogeneous. Nonetheless, we choose to introduce the method with problem (8) of Section 3.2, a problem with homogeneous PDE and homogeneous boundary conditions. We do this because the application of finite Fourier transforms to initial boundary value problems always follows the same pattern whether the problem is homogeneous or nonhomogeneous. As a result, we can clearly illustrate the technique in a homogeneous problem without added complications due to nonhomogeneities.

The separation method on

$$\frac{\partial^2 y}{\partial t^2} = c^2 \frac{\partial^2 y}{\partial x^2}, \qquad 0 < x < L, \qquad t > 0, \tag{4a}$$

$$y(0, t) = 0, \qquad t > 0, \tag{4b}$$

$$y(L, t) = 0, \qquad t > 0, \tag{4c}$$

$$y(x, 0) = f(x), \qquad 0 < x < L, \tag{4d}$$

$$y_t(x, 0) = 0, \qquad 0 < x < L \tag{4e}$$

determines separated functions $y(x, t) = X(x)T(t)$, which satisfy (4a, b, c, e). The result is a Sturm-Liouville system in $X(x)$ and an ordinary differential equation in $T(t)$:

$$X'' + \lambda^2 X = 0, \qquad 0 < x < L, \quad \text{(5a)} \qquad T'' + c^2\lambda^2 T = 0, \qquad t > 0, \qquad \text{(6a)}$$

$$X(0) = 0, \qquad\qquad\qquad \text{(5b)} \qquad\qquad T'(0) = 0. \qquad\qquad\qquad \text{(6b)}$$

$$X(L) = 0; \qquad\qquad\qquad \text{(5c)}$$

From these, separated functions take the form $C\sqrt{2/L} \sin(n\pi x/L)\cos(n\pi ct/L)$ for arbitrary C. The solution of problem (4) is obtained by superposing these functions,

$$y(x, t) = \sum_{n=1}^{\infty} c_n \sqrt{\frac{2}{L}} \sin\frac{n\pi x}{L} \cos\frac{n\pi ct}{L}, \tag{7a}$$

and imposing (4d) to give

$$c_n = \int_0^L f(x) \sqrt{\frac{2}{L}} \sin\frac{n\pi x}{L} dx. \tag{7b}$$

To solve this problem by finite Fourier transforms, we note that the transform associated with Sturm-Liouville system (5) is

$$\tilde{f}(\lambda_n) = \int_0^L f(x) X_n(x) dx, \tag{8}$$

where $\lambda_n^2 = n^2\pi^2/L^2$ and $X_n(x) = \sqrt{2/L} \sin(n\pi x/L)$ are the eigenvalues and orthonormal eigenfunctions. If we apply this transform to both sides of PDE (4a),

$$\int_0^L \frac{\partial^2 y}{\partial t^2} X_n(x) dx = c^2 \int_0^L \frac{\partial^2 y}{\partial x^2} X_n(x) dx. \tag{9}$$

We interchange orders of integration with respect to x and differentiation with respect to t on the left side of this equation. Integration by parts on the right, together with the fact that $X_n(0) = X_n(L) = 0$, gives

$$\frac{\partial^2}{\partial t^2} \int_0^L y X_n dx = c^2 \left\{ \frac{\partial y}{\partial x} X_n \right\}_0^L - c^2 \int_0^L \frac{\partial y}{\partial x} X_n' dx = -c^2 \int_0^L \frac{\partial y}{\partial x} X_n' dx. \tag{10}$$

The integral on the left of this equation is the definition of $\tilde{y}(\lambda_n, t)$, the finite Fourier transform of $y(x, t)$. Integration by parts once again on the right yields

$$\frac{\partial^2}{\partial t^2} \tilde{y}(\lambda_n, t) = -c^2 \{ y X_n' \}_0^L + c^2 \int_0^L y X_n'' dx$$

$$= -c^2 y(L, t) X_n'(L) + c^2 y(0, t) X_n'(0) + c^2 \int_0^L y X_n'' dx. \tag{11}$$

Now, boundary conditions (4b, c) imply that the first two terms on the right vanish. Further, equation (5a) may be used to replace X_n'' with $-\lambda_n^2 X_n$, with the result

$$\frac{\partial^2 \tilde{y}(\lambda_n, t)}{\partial t^2} = c^2 \int_0^L y(-\lambda_n^2 X_n)\, dx = -c^2 \lambda_n^2 \int_0^L y X_n\, dx = -c^2 \lambda_n^2 \tilde{y}(\lambda_n, t). \tag{12}$$

Because $\tilde{y}(\lambda_n, t)$ is a function of only one variable, t, and a parameter, λ_n, the partial derivative may be replaced by an ordinary derivative,

$$\frac{d^2 \tilde{y}}{dt^2} = -c^2 \lambda_n^2 \tilde{y}. \tag{13a}$$

This is an ordinary differential equation for $\tilde{y}(\lambda_n, t)$. When we take finite Fourier transforms of initial conditions (4d, e), we obtain initial conditions for ODE (13a):

$$\tilde{y}(\lambda_n, 0) = \tilde{f}(\lambda_n), \tag{13b}$$

$$\frac{d\tilde{y}(\lambda_n, 0)}{dt} = 0. \tag{13c}$$

What the finite Fourier transform has done, therefore, is replace initial boundary value problem (4) for $y(x, t)$ with initial value problem (13) for $\tilde{y}(\lambda_n, t)$; a PDE has been reduced to an ODE. In actual fact, (13) is an infinite system of ODEs ($n = 1, 2, \ldots$), but because all differential equations have exactly the same form, solving one solves them all.

The general solution of (13a) is

$$\tilde{y}(\lambda_n, t) = A_n \cos c\lambda_n t + B_n \sin c\lambda_n t, \tag{14}$$

where A_n and B_n are constants. Initial conditions (13b, c) require these constants to satisfy

$$A_n = \tilde{f}(\lambda_n), \qquad 0 = c\lambda_n B_n, \tag{15}$$

and therefore

$$\tilde{y}(\lambda_n, t) = \tilde{f}(\lambda_n) \cos c\lambda_n t. \tag{16}$$

The inverse transform defines the solution of problem (4) as

$$y(x, t) = \sum_{n=1}^{\infty} \tilde{y}(\lambda_n, t) X_n(x) = \sum_{n=1}^{\infty} \tilde{f}(\lambda_n) \cos c\lambda_n t\, X_n(x)$$

$$= \sqrt{\frac{2}{L}} \sum_{n=1}^{\infty} \tilde{f}(\lambda_n) \sin \frac{n\pi x}{L} \cos \frac{n\pi c t}{L}, \tag{17}$$

a solution identical to that obtained by separation of variables.

Briefly, the transform technique applied to the PDE replaces the PDE in $y(x, t)$ with an ordinary differential equation in its transform $\tilde{y}(\lambda_n, t)$. Once the differential equation for $\tilde{y}(\lambda_n, t)$ is solved, the inverse transform yields $y(x, t)$. A number of aspects of the method deserve special mention:

(1) Not just any finite Fourier transform will yield a solution to this initial boundary value problem. It must be the transform associated with Sturm-Liouville

system (5); that is, it must be the transform associated with the Sturm-Liouville system $X(x)$ that would result if separation of variables were applied to the problem. In nonhomogeneous problems, we use the transform associated with the Sturm-Liouville system that would result were separation used on the corresponding homogeneous problem. Apparently, then, to use transforms effectively, we must be able to recognize quickly the Sturm-Liouville system that would result were we to use separation of variables.

(2) Boundary conditions on $y(x, t)$ are incorporated in the simplification leading to the ordinary differential equation in $\tilde{y}(\lambda_n, t)$.

(3) Initial conditions on $y(x, t)$ are converted by the transform into initial conditions on $\tilde{y}(\lambda_n, t)$.

(4) Finite Fourier transforms always give a solution in the form of an infinite series (the inverse transform). It may happen that part or all of the solution is the eigenfunction expansion of a simple function. In particular, when nonhomogeneities are time independent, part of the solution is always representable in closed form. However, considerable ingenuity may be required to discover this function. The next example illustrates this point.

It is probably fair to say that the transform technique applied to the above problem is more involved than the separation method. This is in agreement with our earlier statement that the transform method shows its true versatility in problems with nonhomogeneous PDE and/or boundary conditions. To illustrate this, consider problem (34) of Section 3.3, where gravity introduces a nonhomogeneity into the PDE:

$$\frac{\partial^2 y}{\partial t^2} = c^2 \frac{\partial^2 y}{\partial x^2} + g, \qquad 0 < x < L, \qquad t > 0, \qquad (g < 0), \qquad \text{(18a)}$$

$$y(0, t) = 0, \qquad t > 0, \qquad \text{(18b)}$$

$$y(L, t) = 0, \qquad t > 0, \qquad \text{(18c)}$$

$$y(x, 0) = f(x), \qquad 0 < x < L, \qquad \text{(18d)}$$

$$y_t(x, 0) = 0, \qquad 0 < x < L. \qquad \text{(18e)}$$

In Section 3.3 we expressed the solution in the form $y(x, t) = z(x, t) + \psi(x)$, where $\psi(x) = [g/(2c^2)](Lx - x^2)$ is the solution of the corresponding static deflection problem. The function $z(x, t)$ must then satisfy the homogeneous problem

$$\frac{\partial^2 z}{\partial t^2} = c^2 \frac{\partial^2 z}{\partial x^2}, \qquad 0 < x < L, \qquad t > 0, \qquad \text{(19a)}$$

$$z(0, t) = 0, \qquad t > 0, \qquad \text{(19b)}$$

$$z(L, t) = 0, \qquad t > 0, \qquad \text{(19c)}$$

$$z(x, 0) = f(x) - \frac{g}{2c^2}(Lx - x^2), \qquad 0 < x < L, \qquad \text{(19d)}$$

$$z_t(x, 0) = 0, \qquad 0 < x < L. \qquad \text{(19e)}$$

Separation of variables on (19) gives

$$z(x,t) = \sum_{n=1}^{\infty} c_n \sin\frac{n\pi x}{L}\cos\frac{n\pi ct}{L}, \tag{20a}$$

where
$$c_n = \frac{2}{L}\int_0^L \left(f(x) - \frac{g}{2c^2}(Lx - x^2)\right)\sin\frac{n\pi x}{L}\,dx. \tag{20b}$$

The final solution is

$$y(x,t) = z(x,t) + \frac{g}{2c^2}(Lx - x^2). \tag{21}$$

Consider now the finite Fourier transform technique applied to this problem. The transform associated with this problem is again (9), where $\lambda_n^2 = n^2\pi^2/L^2$ and $X_n(x) = \sqrt{2/L}\sin(n\pi x/L)$ are the eigenpairs of (5) (this being the Sturm-Liouville system that would result were separation of variables used on the corresponding homogeneous problem). If we apply the transform to PDE (18a),

$$\int_0^L \frac{\partial^2 y}{\partial t^2}X_n(x)\,dx = \int_0^L \left(c^2\frac{\partial^2 y}{\partial x^2} + g\right)X_n(x)\,dx. \tag{22}$$

Integration by parts on the right, along with the fact that $X_n(0) = X_n(L) = 0$, gives

$$\frac{\partial^2}{\partial t^2}\int_0^L yX_n\,dx = c^2\left\{\frac{\partial y}{\partial x}X_n\right\}_0^L - c^2\int_0^L \frac{\partial y}{\partial x}X_n'\,dx + g\tilde{1}$$

$$= -c^2\int_0^L \frac{\partial y}{\partial x}X_n'\,dx + g\tilde{1}, \tag{23}$$

where $\tilde{1}$ is the transform of the function identically equal to unity,

$$\tilde{1} = \int_0^L X_n(x)\,dx = \int_0^L \sqrt{\frac{2}{L}}\sin\frac{n\pi x}{L}\,dx = \frac{\sqrt{2L}}{n\pi}[1 + (-1)^{n+1}]. \tag{24}$$

Integration by parts again and boundary conditions (18b, c) yield

$$\frac{\partial^2}{\partial t^2}\tilde{y}(\lambda_n, t) = -c^2\{yX_n'\}_0^L + c^2\int_0^L yX_n''\,dx + g\tilde{1}$$

$$= c^2\int_0^L y(-\lambda_n^2 X_n)\,dx + g\tilde{1}$$

or
$$\frac{d^2\tilde{y}}{dt^2} = -c^2\lambda_n^2\tilde{y} + g\tilde{1}. \tag{25a}$$

This is an ordinary differential equation for $\tilde{y}(\lambda_n, t)$. Transforms of initial conditions (18d, e) require $\tilde{y}(\lambda_n, t)$ to satisfy the initial conditions

$$\tilde{y}(\lambda_n, 0) = \tilde{f}(\lambda_n), \tag{25b}$$

$$\frac{d\tilde{y}(\lambda_n, 0)}{dt} = 0. \tag{25c}$$

The general solution of (25a) is

$$\tilde{y}(\lambda_n, t) = A_n \cos c\lambda_n t + B_n \sin c\lambda_n t + \frac{g\tilde{1}}{c^2 \lambda_n^2}, \tag{26}$$

where A_n and B_n are constants. Initial conditions (25b, c) require these constants to satisfy

$$\tilde{f}(\lambda_n) = A_n + \frac{g\tilde{1}}{c^2 \lambda_n^2}, \qquad 0 = c\lambda_n B_n \tag{27}$$

and therefore

$$\tilde{y}(\lambda_n, t) = \left(\tilde{f}(\lambda_n) - \frac{g\tilde{1}}{c^2 \lambda_n^2} \right) \cos c\lambda_n t + \frac{g\tilde{1}}{c^2 \lambda_n^2}. \tag{28}$$

The inverse transform now defines the solution of (18) as

$$
\begin{aligned}
y(x, t) &= \sum_{n=1}^{\infty} \tilde{y}(\lambda_n, t) X_n(x) \\
&= \sum_{n=1}^{\infty} X_n(x) \left(\left[\tilde{f}(\lambda_n) - \frac{g\tilde{1}}{c^2 \lambda_n^2} \right] \cos c\lambda_n t + \frac{g\tilde{1}}{c^2 \lambda_n^2} \right) \\
&= \sqrt{\frac{2}{L}} \sum_{n=1}^{\infty} \sin \frac{n\pi x}{L} \left(\left[\tilde{f}(\lambda_n) - \frac{g\tilde{1}}{c^2 \lambda_n^2} \right] \cos \frac{n\pi c t}{L} + \frac{g\tilde{1}}{c^2 \lambda_n^2} \right).
\end{aligned} \tag{29}
$$

To show that this solution is identical to that obtained by separation, we calculate that for $\psi(x) = [g/(2c^2)](Lx - x^2)$,

$$\tilde{\psi}(\lambda_n) = \int_0^L \psi(x) X_n(x)\, dx = \frac{g}{c^2 n^3 \pi^3} \sqrt{2L^5}\,[1 + (-1)^{n+1}] = \frac{g\tilde{1}}{c^2 \lambda_n^2}. \tag{30}$$

Consequently, the last term of the series in (29) can be expressed as

$$\sum_{n=1}^{\infty} \sqrt{\frac{2}{L}} \sin \frac{n\pi x}{L} \left(\frac{g\tilde{1}}{c^2 \lambda_n^2} \right) = \sum_{n=1}^{\infty} \tilde{\psi}(\lambda_n) X_n(x) = \psi(x).$$

Solution (29) can therefore be written in the form

$$y(x, t) = \sqrt{\frac{2}{L}} \sum_{n=1}^{\infty} \sin \frac{n\pi x}{L} (\tilde{f}(\lambda_n) - \tilde{\psi}(\lambda_n)) \cos \frac{n\pi c t}{L} + \psi(x), \tag{31}$$

which is clearly identical to that obtained by separation.

The transform method applied to this problem with a nonhomogeneous PDE is essentially the same as when applied to the homogeneous problem (4). This is the advantage of the transform method: it does not require homogeneous PDEs or boundary conditions. To illustrate the method applied to nonhomogeneous boundary conditions, we consider Example 4 in Section 3.3:

$$\frac{\partial U}{\partial t} = k \frac{\partial^2 U}{\partial x^2}, \qquad 0 < x < L, \qquad t > 0, \tag{32a}$$

$$U(0, t) = U_0, \qquad t > 0, \tag{32b}$$

$$U(L, t) = U_L, \qquad t > 0, \tag{32c}$$

$$U(x, 0) = f(x), \qquad 0 < x < L. \tag{32d}$$

The finite Fourier transform for this problem is once again (9), where $\lambda_n^2 = n^2\pi^2/L^2$ and $X_n = \sqrt{2/L}\,\sin(n\pi x/L)$ are the eigenpairs of Sturm-Liouville system (5) [obtained by separation when (32b, c) are homogeneous]. If we apply this transform to (32a),

$$\int_0^L \frac{\partial U}{\partial t} X_n(x)\,dx = k\int_0^L \frac{\partial^2 U}{\partial x^2} X_n(x)\,dx. \tag{33}$$

Integration by parts on the right, together with the fact that $X_n(0) = X_n(L) = 0$, gives

$$\frac{\partial}{\partial t}\int_0^L UX_n\,dx = k\left\{\frac{\partial U}{\partial x}X_n\right\}_0^L - k\int_0^L \frac{\partial U}{\partial x}X_n'\,dx = -k\int_0^L \frac{\partial U}{\partial x}X_n'\,dx. \tag{34}$$

Another integration by parts yields

$$\frac{\partial}{\partial t}\tilde{U}(\lambda_n, t) = -k\{UX_n'\}_0^L + k\int_0^L UX_n''\,dx$$

$$= -k\big(U(L, t)X_n'(L) - U(0, t)X_n'(0)\big) + k\int_0^L U(-\lambda_n^2 X_n)\,dx,$$

in which we may use boundary conditions (32b, c):

$$\frac{d\tilde{U}}{dt} = -kU_L\sqrt{\frac{2}{L}}\,\lambda_n(-1)^n + kU_0\sqrt{\frac{2}{L}}\,\lambda_n - k\lambda_n^2\tilde{U}$$

$$= -k\lambda_n^2\tilde{U} + k\sqrt{\frac{2}{L}}\,\lambda_n[U_0 + U_L(-1)^{n+1}]. \tag{35a}$$

Accompanying this ODE in $\tilde{U}(\lambda_n, t)$ is the transform of initial condition (32d),

$$\tilde{U}(\lambda_n, 0) = \tilde{f}(\lambda_n). \tag{35b}$$

The general solution of (35a) is

$$\tilde{U}(\lambda_n, t) = A_n e^{-k\lambda_n^2 t} + \lambda_n^{-1}\sqrt{\frac{2}{L}}[U_0 + U_L(-1)^{n+1}], \tag{36}$$

where A_n is a constant. Initial condition (35b) requires that

$$\tilde{f}(\lambda_n) = A_n + \lambda_n^{-1}\sqrt{\frac{2}{L}}[U_0 + U_L(-1)^{n+1}], \tag{37}$$

and therefore

$$\tilde{U}(\lambda_n, t) = e^{-k\lambda_n^2 t}\left(\tilde{f}(\lambda_n) - \lambda_n^{-1}\sqrt{\frac{2}{L}}[U_0 + U_L(-1)^{n+1}]\right)$$

$$+ \lambda_n^{-1}\sqrt{\frac{2}{L}}[U_0 + U_L(-1)^{n+1}]. \tag{38}$$

Inverse transform (3b) defines the solution of problem (32) as

$$U(x,t) = \sum_{n=1}^{\infty} \tilde{U}(\lambda_n, t) X_n(x)$$

$$= \sum_{n=1}^{\infty} \sqrt{\frac{2}{L}} \sin\frac{n\pi x}{L}\left(e^{-n^2\pi^2 kt/L^2}\left[\tilde{f}(\lambda_n) - \lambda_n^{-1}\sqrt{\frac{2}{L}}[U_0 + U_L(-1)^{n+1}]\right]\right.$$

$$\left. + \lambda_n^{-1}\sqrt{\frac{2}{L}}[U_0 + U_L(-1)^{n+1}]\right). \tag{39}$$

To show that this solution is identical to that obtained by separation of variables in Example 4 of Section 3.3, we calculate that for $\psi(x) = U_0 + (U_L - U_0)x/L$,

$$\tilde{\psi}(\lambda_n) = \int_0^L \psi(x)X_n(x)\,dx = \lambda_n^{-1}\sqrt{\frac{2}{L}}[U_0 + U_L(-1)^{n+1}]. \tag{40}$$

Solution (39) can therefore be written in the form

$$U(x,t) = \sqrt{\frac{2}{L}}\sum_{n=1}^{\infty} e^{-n^2\pi^2 kt/L^2}\left(\tilde{f}(\lambda_n) - \tilde{\psi}(\lambda_n)\right)\sin\frac{n\pi x}{L} + \psi(x), \tag{41}$$

identical to that obtained by separation of variables.

If we set $x = 0$ and $x = L$ in (39), we obtain $U(0,t) = U(L,t) = 0$, whereas $x = 0$ and $x = L$ in (41) give $U(0,t) = U_0$ and $U(L,t) = U_L$. In other words, the function in (39) does not satisfy boundary conditions (32b, c), but (41) does. This is because the series expansion of $\psi(x)$ in (39) is a Fourier sine series, and as such it converges to the odd extension of $\psi(x)$ to a function of period $2L$. At $x = 0$ and $x = L$, this extension (see Figure 6.3) is discontinuous, and the series therefore converges to the average value of the right and left limits, namely zero. For any other value of x between 0 and L, solutions (39) and (41) give identical results.

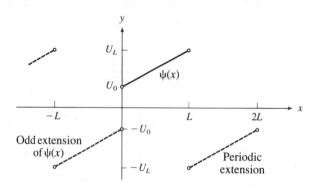

Figure 6.3

Parts of a finite Fourier transform solution that can be expressed in closed form should always be so represented. An additional reason for doing this is that the rate of convergence of the series is enhanced when the closed-form portion is extracted.

In the remainder of this section we consider two additional problems that have nonhomogeneities of a more general nature.

Example 2: Solve the heat conduction problem

$$\frac{\partial U}{\partial t} = k\frac{\partial^2 U}{\partial x^2}, \qquad 0 < x < L, \qquad t > 0, \tag{42a}$$

$$U(0,t) = f_1(t), \qquad t > 0, \tag{42b}$$

$$U_x(L,t) = -\kappa^{-1}f_2(t), \qquad t > 0, \tag{42c}$$

$$U(x,0) = f(x), \qquad 0 < x < L. \tag{42d}$$

Physically described is a rod of length L with insulated sides that at time $t = 0$ has temperature $f(x)$. For $t > 0$, the temperature of its left end is a prescribed $f_1(t)$, and heat is transferred across the right end at a rate $f_2(t)$. When $f_2(t)$ is positive, heat is being removed from the rod, and when $f_2(t)$ is negative, heat is being added.

Solution: Were separation of variables to be applied to the associated homogeneous problem [with $f_1(t) = f_2(t) = 0$], the Sturm-Liouville system

$$X'' + \lambda^2 X = 0, \qquad X(0) = 0, \qquad X'(L) = 0$$

would result. Eigenvalues are $\lambda_n^2 = (2n-1)^2\pi^2/(4L^2)$, with corresponding eigenfunctions $X_n(x) = \sqrt{2/L}\sin\lambda_n x$. If we apply the finite Fourier transform associated with this system to (42a),

$$\int_0^L \frac{\partial U}{\partial t}X_n\,dx = k\int_0^L \frac{\partial^2 U}{\partial x^2}X_n\,dx.$$

Integration by parts on the right integral gives

$$\frac{\partial}{\partial t}\int_0^L UX_n\,dx = k\left\{\frac{\partial U}{\partial x}X_n\right\}_0^L - k\int_0^L \frac{\partial U}{\partial x}X_n'\,dx$$

$$= kU_x(L,t)X_n(L) - k\{UX_n'\}_0^L + k\int_0^L UX_n''\,dx$$

$$= k\left(U_x(L,t)X_n(L) + U(0,t)X_n'(0) + \int_0^L -\lambda_n^2 X_n U\,dx\right). \tag{43}$$

When we use (42c) in the first term and (42b) in the second, we may write

$$\frac{d\tilde{U}}{dt} = k[-\kappa^{-1}f_2(t)X_n(L) + f_1(t)X_n'(0) - \lambda_n^2\tilde{U}(\lambda_n,t)].$$

Thus, $\tilde{U}(\lambda_n, t)$ must satisfy the ODE

$$\frac{d\tilde{U}}{dt} + k\lambda_n^2\tilde{U} = A(\lambda_n, t), \tag{44a}$$

where $A(\lambda_n, t) = k[-\kappa^{-1}f_2(t)X_n(L) + f_1(t)X_n'(0)]$

$$= k\sqrt{\frac{2}{L}}\,[(-1)^n\kappa^{-1}f_2(t) + \lambda_n f_1(t)] \tag{44b}$$

subject to the transform of (42d),

$$\tilde{U}(\lambda_n, 0) = \tilde{f}(\lambda_n). \tag{44c}$$

The general solution of (44a) is

$$\tilde{U}(\lambda_n, t) = e^{-k\lambda_n^2 t} \int A(\lambda_n, t) e^{k\lambda_n^2 t} \, dt,$$

but, in order to incorporate initial condition (44c), it is advantageous to express this solution as a definite integral:

$$\tilde{U}(\lambda_n, t) = e^{-k\lambda_n^2 t} \left(\int_0^t A(\lambda_n, u) e^{k\lambda_n^2 u} \, du + C_n \right)$$

$$= C_n e^{-k\lambda_n^2 t} + \int_0^t A(\lambda_n, u) e^{k\lambda_n^2 (u-t)} \, du.$$

Condition (44c) now requires that $\tilde{f}(\lambda_n) = C_n$, and therefore

$$\tilde{U}(\lambda_n, t) = \tilde{f}(\lambda_n) e^{-k\lambda_n^2 t} + \int_0^t A(\lambda_n, u) e^{k\lambda_n^2 (u-t)} \, du. \tag{45}$$

The solution to problem (42) is defined by the inverse finite Fourier transform,

$$U(x, t) = \sum_{n=1}^{\infty} \tilde{U}(\lambda_n, t) X_n(x)$$

$$= \sum_{n=1}^{\infty} \left(\tilde{f}(\lambda_n) e^{-k\lambda_n^2 t} + \int_0^t A(\lambda_n, u) e^{k\lambda_n^2 (u-t)} \, du \right) \sqrt{\frac{2}{L}} \sin \lambda_n x. \tag{46}$$

As a specific example, suppose the rod is initially at temperature zero $[f(x) \equiv 0]$, its right end is insulated $[f_2(t) \equiv 0]$, and its left end is held at constant temperature 100°C. According to (44b) and (45),

$$\tilde{U}(\lambda_n, t) = \int_0^t k \sqrt{\frac{2}{L}} \lambda_n (100) e^{k\lambda_n^2 (u-t)} \, du = \frac{100\sqrt{2/L}}{\lambda_n} (1 - e^{-k\lambda_n^2 t}),$$

and hence

$$U(x, t) = \sum_{n=1}^{\infty} \frac{100\sqrt{2/L}}{\lambda_n} (1 - e^{-k\lambda_n^2 t}) \sqrt{\frac{2}{L}} \sin \frac{(2n-1)\pi x}{2L}.$$

The solution may be simplified by noting that when $h(x) \equiv 100$,

$$h(\lambda_n) = \int_0^L 100 \sqrt{\frac{2}{L}} \sin \lambda_n x \, dx = \frac{100\sqrt{2/L}}{\lambda_n}.$$

Thus,
$$h(x) = 100 = \sum_{n=1}^{\infty} \frac{100\sqrt{2/L}}{\lambda_n} \sqrt{\frac{2}{L}} \sin \lambda_n x,$$

and it follows that

$$U(x, t) = 100 - \frac{400}{\pi} \sum_{n=1}^{\infty} \frac{e^{-(2n-1)^2 \pi^2 kt/(4L^2)}}{2n-1} \sin \frac{(2n-1)\pi x}{2L}.$$

This function is plotted for various values of t in Figure 6.4 (assuming a thermal diffusivity of $k = 12 \times 10^{-6}$ m²/s).

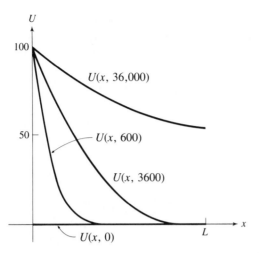

Figure 6.4   ∎

Example 3:   A taut string has one end, at $x = 0$, fixed on the x-axis while the other end, at $x = L$, is forced to undergo periodic vertical motion described by $g(t) = A \sin \omega t$, $t \geq 0$ (A a constant). If the string is initially at rest on the x-axis, find its subsequent displacement.

Solution: The initial boundary value problem for displacements $y(x, t)$ of points on the string is

$$\frac{\partial^2 y}{\partial t^2} = c^2 \frac{\partial^2 y}{\partial x^2}, \qquad 0 < x < L, \qquad t > 0, \tag{47a}$$

$$y(0, t) = 0, \qquad t > 0, \tag{47b}$$

$$y(L, t) = g(t), \qquad t > 0, \tag{47c}$$

$$y(x, 0) = 0, \qquad 0 < x < L, \tag{47d}$$

$$y_t(x, 0) = 0, \qquad 0 < x < L. \tag{47e}$$

The finite Fourier transform associated with x is

$$\tilde{f}(\lambda_n) = \int_0^L f(x) X_n(x) \, dx,$$

where $\lambda_n^2 = n^2 \pi^2 / L^2$ and $X_n(x) = \sqrt{2/L} \sin \lambda_n x$. Application of the transform to PDE (47a) leads to the following ODE in $\tilde{y}(\lambda_n, t)$:

$$\frac{d^2 \tilde{y}}{dt^2} + c^2 \lambda_n^2 \tilde{y} = -c^2 X_n'(L) g(t) \tag{48a}$$

subject to

$$\tilde{y}(\lambda_n, 0) = \tilde{y}'(\lambda_n, 0) = 0. \tag{48b}$$

Variation of parameters on problem (48) gives the solution in the form

$$\tilde{y}(\lambda_n, t) = \frac{-c X_n'(L)}{\lambda_n} \int_0^t g(u) \sin c\lambda_n(t - u) \, du. \tag{49}$$

This is a general formula valid for any function $g(t)$ whatsoever. In this problem, $g(t) = A \sin \omega t$, so that $\tilde{y}(\lambda_n, t)$ could be obtained by evaluation of integral (49). (Try it.) Alternatively, if we return to (48a), the general solution when $g(t) = A \sin \omega t$ is

$$\tilde{y}(\lambda_n, t) = B_n \cos c\lambda_n t + D_n \sin c\lambda_n t - \frac{Ac^2 X_n'(L)}{c^2 \lambda_n^2 - \omega^2} \sin \omega t, \tag{50}$$

provided $\omega \neq c\lambda_n$ for any integer n. Initial conditions (48b) imply that

$$0 = B_n, \qquad 0 = c\lambda_n D_n - \frac{Ac^2 \omega X_n'(L)}{c^2 \lambda_n^2 - \omega^2},$$

from which

$$\tilde{y}(\lambda_n, t) = \frac{Ac\omega X_n'(L)}{\lambda_n(c^2 \lambda_n^2 - \omega^2)} \sin c\lambda_n t - \frac{Ac^2 X_n'(L)}{c^2 \lambda_n^2 - \omega^2} \sin \omega t. \tag{51}$$

Thus, $\quad y(x, t) = \sum_{n=1}^{\infty} \tilde{y}(\lambda_n, t) X_n(x)$

$$= \sum_{n=1}^{\infty} \frac{Ac X_n'(L)}{c^2 \lambda_n^2 - \omega^2} \left(\frac{\omega}{\lambda_n} \sin c\lambda_n t - c \sin \omega t \right) X_n(x)$$

$$= 2cA \sum_{n=1}^{\infty} \frac{(-1)^n}{n^2 \pi^2 c^2 - \omega^2 L^2} \left(\omega L \sin \frac{n\pi ct}{L} - n\pi c \sin \omega t \right) \sin \frac{n\pi x}{L}. \tag{52a}$$

This is the solution of problem (47), provided $\omega \neq c\lambda_n$; that is, provided ω is not equal to a natural frequency of the vibrating string. If this solution is separated into two series,

$$y(x, t) = 2\omega cLA \sum_{n=1}^{\infty} \frac{(-1)^n}{n^2 \pi^2 c^2 - \omega^2 L^2} \sin \frac{n\pi ct}{L} \sin \frac{n\pi x}{L}$$

$$+ 2\pi c^2 A \sin \omega t \sum_{n=1}^{\infty} \frac{(-1)^{n+1}}{n^2 \pi^2 c^2 - \omega^2 L^2} \sin \frac{n\pi x}{L},$$

it is not unreasonable to expect that the second series, since it is void of t, is the Fourier expansion for some function. Indeed, it is straightforward to show that the series represents $(2\pi c^2)^{-1} \sin(\omega x/c)/\sin(\omega L/c)$. In other words, the solution may be expressed in the simplified form

$$y(x, t) = \frac{A \sin(\omega x/c) \sin \omega t}{\sin(\omega L/c)} + 2\omega cLA \sum_{n=1}^{\infty} \frac{(-1)^n}{n^2 \pi^2 c^2 - \omega^2 L^2} \sin \frac{n\pi ct}{L} \sin \frac{n\pi x}{L}. \tag{52b}$$

We now investigate what happens when ω is equal to a natural frequency of the vibrating string; that is, suppose $\omega = m\pi c/L$ for some integer m. When $n \neq m$, solution (51) of (48) is unchanged. But for $n = m$, $\tilde{y}(\lambda_m, t)$ must satisfy

$$\frac{d^2 \tilde{y}}{dt^2} + c^2 \lambda_m^2 \tilde{y} = -c^2 X_m'(L) A \sin c\lambda_m t, \tag{53a}$$

$$\tilde{y}(\lambda_m, 0) = \tilde{y}'(\lambda_m, 0) = 0. \tag{53b}$$

The general solution of (53a) is

$$\tilde{y}(\lambda_m, t) = B_m \cos c\lambda_m t + D_m \sin c\lambda_m t + \frac{Ac X_m'(L)}{2\lambda_m} t \cos c\lambda_m t. \tag{54}$$

Initial conditions (53b) imply that

$$0 = B_m, \qquad 0 = c\lambda_m D_m + \frac{A c X'_m(L)}{2\lambda_m},$$

from which

$$\tilde{y}(\lambda_m, t) = \frac{-A X'_m(L)}{2\lambda_m^2} \sin c\lambda_m t + \frac{A c X'_m(L)}{2\lambda_m} t \cos c\lambda_m t. \tag{55}$$

In other words, when $\omega = c\lambda_m = m\pi c/L$, the sequence $\{\tilde{y}(\lambda_n, t)\}$ remains unchanged except for the mth term, $\tilde{y}(\lambda_m, t)$. The inverse transform now gives

$$y(x, t) = \tilde{y}(\lambda_m, t) X_m(x) + \sum_{\substack{n=1 \\ n \neq m}}^{\infty} \tilde{y}(\lambda_n, t) X_n(x),$$

and substitutions from (55) and (51) lead to

$$
\begin{aligned}
y(x, t) = {} & \frac{A(-1)^m}{L} \left(ct \cos \frac{m\pi c t}{L} - \frac{L}{m\pi} \sin \frac{m\pi c t}{L} \right) \sin \frac{m\pi x}{L} \\
& + \frac{2A}{\pi} \sum_{\substack{n=1 \\ n \neq m}}^{\infty} \frac{(-1)^n}{n^2 - m^2} \left(m \sin \frac{n\pi c t}{L} - n \sin \frac{m\pi c t}{L} \right) \sin \frac{n\pi x}{L}.
\end{aligned} \tag{56}
$$

For large t, the first term in (56) becomes unbounded. This phenomenon is known as *resonance*. When the forcing frequency (ω) is equal to a natural frequency ($c\lambda_n$) of the vibrating system, oscillations may become excessive and destroy the system. ∎

Further instances of resonance are discussed in Exercises 23–32 and 35. In some applications, resonance is disastrous for the system; in others, resonance is exactly what is desired.

In this section we have dealt with initial boundary value problems. Finite Fourier transforms can also be used to solve nonhomogeneous boundary value problems in Cartesian coordinates x and y. We have already suggested (see Section 5.3) that when nonhomogeneities occur only in boundary conditions, the problem can easily be solved by subdivision into homogeneous problems. In other words, finite Fourier transforms need only be used to accommodate nonhomogeneities in the PDE. This is illustrated in Exercises 42–47.

Exercises 6.2

Use finite Fourier transforms to solve all problems in this set of exercises.

Part A—Heat Conduction

1. A cylindrical, homogeneous, isotropic rod with insulated sides has temperature $f(x), 0 \leq x \leq L$, at time $t = 0$. For time $t > 0$, the end $x = 0$ is held at $0°C$ and the end $x = L$ is held at constant temperature $U_L °C$. What is the temperature in the rod for $0 < x < L$ and $t > 0$?

2. A cylindrical, homogeneous, isotropic rod with insulated sides is initially at temperature $10°C$ throughout $(0 \leq x \leq L)$. For time $t > 0$, its ends $(x = 0$ and $x = L)$ are held at temperature $0°C$.

At each position x in the rod, heat generation occurs and is defined by $g(x, t) = e^{-\alpha t}, \alpha > 0, t > 0,$ $0 < x < L$. Find the temperature in the rod as a function of x and t. Assume that $\alpha \neq n^2\pi^2 k/L^2$ for any integer n.

3. Solve Exercise 1 in Section 3.3.

4. Solve Exercise 6 in Section 3.3.

5. A cylindrical, homogeneous, isotropic rod with insulated sides is initially at temperature $U_0(1 - x/L)$, U_0 a constant. For time $t > 0$, the end $x = 0$ is maintained at temperature U_0 and end $x = L$ is insulated. Find the temperature in the rod for $0 < x < L$ and $t > 0$.

6. Solve the initial boundary value problem for temperature in a homogeneous, isotropic rod with insulated sides and ends held at temperature zero. Heat generation is defined at position x and time t by $g(x, t)$, and the initial temperature of the rod is described by $f(x)$.

7. Repeat Exercise 6 if the ends of the rod are insulated.

8. (a) Show that finite Fourier transforms for the problem in Exercise 5 of Section 3.3 leads to the following solution:

$$U(x, t) = 200 \sum_{n=1}^{\infty} \left[\left(\frac{[1 + (-1)^{n+1}]}{n\pi} + \frac{n\pi k(-1)^n}{n^2\pi^2 k - L^2} \right) e^{-n^2\pi^2 kt/L^2} \right.$$
$$\left. + \frac{n\pi k(-1)^{n+1}}{n^2\pi^2 k - L^2} e^{-t} \right] \sin \frac{n\pi x}{L}.$$

(b) Simplify this solution by finding the transform of the function $f(x) = x$ and using the partial fraction decomposition

$$\frac{1}{n(n^2\pi^2 k - L^2)} = \frac{-1/L^2}{n} + \frac{n\pi^2 k/L^2}{n^2\pi^2 k - L^2}$$

on the last term.

9. We have claimed that to solve an initial boundary value problem with finite Fourier transforms, it is necessary to use the transform associated with the Sturm-Liouville system that would result were separation of variables used on the corresponding homogeneous problem. To illustrate this, apply the finite Fourier transform associated with Sturm-Liouville system (2) of Chapter 4 to Exercise 2. Show that an insoluble problem in $\bar{y}(\lambda_n, t)$ is obtained.

10. A cylindrical, homogeneous, isotropic rod with insulated sides is initially at temperature zero throughout. For times $t > 0$, there is located at cross section $x = b$ $(0 < b < L)$ a plane heat source of constant strength g. If the ends $x = 0$ and $x = L$ of the rod are kept at zero temperature, the initial boundary value problem for temperature in the rod is

$$\frac{\partial^2 U}{\partial x^2} = \frac{1}{k} \frac{\partial U}{\partial t} - \frac{g}{\kappa} \delta(x - b), \qquad 0 < x < L, \qquad t > 0,$$

$$U(0, t) = 0, \qquad t > 0,$$
$$U(L, t) = 0, \qquad t > 0,$$
$$U(x, 0) = 0, \qquad 0 < x < L,$$

where $\delta(x - b)$ is the Dirac delta function. Solve this problem for $U(x, t)$, using the fact that

$$\int_0^L f(x)\delta(x - b)\,dx = f(b).$$

11. Solve Exercise 8 in Section 3.3.

12. Repeat Exercise 5 if the temperature of the end $x = 0$ is $U_0 e^{-\alpha t}$ ($\alpha > 0$ a constant). To simplify the solution, use the technique of Exercise 8(b) with $f(x) = 1$. Assume that $\alpha \neq (2n-1)^2 \pi^2 k/(4L^2)$ for any integer n.

13. If the ends $x = 0$ and $x = L$ of the thin-wire problem in Exercise 3 of Section 5.2 are kept at constant temperatures U_0 and U_L, respectively, and the initial temperature is zero throughout, show that

$$U(x, t) = \frac{U_0 \sinh \sqrt{h/k}(L - x) + U_L \sinh \sqrt{h/k}\, x}{\sinh \sqrt{h/k}\, L}$$

$$- 2k\pi e^{-ht} \sum_{n=1}^{\infty} \frac{n[U_0 + (-1)^{n+1} U_L]}{hL^2 + n^2\pi^2 k} e^{-n^2\pi^2 kt/L^2} \sin \frac{n\pi x}{L}.$$

14. Repeat Exercise 5 if heat is added uniformly over the end $x = L$ at a constant rate q W/m^2.

15. (a) A cylindrical, homogeneous, isotropic rod with insulated sides is initially at constant temperature U_0 throughout. For time $t > 0$, the right end, $x = L$, continues to be held at temperature U_0. Heat is added uniformly over the left end, $x = 0$, at a constant rate q W/m^2 for the first t_0 seconds, and the end is insulated thereafter. Find the temperature in the rod for $0 < x < L$ and $0 < t < t_0$.

    (b) Assuming that $U(x, t)$ must be continuous at time t_0, find $U(x, t)$ for $0 < x < L$ and $t > t_0$.

    (c) What is the steady-state solution?

16. Repeat Exercise 15 if the end $x = L$ is insulated.

17. Find a formula for the solution of the general one-dimensional heat conduction problem

$$\frac{\partial U}{\partial t} = k\frac{\partial^2 U}{\partial x^2} + \frac{kg(x, t)}{\kappa}, \qquad 0 < x < L, \qquad t > 0,$$

$$-l_1 \frac{\partial U}{\partial x} + h_1 U = f_1(t), \qquad x = 0, \qquad t > 0,$$

$$l_2 \frac{\partial U}{\partial x} + h_2 U = f_2(t), \qquad x = L, \qquad t > 0,$$

$$U(x, 0) = f(x), \qquad 0 < x < L.$$

18. The general thin-wire problem (see Exercise 31 in Section 1.2) is

$$\frac{\partial U}{\partial t} = k\frac{\partial^2 U}{\partial x^2} - h(U - U_m) + \frac{k}{\kappa}g(x, t), \qquad 0 < x < L, \qquad t > 0,$$

$$-l_1 \frac{\partial U}{\partial x} + h_1 U = f_1(t), \qquad x = 0, \qquad t > 0,$$

$$l_2 \frac{\partial U}{\partial x} + h_2 U = f_2(t), \qquad x = L, \qquad t > 0,$$

$$U(x, 0) = f(x), \qquad 0 < x < L.$$

(a) Show that the change of dependent variable $\bar{U}(x, t) = e^{ht}U(x, t)$ leads to the initial boundary value problem

$$\frac{\partial \bar{U}}{\partial t} = k\frac{\partial^2 \bar{U}}{\partial x^2} + \left(hU_m + \frac{k}{\kappa}g(x, t)\right)e^{ht}, \qquad 0 < x < L, \qquad t > 0,$$

$$-l_1\frac{\partial \bar{U}}{\partial x} + h_1\bar{U} = e^{ht}f_1(t), \qquad x = 0, \qquad t > 0,$$

$$l_2\frac{\partial \bar{U}}{\partial x} + h_2\bar{U} = e^{ht}f_2(t), \qquad x = L, \qquad t > 0,$$

$$\bar{U}(x, 0) = f(x), \qquad 0 < x < L.$$

(b) Use the results of Exercise 17 to find $\bar{U}(x, t)$ and hence $U(x, t)$.

Part B—Vibrations

19. Solve Exercise 13 in Section 3.3.

20. Solve Exercise 14 in Section 3.3.

21. The end $x = 0$ of a horizontal elastic bar of length L is kept fixed, and the other end, $x = L$, is subjected to a constant force per unit area F acting parallel to the bar. If the bar is initially unstrained and at rest, the initial boundary value problem for longitudinal displacement $y(x, t)$ of the cross section originally at position x is

$$\frac{\partial^2 y}{\partial t^2} = c^2\frac{\partial^2 y}{\partial x^2}, \qquad 0 < x < L, \qquad t > 0,$$

$$y(0, t) = 0, \qquad t > 0,$$

$$E\frac{\partial y(L, t)}{\partial x} = F, \qquad t > 0,$$

$$y(x, 0) = 0, \qquad 0 < x < L,$$

$$y_t(x, 0) = 0, \qquad 0 < x < L,$$

where $E/\rho = c^2$ (E = Young's modulus of elasticity and ρ = density).

(a) Show that the solution to this problem is

$$y(x, t) = \frac{8LF}{E\pi^2}\sum_{n=1}^{\infty}\frac{(-1)^{n+1}}{(2n-1)^2}\left(1 - \cos\frac{(2n-1)c\pi t}{2L}\right)\sin\frac{(2n-1)\pi x}{2L}.$$

(b) Find the finite Fourier transform of the function $M(x) = x, 0 < x < L$, and use the result to write $y(x, t)$ in the form

$$y(x, t) = \frac{F}{E}M(x) - \frac{8LF}{E\pi^2}\sum_{n=1}^{\infty}\frac{(-1)^{n+1}}{(2n-1)^2}\cos\frac{(2n-1)c\pi t}{2L}\sin\frac{(2n-1)\pi x}{2L}.$$

(c) Show that $y(x, t)$ can now be expressed in the form

$$y(x, t) = \frac{F}{E}\left(M_L(x) - \frac{1}{2}M_L(x + ct) - \frac{1}{2}M_L(x - ct)\right),$$

where $M_L(x)$ is the extension of $M(x)$ to an odd, odd-harmonic function (see Exercise 21 in Section 2.2).

(d) Evaluate $y(L, t)$ and draw its graph as a function of t to illustrate the motion of the end $x = L$ of the bar.

22. A horizontal elastic bar of natural length L lies along the x-axis between $x = 0$ and $x = L$. At time $t = 0$, it is stretched so that the displacement of the cross section at position x is given by the function kx, $k > 0$ a constant, $0 \leq x \leq L$. The bar is released from rest at this position. If a constant force per unit area F acts parallel to the bar on the end $x = 0$, find subsequent displacements of cross sections of the bar.

23. A taut string initially at rest along the x-axis has its ends $x = 0$ and $x = L$ fixed on the axis. If a periodic external force $F_0 \sin \omega t$, $t \geq 0$, per unit x-length acts at every point on the string, find the displacement of the string. Include a discussion of resonance.

24. A taut string initially at rest along the x-axis has its end $x = 0$ fixed on the x-axis. The end $x = L$ is forced to undergo periodic vertical motion $A \sin \omega t$, $t \geq 0$ (A and ω constants). Find the displacement of the string. Include a discussion of resonance.

In Exercises 25–32, determine frequencies of the applied force that will produce resonance. Do not determine the solution to the initial boundary value problem, only the frequencies.

25. The string in Example 4 if the end $x = L$ is free to slide vertically and an external force $F_0 \sin \omega t$, $t \geq 0$, per unit x-length acts at every point on the string.

26. The string in Example 4 if both ends are free to slide vertically and an external force $F_0 \sin \omega t$, $t \geq 0$, per unit x-length acts at every point on the string. [Find the solution $y(x, t)$ in this case.]

27. The bar in Exercise 21 if the force is $F = F_0 \sin \omega t$.

28. The bar in Exercise 21 if the end $x = 0$ is free and $F = F_0 \sin \omega t$.

29. The bar in Exercise 21 if the end $x = L$ has a prescribed displacement $A_0 \sin \omega t$.

30. The bar in Exercise 21 if the end $x = 0$ is free and the end $x = L$ has a prescribed displacement $A_0 \sin \omega t$.

31. The bar in Exercise 21 if the ends $x = 0$ and $x = L$ have prescribed displacements $A_0 \sin \omega t$ and $B_0 \sin \phi t$, respectively.

32. The bar in Exercise 21 if the ends $x = 0$ and $x = L$ are subjected to forces $F_0 \sin \omega t$ and $G_0 \sin \phi t$ (per unit area), respectively.

33. An elastic bar of natural length L is clamped along its length, turned to the vertical position, and hung from its end $x = 0$. At time $t = 0$, the clamp is removed and gravity is therefore permitted to act on the bar.

(a) Show that vertical displacements of cross sections of the bar are given by

$$y(x, t) = \frac{gx}{2c^2}(2L - x) - \frac{16gL^2}{c^2\pi^3} \sum_{n=1}^{\infty} \frac{1}{(2n-1)^3} \cos \frac{(2n-1)c\pi t}{2L} \sin \frac{(2n-1)\pi x}{2L}.$$

(b) Find a closed-form solution for $y(x, t)$. [*Hint:* See part (c) of Exercise 21.]

(c) Sketch a graph of $y(L, t)$. Does the end $x = L$ of the bar oscillate about its equilibrium position, that is, the position of the lower end of the bar if the bar were to hang motionless under its own weight? (See Exercise 13 in Section 1.3.)

34. (a) Find displacements in the bar of Exercise 33 if the top of the bar is attached to a spring with constant k. Let $x = 0$ correspond to the top end of the bar when the spring is in the unstretched position.

(b) Does the lower end of the bar oscillate about its equilibrium position? (See Exercise 14 in Section 1.3.)

35. Repeat Example 3 if a damping force $-\beta \partial y/\partial t$, proportional to velocity, acts at every point on the string. Assume that $\beta < 2\pi\rho c/L$. Can resonance with unbounded oscillations occur?

36. (a) The ends of a taut string are fixed at $x = 0$ and $x = L$ on the x-axis. The string is initially at rest along the axis and then is allowed to drop under its own weight. Find a series representation for the displacement of the string.

(b) Show that the solution in (a) can be expressed in the closed form

$$y(x, t) = M(x) - \frac{1}{2}[M(x + ct) + M(x - ct)],$$

where $M(x)$ is the odd, 2L-periodic extension of the function $g(Lx - x^2)/(2c^2)$.

37. Repeat Exercise 36 if the string has an initial displacement $f(x)$.

38. The ends of a taut string are looped around smooth vertical supports at $x = 0$ and $x = L$. If the string falls from rest along the x-axis, and a constant vertical force F_0 acts on the loop at $x = L$, find displacements of the string. Take gravity into account.

39. A motionless, horizontal beam has its ends simply supported at $x = 0$ and $x = L$. At time $t = 0$, a concentrated force of magnitude A is suddenly applied at the midpoint.

(a) If the weight per unit length of the beam is negligible compared with A, show that the initial boundary value problem for transverse displacements $y(x, t)$ is

$$\frac{\partial^2 y}{\partial t^2} + c^2\frac{\partial^4 y}{\partial x^4} = -\frac{A}{\rho}\delta\left(x - \frac{L}{2}\right), \qquad 0 < x < L, \qquad t > 0,$$

$$y(0, t) = y(L, t) = 0, \qquad t > 0,$$

$$y_{xx}(0, t) = y_{xx}(L, t) = 0, \qquad t > 0,$$

$$y(x, 0) = y_t(x, 0) = 0, \qquad 0 < x < L,$$

where $c^2 = EI/\rho$ and ρ is the linear density of the beam.

(b) Solve this problem using the finite Fourier transform associated with Sturm-Liouville system (1) of Chapter 4. [See Exercise 10 for the requisite property of the delta function $\delta(x - L/2)$.]

40. Find a formula for the solution of the general one-dimensional vibration problem

$$\frac{\partial^2 y}{\partial t^2} = c^2\frac{\partial^2 y}{\partial x^2} + \frac{F(x, t)}{\rho}, \qquad 0 < x < L, \qquad t > 0,$$

$$-l_1\frac{\partial y}{\partial x} + h_1 y = f_1(t), \qquad x = 0, \qquad t > 0,$$

$$l_2\frac{\partial y}{\partial x} + h_2 y = f_2(t), \qquad x = L, \qquad t > 0,$$

$$y(x, 0) = f(x), \qquad 0 < x < L,$$

$$y_t(x, 0) = g(x), \qquad 0 < x < L.$$

41. The end $x = 0$ of a horizontal elastic bar of length L is kept fixed, and the other end has a mass m attached to it. The mass m is then subjected to a horizontal periodic force $F = F_0 \sin \omega t$. If the bar is initially unstrained and at rest, set up the initial boundary value problem for longitudinal displacements in the bar. Can we solve this problem with finite Fourier transforms?

Part C—Potential, Steady-State Heat Conduction, Static Deflections of Membranes

42. A charge distribution with density $\sigma(x, y)$ coulombs per cubic meter occupies the volume R in space bounded by the planes $x = 0$, $y = 0$, $x = L$, and $y = L'$, and these planes are all held at potential zero.

    (a) Use finite Fourier transforms to find the potential $V(x, y)$ in R when σ is constant. Find two series, one by transforming the x-variable and the other by transforming the y-variable.

    (b) If $\sigma = \sigma(x)$ is a function of x only, find $V(x, y)$.

    (c) Find $V(x, y)$ when $\sigma = xy$.

43. A uniform charge distribution of density σ coulombs per cubic meter occupies the volume R bounded by the planes $x = 0$, $y = 0$, $x = L$, and $y = L'$. If the electrostatic potential on the planes $x = 0$, $y = 0$, and $y = L'$ is zero and that on $x = L$ is $f(y)$, find the potential in R.

44. Repeat Exercise 43 when planes $x = 0$, $x = L$, and $y = L'$ are held at zero potential and $y = 0$ is at potential $g(x)$.

45. Repeat Exercise 43 when planes $x = L$ and $y = L'$ are held at zero potential and $x = 0$ and $y = 0$ are at $f(y)$ and $g(x)$, respectively.

46. Find a formula for the solution of the general two-dimensional Dirichlet boundary value problem

$$\frac{\partial^2 V}{\partial x^2} + \frac{\partial^2 V}{\partial y^2} = F(x, y), \qquad 0 < x < L, \qquad 0 < y < L',$$

$$V(0, y) = f_1(y), \qquad 0 < y < L',$$
$$V(L, y) = f_2(y), \qquad 0 < y < L',$$
$$V(x, 0) = g_1(x), \qquad 0 < x < L,$$
$$V(x, L') = g_2(x), \qquad 0 < x < L.$$

47. We suggested at the end of this section that two-dimensional boundary value problems on rectangles with four nonhomogeneous boundary conditions and homogeneous PDEs can be subdivided into two problems, each of which has two homogeneous and two nonhomogeneous boundary conditions. There is an exception to this, namely the Neumann problem. For example, the Neumann problem associated with Laplace's equation is

$$\frac{\partial^2 V}{\partial x^2} + \frac{\partial^2 V}{\partial y^2} = 0, \qquad 0 < x < L, \qquad 0 < y < L',$$

$$\frac{\partial V(0, y)}{\partial x} = f_1(y), \qquad 0 < y < L',$$

$$\frac{\partial V(L, y)}{\partial x} = f_2(y), \qquad 0 < y < L',$$

$$\frac{\partial V(x, 0)}{\partial y} = g_1(x), \qquad 0 < x < L,$$

$$\frac{\partial V(x, L')}{\partial y} = g_2(x), \qquad 0 < x < L,$$

where the nonhomogeneities must satisfy the consistency condition

$$\int_0^L [g_2(x) - g_1(x)]\, dx + \int_0^{L'} [f_2(y) - f_1(y)]\, dy = 0.$$

Our previous suggestion would indicate that $V(x, y)$ should be set equal to $V(x, y) = V_1(x, y) + V_2(x, y)$, where V_1 and V_2 satisfy Laplace's equation on the rectangle and the following boundary conditions:

$$\frac{\partial V_1(0, y)}{\partial x} = f_1(y), \qquad 0 < y < L', \qquad \frac{\partial V_2(0, y)}{\partial x} = 0, \qquad 0 < y < L',$$

$$\frac{\partial V_1(L, y)}{\partial x} = f_2(y), \qquad 0 < y < L', \qquad \frac{\partial V_2(L, y)}{\partial x} = 0, \qquad 0 < y < L',$$

$$\frac{\partial V_1(x, 0)}{\partial y} = 0, \qquad 0 < x < L, \qquad \frac{\partial V_2(x, 0)}{\partial y} = g_1(x), \qquad 0 < x < L,$$

$$\frac{\partial V_1(x, L')}{\partial y} = 0, \qquad 0 < x < L; \qquad \frac{\partial V_2(x, L')}{\partial y} = g_2(x), \qquad 0 < x < L.$$

But these Neumann problems must satisfy the consistency conditions

$$\int_0^{L'} [f_2(y) - f_1(y)]\, dy = 0 \quad \text{and} \quad \int_0^L [g_2(x) - g_1(x)]\, dx = 0.$$

The difficulty is that the combined consistency condition on f_1, f_2, g_1, and g_2 may not imply these separately. In general, then, solutions for V_1 and V_2 may not exist. With finite Fourier transforms, this difficulty presents no problem. Find $V(x, y)$ using such a transform.

6.3 Higher-Dimensional Problems in Cartesian Coordinates

To solve nonhomogeneous initial boundary value problems in three and four variables, we can once again remove space variables from the problem with finite Fourier transforms, leaving an ODE in the transform function regarded only as a function of time. There are two ways to do this. Successive finite Fourier transforms, each a transform in only one space variable, can be applied to the PDE. This corresponds to successively separating off space variables in homogeneous problems. Alternatively, multidimensional finite Fourier transforms associated with multidimensional eigenvalue problems (see Section 5.5) can be introduced. We take the former approach. To illustrate, consider the following initial boundary value problem.

Example 4:   Solve the heat conduction problem

$$\frac{\partial U}{\partial t} = k\left(\frac{\partial^2 U}{\partial x^2} + \frac{\partial^2 U}{\partial y^2}\right), \qquad 0 < x < L, \qquad 0 < y < L', \qquad t > 0, \qquad \text{(57a)}$$

$$U(0, y, t) = U_1, \qquad 0 < y < L', \qquad t > 0, \tag{57b}$$

$$U(L, y, t) = 0, \qquad 0 < y < L', \qquad t > 0, \tag{57c}$$

$$U(x, 0, t) = U_2, \qquad 0 < x < L, \qquad t > 0, \tag{57d}$$

$$U_y(x, L', t) = 0, \qquad 0 < x < L, \qquad t > 0, \tag{57e}$$

$$U(x, y, 0) = 0, \qquad 0 < x < L, \qquad 0 < y < L'. \tag{57f}$$

Physically described is a horizontal plate that is insulated top and bottom and along the edge $y = L'$. Initially the temperature is zero throughout the plate, and for $t > 0$, faces $x = 0$, $x = L$, and $y = 0$ are held at constant temperatures U_1, 0, and U_2, respectively.

Solution: The finite Fourier transform associated with the x-variable is

$$\tilde{f}(\lambda_n) = \int_0^L f(x) X_n(x)\, dx, \tag{58}$$

where $\lambda_n^2 = n^2\pi^2/L^2$ and $X_n(x) = \sqrt{2/L}\sin(n\pi x/L)$ are the eigenpairs of the Sturm-Liouville system

$$X'' + \lambda^2 X = 0, \qquad 0 < x < L,$$

$$X(0) = X(L) = 0.$$

This is the system that would result were separation of variables applied to problem (57) with homogeneous boundary conditions. If we apply this transform to PDE (57a), and use integration by parts,

$$\int_0^L \frac{\partial U}{\partial t} X_n\, dx = k \int_0^L \left(\frac{\partial^2 U}{\partial x^2} + \frac{\partial^2 U}{\partial y^2} \right) X_n\, dx$$

$$= k\frac{\partial^2}{\partial y^2} \int_0^L U X_n\, dx + k\left\{ \frac{\partial U}{\partial x} X_n \right\}_0^L - k \int_0^L \frac{\partial U}{\partial x} X_n'\, dx.$$

Since $X_n(0) = X_n(L) = 0$,

$$\frac{\partial}{\partial t} \int_0^L U X_n\, dx = k\frac{\partial^2 \tilde{U}(\lambda_n, y, t)}{\partial y^2} - k\{ U X_n' \}_0^L + k \int_0^L U X_n''\, dx.$$

Boundary conditions (57b, c) and the fact that $X_n'' = -\lambda_n^2 X_n$ now give

$$\frac{\partial \tilde{U}}{\partial t} = k\frac{\partial^2 \tilde{U}}{\partial y^2} + kU_1 X_n'(0) + k \int_0^L U(-\lambda_n^2 X_n)\, dx.$$

Thus, $\tilde{U}(\lambda_n, y, t)$ must satisfy the PDE

$$\frac{\partial \tilde{U}}{\partial t} = k\frac{\partial^2 \tilde{U}}{\partial y^2} + kU_1 X_n'(0) - k\lambda_n^2 \tilde{U}, \qquad 0 < y < L', \qquad t > 0 \tag{59a}$$

subject to the transforms of conditions (57d–f),

$$\tilde{U}(\lambda_n, 0, t) = U_2 \tilde{1}_n, \qquad t > 0, \tag{59b}$$

$$\tilde{U}_y(\lambda_n, L', t) = 0, \qquad t > 0, \tag{59c}$$

$$\tilde{U}(\lambda_n, y, 0) = 0, \qquad 0 < y < L', \tag{59d}$$

where

$$\tilde{1}_n = \int_0^L X_n\, dx = \int_0^L \sqrt{\frac{2}{L}} \sin\frac{n\pi x}{L}\, dx = \frac{\sqrt{2L}[1 + (-1)^{n+1}]}{n\pi}. \tag{59e}$$

The finite Fourier transform associated with the y-variable in problem (59) is

$$\tilde{f}(\mu_m) = \int_0^{L'} f(y) Y_m(y)\,dy, \tag{60}$$

where $\mu_m^2 = (2m - 1)^2 \pi^2/(4L'^2)$ and $Y_m(y) = \sqrt{2/L'} \sin[(2m - 1)\pi y/(2L')]$ are eigen-pairs of the Sturm-Liouville system

$$Y'' + \mu^2 Y = 0, \qquad 0 < y < L',$$
$$Y(0) = Y'(L') = 0.$$

If we apply this transform to PDE (59a),

$$\int_0^{L'} \frac{\partial \tilde{U}}{\partial t} Y_m\,dy = k \int_0^{L'} \frac{\partial^2 \tilde{U}}{\partial y^2} Y_m\,dy + \int_0^{L'} [kU_1 X_n'(0) - k\lambda_n^2 \tilde{U}]\, Y_m\,dy,$$

and use integration by parts,

$$\frac{\partial \tilde{\tilde{U}}(\lambda_n, \mu_m, t)}{\partial t} - kU_1 X_n'(0)\tilde{I}_m + k\lambda_n^2 \tilde{\tilde{U}} = k\left\{ \frac{\partial \tilde{U}}{\partial y} Y_m \right\}_0^{L'} - k \int_0^{L'} \frac{\partial \tilde{U}}{\partial y} Y_m'\,dy,$$

where

$$\tilde{I}_m = \int_0^{L'} Y_m\,dy = \int_0^{L'} \sqrt{\frac{2}{L'}} \sin\frac{(2m - 1)\pi y}{2L'}\,dy = \frac{2\sqrt{2L'}}{(2m - 1)\pi}. \tag{61}$$

Since $Y_m(0) = 0$ and $\partial \tilde{U}(\lambda_n, L', t)/\partial y = 0$,

$$\frac{\partial \tilde{\tilde{U}}}{\partial t} - kU_1 X_n'(0)\tilde{I}_m + k\lambda_n^2 \tilde{\tilde{U}} = -k\{\tilde{U} Y_m'\}_0^{L'} + k \int_0^{L'} \tilde{U} Y_m''\,dy.$$

Boundary condition (59b) and the facts that $Y_m'(L') = 0$ and $Y_m'' = -\mu_m^2 Y_m$ yield

$$\frac{\partial \tilde{\tilde{U}}}{\partial t} - kU_1 X_n'(0)\tilde{I}_m + k\lambda_n^2 \tilde{\tilde{U}} = kU_2 Y_m'(0)\tilde{I}_n + k \int_0^{L'} \tilde{U}(-\mu_m^2 Y_m)\,dy$$

or

$$\frac{d\tilde{\tilde{U}}}{dt} + k(\lambda_n^2 + \mu_m^2)\tilde{\tilde{U}} = k[U_2 Y_m'(0)\tilde{I}_n + U_1 X_n'(0)\tilde{I}_m]. \tag{62a}$$

Accompanying this ODE in $\tilde{\tilde{U}}(\lambda_n, \mu_m, t)$ is the transform of initial condition (59d),

$$\tilde{\tilde{U}}(\lambda_n, \mu_m, 0) = 0. \tag{62b}$$

Because the right side of (62a) is a constant with respect to t, a general solution of this ODE is

$$\tilde{\tilde{U}}(\lambda_n, \mu_m, t) = A_{mn} e^{-k(\lambda_n^2 + \mu_m^2)t} + \frac{U_2 Y_m'(0)\, \tilde{I}_n + U_1 X_n'(0)\tilde{I}_m}{\lambda_n^2 + \mu_m^2},$$

where the A_{mn} are constants. Initial condition (62b) requires that

$$0 = A_{mn} + \frac{U_2 Y_m'(0)\tilde{I}_n + U_1 X_n'(0)\tilde{I}_m}{\lambda_n^2 + \mu_m^2},$$

and therefore

$$\tilde{\tilde{U}}(\lambda_n, \mu_m, t) = \frac{U_2 Y_m'(0)\tilde{I}_n + U_1 X_n'(0)\tilde{I}_m}{\lambda_n^2 + \mu_m^2} (1 - e^{-k(\lambda_n^2 + \mu_m^2)t}). \tag{63}$$

To find $U(x, y, t)$, we now invert transforms (60) and (58):

$$U(x, y, t) = \sum_{m=1}^{\infty} \sum_{n=1}^{\infty} \tilde{\tilde{U}}(\lambda_n, \mu_m, t) Y_m(y) X_n(x).$$

Substitutions for $\tilde{\tilde{U}}(\lambda_n, \mu_m, t)$, $Y_m(y)$, and $X_n(x)$ lead to

$$U(x, y, t) = 8 \sum_{m=1}^{\infty} \sum_{n=1}^{\infty} B_{mn}(1 - e^{-[4n^2\pi^2 L'^2 + (2m-1)^2\pi^2 L^2]kt/(4L^2 L'^2)})$$

$$\times \sin\frac{n\pi x}{L} \sin\frac{(2m-1)\pi y}{2L'}, \tag{64a}$$

where

$$B_{mn} = \frac{[1 + (-1)^{n+1}](2m-1)^2 L^2 U_2 + 4n^2 L'^2 U_1}{n(2m-1)[4n^2\pi^2 L'^2 + (2m-1)^2\pi^2 L^2]}. \quad \blacksquare \tag{64b}$$

As a second example, we consider a boundary value problem in three dimensions.

Example 5: Find the potential inside the region bounded by the planes $x = 0$, $x = L$, $y = 0$, $y = L'$, $z = 0$, and $z = L''$ if all such planes are held at potential zero and the region contains a uniform charge distribution with density σ coulombs per cubic meter.

Solution: The boundary value problem for potential $V(x, y, z)$ in the region is

$$\frac{\partial^2 V}{\partial x^2} + \frac{\partial^2 V}{\partial y^2} + \frac{\partial^2 V}{\partial z^2} = -\frac{\sigma}{\varepsilon}, \qquad 0 < x < L, \qquad 0 < y < L', \qquad 0 < z < L'', \tag{65a}$$

$$V(0, y, z) = 0, \qquad 0 < y < L', \qquad 0 < z < L'', \tag{65b}$$

$$V(L, y, z) = 0, \qquad 0 < y < L', \qquad 0 < z < L'', \tag{65c}$$

$$V(x, 0, z) = 0, \qquad 0 < x < L, \qquad 0 < z < L'', \tag{65d}$$

$$V(x, L', z) = 0, \qquad 0 < x < L, \qquad 0 < z < L'', \tag{65e}$$

$$V(x, y, 0) = 0, \qquad 0 < x < L, \qquad 0 < y < L', \tag{65f}$$

$$V(x, y, L'') = 0, \qquad 0 < x < L, \qquad 0 < y < L'. \tag{65g}$$

The finite Fourier transform associated with the x-variable is

$$\tilde{f}(\lambda_n) = \int_0^L f(x) X_n(x) \, dx, \tag{66}$$

where $\lambda_n^2 = n^2\pi^2/L^2$ and $X_n(x) = \sqrt{2/L} \sin(n\pi x/L)$ are the eigenpairs of the Sturm-Liouville system

$$X'' + \lambda^2 X = 0, \qquad 0 < x < L,$$

$$X(0) = 0 = X(L).$$

When we apply this transform to PDE (65a) and use integration by parts,

$$\int_0^L \left(\frac{\partial^2 V}{\partial y^2} + \frac{\partial^2 V}{\partial z^2} + \frac{\sigma}{\varepsilon} \right) X_n \, dx = -\int_0^L \frac{\partial^2 V}{\partial x^2} X_n \, dx$$

$$= -\left\{ \frac{\partial V}{\partial x} X_n \right\}_0^L + \int_0^L \frac{\partial V}{\partial x} X_n' \, dx$$

[and since $X_n(0) = X_n(L) = 0$]

$$= \{V X_n'\}_0^L - \int_0^L V X_n'' \, dx$$

[and since $V(L, y, z) = V(0, y, z) = 0$]

$$= -\int_0^L V(-\lambda_n^2 X_n) \, dx$$

$$= \lambda_n^2 \tilde{V}(\lambda_n, y, z).$$

Thus, $\tilde{V}(\lambda_n, y, z)$ must satisfy the PDE

$$\frac{\partial^2 \tilde{V}}{\partial y^2} + \frac{\partial^2 \tilde{V}}{\partial z^2} - \lambda_n^2 \tilde{V} = -\frac{\sigma}{\varepsilon} \tilde{1}_n, \qquad 0 < y < L', \qquad 0 < z < L'', \qquad \text{(67a)}$$

subject to the boundary conditions

$$\tilde{V}(\lambda_n, 0, z) = 0, \qquad 0 < z < L'', \tag{67b}$$

$$\tilde{V}(\lambda_n, L', z) = 0, \qquad 0 < z < L'', \tag{67c}$$

$$\tilde{V}(\lambda_n, y, 0) = 0, \qquad 0 < y < L', \tag{67d}$$

$$\tilde{V}(\lambda_n, y, L'') = 0, \qquad 0 < y < L' \tag{67e}$$

and

$$\tilde{1}_n = \int_0^L 1 X_n \, dx = \frac{\sqrt{2L}[1 + (-1)^{n+1}]}{n\pi}. \tag{67f}$$

To eliminate y from problem (67), we use the finite Fourier transform

$$\tilde{f}(\mu_m) = \int_0^{L'} f(y) Y_m(y) \, dy, \tag{68}$$

where $\mu_m^2 = m^2 \pi^2 / L'^2$ and $Y_m(y) = \sqrt{2/L'} \sin(m\pi y / L')$ are eigenpairs of the Sturm-Liouville system

$$Y'' + \mu^2 Y = 0, \qquad 0 < y < L',$$

$$Y(0) = 0 = Y(L').$$

Application of this transform to (67a) yields

$$\int_0^{L'} \left(\frac{\partial^2 \tilde{V}}{\partial z^2} - \lambda_n^2 \tilde{V} + \frac{\sigma}{\varepsilon} \tilde{1}_n \right) Y_m \, dy = -\int_0^{L'} \frac{\partial^2 \tilde{V}}{\partial y^2} Y_m \, dy$$

$$= -\left\{ \frac{\partial \tilde{V}}{\partial y} Y_m \right\}_0^{L'} + \int_0^{L'} \frac{\partial \tilde{V}}{\partial y} Y_m' \, dy$$

[and since $Y_m(0) = Y_m(L') = 0$]

$$= \{\tilde{V} Y_m'\}_0^{L'} - \int_0^{L'} \tilde{V} Y_m'' \, dy$$

$$[\text{and since } \tilde{V}(\lambda_n, 0, z) = \tilde{V}(\lambda_n, L', z) = 0]$$

$$= -\int_0^{L'} \tilde{V}(-\mu_m^2 Y_m) \, dy$$

$$= \mu_m^2 \tilde{\tilde{V}}(\lambda_n, \mu_m, z).$$

Thus, $\tilde{\tilde{V}}(\lambda_n, \mu_m, z)$ must satisfy the ODE

$$\frac{d^2 \tilde{\tilde{V}}}{dz^2} - (\lambda_n^2 + \mu_m^2)\tilde{\tilde{V}} = -\frac{\sigma}{\varepsilon}\tilde{\tilde{1}}_{nm}, \qquad 0 < z < L'', \tag{69a}$$

subject to

$$\tilde{\tilde{V}}(\lambda_n, \mu_m, 0) = 0, \tag{69b}$$

$$\tilde{\tilde{V}}(\lambda_n, \mu_m, L'') = 0 \tag{69c}$$

and

$$\tilde{\tilde{1}}_{nm} = \int_0^{L'} \tilde{1}_n Y_m \, dy = \frac{2\sqrt{LL'}[1 + (-1)^{n+1}][1 + (-1)^{m+1}]}{mn\pi^2}. \tag{69d}$$

The general solution of (69a) is

$$\tilde{\tilde{V}}(\lambda_n, \mu_m, z) = A_{mn} \cosh\sqrt{\lambda_n^2 + \mu_m^2}\,z + B_{mn}\sinh\sqrt{\lambda_n^2 + \mu_m^2}\,z + \frac{(\sigma/\varepsilon)\tilde{\tilde{1}}_{nm}}{\lambda_n^2 + \mu_m^2}. \tag{70}$$

Boundary conditions (69b, c) require that

$$0 = A_{mn} + \frac{(\sigma/\varepsilon)\tilde{\tilde{1}}_{nm}}{\lambda_n^2 + \mu_m^2},$$

$$0 = A_{mn} \cosh\sqrt{\lambda_n^2 + \mu_m^2}\,L'' + B_{mn}\sinh\sqrt{\lambda_n^2 + \mu_m^2}\,L'' + \frac{(\sigma/\varepsilon)\tilde{\tilde{1}}_{nm}}{\lambda_n^2 + \mu_m^2}.$$

When these are solved for A_{mn} and B_{mn} and the results are substituted into (70), $\tilde{\tilde{V}}(\lambda_n, \mu_m, z)$ simplifies to

$$\tilde{\tilde{V}}(\lambda_n, \mu_m, z) = \frac{-(\sigma/\varepsilon)\tilde{\tilde{1}}_{nm}}{(\lambda_n^2 + \mu_m^2)\sinh\sqrt{\lambda_n^2 + \mu_m^2}\,L''}\left(\sinh\sqrt{\lambda_n^2 + \mu_m^2}\,(L'' - z)\right.$$

$$\left. + \sinh\sqrt{\lambda_n^2 + \mu_m^2}\,z - \sinh\sqrt{\lambda_n^2 + \mu_m^2}\,L''\right). \tag{71}$$

The solution of problem (65) is therefore

$$V(x, y, z) = \sum_{m=1}^{\infty} \sum_{n=1}^{\infty} \tilde{\tilde{V}}(\lambda_n, \mu_m, z) X_n(x)\, Y_m(y). \qquad \blacksquare \tag{72}$$

Exercises 6.3

Part A—Heat Conduction

1. An isotropic, homogeneous, horizontal plate has its top and bottom faces insulated. Edges $x = 0$, $x = L$, $y = 0$, and $y = L'$ are all held at constant temperatures U_1, U_2, U_3, and U_4, respectively,

for time $t > 0$. If the temperature in the plate at time $t = 0$ is $f(x, y), 0 \le x \le L, 0 \le y \le L'$, find its temperature thereafter.

2. (a) Solve the following heat conduction problem:

$$\frac{\partial U}{\partial t} = k\left(\frac{\partial^2 U}{\partial x^2} + \frac{\partial^2 U}{\partial y^2}\right), \qquad 0 < x < L, \qquad 0 < y < L', \qquad t > 0,$$

$$U(0, y, t) = U_1, \qquad 0 < y < L', \qquad t > 0,$$

$$U(L, y, t) = U_2, \qquad 0 < y < L', \qquad t > 0,$$

$$U_y(x, 0, t) = \kappa_1^{-1}\phi_1, \qquad 0 < x < L, \qquad t > 0,$$

$$U_y(x, L', t) = -\kappa_2^{-1}\phi_2, \qquad 0 < x < L, \qquad t > 0,$$

$$U(x, y, 0) = 0, \qquad 0 < x < L, \qquad 0 < y < L',$$

where U_1, U_2, ϕ_1, and ϕ_2 are constants. Interpret the problem physically.

(b) What is the solution when $\phi_1 = \phi_2 = 0$?

3. Repeat Exercise 2(a) when U_1, U_2, ϕ_1, and ϕ_2 are functions of time t.

4. Find a formula for the solution of the general two-dimensional heat conduction problem

$$\frac{\partial U}{\partial t} = k\left(\frac{\partial^2 U}{\partial x^2} + \frac{\partial^2 U}{\partial y^2}\right) + \frac{kg(x, y, t)}{\kappa}, \quad 0 < x < L, \quad 0 < y < L', \quad t > 0,$$

$$-l_1\frac{\partial U}{\partial x} + h_1 U = f_1(y, t), \qquad x = 0, \qquad 0 < y < L', \qquad t > 0,$$

$$l_2\frac{\partial U}{\partial x} + h_2 U = f_2(y, t), \qquad x = L, \qquad 0 < y < L', \qquad t > 0,$$

$$-l_3\frac{\partial U}{\partial y} + h_3 U = f_3(x, t), \qquad y = 0, \qquad 0 < x < L, \qquad t > 0,$$

$$l_4\frac{\partial U}{\partial y} + h_4 U = f_4(x, t), \qquad y = L', \qquad 0 < x < L, \qquad t > 0,$$

$$U(x, y, 0) = f(x, y), \qquad 0 < x < L, \qquad 0 < y < L'.$$

Part B—Vibrations

5. A rectangular membrane of side lengths L and L' has its edges fixed on the xy-plane. If it is released from rest at a displacement given by $f(x, y)$, find subsequent displacements of the membrane if gravity is taken into account.

6. A square membrane of side length L, which is initially at rest on the xy-plane, has its edges fixed on the xy-plane. If a periodic force per unit area $A \cos(\omega t), t > 0$ (A a constant) acts at every point in the membrane, find displacements in the membrane. Assume that $\omega \ne c\pi\sqrt{n^2 + m^2}/L$ for any positive integers m and n.

7. Repeat Exercise 6 if $\omega = \sqrt{2}\,\pi c/L$.

8. Repeat Exercise 6 if $\omega = \sqrt{17}\,\pi c/L$.

9. Repeat Exercise 6 if $\omega = \sqrt{65}\,\pi c/L$.

10. Repeat Exercise 6 if $\omega = \sqrt{10}\,\pi c/L$.

11. Repeat Exercise 6 if $\omega = \sqrt{130}\,\pi c/L$.

12. Find a formula for the solution of the general two-dimensional vibration problem

$$\frac{\partial^2 z}{\partial t^2} = c^2 \left(\frac{\partial^2 z}{\partial x^2} + \frac{\partial^2 z}{\partial y^2} \right) + \frac{F(x, y, t)}{\rho}, \qquad 0 < x < L, \qquad 0 < y < L', \qquad t > 0,$$

$$-l_1 \frac{\partial z}{\partial x} + h_1 z = f_1(y, t), \qquad x = 0, \qquad 0 < y < L', \qquad t > 0,$$

$$l_2 \frac{\partial z}{\partial x} + h_2 z = f_2(y, t), \qquad x = L, \qquad 0 < y < L', \qquad t > 0,$$

$$-l_3 \frac{\partial z}{\partial y} + h_3 z = f_3(x, t), \qquad y = 0, \qquad 0 < x < L, \qquad t > 0,$$

$$l_4 \frac{\partial z}{\partial y} + h_4 z = f_4(x, t), \qquad y = L', \qquad 0 < x < L, \qquad t > 0,$$

$$z(x, y, 0) = g(x, y), \qquad 0 < x < L, \qquad 0 < y < L',$$

$$z_t(x, y, 0) = h(x, y), \qquad 0 < x < L, \qquad 0 < y < L'.$$

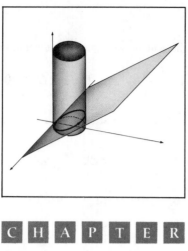

Problems on Infinite Spatial Domains

7.1 Introduction

In Chapters 2–6 we restricted consideration to problems on bounded spatial domains, but many important problems take place on infinite or semi-infinite domains. For example, suppose a rod of infinite length is initially at temperature $f(x)$, $-\infty < x < \infty$. The initial value problem for temperature $U(x, t)$ in the rod when the sides are insulated is

$$\frac{\partial U}{\partial t} = k\frac{\partial^2 U}{\partial x^2}, \qquad -\infty < x < \infty, \qquad t > 0, \tag{1a}$$

$$U(x, 0) = f(x), \qquad -\infty < x < \infty. \tag{1b}$$

It may be argued that there is no such thing as an infinite rod. Physically it must be finite, and therefore boundary effects must be taken into account. This can be countered by stating that the rod may be so long that boundary effects are negligibly small in that part of the rod under consideration. Consequently, if there is a simple solution to the infinite problem that is an excellent approximation to the Fourier series solution of the bounded problem, then clearly there is an advantage in considering the infinite problem.

In this chapter we illustrate that separation of variables on problems with infinite spatial domains leads to integral representations of the solution called *Fourier integrals*. The Fourier integral replaces the Fourier series representation for finite intervals; it is a direct result of the fact that eigenvalues of the separated equation form a continuous, rather than discrete, set. When the solution of an infinite spatial problem is known to be even or odd, the Fourier integral takes on a simplified form called the *Fourier cosine* or *sine integral*. These integrals also arise naturally in problems on semi-infinite intervals ($0 < x < \infty$) when the boundary condition at $x = 0$ is Neumann or Dirichlet. Generalized Fourier integrals arise when the boundary condition at $x = 0$ is of Robin type. Associated with each Fourier integral is an integral transform that provides a convenient alternative to separation of variables. These transforms are as valuable for homogeneous problems as they are for nonhomogeneous problems (unlike finite Fourier transforms, which are not normally used on homogeneous problems).

We begin by illustrating the continuous nature of "eigenvalues" for infinite spatial problems. Separation of variables $U(x,t) = X(x)T(t)$ in problem (1) yields

$$X'' + \alpha X = 0, \qquad T' + k\alpha T = 0, \qquad \alpha = \text{constant}. \tag{2}$$

The solution for $T(t)$ is $Ce^{-k\alpha t}$, which clearly indicates that α must be nonnegative. We therefore set $\alpha = \lambda^2$, in which case

$$X(x) = A \cos \lambda x + B \sin \lambda x. \tag{3}$$

[Alternatively, we could argue that the solution $X(x)$ of $X'' + \alpha X = 0$ must be bounded as $x \to \pm\infty$, and this would again imply that α be nonnegative.] Thus, any function of the form

$$e^{-k\lambda^2 t}(A \cos \lambda x + B \sin \lambda x)$$

for arbitrary A, B, and λ satisfies PDE (1a). For problems on bounded intervals, boundary conditions determine a discrete set of eigenvalues λ_n and equations expressing A and B in terms of λ_n. Separated functions are then superposed as infinite series. For infinite intervals, no boundary conditions exist, and hence A, B, and λ are all arbitrary. But suppose for the moment that A and B are functions of λ. It is straightforward to show that when the integral

$$U(x,t) = \int_0^\infty e^{-k\lambda^2 t}[A(\lambda) \cos \lambda x + B(\lambda) \sin \lambda x]\, d\lambda \tag{4}$$

is suitably convergent so that integrations with respect to λ may be interchanged with differentiations with respect to x and y, such a function satisfies (1a) (see Exercise 2). This integral is a superposition of separated functions over all values of the parameter λ, and it satisfies (1a) for arbitrary $A(\lambda)$ and $B(\lambda)$. To determine these functions, we demand that (4) satisfy initial condition (1b):

$$f(x) = \int_0^\infty [A(\lambda) \cos \lambda x + B(\lambda) \sin \lambda x]\, d\lambda, \qquad -\infty < x < \infty. \tag{5}$$

The solution of (1) is therefore defined by improper integral (4), provided we can find functions $A(\lambda)$ and $B(\lambda)$ satisfying (5). Equation (5) is called the Fourier integral representation of $f(x)$; it is the integral analog of the Fourier series of a periodic function. In Section 7.2 we investigate conditions under which a function has a Fourier integral representation, and we determine formulas for $A(\lambda)$ and $B(\lambda)$.

Exercises 7.1

1. Why does the integral superposition in equation (4) not extend over the interval $-\infty < \lambda < \infty$?

2. Show that if partial derivatives of the improper integral in (4) with respect to x and y may be interchanged with the λ-integration, then $U(x, t)$ satisfies PDE (1a).

7.2 The Fourier Integral Formulas

To state conditions under which the Fourier integral of a function does indeed represent the function, we require the concept of absolute integrability.

Definition 1

A function $f(x)$ is said to be absolutely integrable on the interval $-\infty < x < \infty$ if

$$\int_{-\infty}^{\infty} |f(x)|\, dx$$

converges.

For example, the functions e^{-x^2} and $(x^2 + 1)^{-1}$ are absolutely integrable on $-\infty < x < \infty$, but x, $\sin x$, and $1/\sqrt{|x|}$ are not.

Corresponding to Theorem 2 in Section 2.1 for Fourier series, we have the following result for Fourier integrals.

Theorem 1

If $f(x)$ is piecewise continuous on every finite interval and absolutely integrable on $-\infty < x < \infty$, then at every x at which $f(x)$ has a right and left derivative,

$$\frac{f(x+) + f(x-)}{2} = \int_0^{\infty} [A(\lambda)\cos \lambda x + B(\lambda)\sin \lambda x]\, d\lambda \qquad (6a)$$

$$\text{when} \quad A(\lambda) = \frac{1}{\pi}\int_{-\infty}^{\infty} f(x)\cos \lambda x\, dx, \qquad B(\lambda) = \frac{1}{\pi}\int_{-\infty}^{\infty} f(x)\sin \lambda x\, dx. \qquad (6b)$$

Equation (6) is called the *Fourier integral formula* for the function $f(x)$. It is proved in Appendix B. Since functions that are piecewise smooth must have right and left derivatives, we may state the following corollary to Theorem 1.

Corollary

If $f(x)$ is absolutely integrable on $-\infty < x < \infty$ and is piecewise smooth on every finite interval, then $f(x)$ can be expressed in Fourier integral form (6).

One of the most important functions that we encounter in this chapter is contained in the following example.

Example 1:   Find the Fourier integral representation of the Gaussian $f(x) = e^{-kx^2}$, $k > 0$ a constant.

Solution: Since this function and its derivative are continuous, and the function is absolutely integrable, we may write

$$e^{-kx^2} = \int_0^\infty [A(\lambda)\cos \lambda x + B(\lambda)\sin \lambda x]\, dx,$$

where $A(\lambda) = \dfrac{1}{\pi}\displaystyle\int_{-\infty}^\infty e^{-kx^2}\cos \lambda x\, dx$ and $B(\lambda) = \dfrac{1}{\pi}\displaystyle\int_{-\infty}^\infty e^{-kx^2}\sin \lambda x\, dx.$

To evaluate $A(\lambda)$, we note that the presence of the exponential e^{-kx^2} permits differentiation under the integral to obtain

$$\frac{dA}{d\lambda} = \frac{1}{\pi}\int_{-\infty}^\infty -xe^{-kx^2}\sin \lambda x\, dx.$$

Integration by parts now gives

$$\frac{dA}{d\lambda} = \frac{1}{\pi}\left\{\frac{e^{-kx^2}}{2k}\sin \lambda x\right\}_{-\infty}^\infty - \frac{1}{\pi}\int_{-\infty}^\infty \frac{e^{-kx^2}}{2k}\lambda\cos \lambda x\, dx = -\frac{\lambda}{2k}A(\lambda).$$

In other words, $A(\lambda)$ must satisfy the ODE

$$\frac{dA}{d\lambda} + \frac{\lambda}{2k}A = 0.$$

An initial condition for this differential equation is

$$A(0) = \frac{1}{\pi}\int_{-\infty}^\infty e^{-kx^2}\, dx = \frac{1}{\sqrt{k\pi}}$$

(see Exercise 24 for the value of this integral). The solution of this problem is

$$A(\lambda) = \frac{1}{\sqrt{k\pi}}e^{-\lambda^2/(4k)}.$$

Because $e^{-kx^2}\sin \lambda x$ is an odd function, we quickly conclude that $B(\lambda) = 0$. We may therefore write

$$e^{-kx^2} = \int_0^\infty \frac{e^{-\lambda^2/(4k)}}{\sqrt{k\pi}}\cos \lambda x\, d\lambda.$$

An alternative derivation of $A(\lambda)$ using complex contour integrals is given in Exercise 25. ∎

When a function $f(x)$ satisfying the conditions of Theorem 1 (or its corollary) is even, it is obvious that

$$A(\lambda) = \frac{2}{\pi} \int_0^\infty f(x) \cos \lambda x \, dx, \qquad B(\lambda) = 0, \tag{7b}$$

in which case

$$\boxed{\frac{f(x+) + f(x-)}{2} = \int_0^\infty A(\lambda) \cos \lambda x \, d\lambda.} \tag{7a}$$

This result is called the *Fourier cosine integral formula*. The function e^{-kx^2} in Example 1 is represented in the form of a Fourier cosine integral.

Example 2:   Find an integral representation for the function

$$f(x) = \begin{cases} k(L - |x|)/L & |x| \le L \\ 0 & |x| > L \end{cases}.$$

Solution: Because $f(x)$ is even (Figure 7.1), it has a cosine integral representation, where

$$A(\lambda) = \frac{2}{\pi} \int_0^\infty f(x) \cos \lambda x \, dx = \frac{2}{\pi} \int_0^L \frac{k}{L}(L - x) \cos \lambda x \, dx$$

$$= \frac{2k}{\pi L}\left\{ \frac{L - x}{\lambda} \sin \lambda x - \frac{1}{\lambda^2} \cos \lambda x \right\}_0^L = \frac{2k}{\pi L \lambda^2}(1 - \cos \lambda L).$$

Since $f(x)$ is continuous, we may write

$$f(x) = \int_0^\infty \frac{2k}{\pi L \lambda^2}(1 - \cos \lambda L) \cos \lambda x \, d\lambda = \frac{2k}{\pi L} \int_0^\infty \frac{1 - \cos \lambda L}{\lambda^2} \cos \lambda x \, d\lambda.$$

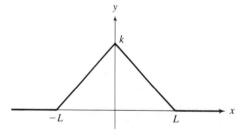

Figure 7.1

When $f(x)$ is an odd function, coefficient $A(\lambda) = 0$, and $f(x)$ may be represented by the *Fourier sine integral formula*

$$\boxed{\frac{f(x+) + f(x-)}{2} = \int_0^\infty B(\lambda) \sin \lambda x \, d\lambda,} \tag{8a}$$

where

$$B(\lambda) = \frac{2}{\pi} \int_0^\infty f(x) \sin \lambda x \, dx. \tag{8b}$$

Example 3:   Find an integral representation for the function

$$(\operatorname{sgn} x)e^{-|x|} = \begin{cases} e^{-x} & x > 0 \\ -e^{x} & x < 0 \end{cases}.$$

Solution: Because $(\operatorname{sgn} x)e^{-|x|}$ is odd (Figure 7.2), it has a sine integral representation, where

$$B(\lambda) = \frac{2}{\pi}\int_{0}^{\infty} e^{-x}\sin \lambda x\, dx = \frac{2}{\pi}\left\{\frac{-e^{-x}}{1+\lambda^2}(\sin \lambda x + \lambda \cos \lambda x)\right\}_{0}^{\infty} = \frac{2\lambda}{\pi(1+\lambda^2)}.$$

Hence, $$(\operatorname{sgn} x)e^{-|x|} = \int_{0}^{\infty}\frac{2\lambda}{\pi(1+\lambda^2)}\sin \lambda x\, d\lambda,$$

provided the function is assigned the value zero at $x = 0$.

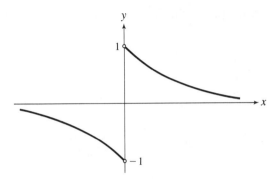

Figure 7.2

The Fourier sine and cosine integral formulas also provide integral representations for functions that are defined only for $0 < x < \infty$. Indeed, when $f(x)$ is absolutely integrable on $0 < x < \infty$, and $f(x)$ is piecewise smooth on every finite interval $0 \le x \le X$, integrals (7) and (8) converge to $[f(x+) + f(x-)]/2$ for $x > 0$. For $x < 0$, they converge to the even and odd extensions of $f(x)$, respectively. At $x = 0$, the Fourier cosine integral converges to $f(0+)$, and the sine integral yields the value zero.

Theorem 1 would seem to eliminate many functions that we might wish to represent in the form of a Fourier integral. For instance, it would be quite reasonable to have a sinusoidal initial temperature distribution $f(x)$ in problem (1). But such a function is not absolutely integrable on $-\infty < x < \infty$; absolutely integrable functions must necessarily have limit zero as $x \to \pm\infty$. Thus, Fourier integrals cannot presently be used to solve problem (1) when $f(x)$ is sinusoidal. "Generalized functions," the class of functions that contain the Dirac delta function as a special case (see Chapter 11) can be used to weaken the condition of absolute integrability. In this chapter, however, we shall maintain this restriction unless otherwise specified and concentrate our attention on how Fourier integrals and Fourier transforms are used to solve problems, rather than attempt to enlarge the class of problems to which the techniques can be applied.

Fourier integral formula (6) can be used, in conjunction with separation of variables, to solve problems with spatial domain $-\infty < x < \infty$ (see Example 4). In many of these problems, Fourier integral (6) reduces to the cosine or sine integral (7) or (8). Additionally, sine and cosine integrals are useful for problems on the semi-infinite domain $0 < x < \infty$ when the boundary condition at $x = 0$ is homogeneous and of Dirichlet or Neumann type. We illustrate this in Examples 5 and 6.

Example 4:   Solve heat conduction problem (1) when

$$f(x) = \begin{cases} x(L-x) & 0 \le x \le L \\ 0 & \text{otherwise} \end{cases}.$$

Solution: Separation of variables and superposition lead to solution (4),

$$U(x,t) = \int_0^\infty e^{-k\lambda^2 t}[A(\lambda)\cos \lambda x + B(\lambda)\sin \lambda x]\, d\lambda,$$

where boundary condition (1b) requires (5):

$$f(x) = \int_{-\infty}^\infty [A(\lambda)\cos \lambda x + B(\lambda)\sin \lambda x]\, d\lambda, \qquad -\infty < x < \infty.$$

Consequently, $A(\lambda)$ and $B(\lambda)$ are coefficients in the Fourier integral representation of $f(x)$, defined by (6b):

$$A(\lambda) = \frac{1}{\pi}\int_{-\infty}^\infty f(x)\cos \lambda x\, dx = \frac{1}{\pi}\int_0^L x(L-x)\cos \lambda x\, dx$$

$$= \frac{1}{\pi}\left\{\frac{x(L-x)}{\lambda}\sin \lambda x + \frac{L-2x}{\lambda^2}\cos \lambda x + \frac{2}{\lambda^3}\sin \lambda x\right\}_0^L$$

$$= \frac{-L}{\pi\lambda^2}(1 + \cos \lambda L) + \frac{2\sin \lambda L}{\pi\lambda^3};$$

$$B(\lambda) = \frac{1}{\pi}\int_{-\infty}^\infty f(x)\sin \lambda x\, dx = \frac{1}{\pi}\int_0^L x(L-x)\sin \lambda x\, dx$$

$$= \frac{1}{\pi}\left\{\frac{x(x-L)}{\lambda}\cos \lambda x + \frac{L-2x}{\lambda^2}\sin \lambda x - \frac{2}{\lambda^3}\cos \lambda x\right\}_0^L$$

$$= \frac{-L}{\pi\lambda^2}\sin \lambda L + \frac{2}{\pi\lambda^3}(1 - \cos \lambda L).$$

Thus, $U(x,t) = \int_0^\infty \dfrac{e^{-k\lambda^2 t}}{\pi\lambda^3}([-\lambda L(1 + \cos \lambda L) + 2\sin \lambda L]\cos \lambda x$

$$+ [-\lambda L\sin \lambda L + 2(1 - \cos \lambda L)]\sin \lambda x)\, d\lambda. \qquad\blacksquare$$

This particular representation is of little practical use. With the Fourier transform of Section 7.3, we derive a simpler representation in Section 7.4. (See also Exercise 5 in this section.)

Example 5:   A taut string of semi-infinite length is given an initial displacement $f(x)$, $x > 0$, but no initial velocity. If the end $x = 0$ is free to move vertically for $t > 0$, find an integral representation for subsequent displacements of points on the string.

Solution: The initial boundary value problem for displacements $y(x,t)$ is

$$\frac{\partial^2 y}{\partial t^2} = c^2\frac{\partial^2 y}{\partial x^2}, \qquad x > 0, \qquad t > 0, \tag{9a}$$

$$y_x(0,t) = 0, \qquad t > 0, \tag{9b}$$

$$y(x, 0) = f(x), \qquad x > 0, \tag{9c}$$

$$y_t(x, 0) = 0, \qquad x > 0. \tag{9d}$$

Separation of variables $y(x, t) = X(x)T(t)$ on (9a, b, d) leads to the ODEs

$$X'' + \lambda^2 X = 0, \qquad x > 0, \qquad T'' + c^2\lambda^2 T = 0, \qquad t > 0,$$

$$X'(0) = 0; \qquad\qquad\qquad T'(0) = 0.$$

These yield $X(x) = A \cos \lambda x$ and $T(t) = D \cos c\lambda t$. Superposition of separated functions in integral form gives

$$y(x, t) = \int_0^\infty A(\lambda) \cos \lambda x \cos c\lambda t \, d\lambda. \tag{10}$$

Initial condition (9c) requires $A(\lambda)$ to satisfy

$$f(x) = \int_0^\infty A(\lambda) \cos \lambda x \, d\lambda; \tag{11}$$

that is, $A(\lambda)$ is the coefficient in the Fourier cosine integral representation of $f(x)$,

$$A(\lambda) = \frac{2}{\pi} \int_0^\infty f(x) \cos \lambda x \, dx.$$

If we replace the variable of integration by u and substitute into (10), the solution of problem (9) is

$$y(x, t) = \int_0^\infty \left(\frac{2}{\pi} \int_0^\infty f(u) \cos \lambda u \, du \right) \cos \lambda x \cos c\lambda t \, d\lambda$$

$$= \frac{2}{\pi} \int_0^\infty \int_0^\infty f(u) \cos \lambda u \cos \lambda x \cos c\lambda t \, du \, d\lambda. \tag{12}$$

This is not a particularly useful representation for $y(x, t)$. If we return to equation (10), we can obtain the solution in closed form:

$$y(x, t) = \int_0^\infty A(\lambda) \left(\frac{1}{2} \right) (\cos \lambda(x + ct) + \cos \lambda(x - ct)) \, d\lambda$$

$$= \frac{1}{2} \int_0^\infty A(\lambda) \cos \lambda(x + ct) \, d\lambda + \frac{1}{2} \int_0^\infty A(\lambda) \cos \lambda(x - ct) \, d\lambda.$$

But if equation (11) is a representation of $f(x)$, these integrals must represent $f(x + ct)$ and $f(x - ct)$. In other words,

$$y(x, t) = \frac{1}{2} [f(x + ct) + f(x - ct)]. \tag{13}$$

Although $f(x)$ is defined only for $x > 0$, the fact that it has been represented in cosine integral form requires that for this solution, it must be extended as an even function. This form for $y(x, t)$ is d'Alembert's representation on the interval $x > 0$. It can be interpreted in exactly the same way as d'Alembert's solution for the finite string in Section 1.7. Geometrically, the position of the string at any given time t is the algebraic sum of one-half the original displacement $f(x)$, $-\infty < x < \infty$, shifted ct units to the right, $[f(x - ct)]/2$, and one-half the same curve shifted ct units to the left, $[f(x + ct)]/2$. From a physical standpoint, initial displacement $f(x)$, $0 < x < \infty$, separates into two equal disturbances $f(x)/2$, one of which travels with speed c to the right, $[f(x - ct)]/2$, and the other of which travels with speed c to the left, $[f(x + ct)]/2$. The left-traveling wave is reflected at $x = 0$ (with no reversal in sign) and combines with what remains of this same wave. A specific example is discussed in Exercise 8. In Exercise 9, the motion of individual particles is examined. ∎

Example 6:   Find an integral representation for electrostatic potential in the source-free region $0 < x < L$, $y > 0$ (Figure 7.3) when potential along $y = 0$ is zero and potentials along $x = 0$ and $x = L$ are arbitrarily specified functions.

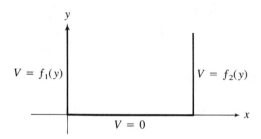

Figure 7.3

Solution: The boundary value problem for $V(x, y)$ is

$$\frac{\partial^2 V}{\partial x^2} + \frac{\partial^2 V}{\partial y^2} = 0, \qquad 0 < x < L, \qquad y > 0, \tag{14a}$$

$$V(0, y) = f_1(y), \qquad y > 0, \tag{14b}$$

$$V(L, y) = f_2(y), \qquad y > 0, \tag{14c}$$

$$V(x, 0) = 0, \qquad 0 < x < L. \tag{14d}$$

Separation of variables $V(x, y) = X(x)Y(y)$ on (14a, d) leads to the ODEs

$$X'' - \lambda^2 X = 0, \qquad 0 < x < L; \qquad Y'' + \lambda^2 Y = 0, \qquad y > 0,$$

$$Y(0) = 0.$$

Solutions of these are $X(x) = A \cosh \lambda x + B \sinh \lambda x$ and $Y(y) = D \sin \lambda y$, which we superpose in integral form:

$$V(x, y) = \int_0^\infty [A(\lambda) \cosh \lambda x + B(\lambda) \sinh \lambda x] \sin \lambda y \, d\lambda. \tag{15}$$

Boundary conditions (14b, c) require that

$$f_1(y) = \int_0^\infty A(\lambda) \sin \lambda y \, d\lambda, \tag{16a}$$

$$f_2(y) = \int_0^\infty [A(\lambda) \cosh \lambda L + B(\lambda) \sinh \lambda L] \sin \lambda y \, d\lambda. \tag{16b}$$

These are Fourier sine integral representations of $f_1(y)$ and $f_2(y)$; hence, by (8b),

$$A(\lambda) = \frac{2}{\pi} \int_0^\infty f_1(y) \sin \lambda y \, dy,$$

$$A(\lambda) \cosh \lambda L + B(\lambda) \sinh \lambda L = \frac{2}{\pi} \int_0^\infty f_2(y) \sin \lambda y \, dy.$$

When these are solved for $A(\lambda)$ and $B(\lambda)$ and substituted into (15), the solution of problem (14) is

$$V(x, y) = \int_0^\infty \left(\frac{2 \cosh \lambda x}{\pi} \int_0^\infty f_1(u) \sin \lambda u \, du + \frac{2 \sinh \lambda x}{\pi \sinh \lambda L} \int_0^\infty f_2(u) \sin \lambda u \, du \right.$$

$$\left. - \frac{2 \sinh \lambda x \cosh \lambda L}{\pi \sinh \lambda L} \int_0^\infty f_1(u) \sin \lambda u \, du \right) \sin \lambda y \, d\lambda$$

$$= \frac{2}{\pi} \int_0^\infty \frac{\sin \lambda y}{\sinh \lambda L} \left(\int_0^\infty \left[f_1(u)(\cosh \lambda x \sinh \lambda L - \sinh \lambda x \cosh \lambda L) \right. \right.$$

$$\left. \left. + f_2(u) \sinh \lambda x \right] \sin \lambda u \, du \right) d\lambda$$

$$= \frac{2}{\pi} \int_0^\infty \frac{\sin \lambda y}{\sinh \lambda L} \left(\int_0^\infty \left[f_1(u) \sinh \lambda (L - x) + f_2(u) \sinh \lambda x \right] \sin \lambda u \right) d\lambda. \qquad \blacksquare \; (17)$$

When the nonhomogeneity in Example 6 is along $y = 0$ instead of $x = 0$ and $x = L$, Fourier integrals are not needed. This is illustrated in the next example.

Example 7:   Solve the boundary value problem

$$\frac{\partial^2 V}{\partial x^2} + \frac{\partial^2 V}{\partial y^2} = 0, \qquad 0 < x < L, \qquad y > 0, \qquad \text{(18a)}$$

$$V(0, y) = 0, \qquad y > 0, \qquad \text{(18b)}$$

$$V(L, y) = 0, \qquad y > 0, \qquad \text{(18c)}$$

$$V(x, 0) = f(x), \qquad 0 < x < L. \qquad \text{(18d)}$$

Solution: Separation of variables $V(x, y) = X(x)Y(y)$ on (18a–c) leads to

$$X'' + \lambda^2 X = 0, \qquad 0 < x < L, \qquad Y'' - \lambda^2 Y = 0, \qquad y > 0.$$

$$X(0) = 0 = X(L);$$

Eigenfunctions of the Sturm-Liouville system are $X_n(x) = \sqrt{2/L} \sin(n\pi x/L)$, and the corresponding solutions for $Y(y)$ are

$$Y(y) = Ae^{-n\pi y/L} + Be^{n\pi y/L}.$$

For the solution to remain bounded for large y, we must set $B = 0$, in which case superposition of separated functions gives

$$V(x, y) = \sum_{n=1}^\infty A_n e^{-n\pi y/L} X_n(x). \qquad \text{(19)}$$

The boundary condition along $y = 0$ requires that

$$f(x) = \sum_{n=1}^{\infty} A_n X_n(x), \qquad 0 < x < L,$$

and therefore

$$A_n = \int_0^L f(x) X_n(x)\, dx. \qquad \blacksquare$$

Exercises 7.2

Do the exercises in Part D first.

Part A—Heat Conduction

1. Solve Example 4 if the rod occupies only the region $x \geq 0$ and the end $x = 0$ of the rod is held at temperature zero.

2. Solve Exercise 1 if the end $x = 0$ of the rod is insulated.

3. Repeat Example 4 if $f(x) = e^{-ax^2}$, $a > 0$ constant.

4. (a) Show that the solution of problem (1) can be expressed in the form

$$U(x, t) = \frac{1}{\pi} \int_0^{\infty} \int_{-\infty}^{\infty} e^{-k\lambda^2 t} f(u) \cos \lambda(u - x)\, du\, d\lambda.$$

(b) Formally interchange orders of integration and use the result of Example 1 to replace this iterated integral with the single integral

$$U(x, t) = \frac{1}{2\sqrt{k\pi t}} \int_{-\infty}^{\infty} f(u) e^{-(u-x)^2/(4kt)}\, du.$$

5. Use the result of Exercise 4 to simplify the solution to Example 4.

6. Use the technique of Exercise 4 to solve problem (1) on the semi-infinite interval $x \geq 0$ if the end $x = 0$ of the rod is held at temperature $0°C$.

7. Repeat Exercise 6 if the end $x = 0$ is insulated.

Part B—Vibrations

8. Suppose the initial displacement of the string in Example 5 is

$$f(x) = \begin{cases} k - k|x - a|/\varepsilon & |x - a| \leq \varepsilon \\ 0 & |x - a| > \varepsilon, \end{cases}$$

where a, ε, and k are positive constants with $a > 2\varepsilon$.

(a) Use the geometric interpretation of solution (13) as the superposition of $f(x)/2$ shifted ct units to the left and right to draw the position of the string for the following times:

(i) $\varepsilon/(2c)$	(ii) ε/c	(iii) $(2a - \varepsilon)/(2c)$
(iv) a/c	(v) $(2a + \varepsilon)/(2c)$	(vi) $(a + \varepsilon)/c$.

Describe the position of the string for $t > (a + \varepsilon)/c$.

(b) What difference to the analysis in (a) occurs if the physical interpretation of left- and right-traveling waves is used?

9. (a) Discuss the motion of the end of the string in Example 5.

   (b) Discuss the motion of other points on the string.

10. (a) Repeat Example 5 if end $x = 0$ of the string is held fixed on the x-axis.

    (b) Discuss the motion of points on the string.

11. Repeat Exercise 10(a) if the string has no initial displacement but is given an initial velocity $g(x)$, where $g(0) = 0$.

Part C—Potential, Steady-State Heat Conduction, Static Deflections of Membranes

12. Solve Example 6 if the boundary condition along $y = 0$ is homogeneous Neumann.

13. (a) Prove that for $0 \leq r < 1$,

$$\sum_{n=1}^{\infty} \frac{r^{2n-1}}{2n-1} \sin(2n-1)\theta = \frac{1}{2}\mathrm{Tan}^{-1}\left(\frac{2r\sin\theta}{1-r^2}\right).$$

(b) Use this result to find a closed-form solution to Example 7 when $f(x) = V_0 = $ constant.

Part D—General Results

In Exercises 14–18, find the Fourier integral representation of the function. Sketch a graph of the function to which the integral converges.

14. $f(x) = e^{-a|x|}$, $a > 0$ constant

15. $f(x) = H(x - a) - H(x - b)$, $b > a$ constants. $H(x - a)$ is the *Heaviside unit step function*, defined as

$$H(x - a) = \begin{cases} 0 & x < a \\ 1 & x > a \end{cases}.$$

16. $f(x) = \begin{cases} (b/a)(a - |x|) & |x| < a \\ 0 & |x| > a \end{cases}$, $a > 0, b > 0$ constants

17. $f(x) = \begin{cases} b(a^2 - x^2)/a^2 & |x| < a \\ 0 & |x| > a \end{cases}$, $a > 0, b > 0$ constants

18. $f(x) = e^{-ax}H(x)$, $a > 0$ constant

19. What is the Fourier cosine integral for the function $f(x) = e^{-kx^2}$ ($k > 0$), defined only for $x \geq 0$?

In Exercises 20–23, $f(x)$ is defined only for $x \geq 0$. Find its Fourier sine and cosine integral representations. To what does each integral converge at $x = 0$?

20. $f(x) = H(x - a) - H(x - b)$, $b > a > 0$ constants

21. $f(x) = \begin{cases} (b/a)(a - |x - c|) & |x - c| < a \\ 0 & |x - c| > a \end{cases}$, $a, b,$ and c all positive constants with $c > a > 0$

22. $f(x) = e^{-ax}\cos bx$, $a > 0, b > 0$ constants

23. $f(x) = e^{-ax}\sin bx$, $a > 0, b > 0$ constants

24. To evaluate

$$I = \int_{-\infty}^{\infty} e^{-kx^2}\, dx = 2 \int_{0}^{\infty} e^{-kx^2}\, dx,$$

we write

$$\frac{I^2}{4} = \left(\int_{0}^{\infty} e^{-kx^2}\, dx \right) \left(\int_{0}^{\infty} e^{-ky^2}\, dy \right) = \int_{0}^{\infty} \int_{0}^{\infty} e^{-k(x^2+y^2)}\, dy\, dx$$

and transform the double integral into polar coordinates. Show that $I = \sqrt{\pi/k}$.

25. In this exercise we use complex contour integrals to evaluate $A(\lambda)$ in Example 1.

(a) Transform the complex combination of real integrals

$$I = \int_{-\infty}^{\infty} e^{-kx^2} e^{i\lambda x}\, dx$$

by means of $z = x - i\lambda/(2k)$ into the contour integral

$$I = e^{-\lambda^2/(4k)} \int_{C} e^{-kz^2}\, dz$$

along the line $\text{Im}(z) = -i\lambda/(2k)$.

(b) Use the contour integral

$$\oint_{C'} e^{-kz^2}\, dz,$$

where C' is the rectangle in Figure 7.4, to find I.

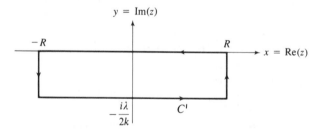

Figure 7.4

(c) Take real and imaginary parts of I to find $A(\lambda)$ and $B(\lambda)$.

7.3 Fourier Transforms

In Section 7.2 we used separation of variables to solve homogeneous problems on infinite and semi-infinite intervals. In this section we develop Fourier transforms in order to handle nonhomogeneities. We shall also find that the transforms yield solutions to homogeneous problems that are often simpler than those obtained by separation of variables. We begin with the transform associated with Fourier integral (6) for a function $f(x)$ absolutely integrable on $-\infty < x < \infty$. To obtain the transform, we express integral (6a) in complex form, reminiscent of the complex form for Fourier series (see Exercise 27 in Section 2.1):

$$\frac{f(x+) + f(x-)}{2} = \int_0^\infty \left[A(\lambda)\left(\frac{e^{i\lambda x} + e^{-i\lambda x}}{2}\right) + B(\lambda)\left(\frac{e^{i\lambda x} - e^{-i\lambda x}}{2i}\right) \right] d\lambda$$

$$= \int_0^\infty \left[e^{i\lambda x}\left(\frac{A(\lambda) - iB(\lambda)}{2}\right) + e^{-i\lambda x}\left(\frac{A(\lambda) + iB(\lambda)}{2}\right) \right] d\lambda$$

$$= \int_0^\infty e^{i\lambda x}\left(\frac{A(\lambda) - iB(\lambda)}{2}\right) d\lambda + \int_0^{-\infty} e^{i\lambda x}\left(\frac{A(-\lambda) + iB(-\lambda)}{2}\right)(-d\lambda)$$

$$= \int_0^\infty C(\lambda)e^{i\lambda x}\, d\lambda + \int_{-\infty}^0 C(\lambda)e^{i\lambda x}\, d\lambda = \int_{-\infty}^\infty C(\lambda)e^{i\lambda x}\, d\lambda,$$

where
$$C(\lambda) = \begin{cases} [A(\lambda) - iB(\lambda)]/2 & \lambda > 0 \\ [A(-\lambda) + iB(-\lambda)]/2 & \lambda < 0 \end{cases}.$$

But using (6b), we may write, for $\lambda > 0$,

$$C(\lambda) = \frac{1}{2\pi} \int_{-\infty}^\infty f(x)\cos \lambda x\, dx - \frac{i}{2\pi} \int_{-\infty}^\infty f(x)\sin \lambda x\, dx = \frac{1}{2\pi} \int_{-\infty}^\infty f(x)e^{-i\lambda x}\, dx,$$

and for $\lambda < 0$,

$$C(\lambda) = \frac{1}{2\pi} \int_{-\infty}^\infty f(x)\cos(-\lambda x)\, dx + \frac{i}{2\pi} \int_{-\infty}^\infty f(x)\sin(-\lambda x)\, dx$$

$$= \frac{1}{2\pi} \int_{-\infty}^\infty f(x)e^{-i\lambda x}\, dx.$$

If, as has been our custom, we define, or redefine if necessary, $f(x)$ as the average value of left- and right-hand limits at any point of discontinuity, we have shown that Fourier integral (6) may be expressed in the complex form

$$f(x) = \int_{-\infty}^\infty C(\lambda)e^{i\lambda x}\, d\lambda, \tag{20a}$$

where
$$C(\lambda) = \frac{1}{2\pi} \int_{-\infty}^\infty f(x)e^{-i\lambda x}\, dx. \tag{20b}$$

A somewhat more critical analysis of the improper integrals leading to (20a) indicates that the integral should be taken in the sense of Cauchy's principal value,

$$f(x) = \lim_{R \to \infty} \int_{-R}^R C(\lambda)e^{i\lambda x}\, dx \tag{20c}$$

(see Exercise 23). We shall continue to write (20a) for brevity, but if convergence difficulties arise, we shall replace (20a) with (20c).

It is clear that by redefining $C(\lambda)$, we could also write

$$f(x) = \frac{1}{2\pi} \int_{-\infty}^\infty C(\lambda)e^{i\lambda x}\, d\lambda, \tag{21a}$$

where

$$C(\lambda) = \int_{-\infty}^{\infty} f(x)e^{-i\lambda x}\,dx, \tag{21b}$$

or

$$f(x) = \frac{1}{\sqrt{2\pi}} \int_{-\infty}^{\infty} C(\lambda)e^{i\lambda x}\,d\lambda \tag{22a}$$

with

$$C(\lambda) = \frac{1}{\sqrt{2\pi}} \int_{-\infty}^{\infty} f(x)e^{-i\lambda x}\,dx. \tag{22b}$$

Any of the pairs (20), (21), or (22) can be used to define the Fourier transform; we pick (21) simply because it involves the factor 2π only in the latter stages of applications. It is customary to use ω in place of λ for Fourier transforms.

Definition 2

The Fourier transform of a function $f(x)$ is defined as

$$\boxed{\mathscr{F}\{f(x)\} = \tilde{f}(\omega) = \int_{-\infty}^{\infty} f(x)e^{-i\omega x}\,dx.} \tag{23a}$$

The associated inverse transform is

$$\boxed{\mathscr{F}^{-1}\{\tilde{f}(\omega)\} = f(x) = \frac{1}{2\pi} \int_{-\infty}^{\infty} \tilde{f}(\omega)e^{i\omega x}\,d\omega.} \tag{23b}$$

The transform of $f(x)$ exists if the function is piecewise smooth on every finite interval and absolutely integrable on $-\infty < x < \infty$. Once again, we point out that (23b) should be interpreted as Cauchy's principal value,

$$f(x) = \frac{1}{2\pi} \lim_{R \to \infty} \int_{-R}^{R} \tilde{f}(\omega)e^{i\omega x}\,d\omega. \tag{23c}$$

Definition 2 should be compared with equation (3) in Chapter 6 for the finite Fourier transform. Finite Fourier transforms are associated with Sturm-Liouville systems. When $[\lambda_n, y_n(x)]$ are eigenpairs of Sturm-Liouville system (3) in Chapter 4, the finite Fourier transform of a function $f(x)$, defined on $0 < x < L$, is

$$\tilde{f}(\lambda_n) = \int_{0}^{L} p(x)f(x)y_n(x)\,dx,$$

and the inverse transform is

$$f(x) = \sum_{n=1}^{\infty} \tilde{f}(\lambda_n)y_n(x).$$

The finite Fourier transform is a sequence of numbers $\{\tilde{f}(\lambda_n)\}$, or a discrete function defined only for integers n; the inverse transform is a superposition over all eigenfunctions. Fourier transform (23a), on the other hand, defines a continuous function $\tilde{f}(\omega)$, and this is due to the fact that "eigenfunctions" of the differential equation

$$\frac{d^2X}{dx^2} + \omega^2 X = 0, \qquad X(x) \text{ bounded,}$$

are $A \cos \omega x + B \sin \omega x$, where "eigenvalues" ω are arbitrary. Inverse transform (23b) is an integral superposition over all ω.

From Example 1 we obtain the most important transform pair.

Example 8:   Find the Fourier transform of e^{-kx^2} and the inverse Fourier transform of $e^{-a\omega^2}$.

Solution: By definition (23a), the Fourier transform of $f(x) = e^{-kx^2}$ is

$$\tilde{f}(\omega) = \int_{-\infty}^{\infty} e^{-kx^2} e^{-i\omega x} \, dx = \int_{-\infty}^{\infty} e^{-kx^2}(\cos \omega x - i \sin \omega x) \, dx = \int_{-\infty}^{\infty} e^{-kx^2} \cos \omega x \, dx,$$

because $e^{-kx^2} \sin \omega x$ is odd. But according to Example 1 in Section 7.1,

$$\frac{1}{\pi} \int_{-\infty}^{\infty} e^{-kx^2} \cos \lambda x \, dx = \frac{1}{\sqrt{k\pi}} e^{-\lambda^2/(4k)}$$

and therefore

$$\tilde{f}(\omega) = \sqrt{\frac{\pi}{k}} e^{-\omega^2/(4k)}.$$

A similar analysis shows that the inverse Fourier transform of $\tilde{g}(\omega) = e^{-a\omega^2}$ is

$$g(x) = \frac{1}{2\sqrt{a\pi}} e^{-x^2/(4a)}. \qquad \blacksquare$$

Fourier transforms are also associated with the Fourier cosine and sine integrals (7) and (8). They can be regarded as special cases of the Fourier transform when the function is either even or odd, or as transforms for functions defined on the semi-infinite interval $0 < x < \infty$. We take the latter approach in the following definition.

Definition 3
_____

The Fourier cosine transform of a function $f(x)$ defined for $0 < x < \infty$ is

$$\boxed{\mathscr{F}_C\{f(x)\} = \tilde{f}(\omega) = \int_0^{\infty} f(x) \cos \omega x \, dx,} \qquad \text{(24a)}$$

with inverse transform

$$\boxed{\mathscr{F}_C^{-1}\{\tilde{f}(\omega)\} = f(x) = \frac{2}{\pi} \int_0^{\infty} \tilde{f}(\omega) \cos \omega x \, d\omega.} \qquad \text{(24b)}$$

The Fourier sine transform of a function $f(x)$ defined for $0 < x < \infty$ is

$$\mathscr{F}_s\{f(x)\} = \tilde{f}(\omega) = \int_0^\infty f(x)\sin \omega x \, dx, \qquad\qquad \text{(25a)}$$

with inverse transform

$$\mathscr{F}_s^{-1}\{\tilde{f}(\omega)\} = f(x) = \frac{2}{\pi}\int_0^\infty \tilde{f}(\omega)\sin \omega x \, d\omega. \qquad\qquad \text{(25b)}$$

According to (7) and (8), these transforms are the coefficients in the Fourier cosine and sine integrals of $f(x)$, and the inverse transforms are the integral formulas.

Example 9:   What are the Fourier cosine and sine transforms of the function $f(x) = e^{-ax}$ $(a > 0)$, defined for $x \geq 0$?

Solution: The Fourier cosine transform is

$$\int_0^\infty e^{-ax}\cos \omega x \, dx = \text{Re}\left(\int_0^\infty e^{-ax}e^{-i\omega x}\, dx\right) = \text{Re}\left\{\frac{e^{-x(a+i\omega)}}{-(a+i\omega)}\right\}_0^\infty$$

$$= \text{Re}\left(\frac{1}{a+i\omega}\right) = \frac{a}{\omega^2 + a^2}.$$

The Fourier sine transform is

$$\int_0^\infty e^{-ax}\sin \omega x \, dx = -\text{Im}\left(\frac{1}{a+i\omega}\right) = \frac{\omega}{\omega^2 + a^2}.$$

With these transforms we may write the function e^{-ax}, for $x > 0$, in either of the forms

$$e^{-ax} = \frac{2}{\pi}\int_0^\infty \frac{a}{\omega^2+a^2}\cos \omega x \, d\omega = \frac{2a}{\pi}\int_0^\infty \frac{\cos \omega x}{\omega^2 + a^2}\, d\omega$$

or $\qquad\qquad\qquad e^{-ax} = \frac{2}{\pi}\int_0^\infty \frac{\omega}{\omega^2 + a^2}\sin \omega x \, d\omega.$ ∎

We have introduced Fourier transforms (23), (24), and (25) in order to solve (initial) boundary value problems on infinite and semi-infinite spatial domains. We shall show how to do this in Section 7.4. Although the finite Fourier transform of Chapter 6 was introduced for similar problems on finite domains, our treatments of the finite and "infinite" transforms are quite different. There are many finite Fourier transforms (each associated with a Sturm-Liouville system); because of this, we made no attempt to discuss general properties of finite Fourier transforms. As a result, when we apply a finite Fourier transform to a PDE, we must work our way through the integrals involved, bringing into play boundary and/or initial conditions at appropriate times. On the other hand, because there are only three Fourier transforms, it is possible to develop properties of these transforms that make it unnecessary to return to their integral definitions when solving (initial) boundary value problems. This makes it much simpler to apply Fourier transforms.

We shall state elementary properties of the Fourier transforms, leaving verifications to the exercises, and concentrate on those aspects that are crucial to our discussions of PDEs. All three Fourier transforms and their inverses are linear operators. For example,

$$\mathscr{F}\{c_1 f_1(x) + c_2 f_2(x)\} = c_1 \mathscr{F}\{f_1(x)\} + c_2 \mathscr{F}\{f_2(x)\}, \tag{26}$$

and similar results apply to $\mathscr{F}_C$ and $\mathscr{F}_S$ and their inverses (see Exercise 1).

When a is a real constant

$$\mathscr{F}\{f(ax)\} = \frac{1}{|a|} \mathscr{F}\{f(x)\}_{|\omega/a} \tag{27a}$$

and

$$\mathscr{F}^{-1}\{\tilde{f}(a\omega)\} = \frac{1}{|a|} \mathscr{F}^{-1}\{\tilde{f}(\omega)\}_{|x/a} \tag{27b}$$

(see Exercise 2). Similar properties hold for $\mathscr{F}_S$ and $\mathscr{F}_C$, but in these cases $a > 0$, since $f(x)$ is not defined for $x < 0$.

Translation of a function $f(x)$ along the x-axis by an amount a results in its Fourier transform being multiplied by $e^{-ia\omega}$:

$$\mathscr{F}\{f(x - a)\} = e^{-ia\omega}\mathscr{F}\{f(x)\}, \tag{28a}$$

$$\mathscr{F}^{-1}\{e^{-ia\omega}\tilde{f}(\omega)\} = \mathscr{F}^{-1}\{\tilde{f}(\omega)\}_{|x-a} \tag{28b}$$

(see Exercise 3). Properties similar to (28a) hold for $\mathscr{F}_C$ and $\mathscr{F}_S$ in the case in which $a > 0$, provided $f(x - a)$ is multiplied by the Heaviside function $H(x - a)$:

$$\mathscr{F}_S\{f(x - a)H(x - a)\} = (\cos a\omega)\mathscr{F}_S\{f(x)\} + (\sin a\omega)\mathscr{F}_C\{f(x)\}, \tag{28c}$$

$$\mathscr{F}_C\{f(x - a)H(x - a)\} = (\cos a\omega)\mathscr{F}_C\{f(x)\} - (\sin a\omega)\mathscr{F}_S\{f(x)\}. \tag{28d}$$

[Once again, the presence of $H(x - a)$ is attributable to the fact that $f(x)$ need not be defined for $x < 0$.]

Multiplication of a function $f(x)$ by an exponential e^{-ax} $(a > 0)$ results in a "translation" of its Fourier transform,

$$\mathscr{F}\{e^{-ax}f(x)\} = \tilde{f}(\omega - ai) \tag{29}$$

(see Exercise 4). No such property holds for the sine and cosine transforms.

The following theorem and its corollary eliminate much of the work when Fourier transforms are applied to (initial) boundary value problems.

Theorem 2

Suppose $f(x)$ is continuous for $-\infty < x < \infty$ and $f'(x)$ is piecewise continuous on every finite interval. If both functions are absolutely integrable on $-\infty < x < \infty$,

$$\mathscr{F}\{f'(x)\} = i\omega\mathscr{F}\{f(x)\}, \tag{30a}$$

$$\mathscr{F}^{-1}\{i\omega\tilde{f}(\omega)\} = \frac{d}{dx}(\mathscr{F}^{-1}\{\tilde{f}(\omega)\}). \tag{30b}$$

Proof: When integration by parts is used on the definition of $\mathscr{F}\{f'(x)\}$,

$$\mathscr{F}\{f'(x)\} = \int_{-\infty}^{\infty} f'(x)e^{-i\omega x}\,dx = \{f(x)e^{-i\omega x}\}_{-\infty}^{\infty} - \int_{-\infty}^{\infty} f(x)(-i\omega)e^{-i\omega x}\,dx$$

$$= i\omega \int_{-\infty}^{\infty} f(x)e^{i\omega x}\,dx = i\omega\mathscr{F}\{f(x)\}. \qquad\blacksquare$$

It is straightforward to extend this result to second derivatives (see the corollary below) and higher-order derivatives (see Exercise 5).

Corollary

Suppose $f(x)$ and $f'(x)$ are continuous for $-\infty < x < \infty$ and $f''(x)$ is piecewise continuous on every finite interval. If all three functions are absolutely integrable on $-\infty < x < \infty$,

$$\mathscr{F}\{f''(x)\} = -\omega^2\mathscr{F}\{f(x)\}, \tag{31a}$$

$$\mathscr{F}^{-1}\{-\omega^2\tilde{f}(\omega)\} = \frac{d^2}{dx^2}\left(\mathscr{F}^{-1}\{\tilde{f}(\omega)\}\right). \qquad\blacksquare \tag{31b}$$

Results corresponding to (30a) and (31a) for the sine and cosine transforms are

$$\mathscr{F}_C\{f'(x)\} = \omega\mathscr{F}_S\{f(x)\} - f(0+), \tag{31c}$$

$$\mathscr{F}_C\{f''(x)\} = -\omega^2\mathscr{F}_C\{f(x)\} - f'(0+), \tag{31d}$$

$$\mathscr{F}_S\{f'(x)\} = -\omega\mathscr{F}_C\{f(x)\}, \tag{31e}$$

$$\mathscr{F}_S\{f''(x)\} = -\omega^2\mathscr{F}_S\{f(x)\} + \omega f(0+). \tag{31f}$$

The limits in (31c, d, f) allow for the possibility of $f(x)$ being undefined at $x = 0$ (but its right-hand limit must exist).

In applications of Fourier transforms to initial boundary value problems, it is often necessary to find the inverse transform of the product of two functions $\tilde{f}(\omega)$ and $\tilde{g}(\omega)$, both of whose inverse transforms are known; that is, we require $\mathscr{F}^{-1}\{\tilde{f}(\omega)\tilde{g}(\omega)\}$, knowing that $\mathscr{F}^{-1}\{\tilde{f}(\omega)\} = f(x)$ and $\mathscr{F}^{-1}\{\tilde{g}(\omega)\} = g(x)$. In Theorem 3 it is shown that

$$\mathscr{F}^{-1}\{\tilde{f}(\omega)\tilde{g}(\omega)\} = \int_{-\infty}^{\infty} f(u)g(x-u)\,du.$$

This integral, called the *convolution* of the functions $f(x)$ and $g(x)$, is often given the notation $f * g$:

$$f(x) * g(x) = \int_{-\infty}^{\infty} f(u)g(x-u)\,du. \tag{32}$$

Theorem 3

Suppose that $f(x)$ and $g(x)$ and their first derivatives are piecewise continuous on every finite interval and that $f(x)$ and $g(x)$ are absolutely integrable on $-\infty < x < \infty$. If either $\tilde{f}(\omega)$ or $\tilde{g}(\omega)$ is absolutely integrable on $-\infty < \omega < \infty$, then

$$\boxed{\mathscr{F}^{-1}\{\tilde{f}(\omega)\tilde{g}(\omega)\} = f * g = \int_{-\infty}^{\infty} f(u)g(x - u)\, du.}$$ (33)

Proof: Let us assume that $\tilde{g}(\omega)$ is absolutely integrable. [The proof is similar if $\tilde{f}(\omega)$ is absolutely integrable.] By definition (23b),

$$\mathscr{F}^{-1}\{\tilde{f}(\omega)\tilde{g}(\omega)\} = \frac{1}{2\pi}\int_{-\infty}^{\infty} \tilde{f}(\omega)\tilde{g}(\omega)e^{i\omega x}\, d\omega,$$

and when we substitute the integral definition of $\tilde{f}(\omega)$,

$$\mathscr{F}^{-1}\{\tilde{f}(\omega)\tilde{g}(\omega)\} = \frac{1}{2\pi}\int_{-\infty}^{\infty} \left(\int_{-\infty}^{\infty} f(u)e^{-i\omega u}\, du\right)\tilde{g}(\omega)e^{i\omega x}\, d\omega.$$

The fact that $f(x)$ and $\tilde{g}(\omega)$ are both absolutely integrable permits us to interchange the order of integration and write

$$\mathscr{F}^{-1}\{\tilde{f}(\omega)\tilde{g}(\omega)\} = \int_{-\infty}^{\infty} \left(\frac{1}{2\pi}\int_{-\infty}^{\infty} \tilde{g}(\omega)e^{i\omega(x-u)}\, d\omega\right)f(u)\, du$$

$$= \int_{-\infty}^{\infty} f(u)g(x - u)\, du. \qquad\blacksquare$$

The simplicity of the proof of Theorem 3 is a direct result of the assumption that $\tilde{g}(\omega)$ is absolutely integrable. This condition can be weakened, but because functions that we encounter satisfy this condition, we pursue the discussion no further.

By making a change of variable of integration in (32), it is easily shown that convolutions are symmetric; that is, $f * g = g * f$. Other properties of convolutions are discussed in Exercise 7. An example of convolutions that we encounter in heat conduction problems is

$$\mathscr{F}^{-1}\left(\tilde{f}(\omega)e^{-k\omega^2 t}\right),$$

where $\tilde{f}(\omega)$ is the transform of an initial temperature distribution, k is thermal diffusivity, and t is time. According to Example 8, $\mathscr{F}^{-1}(e^{-k\omega^2 t}) = [1/(2\sqrt{k\pi t})]e^{-x^2/(4kt)}$, and hence convolutions yield

$$\mathscr{F}^{-1}\left(\tilde{f}(\omega)e^{-k\omega^2 t}\right) = \int_{-\infty}^{\infty} f(u)\frac{1}{2\sqrt{k\pi t}}e^{-(x-u)^2/(4kt)}\, du$$

$$= \frac{1}{2\sqrt{k\pi t}}\int_{-\infty}^{\infty} f(u)e^{-(x-u)^2/(4kt)}\, du.$$

The following convolution properties for sine and cosine transforms are verified in Exercise 8.

When $f(x) = \mathscr{F}_C^{-1}\{\tilde{f}(\omega)\}$ and $g(x) = \mathscr{F}_C^{-1}\{\tilde{g}(\omega)\}$,

$$\mathscr{F}_C^{-1}\{\tilde{f}(\omega)\tilde{g}(\omega)\} = \frac{1}{2}\int_0^\infty f(u)[g(x-u) + g(x+u)]\,du, \qquad (34\text{a})$$

$$= \frac{1}{2}\int_0^\infty g(u)[f(x-u) + f(x+u)]\,du, \qquad (34\text{b})$$

provided $f(x)$ and $g(x)$ are extended as even functions for $x < 0$.

When $f(x) = \mathscr{F}_S^{-1}\{\tilde{f}(\omega)\}$ and $g(x) = \mathscr{F}_C^{-1}\{\tilde{g}(\omega)\}$ [note that $\tilde{g}(\omega)$ is a Fourier cosine transform],

$$\mathscr{F}_S^{-1}\{\tilde{f}(\omega)\tilde{g}(\omega)\} = \frac{1}{2}\int_0^\infty f(u)[g(x-u) - g(x+u)]\,du, \qquad (34\text{c})$$

$$= \frac{1}{2}\int_0^\infty g(u)[f(x-u) + f(x+u)]\,du, \qquad (34\text{d})$$

provided $f(x)$ and $g(x)$, respectively, are extended as odd and even functions for $x < 0$.

In Section 7.4 we make use of these properties when Fourier transforms are applied to (initial) boundary value problems.

Exercises 7.3

1. Verify that the Fourier transforms and their inverses are linear operators.

2. Verify properties (27) and similar properties for the sine and cosine transforms.

3. Verify properties (28).

4. Verify property (29).

5. (a) Extend the result of Theorem 2 to nth derivatives.

   (b) Verify the transforms in (31).

6. (a) Verify that for $n \geq 1$,

$$\mathscr{F}\{x^n f(x)\} = i^n \frac{d^n}{d\omega^n}\mathscr{F}\{f(x)\}, \qquad (35\text{a})$$

$$\mathscr{F}^{-1}\{\tilde{f}^{(n)}(\omega)\} = (-ix)^n \mathscr{F}^{-1}\{\tilde{f}(\omega)\}. \qquad (35\text{b})$$

   (b) What are the results corresponding to (35a) for $\mathscr{F}_S$ and $\mathscr{F}_C$ when $n = 1$ and $n = 2$?

7. Verify the following properties for convolution (32):

   (a) $f * g = g * f$ (36a)

   (b) $f * (kg) = (kf) * g = k(f * g)$, $k = $ constant   (36b)

   (c) $(f * g) * h = f * (g * h)$ (36c)

   (d) $f * (g + h) = f * g + f * h$ (36d)

8. (a) Verify convolution properties (34a, b) for the Fourier cosine transform.

   (b) Verify convolution properties (34c, d) for the Fourier sine transform.

9. **(a)** Prove that when $f(x)$ is an even function with a Fourier transform,

$$\mathscr{F}\{f(x)\} = 2\mathscr{F}_C\{f(x)\}. \tag{37a}$$

(b) Prove that when $f(x)$ is an odd function with a Fourier transform,

$$\mathscr{F}\{f(x)\} = -2i\mathscr{F}_S\{f(x)\}. \tag{37b}$$

10. **(a)** Show that when $\tilde{f}(\omega) = \mathscr{F}\{f(x)\}$,

$$\mathscr{F}\{\tilde{f}(x)\} = 2\pi f(-\omega). \tag{38}$$

(b) What are corresponding results for Fourier sine and cosine transforms?

11. **(a)** Show that

$$\mathscr{F}\left(\int_{-\infty}^{x} f(u)\,du\right) = \frac{\tilde{f}(\omega)}{i\omega}, \tag{39a}$$

provided the integral does have a transform, and

$$\mathscr{F}^{-1}\left(\frac{\tilde{f}(\omega)}{\omega}\right) = i\int_{-\infty}^{x} f(u)\,du. \tag{39b}$$

(b) What are corresponding results for the sine and cosine transforms?

In Exercises 12–17, find the Fourier transform of the function.

12. $f(x) = e^{-a|x|}$, $a > 0$ constant

13. $f(x) = x^n e^{-ax} H(x)$, $a > 0$ constant, $n \geq 0$ an integer

14. $f(x) = H(x - a) - H(x - b)$, $b > a$ constants

15. $f(x) = \dfrac{\sin ax}{x}$, $a > 0$ constant. (*Hint:* Use Exercises 10 and 14.)

16. $f(x) = \begin{cases} (b/a)(a - |x|) & |x| < a \\ 0 & |x| > a \end{cases}$, $a > 0, b > 0$ constants

17. $f(x) = \begin{cases} b(a^2 - x^2)/a^2 & |x| < a \\ 0 & |x| > a \end{cases}$, $a > 0, b > 0$ constants

In Exercises 18–20, find the Fourier sine and cosine transforms of the function.

18. $f(x) = e^{-ax^2}$, $a > 0$ constant. (*Hint:* See Exercises 24 and 25 in Section 7.2.)

19. $f(x) = H(x - a) - H(x - b)$, $b > a > 0$ constants

20. $f(x) = \begin{cases} (b/a)(a - |x - c|) & |x - c| < a \\ 0 & |x - c| > a \end{cases}$, $a, b,$ and c all positive constants with $c > a$

21. The *error function*, erf(x), is defined as

$$\text{erf}(x) = \frac{2}{\sqrt{\pi}} \int_0^x e^{-u^2}\,du.$$

Because this function is increasing for $x > 0$ and $\lim_{x\to\infty} \text{erf}(x) = 1$, it does not have Fourier transforms. The *complementary error function*, erfc(x), defined by

$$\text{erfc}(x) = 1 - \text{erf}(x) = \frac{2}{\sqrt{\pi}} \int_x^{\infty} e^{-u^2}\,du,$$

does have Fourier transforms. Use properties (31) and Exercise 18 to derive the following results:

(a) $\mathscr{F}_S\{\text{erfc}(ax)\} = (1 - e^{-\omega^2/(4a^2)})/\omega$, $a > 0$ constant

(b) $\mathscr{F}_C(ax \, \text{erfc}(ax) - (1/\sqrt{\pi})e^{-a^2x^2}) = (a/\omega^2)(-1 + e^{-\omega^2/(4a^2)})$, $a > 0$ constant

22. Verify formally each of the following results, often called *Parseval's relations*:

(a) $$\int_{-\infty}^{\infty} \tilde{f}(x)g(x)\,dx = \int_{-\infty}^{\infty} f(x)\tilde{g}\,(x)\,dx \tag{40a}$$

(b) $$2\pi \int_{-\infty}^{\infty} f(x)g(x)\,dx = \int_{-\infty}^{\infty} \tilde{f}(\omega)\tilde{g}(-\omega)\,d\omega \tag{40b}$$

(c) $$2\pi \int_{-\infty}^{\infty} [f(x)]^2\,dx = \int_{-\infty}^{\infty} |\tilde{f}(\omega)|^2\,d\omega \tag{40c}$$

23. Verify that improper integral (20a) should be taken in the sense of Cauchy's principal value (20c).

24. When the boundary condition at $x = 0$ for an initial boundary value problem on the semi-infinite interval $x > 0$ is of Robin type, separation of variables leads to the system

$$X'' + \omega^2 X = 0, \qquad x > 0,$$
$$-lX' + hX = 0, \qquad x = 0,$$
$$X(x) \text{ bounded as } x \to \infty.$$

Eigenfunctions of this system are

$$X_\omega(x) = \frac{1}{\sqrt{1 + [h/(\omega l)]^2}}\left(\cos \omega x + \frac{h}{\omega l}\sin \omega x\right) \tag{41}$$

for arbitrary ω, which we take as positive. Associated therewith is a generalized Fourier integral formula that states that a function $f(x)$ satisfying the conditions of Theorem 1 can be represented in the form

$$\frac{f(x+) + f(x-)}{2} = \frac{2}{\pi}\int_0^\infty G(\omega)X_\omega(x)\,d\omega, \tag{42a}$$

where

$$G(\omega) = \int_0^\infty f(x)X_\omega(x)\,dx. \tag{42b}$$

From this formula we define a generalized Fourier transform,

$$\tilde{f}(\omega) = \mathscr{G}\{f(x)\} = \int_0^\infty f(x)X_\omega(x)\,dx, \tag{43a}$$

and an inverse transform,

$$f(x) = \mathscr{G}^{-1}\{\tilde{f}(\omega)\} = \frac{2}{\pi}\int_0^\infty \tilde{f}(\omega)X_\omega(x)\,d\omega. \tag{43b}$$

Find transforms of the following functions:

(a) $f(x) = e^{-ax}$, $a > 0$ constant

(b) $f(x) = H(x - a) - H(x - b)$, $b > a > 0$ constants

The following exercises should be attempted only by readers who are already familiar with the Laplace transform. In these exercises $\mathscr{L}\{f(x)\}$ denotes the Laplace transform of a function $f(x)$.

25. (a) Show that when $f(x)$ is absolutely integrable on $0 < x < \infty$, and $f(x) = 0$ for $x < 0$,

$$\mathscr{F}\{f(x)\} = \mathscr{L}\{f(x)\}_{|s=i\omega}, \tag{44a}$$

$$\mathscr{F}_S\{f(x)\} = -\operatorname{Im}(\mathscr{L}\{f(x)\}_{|s=i\omega}), \tag{44b}$$

$$\mathscr{F}_C\{f(x)\} = \operatorname{Re}(\mathscr{L}\{f(x)\}_{|s=i\omega}). \tag{44c}$$

(b) Use the results in (a) to calculate Fourier transforms for the following:

    (i) $f(x)$ in Exercise 14.   (ii) $f(x)$ in Exercise 13.

(c) Use the results in (a) to calculate Fourier sine and cosine transforms for the following:

    (i) $f(x)$ in Exercise 19.   (ii) $f(x)$ in Exercise 20.

26. (a) The inverse result of (44a) can be stated as follows: Suppose that when ω in a function $\tilde{f}(\omega)$ is replaced by $-is$, the function $\tilde{f}(-is)$ has no poles on the imaginary s-axis or in the right half-plane. If $\tilde{f}(-is)$ has an inverse Laplace transform, this is also the inverse Fourier transform of $\tilde{f}(\omega)$,

$$\mathscr{F}^{-1}\{\tilde{f}(\omega)\} = \begin{cases} \mathscr{L}^{-1}\{\tilde{f}(-is)\} & x > 0 \\ 0 & x < 0 \end{cases}. \tag{45}$$

Use (45) to find inverse Fourier transforms for the following:

    (i) $\tilde{f}(\omega) = 1/(8 + i\omega)^3$

    (ii) $\tilde{f}(\omega) = (b/a)[(1 - e^{-i\omega a})/\omega^2 - ia/\omega]$, $a > 0$, $b > 0$ constants

(b) Can the result in (45) be used to find $\mathscr{F}^{-1}\{(i/\omega)e^{-ia\omega}\}$?

27. (a) Show that when $f(x)$ is absolutely integrable on $-\infty < x < 0$, and $f(x) = 0$ for $x > 0$,

$$\mathscr{F}\{f(x)\} = \mathscr{L}\{f(-x)\}_{|s=-i\omega}. \tag{46}$$

(b) Use (46) to find Fourier transforms for the following:

    (i) $f(x) = \begin{cases} -x(x + L) & -L \le x \le 0 \\ 0 & \text{otherwise} \end{cases}$

    (ii) $f(x) = e^{cx}[H(x - a) - H(x - b)]$, $a < b < 0$, $c > 0$

28. (a) Let $f(x)$ be a function that has a Fourier transform. Denote by $f^+(x)$ and $f^-(x)$ the right and left halves respectively, of $f(x)$:

$$f^+(x) = \begin{cases} 0 & x < 0 \\ f(x) & x > 0 \end{cases}; \qquad f^-(x) = \begin{cases} f(x) & x < 0 \\ 0 & x > 0 \end{cases}.$$

Show that

$$\mathscr{F}\{f(x)\} = \mathscr{F}\{f^+(x)\} + \mathscr{F}\{f^-(x)\}.$$

(b) Use the result in (a) in conjunction with the results of (44a) and (46) to find Fourier transforms for the following:

    (i) $f(x)$ in Exercise 16.

    (ii) $f(x) = \sin(ax)[H(x + 2\pi n/a) - H(x - 2\pi n/a)]$, $n > 0$ an integer, $a > 0$.

7.4 Applications of Fourier Transforms to Initial Boundary Value Problems

Fourier transform (23) is an alternative to separation of variables in problems over infinite intervals. We begin with heat conduction problem (1). When we apply Fourier transform (23) to PDE (1a),

$$\int_{-\infty}^{\infty} \frac{\partial U}{\partial t} e^{-i\omega x}\, dx = k \int_{-\infty}^{\infty} \frac{\partial^2 U}{\partial x^2} e^{-i\omega x}\, dx.$$

When we interchange the operations of integration with respect to x and differentiation with respect to t on the left, and use property (31a) for the transform on the right,

$$\frac{d\tilde{U}}{dt} = -k\omega^2 \tilde{U}(\omega, t).$$

We should not forget that use of (31a) assumes that U, $\partial U/\partial x$, and $\partial^2 U/\partial x^2$ are all absolutely integrable, that U and $\partial U/\partial x$ are continuous, and that $\partial^2 U/\partial x^2$ is piecewise continuous on every finite interval. The general solution of this ODE in $\tilde{U}(\omega, t)$ is

$$\tilde{U}(\omega, t) = Ce^{-k\omega^2 t}.$$

The Fourier transform of initial condition (1b) is $\tilde{U}(\omega, 0) = \tilde{f}(\omega)$, and this condition requires that $C = \tilde{f}(\omega)$. Thus,

$$\tilde{U}(\omega, t) = \tilde{f}(\omega)e^{-k\omega^2 t}$$

and
$$U(x, t) = \frac{1}{2\pi} \int_{-\infty}^{\infty} \tilde{f}(\omega)e^{-k\omega^2 t} e^{i\omega x}\, d\omega. \tag{47a}$$

A much more useful form of the solution, which expresses $U(x, t)$ as a real integral involving $f(x)$, rather than a complex integral in $\tilde{f}(\omega)$, can be obtained with convolutions. Because the inverse transform of $e^{-k\omega^2 t}$ is $1/(2\sqrt{k\pi t})e^{-x^2/(4kt)}$ (see Example 8), convolution property (33) yields

$$U(x, t) = \int_{-\infty}^{\infty} f(u)\frac{1}{2\sqrt{k\pi t}} e^{-(x-u)^2/(4kt)}\, du$$

$$= \frac{1}{2\sqrt{k\pi t}} \int_{-\infty}^{\infty} f(u)e^{-(x-u)^2/(4kt)}\, du. \tag{47b}$$

This form of the solution clearly indicates the dependence of $U(x, t)$ on the initial temperature distribution $f(x)$. It also has another advantage. Because (47b) does not contain the Fourier transform of $f(x)$, it may represent a solution to (1) even when $f(x)$ has no Fourier transform. Indeed, provided $f(x)$ is piecewise continuous on some bounded interval, and continuous and bounded outside this interval, it can be shown that $U(x, t)$ so defined satisfies (1). This is illustrated in the first two special cases that follow on the next page.

Case 1: $f(x) = U_0$, **a constant.**

In this case, we would expect that $U(x, t) = U_0$ for all x and t. That (47b) gives this result is easily demonstrated by setting $v = (x - u)/(2\sqrt{kt})$ and $dv = -du/(2\sqrt{kt})$:

$$U(x, t) = \frac{U_0}{2\sqrt{k\pi t}} \int_\infty^{-\infty} e^{-v^2}(-2\sqrt{kt}\, dv) = \frac{U_0}{\sqrt{\pi}} \int_{-\infty}^\infty e^{-v^2}\, dv = U_0$$

(see Exercise 24 in Section 7.2 for the value of this integral). Thus, integral (47b) has given the correct solution in spite of the fact that the function $f(x) = U_0$ does not have a Fourier transform.

Case 2: $f(x) = U_0 H(x)$.

In this case, we set $v = (x - u)/(2\sqrt{kt})$ and $dv = -du/(2\sqrt{kt})$ in

$$U(x, t) = \frac{U_0}{2\sqrt{k\pi t}} \int_0^\infty e^{-(x-u)^2/(4kt)}\, du$$

to obtain

$$U(x, t) = \frac{U_0}{2\sqrt{k\pi t}} \int_{x/(2\sqrt{kt})}^{-\infty} e^{-v^2}(-2\sqrt{kt}\, dv)$$

$$= \frac{U_0}{\sqrt{\pi}} \int_{-\infty}^{x/(2\sqrt{kt})} e^{-v^2}\, dv$$

$$= \frac{U_0}{\sqrt{\pi}} \left(\int_{-\infty}^0 e^{-v^2}\, dv + \int_0^{x/(2\sqrt{kt})} e^{-v^2}\, dv \right)$$

$$= \frac{U_0}{\sqrt{\pi}} \left[\frac{\sqrt{\pi}}{2} + \frac{\sqrt{\pi}}{2}\operatorname{erf}\left(\frac{x}{2\sqrt{kt}}\right) \right] = \frac{U_0}{2}\left[1 + \operatorname{erf}\left(\frac{x}{2\sqrt{kt}}\right) \right]$$

where

$$\operatorname{erf}(x) = \frac{2}{\sqrt{\pi}} \int_0^x e^{-u^2}\, du \qquad (48)$$

is the error function. This solution indicates how heat that is concentrated in one-half of a rod diffuses into the other half. It indicates, in particular, that temperature at every point in the left half of the rod $(x < 0)$ is positive for every $t > 0$. This substantiates our claim in Section 5.6 that heat propagates with infinite speed.

Case 3: $f(x) = x(L - x)$, $0 \le x \le L$, **and vanishes otherwise.**

This is the initial temperature distribution in Example 4. In this case, (47b) gives

$$U(x, t) = \frac{1}{2\sqrt{k\pi t}} \int_0^L u(L - u)e^{-(x-u)^2/(4kt)}\, du,$$

an integral representation that is preferable to that in Example 4, principally because it is not improper.

In the following example, heat is generated over the interval $-x_0 \le x \le x_0$ at a constant rate.

Example 10:   Solve the heat conduction problem

$$\frac{\partial U}{\partial t} = k\frac{\partial^2 U}{\partial x^2} + \frac{k}{\kappa}[H(x + x_0) - H(x - x_0)], \qquad -\infty < x < \infty, \qquad t > 0, \quad \text{(49a)}$$

$$U(x, 0) = f(x), \qquad -\infty < x < \infty. \tag{49b}$$

Solution: When we take Fourier transforms of the PDE [and use (31a) and Exercise 14 in Section 7.3],

$$\frac{d\tilde{U}}{dt} = -k\omega^2\tilde{U} + \frac{2k}{\kappa\omega}\sin x_0\omega. \tag{50a}$$

The transform $\tilde{U}(\omega, t)$ must satisfy this ODE subject to the transform of (49b),

$$\tilde{U}(\omega, 0) = \tilde{f}(\omega). \tag{50b}$$

The general solution of (50a) is

$$\tilde{U} = Ce^{-k\omega^2 t} + \frac{2}{\kappa\omega^3}\sin x_0\omega,$$

and condition (50b) requires that

$$\tilde{f}(\omega) = C + \frac{2}{\kappa\omega^3}\sin x_0\omega.$$

Thus, $$\tilde{U}(\omega, t) = \left(\tilde{f}(\omega) - \frac{2}{\kappa\omega^3}\sin x_0\omega\right)e^{-k\omega^2 t} + \frac{2}{\kappa\omega^3}\sin x_0\omega,$$

and $U(x, t)$ is the inverse transform thereof. According to (33), the inverse transform of $\tilde{f}(\omega)e^{-k\omega^2 t}$ can be expressed as

$$\frac{1}{2\sqrt{k\pi t}}\int_{-\infty}^{\infty} f(u)e^{-(x-u)^2/(4kt)}\,du,$$

and therefore

$$U(x, t) = \frac{1}{2\sqrt{k\pi t}}\int_{-\infty}^{\infty} f(u)e^{-(x-u)^2/(4kt)}\,du$$

$$-\frac{1}{\kappa\pi}\int_{-\infty}^{\infty}\frac{1}{\omega^3}(1 - e^{-k\omega^2 t})\sin x_0\omega\, e^{i\omega x}\,d\omega. \qquad \blacksquare \quad \text{(51)}$$

   Fourier sine and cosine transforms are used to solve problems on the semi-infinite interval $x > 0$ in Examples 11 and 12. The sine transform is applied to problems with a Dirichlet boundary condition at $x = 0$. This is because separation of variables on such a problem leads to the ODE

$$X'' + \omega^2 X = 0, \qquad x > 0, \tag{52a}$$

$$X(0) = 0, \tag{52b}$$

and the only bounded solution of this equation is $\sin \omega x$. Similarly, on Neumann problems, we use the cosine transform, since separation leads to

$$X'' + \omega^2 X = 0, \qquad x > 0, \tag{53a}$$

$$X'(0) = 0, \tag{53b}$$

the bounded solution of which is $\cos \omega x$.

Example 11: Solve the vibration problem

$$\frac{\partial^2 y}{\partial t^2} = c^2 \frac{\partial^2 y}{\partial x^2}, \qquad x > 0, \qquad t > 0, \tag{54a}$$

$$y(0, t) = f_1(t), \qquad t > 0, \tag{54b}$$

$$y(x, 0) = f(x), \qquad x > 0, \tag{54c}$$

$$y_t(x, 0) = g(x), \qquad x > 0, \tag{54d}$$

for displacement of a semi-infinite bar (or string) with prescribed motion at its one end, $x = 0$.

Solution: We apply the Fourier sine transform to the PDE and use property (31f) for the transform of $\partial^2 y / \partial x^2$:

$$\frac{d^2 \tilde{y}}{dt^2} = -\omega^2 c^2 \tilde{y}(\omega, t) + \omega c^2 f_1(t).$$

Thus, the Fourier sine transform $\tilde{y}(\omega, t)$ of $y(x, t)$ must satisfy the ODE

$$\frac{d^2 \tilde{y}}{dt^2} + \omega^2 c^2 \tilde{y} = \omega c^2 f_1(t) \tag{55a}$$

subject to transforms of initial conditions (54c, d):

$$\tilde{y}(\omega, 0) = \tilde{f}(\omega), \tag{55b}$$

$$\tilde{y}'(\omega, 0) = \tilde{g}(\omega). \tag{55c}$$

Variation of parameters leads to the following general solution of ODE (55a):

$$\tilde{y}(\omega, t) = A \cos c\omega t + B \sin c\omega t + c \int_0^t f_1(u) \sin c\omega(t - u) \, du.$$

Initial conditions (55b, c) require the constants A and B to satisfy

$$\tilde{f}(\omega) = A, \qquad \tilde{g}(\omega) = c\omega B.$$

Hence,

$$\tilde{y}(\omega, t) = \tilde{f}(\omega) \cos c\omega t + \frac{\tilde{g}(\omega)}{c\omega} \sin c\omega t + c \int_0^t f_1(u) \sin c\omega(t - u) \, du, \tag{56}$$

and $y(x, t)$ is the inverse transform of this function:

$$y(x, t) = \frac{2}{\pi} \int_0^\infty \tilde{y}(\omega, t) \sin \omega x \, d\omega. \tag{57}$$

The first term in this integral is

$$\frac{2}{\pi} \int_0^\infty \tilde{f}(\omega) \cos c\omega t \sin \omega x \, d\omega = \frac{2}{\pi} \int_0^\infty \frac{1}{2} \tilde{f}(\omega)(\sin \omega(x - ct) + \sin \omega(x + ct)) \, d\omega$$

$$= \frac{1}{2} [f(x - ct) + f(x + ct)],$$

provided $f(x)$ is extended as an odd function.

According to Exercise 19 in Section 7.3, the Fourier cosine transform of $H(x) - H(x - ct)$ is $(\sin c\omega t)/\omega$. Consequently, convolution identity (34d) implies that the inverse sine transform of $[\tilde{g}(\omega)/(c\omega)] \sin c\omega t$ is

$$\frac{1}{2c} \int_0^\infty [H(u) - H(u - ct)][g(x + u) + g(x - u)] \, du$$

$$= \frac{1}{2c} \left(\int_0^{ct} g(x + u) \, du + \int_0^{ct} g(x - u) \, du \right),$$

provided $g(x)$ is extended as an odd function for $x < 0$. When we set $v = x + u$ and $v = x - u$, respectively, in these integrals, the result is

$$\frac{1}{2c} \left(\int_x^{x+ct} g(v) \, dv + \int_x^{x-ct} g(v)(-dv) \right) = \frac{1}{2c} \int_{x-ct}^{x+ct} g(v) \, dv.$$

The inverse transform of the integral term in $\tilde{y}(\omega, t)$ can also be expressed in closed form if we set $v = c(t - u)$:

$$c \int_0^t f_1(u) \sin c\omega(t - u) \, du = c \int_{ct}^0 f_1 \left(t - \frac{v}{c} \right) \sin \omega v \left(-\frac{dv}{c} \right)$$

$$= \int_0^{ct} f_1 \left(t - \frac{v}{c} \right) \sin \omega v \, dv.$$

But this is the Fourier sine transform of the function

$$\begin{cases} f_1 \left(t - \dfrac{x}{c} \right) & x < ct \\ 0 & x > ct \end{cases}$$

or

$$\begin{cases} 0 & t < x/c \\ f_1 \left(t - \dfrac{x}{c} \right) & t > x/c \end{cases} = f_1 \left(t - \frac{x}{c} \right) H \left(t - \frac{x}{c} \right).$$

The solution is therefore

$$y(x, t) = \frac{1}{2} [f(x - ct) + f(x + ct)] + \frac{1}{2c} \int_{x-ct}^{x+ct} g(u) \, du + f_1 \left(t - \frac{x}{c} \right) H \left(t - \frac{x}{c} \right). \tag{58}$$

The first two terms constitute the d'Alembert part of the solution (see also Section 1.7). The last term is due to the nonhomogeneity at the end $x = 0$; it can be interpreted physically, and this is most easily done when $f(x) = g(x) = 0$. In this case, the complete solution is

$$y(x,t) = f_1\left(t - \frac{x}{c}\right) H\left(t - \frac{x}{c}\right).$$

A point x on the string remains at rest until time $t = x/c$, when it begins to execute the same motion as the end $x = 0$. The time x/c taken by the disturbance to reach x is called *retarded time*. The disturbance $f_1(t)$ at $x = 0$ therefore travels down the string with velocity c.

    The solution of the original problem is a superposition of the d'Alembert displacement and the displacement due to the end effect at $x = 0$.   ■

Example 12: The temperature of a semi-infinite rod at time $t = 0$ is $f(x)$, $x \geq 0$. For time $t > 0$, heat is added to the rod uniformly over the end $x = 0$ at a variable rate $f_1(t)$ W/m². Find the temperature in the rod.

Solution: The initial boundary value problem for temperature $U(x,t)$ in the rod is

$$\frac{\partial U}{\partial t} = k\frac{\partial^2 U}{\partial x^2}, \qquad x > 0, \qquad t > 0, \tag{59a}$$

$$U_x(0,t) = -\kappa^{-1}f_1(t), \qquad t > 0, \tag{59b}$$

$$U(x,0) = f(x), \qquad x > 0. \tag{59c}$$

When we apply the Fourier cosine transform to the PDE and use property (31d),

$$\frac{d\tilde{U}}{dt} = -k\omega^2\tilde{U}(\omega,t) + \kappa^{-1}f_1(t).$$

Thus, the Fourier cosine transform $\tilde{U}(\omega,t)$ of $U(x,t)$ must satisfy the ODE

$$\frac{d\tilde{U}}{dt} + k\omega^2\tilde{U} = \kappa^{-1}f_1(t) \tag{60a}$$

subject to the transform of (59c),

$$\tilde{U}(\omega,0) = \tilde{f}(\omega). \tag{60b}$$

The general solution of (60a) is

$$\tilde{U}(\omega,t) = Ce^{-k\omega^2 t} + \frac{1}{\kappa}\int_0^t e^{-k\omega^2(t-u)}f_1(u)\,du,$$

and condition (60b) requires that $\tilde{f}(\omega) = C$. Consequently,

$$\tilde{U}(\omega,t) = \tilde{f}(\omega)e^{-k\omega^2 t} + \frac{1}{\kappa}\int_0^t e^{-k\omega^2(t-u)}f_1(u)\,du, \tag{61}$$

and the required temperature is the inverse transform of $\tilde{U}(\omega,t)$,

$$U(x,t) = \frac{2}{\pi}\int_0^\infty \tilde{U}(\omega,t)\cos\omega x\,d\omega. \tag{62}$$

The first term in this integral is the inverse cosine transform of $\tilde{f}(\omega)e^{-k\omega^2 t}$. According to Exercise 18 in Section 7.3, the Fourier cosine transform of e^{-ax^2} is $(1/2)\sqrt{\pi/a}\,e^{-\omega^2/(4a)}$, or, conversely, the inverse Fourier cosine transform of $e^{-k\omega^2 t}$ is $1/(\sqrt{k\pi t})e^{-x^2/(4kt)}$. Convolution property (34a) therefore gives the inverse cosine transform of $\tilde{f}(\omega)e^{-k\omega^2 t}$ as

$$\frac{1}{2}\int_0^\infty f(u)\frac{1}{\sqrt{k\pi t}}(e^{-(x-u)^2/(4kt)} + e^{-(x+u)^2/(4kt)})\,du$$

$$= \frac{1}{2\sqrt{k\pi t}}\int_0^\infty f(u)(e^{-(x-u)^2/(4kt)} + e^{-(x+u)^2/(4kt)})\,du.$$

Finally,

$$U(x,t) = \frac{1}{2\sqrt{k\pi t}}\int_0^\infty f(u)(e^{-(x-u)^2/(4kt)} + e^{-(x+u)^2/(4kt)})\,du$$

$$+ \frac{2}{k\pi}\int_0^\infty \left(\int_0^t e^{-k\omega^2(t-u)}f_1(u)\,du\right)\cos\omega x\,d\omega. \qquad ■ \quad (63)$$

Example 13:   Solve Laplace's equation for the quarter-plane $x > 0$, $y > 0$,

$$\frac{\partial^2 V}{\partial x^2} + \frac{\partial^2 V}{\partial y^2} = 0, \qquad x > 0, \qquad y > 0, \qquad (64a)$$

subject to the boundary conditions

$$V(0,y) = g(y), \qquad y > 0, \qquad (64b)$$

$$V_y(x,0) = f(x), \qquad x > 0. \qquad (64c)$$

Solution: Superposition can be used to express $V(x,y)$ as the sum of functions $V_1(x,y)$ and $V_2(x,y)$, satisfying

$$\frac{\partial^2 V_1}{\partial x^2} + \frac{\partial^2 V_1}{\partial y^2} = 0, \quad x > 0, \quad y > 0, \quad (65a) \qquad \frac{\partial^2 V_2}{\partial x^2} + \frac{\partial^2 V_2}{\partial y^2} = 0, \quad x > 0, \quad y > 0, \quad (66a)$$

$$V_1(0,y) = g(y), \quad y > 0, \qquad (65b) \qquad\qquad V_2(0,y) = 0, \quad y > 0, \qquad (66b)$$

$$\frac{\partial V_1(x,0)}{\partial y} = 0, \quad x > 0; \qquad (65c) \qquad\qquad \frac{\partial V_2(x,0)}{\partial y} = f(x), \quad x > 0. \qquad (66c)$$

To find $V_1(x,y)$, we apply Fourier cosine transform (24a) (with respect to y) to PDE (65a) and use property (31d):

$$\frac{d^2\tilde{V}_1}{dx^2} - \omega^2\tilde{V}_1(x,\omega) = 0, \qquad x > 0. \qquad (67a)$$

This transform function $\tilde{V}_1(x,\omega)$ is also subject to

$$\tilde{V}_1(0,\omega) = \tilde{g}(\omega). \qquad (67b)$$

The general solution of (67a) is

$$\tilde{V}_1(x,\omega) = Ae^{\omega x} + Be^{-\omega x}.$$

For $\tilde{V}_1(x,\omega)$ to remain bounded as $x \to \infty$, A must be zero, and the boundary condition $\tilde{V}_1(0,\omega) = \tilde{g}(\omega)$ then implies that $B = \tilde{g}(\omega)$. Hence,

$$\tilde{V}_1(x,\omega) = \tilde{g}(\omega)e^{-\omega x}. \qquad (68)$$

To invert this transform, we first recall from Example 9 that the Fourier cosine transform of e^{-ay} is $a/(\omega^2 + a^2)$. The result of Exercise 10(b) in Section 7.3 implies, then, that the Fourier cosine transform of $a/(y^2 + a^2)$ is $(\pi/2)e^{-a\omega}$. In other words, the inverse cosine transform of $e^{-\omega x}$ is $(2/\pi)x/(y^2 + x^2)$. Convolution property (34b) now gives

$$V_1(x, y) = \frac{1}{2}\int_0^\infty g(u)\left(\frac{2}{\pi}\right)\left(\frac{x}{(y - u)^2 + x^2} + \frac{x}{(y + u)^2 + x^2}\right)du$$

$$= \frac{x}{\pi}\int_0^\infty g(u)\left(\frac{1}{x^2 + (y - u)^2} + \frac{1}{x^2 + (y + u)^2}\right)du. \qquad (69)$$

Taking Fourier sine transforms with respect to x in order to find $V_1(x, y)$ leads to a nonhomogeneous ODE in $\tilde{V}_1(\omega, y)$ that is more difficult to solve.

To find $V_2(x, y)$, we apply Fourier sine transform (25a) (with respect to x) to PDE (66a) and use property (31f):

$$-\omega^2 \tilde{V}_2(\omega, y) + \frac{d^2\tilde{V}_2}{dy^2} = 0. \qquad (70a)$$

The transform of (66c) requires that

$$\frac{d\tilde{V}_2(\omega, 0)}{dy} = \tilde{f}(\omega). \qquad (70b)$$

The general solution of (70a) is

$$\tilde{V}_2(\omega, y) = Ae^{\omega y} + Be^{-\omega y}.$$

For $\tilde{V}_2(\omega, y)$ to remain bounded as $y \to \infty$, A must be zero, and the boundary condition on $\tilde{V}_2$ then implies that $B = -\tilde{f}(\omega)/\omega$. Hence,

$$\tilde{V}_2(\omega, y) = -\frac{\tilde{f}(\omega)}{\omega}e^{-\omega y} \qquad (71)$$

and

$$V_2(x, y) = \frac{2}{\pi}\int_0^\infty -\frac{\tilde{f}(\omega)}{\omega}e^{-\omega y}\sin \omega x\, d\omega. \qquad (72)$$

The final solution is therefore $V(x, y) = V_1(x, y) + V_2(x, y)$. ∎

Exercises 7.4

Part A—Heat Conduction

1. (a) Use a Fourier transform to find an integral representation for the solution of the heat conduction problem

$$\frac{\partial U}{\partial t} = k\frac{\partial^2 U}{\partial x^2} + \frac{k}{\kappa}g(x, t), \qquad -\infty < x < \infty, \qquad t > 0,$$

$$U(x, 0) = f(x), \qquad -\infty < x < \infty.$$

(b) Simplify the solution in (a) in the case that $g(x, t) \equiv 0$ and

(i) $f(x) = \begin{cases} 1 & |x| < a \\ 0 & |x| > a \end{cases}$;   (ii) $f(x) = \begin{cases} 0 & |x| < a \\ 1 & |x| > a \end{cases}$.

2. (a) Use the Fourier sine transform to find an integral representation for the solution of the heat conduction problem

$$\frac{\partial U}{\partial t} = k\frac{\partial^2 U}{\partial x^2}, \qquad x > 0, \qquad t > 0,$$

$$U(0, t) = \bar{U} = \text{constant}, \qquad t > 0,$$

$$U(x, 0) = 0, \qquad x > 0.$$

(*Hint:* See Exercise 21 in Section 7.3 when inverting the transform.)

(b) Comment on the possibility of using the transformation $W = U - \bar{U}$ to remove the non-homogeneity from the boundary condition.

3. Use the Fourier cosine transform to find an integral representation for the solution of the heat conduction problem

$$\frac{\partial U}{\partial t} = k\frac{\partial^2 U}{\partial x^2}, \qquad x > 0, \qquad t > 0,$$

$$U_x(0, t) = -\kappa^{-1}Q_0 = \text{constant}, \qquad t > 0,$$

$$U(x, 0) = 0, \qquad x > 0.$$

(*Hint:* See Exercise 21 in Section 7.3 when inverting the transform.)

4. (a) Use a Fourier transform to find an integral representation for the solution of the heat conduction problem

$$\frac{\partial U}{\partial t} = k\frac{\partial^2 U}{\partial x^2} + \frac{k}{\kappa}g(x, t), \qquad x > 0, \qquad t > 0,$$

$$U(0, t) = f_1(t), \qquad t > 0,$$

$$U(x, 0) = f(x), \qquad x > 0.$$

(b) Simplify the solution in (a) when $g(x, t) \equiv 0$, $f_1(t) \equiv 0$, and $f(x) = U_0 = \text{constant}$.

(c) Simplify the solution in (a) when $g(x, t) \equiv 0$, $f(x) \equiv 0$, and $f_1(t) = \bar{U} = \text{constant}$. Is it the solution of Exercise 2?

5. (a) Use a Fourier transform to find an integral representation for the solution of the heat conduction problem

$$\frac{\partial U}{\partial t} = k\frac{\partial^2 U}{\partial x^2} + \frac{k}{\kappa}g(x, t), \qquad x > 0, \qquad t > 0,$$

$$U_x(0, t) = -\kappa^{-1}f_1(t), \qquad t > 0,$$

$$U(x, 0) = f(x), \qquad x > 0.$$

(b) Simplify the solution in (a) when $g(x, t) \equiv 0, f_1(t) \equiv 0$, and $f(x) = U_0 = \text{constant}$.

(c) Simplify the solution in (a) when $g(x, t) \equiv 0$, $f(x) \equiv 0$, and $f_1(t) = Q_0 = \text{constant}$. Is it the solution of Exercise 3?

6. Use the Fourier transform of Exercise 24 in Section 7.3 to find an integral representation for the solution of the heat conduction problem

$$\frac{\partial U}{\partial t} = k\frac{\partial^2 U}{\partial x^2}, \qquad x > 0, \qquad t > 0,$$

$$-\kappa\frac{\partial U(0,t)}{\partial x} + \mu U(0,t) = \mu U_m = \text{constant}, \qquad t > 0,$$

$$U(x,0) = 0, \qquad x > 0.$$

7. Use the Fourier transform of Exercise 24 in Section 7.3 to find an integral representation for the solution of the heat conduction problem

$$\frac{\partial U}{\partial t} = k\frac{\partial^2 U}{\partial x^2} + \frac{k}{\kappa}g(x,t), \qquad x > 0, \qquad t > 0,$$

$$-\kappa\frac{\partial U(0,t)}{\partial x} + \mu U(0,t) = \mu f_1(t), \qquad t > 0,$$

$$U(x,0) = f(x), \qquad x > 0.$$

Part B—Vibrations

8. Repeat Example 11 if the Dirichlet boundary condition at $x = 0$ is replaced by the Neumann condition

$$y_x(0,t) = -\tau^{-1}f_1(t), \qquad \tau = \text{constant}.$$

Part C—Potential, Steady-State Heat Conduction, Static Deflection of Membranes

9. Solve Example 6 in Section 7.2 using Fourier transforms.

10. (a) Solve the boundary value problem for potential in the semi-infinite strip $0 \leq y \leq L'$, $x \geq 0$ when

   (i) potential on $y = 0$ and $y = L'$ is zero and that on $x = 0$ is $f(y)$.
   (ii) potential on $x = 0$ and $y = 0$ is zero and that on $y = L'$ is $g(x)$.
   (iii) potential on $x = 0$ and $y = L'$ is zero and that on $y = 0$ is $g(x)$.
   (iv) potentials on $x = 0$, $y = 0$, and $y = L'$ are $f(y)$, $g_1(x)$, and $g_2(x)$, respectively. [*Hint:* Superpose solutions of the types in (i), (ii), and (iii).]

   (b) Try to solve the problem in (iv) by using

   (i) a Fourier sine transform on x.   (ii) a finite Fourier transform on y.

11. A thin plate has edges along $y = 0$, $y = L'$, and $x = 0$ for $0 \leq y \leq L'$. The other edge is so far to the right that its effect may be considered negligible. Assuming no heat flow in the z-direction, find the steady-state temperature inside the plate (for $x > 0$, $0 < y < L'$) if side $y = 0$ is held at temperature $0°C$, side $y = L'$ is insulated, and, along $x = 0$,

   (a) temperature is held at a constant $U_0°C$.
   (b) heat is added to the plate at a constant rate $Q_0 > 0$ W/m^2 over the interval $0 < y < L'/2$ and extracted at the same rate for $L'/2 < y < L'$.
   (c) heat is transferred to a medium at constant temperature U_m according to Newton's law of cooling.

12. What are the solutions to Exercise 11 if edge $y = 0$ is insulated instead of held at temperature $0°C$?

13. Does the function

$$U(x, y) = \begin{cases} -Q_0 x/\kappa & 0 < y < L'/2 \\ Q_0 x/\kappa & L'/2 < y < L' \end{cases}$$

satisfy the PDE and the boundary conditions on $x = 0, y = 0,$ and $y = L'$ in Exercise 11(b)? Why is this not the solution?

14. (a) A uniform charge distribution of density σ coulombs per cubic meter occupies the region bounded by the planes $x = 0, y = 0,$ and $x = L$ ($y \geq 0$). If the planes $x = 0$ and $y = 0$ are kept at zero potential and $x = L$ is maintained at a constant potential V_L, find the potential between the planes using

   (i) a finite Fourier transform.
   (ii) a transformation to remove the constant nonhomogeneities σ and V_L.

   (b) Can we apply a Fourier sine transform with respect to y?

15. If the charge distribution in Exercise 14 is a function of $y, \sigma(y) = e^{-y}$, find the potential between the plates.

16. Solve Exercise 15 when $V_L = 0$, using

   (a) a finite Fourier transform.   (b) the Fourier sine transform.

17. (a) Show that the Fourier sine transform with respect to x of the solution of the boundary value problem

$$\frac{\partial^2 V}{\partial x^2} + \frac{\partial^2 V}{\partial y^2} = 0, \qquad x > 0, \qquad y > 0,$$

$$V(0, y) = 0, \qquad y > 0,$$

$$V(x, 0) = f(x), \qquad x > 0,$$

   is
$$\tilde{V}(\omega, y) = \tilde{f}(\omega)e^{-\omega y}.$$

   (b) Use Example 9 and the result of Exercise 10(b) in Section 7.3 to show that

$$\mathscr{F}_c\left(\frac{y}{x^2 + y^2}\right) = \frac{\pi}{2}e^{-\omega y}, \qquad y > 0.$$

   (c) Now use convolution property (34c) to show that

$$V(x, y) = \frac{y}{\pi}\int_0^\infty f(u)\left(\frac{1}{(x-u)^2 + y^2} - \frac{1}{(x+u)^2 + y^2}\right)du.$$

   (d) Simplify the solution in (c) when $f(x) \equiv 1$.

18. (a) Use the technique of Exercise 17 to solve Laplace's equation for the upper half-plane subject to the condition that $V(x, 0) = f(x)$. The result is called *Poisson's integral formula for the half-plane*.

   (b) What is the solution when $f(x) = H(x)$?

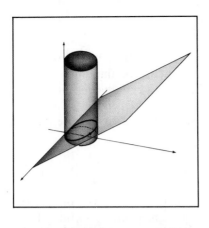

E I G H T

Special Functions

8.1 Introduction

In Chapters 3–7, discussions have been confined to (initial) boundary value problems expressed in Cartesian coordinates (with the exception of Laplace's equation in polar coordinates in Section 5.3). When separation of variables, finite Fourier transforms, and Laplace transforms are applied to initial boundary value problems in polar, cylindrical, and spherical coordinates, new functions arise, namely, Bessel functions and Legendre functions. In Sections 8.3 and 8.5, we introduce these functions as solutions of ordinary differential equations, as this is how they arise in the context of PDEs. Bessel's differential equation and Legendre's differential equation are homogeneous, second-order, linear differential equations with variable coefficients. The most general form of such an equation is

$$P(x)\frac{d^2y}{dx^2} + Q(x)\frac{dy}{dx} + R(x)y = 0. \tag{1}$$

A point x_0 is said to be an *ordinary point* of this differential equation when the functions $Q(x)/P(x)$ and $R(x)/P(x)$ have convergent Taylor series about x_0; otherwise, x_0 is called a *singular point*. When x_0 is an ordinary point of (1), there exist two independent solutions $y_1(x)$ and $y_2(x)$, both with Taylor series convergent in some interval $|x - x_0| < \delta$. A general solution of the differential equation valid in this interval is $c_1 y_1(x) + c_2 y_2(x)$, where c_1 and c_2 are constants.

When x_0 is a singular point of (1), independent solutions in the form of power series $\sum_{n=0}^{\infty} a_n(x - x_0)^n$ about x_0 may not exist. In this case, it is customary to search for solutions in the form

$$(x - x_0)^r \sum_{n=0}^{\infty} a_n(x - x_0)^n = \sum_{n=0}^{\infty} a_n(x - x_0)^{n+r}, \tag{2}$$

called *Frobenius* solutions. Solutions of this type may or may not exist, depending on the severity of the singularity. A singular point x_0 is said to be *regular* if

$$(x - x_0)\frac{Q(x)}{P(x)} \quad \text{and} \quad (x - x_0)^2 \frac{R(x)}{P(x)}$$

both have Taylor series expansions about x_0. Otherwise, x_0 is said to be an *irregular* singular point.

When x_0 is a regular singular point of (1), a Frobenius solution (2) always leads to a quadratic equation for the unknown index r. Depending on the nature of the roots of this quadratic, called the *indicial equation*, three situations arise; they are summarized in the following theorem.

Theorem 1

Let r_1 and r_2 be the indicial roots for a Frobenius solution of (1) about a regular singular point x_0. To find linearly independent solutions of (1), it is necessary to consider the cases in which the difference $r_1 - r_2$ is not an integer, is zero, or is a positive integer.

Case 1: $r_1 \neq r_2$ and $r_1 - r_2 \neq$ integer.
In this case, two linearly independent solutions,

$$y_1(x) = (x - x_0)^{r_1} \sum_{n=0}^{\infty} a_n(x - x_0)^n \quad \text{with } a_0 = 1 \tag{3a}$$

and

$$y_2(x) = (x - x_0)^{r_2} \sum_{n=0}^{\infty} b_n(x - x_0)^n \quad \text{with } b_0 = 1, \tag{3b}$$

always exist.

Case 2: $r_1 = r_2 = r$.
In this case, one Frobenius solution,

$$y_1(x) = (x - x_0)^r \sum_{n=0}^{\infty} a_n(x - x_0)^n \quad \text{with} \quad a_0 = 1, \tag{4a}$$

is obtained. A second (independent) solution exists in the form

$$y_2(x) = y_1(x)\ln(x - x_0) + (x - x_0)^r \sum_{n=1}^{\infty} A_n(x - x_0)^n, \qquad x > x_0. \tag{4b}$$

Case 3: $r_1 - r_2$ = positive integer.

In this case, one Frobenius solution can always be obtained from the larger root r_1:

$$y_1(x) = (x - x_0)^{r_1} \sum_{n=0}^{\infty} a_n(x - x_0)^n \quad \text{with } a_0 = 1. \tag{5a}$$

The smaller root r_2 may yield no solution, one solution, or a general solution. In the event that it yields no solution, a second (independent) solution can always be found in the form

$$y_2(x) = Ay_1(x)\ln(x - x_0) + (x - x_0)^{r_2} \sum_{n=0}^{\infty} A_n(x - x_0)^n \quad \text{with } A_0 = 1, x > x_0. \tag{5b}$$

In all cases, a general solution of the differential equation is

$$y(x) = c_1 y_1(x) + c_2 y_2(x).$$

8.2 Gamma Function

The gamma function is a generalization of the factorial operation to noninteger values. For $v > 0$, it is defined by the convergent improper integral

$$\boxed{\Gamma(v) = \int_0^{\infty} x^{v-1} e^{-x}\, dx.} \tag{6}$$

Integration by parts yields the recursive formula

$$\Gamma(v + 1) = v\Gamma(v), \qquad v > 0. \tag{7a}$$

With this formula, and the fact that the gamma function is well tabulated in many references[†] for $1 \le v < 2$, $\Gamma(v)$ can be calculated quickly for all $v > 0$. We note, in particular, that

$$\Gamma(1) = \int_0^{\infty} e^{-x}\, dx = 1, \tag{8}$$

and hence for v a positive integer,

$$\Gamma(v + 1) = v!. \tag{9}$$

Example 1:   Evaluate $\Gamma(4.2)$.

Solution: With recursive formula (7a),

$$\Gamma(4.2) = (3.2)\Gamma(3.2) = (3.2)(2.2)\Gamma(2.2)$$
$$= (3.2)(2.2)(1.2)\Gamma(1.2).$$

[†] See, for example, M. Abramowitz and I. Stegun, *Handbook of Mathematical Functions* (New York: Dover, 1965).

But from tables, $\Gamma(1.2) = 0.918169$, and therefore

$$\Gamma(4.2) = (3.2)(2.2)(1.2)(0.918169) = 7.7567.$$ ■

If $v \le 0$, the improper integral in (1) diverges (at $x = 0$), so the integral cannot be used to define $\Gamma(v)$ for $v \le 0$. Instead we reverse recursive formula (7a),

$$\Gamma(v) = \frac{\Gamma(v + 1)}{v},$$ (7b)

and iterate to define

$$\Gamma(v) = \frac{\Gamma(v + k)}{v(v + 1)(v + 2)\cdots(v + k - 1)},$$ (10)

where k is chosen such that $1 < v + k < 2$. With (10) as the definition of $\Gamma(v)$ for $v < 1$, $\Gamma(v)$ is now defined for all v except $v = 0, -1, -2,\ldots$, and its graph is as shown in Figure 8.1.

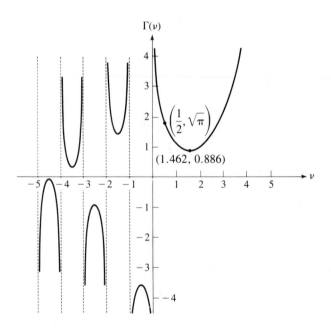

Figure 8.1

Example 2:   Evaluate $\Gamma(-2.3)$.

Solution: We use (7b) to write

$$\Gamma(-2.3) = \frac{\Gamma(-1.3)}{-2.3} = \frac{\Gamma(-0.3)}{(-2.3)(-1.3)} = \frac{\Gamma(0.7)}{(-2.3)(-1.3)(-0.3)}$$

$$= \frac{\Gamma(1.7)}{(-2.3)(-1.3)(-0.3)(0.7)}.$$

But from tables, $\Gamma(1.7) = 0.908639$, and therefore

$$\Gamma(-2.3) = \frac{0.908639}{(-2.3)(-1.3)(-0.3)(0.7)} = -1.4471.$$ ∎

Exercises 8.2

1. Use tables for the gamma function, or otherwise, to evaluate the following:

   (a) $\Gamma(6)$ (b) $\Gamma(3.4)$ (c) $\Gamma(4.16)$

   (d) $\Gamma(-0.8)$ (e) $\Gamma(-3.2)$ (f) $\Gamma(-2.44)$

2. Show that

$$\int_0^\infty x^v e^{-\alpha x}\, dx = \frac{\Gamma(v+1)}{\alpha^{v+1}}, \qquad v > -1, \qquad \alpha > 0.$$

3. By definition,

$$\Gamma\left(\frac{1}{2}\right) = \int_0^\infty x^{-1/2} e^{-x}\, dx.$$

   Set $x = y^2$ to show that

$$\Gamma\left(\frac{1}{2}\right) = 2 \int_0^\infty e^{-y^2}\, dy,$$

   and use the result of Exercise 24 in Section 7.2 to obtain $\Gamma(1/2) = \sqrt{\pi}$.

4. Prove that for n a positive integer,

$$\Gamma\left(n + \frac{1}{2}\right) = \frac{(2n)!\,\sqrt{\pi}}{2^{2n} n!}.$$

8.3 Bessel Functions

Bessel functions arise when separation of variables is applied to initial boundary value problems expressed in polar, cylindrical, and spherical coordinates. They are solutions of the linear, homogeneous, second-order ODE

$$x^2 \frac{d^2 y}{dx^2} + x \frac{dy}{dx} + (x^2 - v^2)y = 0, \qquad v \geq 0, \tag{11}$$

called *Bessel's differential equation of order v*. When we assume a Frobenius solution $y(x) = \sum_{n=0}^\infty a_n x^{n+r}$ ($x = 0$ being a regular singular point for the differential equation), we obtain the indicial equation

$$r^2 - v^2 = 0, \tag{12a}$$

and from the remaining coefficients,

$$a_1[(r+1)^2 - v^2] = 0, \tag{12b}$$

$$a_n[(n+r)^2 - v^2] + a_{n-2} = 0, \qquad n \geq 2. \tag{12c}$$

For the nonnegative indicial root $r = v$, we must choose $a_1 = 0$, and iteration of (12c) yields, for $n > 0$,

$$a_{2n+1} = 0, \tag{13a}$$

$$a_{2n} = \frac{(-1)^n a_0}{2^{2n} n!(v+1)(v+2)\cdots(v+n)}. \tag{13b}$$

If we choose $a_0 = 1/[2^v \Gamma(v+1)]$, the particular solution of Bessel's differential equation corresponding to the indicial root $r = v$ is denoted by

$$J_v(x) = \left(\frac{x}{2}\right)^v \sum_{n=0}^{\infty} \frac{(-1)^n}{n! \Gamma(n+v+1)} \left(\frac{x}{2}\right)^{2n} \tag{14}$$

and is called the *Bessel function of the first kind of order v*. The ratio test shows that this series converges for all x, and hence $J_v(x)$ is a solution of Bessel's differential equation for all x (provided, of course, that x^v is defined).

When v is a nonnegative integer, the gamma function can be expressed as a factorial:

$$J_v(x) = \left(\frac{x}{2}\right)^v \sum_{n=0}^{\infty} \frac{(-1)^n}{n!(n+v)!} \left(\frac{x}{2}\right)^{2n}, \qquad v = 0, 1, 2, \ldots. \tag{15}$$

Graphs of $J_v(x)$ for $v = 0, 1, 2$ are shown in Figure 8.2.

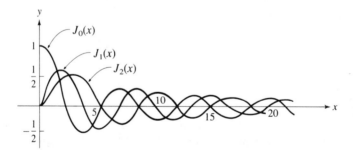

Figure 8.2

To obtain a second independent solution of Bessel's differential equation, three different cases arise, depending on whether v is not an integer, v is zero, or v is a positive integer.

Case 1: v is not an integer.
We could iterate recursive relation (12c) with the negative indicial root $r = -v$ (see Exercise 1), but there is a more direct route to the same solution. We examine the function obtained by replacing v by $-v$ in $J_v(x)$:

$$J_{-v}(x) = \left(\frac{x}{2}\right)^{-v} \sum_{n=0}^{\infty} \frac{(-1)^n}{n! \Gamma(n-v+1)} \left(\frac{x}{2}\right)^{2n}. \tag{16}$$

It is clear that this function also satisfies Bessel's differential equation (since the differential equation involves only v^2). Further, it is independent of $J_v(x)$, since $J_v(0) = 0$ and $\lim_{x \to 0^+} J_{-v}(x) = \infty$. Thus, if v is not an integer, a general solution of Bessel's differential equation is

$$y(x) = AJ_v(x) + BJ_{-v}(x), \qquad (17)$$

which certainly is valid for $x > 0$ (and may or may not be valid for $x < 0$, depending on the value of v). In the special case that v is one-half an odd integer $(1/2, 3/2, 5/2,$ etc.), the indicial roots differ by an integer, and this general solution is generated by the negative indicial root alone. The solutions in this case are called *spherical Bessel functions* (see Exercise 6).

Case 2: $v = 0$.
When $v = 0$, the indicial roots are equal, and a solution of Bessel's differential equation of order zero,

$$x\frac{d^2y}{dx^2} + \frac{dy}{dx} + xy = 0, \qquad (18)$$

independent of

$$J_0(x) = \sum_{n=0}^{\infty} \frac{(-1)^n}{(n!)^2} \left(\frac{x}{2}\right)^{2n}, \qquad (19)$$

can be found in the form

$$y(x) = J_0(x)\ln x + \sum_{n=1}^{\infty} A_n x^n$$

(see Case 2 of Theorem 1 in Section 8.1). Substitution of this solution into Bessel's differential equation leads to

$$2xJ_0' + \sum_{n=1}^{\infty} n(n-1)A_n x^n + \sum_{n=1}^{\infty} nA_n x^n + \sum_{n=1}^{\infty} A_n x^{n+2} = 0.$$

When $J_0'(x)$ is calculated from (19) and the remaining three summations are combined, the result is

$$A_1 x + 4A_2 x^2 + \sum_{n=3}^{\infty} (n^2 A_n + A_{n-2})x^n + \sum_{n=1}^{\infty} \frac{(-1)^n}{n!(n-1)!2^{2n-2}} x^{2n} = 0.$$

Evidently, $A_1 = 0$, and if n is odd, the recursive formula

$$n^2 A_n + A_{n-2} = 0$$

yields $A_{2n+1} = 0$ for $n > 0$. From the terms in x^2, $A_2 = 1/4$, and from those in x^{2n}, $n \geq 2$,

$$(2n)^2 A_{2n} + A_{2n-2} + \frac{(-1)^n}{n!(n-1)!2^{2n-2}} = 0. \qquad (20)$$

Iteration of this result gives

$$A_{2n} = \frac{(-1)^{n+1}}{2^{2n}(n!)^2}\left(1 + \frac{1}{2} + \frac{1}{3} + \cdots + \frac{1}{n}\right), \qquad n \geq 1. \qquad (21)$$

With the notation

$$\phi(n) = \sum_{r=1}^{n} \frac{1}{r}, \tag{22}$$

we obtain the independent solution

$$y(x) = J_0(x) \ln x + \sum_{n=1}^{\infty} \frac{(-1)^{n+1}\phi(n)}{(n!)^2}\left(\frac{x}{2}\right)^{2n}, \tag{23}$$

called *Neumann's Bessel function (of the second kind) of order zero*. The series in (23) converges for all x, but the logarithm term restricts the function to $x > 0$. Any linear combination of this solution and $J_0(x)$,

$$aJ_0(x) + by(x),$$

constitutes a general solution of Bessel's differential equation of order zero. Often taken are

$$a = A + \frac{2B}{\pi}(\gamma - \ln 2), \qquad b = \frac{2}{\pi}B,$$

where γ is Euler's constant, defined by

$$\gamma = \lim_{n \to \infty}\left(1 + \frac{1}{2} + \frac{1}{3} + \cdots + \frac{1}{n} - \ln n\right), \tag{24}$$

and A and B are arbitrary constants. In this case, the general solution of Bessel's differential equation of order zero is

$$y(x) = AJ_0(x) + BY_0(x), \tag{25a}$$

where

$$\boxed{Y_0(x) = \frac{2}{\pi}\left\{J_0(x)\left[\ln\left(\frac{x}{2}\right) + \gamma\right] + \sum_{n=1}^{\infty}\frac{(-1)^{n+1}\phi(n)}{(n!)^2}\left(\frac{x}{2}\right)^{2n}\right\}.} \tag{25b}$$

The solution $Y_0(x)$ is called *Weber's Bessel function (of the second kind) of order zero*.

Case 3: v is a positive integer.

When v is a positive integer, the indicial roots differ by an integer, and we find that $r = -v$ once again yields $J_v(x)$ (see Exercise 2). A second solution can be found in the form

$$y(x) = AJ_v(x) \ln x + \sum_{n=0}^{\infty} A_n x^{n-v} \tag{26}$$

(see Case 3 in Theorem 1 of Section 8.1). Substitution of this series into Bessel's differential equation (11) gives

$$2AxJ'_v + \sum_{n=0}^{\infty}(n-v)(n-v-1)A_n x^{n-v} + \sum_{n=0}^{\infty}(n-v)A_n x^{n-v} + (x^2-v^2)\sum_{n=0}^{\infty}A_n x^{n-v} = 0,$$

and, if this equation is multiplied by x^v and the summations are combined,

$$(1 - 2v)A_1 x + \sum_{n=2}^{\infty} [n(n - 2v)A_n + A_{n-2}]x^n + \sum_{n=0}^{\infty} \frac{(-1)^n A(2n + v)}{n!(n + v)!2^{2n+v-1}} x^{2n+2v} = 0.$$

Evidently, $A_1 = 0$, and if n is odd, the recursive formula

$$n(n - 2v)A_n + A_{n-2} = 0$$

requires that $A_{2n+1} = 0$ for $n > 0$. Since this recursive formula is also valid for even n and $0 < n < 2v$, iteration gives

$$A_{2n} = \frac{A_0(v - n - 1)!}{2^{2n}n!(v - 1)!}, \qquad 0 < n < v. \tag{27}$$

From the coefficient of x^{2v},

$$A_{2v-2} + \frac{Av}{v!2^{v-1}} = 0,$$

which can be solved for

$$A = \frac{-A_0}{2^{v-1}(v - 1)!}. \tag{28}$$

From the terms in x^{2n+2v}, $n > 0$,

$$2n(2n + 2v)A_{2n+2v} + A_{2n+2v-2} + \frac{(-1)^n A(2n + v)}{n!(n + v)!2^{2n+v-1}} = 0.$$

Iteration of this result gives

$$A_{2n+2v} = \frac{(-1)^{n+1}A[\phi(n) + \phi(n + v)]}{n!(n + v)!2^{2n+v+1}}, \qquad n > 0, \tag{29a}$$

provided we make the choice

$$A_{2v} = \frac{-A\phi(v)}{2^{v+1}v!}. \tag{29b}$$

Finally, then, the solution is

$$y(x) = AJ_v(x) \ln x + x^{-v}\left(\sum_{n=0}^{v-1} \frac{A_0(v - n - 1)!}{n!(v - 1)!} \left(\frac{x}{2}\right)^{2n} - \frac{A\phi(v)}{2^{v+1}v!}x^{2v} \right.$$

$$\left. + \sum_{n=1}^{\infty} \frac{(-1)^{n+1}A[\phi(n) + \phi(n + v)]}{n!(n + v)!2^{2n+v+1}} x^{2n+2v} \right). \tag{30}$$

The particular solution obtained by setting $A_0 = -2^{v-1}(v - 1)!$ is

$$y(x) = J_v(x) \ln x - \frac{1}{2}\left(\frac{x}{2}\right)^{-v} \sum_{n=0}^{v-1} \frac{(v - n - 1)!}{n!} \left(\frac{x}{2}\right)^{2n}$$

$$- \frac{1}{2}\left(\frac{x}{2}\right)^{v} \sum_{n=0}^{\infty} \frac{(-1)^n [\phi(n) + \phi(n + v)]}{n!(n + v)!} \left(\frac{x}{2}\right)^{2n}, \tag{31}$$

where we have adopted the convention that $\phi(0) = 0$. This solution is called *Neumann's Bessel function (of the second kind) of order v*. Any linear combination of this solution and $J_v(x)$,

$$aJ_v(x) + by(x),$$

constitutes a general solution of Bessel's differential equation of order v, v a positive integer. Often taken are a and b, as in the $v = 0$ case, in which case the general solution of Bessel's differential equation of positive integer order v is

$$y(x) = AJ_v(x) + BY_v(x), \tag{32a}$$

where

$$Y_v(x) = \frac{2}{\pi}\left\{J_v(x)\left[\ln\left(\frac{x}{2}\right) + \gamma\right] - \frac{1}{2}\left(\frac{x}{2}\right)^{-v}\sum_{n=0}^{v-1}\frac{(v-n-1)!}{n!}\left(\frac{x}{2}\right)^{2n}\right.$$
$$\left. - \frac{1}{2}\left(\frac{x}{2}\right)^{v}\sum_{n=0}^{\infty}\frac{(-1)^{n}[\phi(n) + \phi(n+v)]}{n!(n+v)!}\left(\frac{x}{2}\right)^{2n}\right\}. \tag{32b}$$

The solution $Y_v(x)$ is called *Weber's Bessel function (of the second kind) of order v*.

Notice that in the special case that $v = 0$, $Y_v(x)$ reduces to $Y_0(x)$, provided we stipulate that the first sum vanish. Graphs of $Y_0(x)$ and $Y_1(x)$ are shown in Figure 8.3.

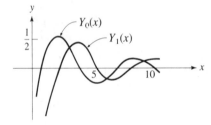

Figure 8.3

For nonnegative integer values of v, a general solution of Bessel's differential equation has been obtained in the form $y(x) = AJ_v(x) + BY_v(x)$, and, for noninteger v, the solution is $y(x) = AJ_v(x) + BJ_{-v}(x)$. This situation is not completely satisfactory because the second solution is defined differently, depending on whether v is an integer. To provide uniformity of formalism and numerical tabulation, a form of the second solution valid for all orders is sometimes preferable. Such a form is contained in

$$Y_v(x) = \frac{1}{\sin v\pi}(J_v(x)\cos v\pi - J_{-v}(x)), \qquad v \neq \text{integer}, \tag{33a}$$

$$Y_n(x) = \lim_{v \to n} Y_v(x), \qquad n = \text{integer}. \tag{33b}$$

If v is not an integer, $Y_v(x)$ is simply a linear combination of $J_v(x)$ and $J_{-v}(x)$, and since $J_v(x)$ and $Y_v(x)$ must therefore be independent,

$$AJ_v(x) + BY_v(x) \tag{34}$$

is a general solution of Bessel's differential equation. It can be shown that as v approaches n, $Y_v(x)$ is also given by (25b) or (32b). Consequently, a general solution of Bessel's differential equation (11) is (34), where $J_v(x)$ is given by (14) and $Y_v(x)$ is given by (33). When v is an integer, $Y_v(x)$ is also given by (25b) or (32b).

Recurrence Relations

Bessel functions of lower orders are well tabulated.[†] With recurrence relations, it is then possible to evaluate Bessel functions of higher orders. We now develop some of these relations.

Using series (14),

$$
\begin{aligned}
J_{v-1}(x) + J_{v+1}(x) &= \sum_{n=0}^{\infty} \frac{(-1)^n}{n!\,\Gamma(n+v)}\left(\frac{x}{2}\right)^{2n+v-1} + \sum_{n=0}^{\infty} \frac{(-1)^n}{n!\,\Gamma(n+v+2)}\left(\frac{x}{2}\right)^{2n+v+1} \\
&= \sum_{n=0}^{\infty} \frac{(-1)^n}{n!\,\Gamma(n+v)}\left(\frac{x}{2}\right)^{2n+v-1} + \sum_{n=1}^{\infty} \frac{(-1)^{n-1}}{(n-1)!\,\Gamma(n+v+1)}\left(\frac{x}{2}\right)^{2n+v-1} \\
&= \frac{1}{\Gamma(v)}\left(\frac{x}{2}\right)^{v-1} + \sum_{n=1}^{\infty} \frac{(-1)^{n-1}}{n!\,\Gamma(n+v+1)}(-(n+v)+n)\left(\frac{x}{2}\right)^{2n+v-1} \\
&= \frac{v}{\Gamma(v+1)}\left(\frac{x}{2}\right)^{v-1} + \sum_{n=1}^{\infty} \frac{(-1)^n v}{n!\,\Gamma(n+v+1)}\left(\frac{x}{2}\right)^{2n+v-1} \\
&= \sum_{n=0}^{\infty} \frac{(-1)^n v}{n!\,\Gamma(n+v+1)}\left(\frac{x}{2}\right)^{2n+v-1} \\
&= \frac{2v}{x} \sum_{n=0}^{\infty} \frac{(-1)^n}{n!\,\Gamma(n+v+1)}\left(\frac{x}{2}\right)^{2n+v} = \frac{2v}{x} J_v(x).
\end{aligned}
$$

Thus, we have the recurrence relation

$$
J_{v+1}(x) = \frac{2v}{x} J_v(x) - J_{v-1}(x), \qquad v \geq 1, \tag{35}
$$

which allows evaluation of Bessel functions of higher order by means of Bessel functions of lower orders.

In addition to this functional relation, there exist many relationships among the Bessel functions and their derivatives. A derivation similar to the above yields

$$
2J_v'(x) = J_{v-1}(x) - J_{v+1}(x), \qquad v \geq 1, \tag{36}
$$

(see Exercise 5). This result combines with recurrence relation (35) to give

$$
J_v'(x) = -\frac{v}{x} J_v(x) + J_{v-1}(x), \qquad v \geq 1, \tag{37}
$$

and

$$
J_v'(x) = \frac{v}{x} J_v(x) - J_{v+1}(x), \qquad v \geq 0. \tag{33}
$$

[†] Ibid.

Further, multiplication of these equations by x^v and x^{-v}, respectively, implies that

$$\frac{d}{dx}\left(x^v J_v(x)\right) = x^v J_{v-1}(x), \qquad v \geq 1, \tag{39}$$

and

$$\frac{d}{dx}\left(x^{-v} J_v(x)\right) = -x^{-v} J_{v+1}(x), \qquad v \geq 0. \tag{40}$$

The results in (35)–(40) are also valid for $Y_v(x)$.

Zeros of Bessel Functions

Zeros of Bessel functions play an important role in Sturm-Liouville systems involving Bessel's differential equation (see Section 8.4). We shall show that $J_v(x)$ has an infinite number of positive zeros and that these zeros cannot be contained in an interval of finite length; that is, there must be arbitrarily large zeros of $J_v(x)$. [The results will also be valid for $Y_v(x)$, but our interest is in $J_v(x)$, and we shall therefore deal directly with $J_v(x)$.] We begin by changing dependent variables in Bessel's differential equation (11) according to $R = \sqrt{x}\, y(x)$ for $x > 0$ (see Exercise 7). The result is

$$\frac{d^2 R}{dx^2} + \left(1 + \frac{1/4 - v^2}{x^2}\right) R = 0, \qquad x > 0, \tag{41}$$

and $R(x) = \sqrt{x}\, J_v(x)$ is a solution of this equation. When $0 < \varepsilon < 1$, the differential equation

$$\frac{d^2 R}{dx^2} + \varepsilon^2 R = 0, \qquad x > 0, \tag{42}$$

has general solution $R(x) = A \sin(\varepsilon x + \phi)$, where A and ϕ $(0 < \phi < \pi)$ are arbitrary constants, and this solution has an infinity of positive zeros, $x = (n\pi - \phi)/\varepsilon$ $(n > 0)$.

According to the Sturm comparison theorem in Section 4.3, if $1 + (1/4 - v^2)/x^2$ is greater than or equal to ε^2, every solution of (41) has a zero between every consecutive pair of zeros of $A \sin(\varepsilon x + \phi)$. But

$$1 + \frac{1/4 - v^2}{x^2} > \varepsilon^2 \tag{43}$$

if, and only if,

$$x^2 > \frac{v^2 - 1/4}{1 - \varepsilon^2}.$$

When $0 \leq v \leq 1/2$, this is valid for all $x > 0$. When $v > 1/2$, this is valid for all $x > x_0$ if $x_0 = \sqrt{(v^2 - 1/4)/(1 - \varepsilon^2)}$. In other words, it is always possible to find an interval $x > x_0 \geq 0$ on which inequality (43) is valid. On this interval, then, $R(x)$, and therefore $J_v(x)$, has at least one zero between every consecutive pair of zeros of $A \sin(\varepsilon x + \phi)$. Since the zeros $x = (n\pi - \phi)/\varepsilon$ of $A \sin(\varepsilon x + \phi)$ become indefinitely large with increasing n, it follows that $J_v(x)$ must also have arbitrarily large zeros. The first five zeros of $J_0(x)$ and $J_1(x)$ are shown in Figure 8.2.

Exercises 8.3

1. Show that when v is not an integer, solution (16) of Bessel's differential equation can be obtained from the negative indicial root.

2. Show that when v is a positive integer, the solution obtained from the negative indicial root $r = -v$ is $J_v(x)$.

3. Use series (15) to find values of the following, correct to four decimals.

   (a) $J_0(0.4)$ (b) $J_0(1.3)$ (c) $J_1(0.8)$ (d) $J_1(3.6)$

   (e) $J_2(3.6)$ (f) $J_2(6.2)$ (g) $J_3(4.1)$ (h) $J_4(2.9)$

4. Calculate the following, using recurrence relation (35) and tabulated values of J_0 and J_1:

   (a) $J_2(3.6)$ (b) $J_2(6.2)$ (c) $J_3(4.1)$ (d) $J_4(2.9)$

5. Verify identity (36).

6. Bessel functions of the first kind of order $\pm(n + 1/2)$, n a nonnegative integer, are called *spherical Bessel functions*. They can be expressed in terms of sines and cosines.

   (a) Use series (14) and the result of Exercise 4 in Section 8.2 to show that

   $$J_{1/2}(x) = \sqrt{\frac{2}{\pi x}} \sin x, \qquad J_{-1/2}(x) = \sqrt{\frac{2}{\pi x}} \cos x.$$

   (b) Use (39) and (40) to show that

   $$\left(\frac{1}{x}\frac{d}{dx}\right)^n (x^{-v}J_v(x)) = (-1)^n x^{-v-n}J_{v+n}(x)$$

   and

   $$\left(\frac{1}{x}\frac{d}{dx}\right)^n (x^v J_v(x)) = x^{v-n}J_{v-n}(x),$$

   where the left sides mean to apply the operator $x^{-1}d/dx$ successively n times.

   (c) Prove that for $n = 0, 1, 2, \ldots,$

   $$J_{n+1/2}(x) = (-1)^n \sqrt{\frac{2}{\pi}} x^{n+1/2} \left(\frac{1}{x}\frac{d}{dx}\right)^n \left(\frac{\sin x}{x}\right),$$

   $$J_{1/2-n}(x) = \sqrt{\frac{2}{\pi}} x^{n-1/2} \left(\frac{1}{x}\frac{d}{dx}\right)^n (\sin x).$$

7. Show that the change of dependent variable $R(x) = \sqrt{x}\,y(x)$ transforms Bessel's differential equation into equation (41).

8. Show that the function $e^{x(t-1/t)/2}$ can be expressed as the product of the series

   $$e^{x(t-1/t)/2} = \left(\sum_{k=0}^{\infty}\left(\frac{x}{2}\right)^k \frac{t^k}{k!}\right)\left(\sum_{n=0}^{\infty}\left(-\frac{x}{2}\right)^n \frac{t^{-n}}{n!}\right)$$

   and that the product can be rearranged into the form

   $$e^{x(t-1/t)/2} = J_0(x) + \sum_{m=1}^{\infty} [J_m(x)t^m + (-1)^m J_m(x)t^{-m}].$$

   Because of this, $e^{x(t-1/t)/2}$ is said to be a *generating function* for $J_m(x)$, m a nonnegative integer.

9. Use integration by parts and the facts that $d[xJ_1(x)]/dx = xJ_0(x)$ and $dJ_0(x)/dx = -J_1(x)$ [see identities (39) and (38)] to derive the reduction formula

$$\int x^n J_0(x)\,dx = x^n J_1(x) + (n-1)x^{n-1}J_0(x) - (n-1)^2 \int x^{n-2}J_0(x)\,dx, \qquad n \geq 2.$$

10. (a) The differential equation

$$x^2 \frac{d^2y}{dx^2} + x \frac{dy}{dx} - (x^2 + v^2)y = 0, \qquad v \geq 0,$$

is called *Bessel's modified differential equation of order v.* Show that the change of independent variable $z = ix$ reduces it to Bessel's differential equation of order v.

(b) Verify that the function $I_v(x) = i^{-v}J_v(ix)$, called the *modified Bessel function of the first kind of order v*, is a solution of Bessel's modified differential equation. Find the Maclaurin series for $I_v(x)$ to illustrate why the factor i^{-v} is included in its definition.

(c) Sketch graphs of $I_0(x)$ and $I_1(x)$ for $x \geq 0$.

(d) A second (linearly independent) solution of the modified equation is called the *modified Bessel function of the second kind of order v.* Its definition is analogous to definition (33) for $Y_v(x)$:

$$K_v(x) = \frac{\pi}{2\sin v\pi}[I_{-v}(x) - I_v(x)], \qquad v \neq \text{integer},$$

$$K_n(x) = \lim_{v \to n} K_v(x), \qquad n = \text{integer}.$$

It can be shown that this definition leads to the following expressions for $K_v(x)$ when v is an integer:

$$K_0(x) = -I_0(x)\left[\ln\left(\frac{x}{2}\right) + \gamma\right] + \sum_{n=1}^{\infty} \frac{\phi(n)}{(n!)^2}\left(\frac{x}{2}\right)^{2n},$$

$$K_v(x) = (-1)^{v+1}I_v(x)\left[\ln\left(\frac{x}{2}\right) + \gamma\right] + \frac{1}{2}\left(\frac{x}{2}\right)^{-v}\sum_{n=0}^{v-1}\frac{(-1)^n(v-n-1)!}{n!}\left(\frac{x}{2}\right)^{2n}$$

$$+ \frac{1}{2}\left(-\frac{x}{2}\right)^v\sum_{n=0}^{\infty}\frac{[\phi(n) + \phi(n+v)]}{n!(v+n)!}\left(\frac{x}{2}\right)^{2n}, \qquad v > 0.$$

Express $K_v(x)$ in terms of $J_v(ix)$ and $Y_v(ix)$ when v is an integer.

(e) Show that $K_v(x)$ is unbounded near $x = 0$ when v is an integer.

8.4 Sturm-Liouville Systems and Bessel's Differential Equation

When separation of variables is applied to initial boundary value problems in polar and cylindrical coordinates (and we shall do this in Chapter 9), both regular and singular Sturm-Liouville systems in the radial coordinate r occur. Regular systems take the form

$$\frac{d}{dr}\left(r\frac{dR}{dr}\right) + \left(\lambda^2 r - \frac{v^2}{r}\right)R = 0, \qquad 0 < r_1 < r < r_2, \tag{44a}$$

$$-l_1 R'(r_1) + h_1 R(r_1) = 0, \tag{44b}$$

$$l_2 R'(r_2) + h_2 R(r_2) = 0; \tag{44c}$$

singular systems appear as

$$\frac{d}{dr}\left(r\frac{dR}{dr}\right) + \left(\lambda^2 r - \frac{v^2}{r}\right)R = 0, \qquad 0 < r < r_2, \tag{45a}$$

$$l_2 R'(r_2) + h_2 R(r_2) = 0, \tag{45b}$$

where l_1, l_2, h_1, h_2, and v are nonnegative constants. Eigenvalues have been represented as λ^2, since (44) is a proper Sturm-Liouville system (the eigenvalues of which must be nonnegative).

Properties of system (44) are a straightforward application of the general theory in Section 4.1. Although we make limited use of the results, we include a brief discussion for two reasons. First, it affords us the opportunity to review the theory of Sturm-Liouville systems; second, the notation introduced and some of the results obtained are useful in the discussion of singular system (45).

We begin by making a change of independent variable $x = \lambda r$ in (44a). Since $d/dr = \lambda d/dx$, the resulting differential equation is

$$\lambda\frac{d}{dx}\left(x\frac{dR}{dx}\right) + \left(\lambda x - \frac{\lambda}{x}v^2\right)R = 0,$$

or

$$x^2\frac{d^2 R}{dx^2} + x\frac{dR}{dx} + (x^2 - v^2)R = 0, \tag{46}$$

Bessel's differential equation of order v. According to equation (34), the general solution of this equation is

$$R = AJ_v(x) + BY_v(x), \tag{47}$$

where A and B are arbitrary constants and J_v and Y_v are Bessel functions of the first and second kind of order v. Consequently, the general solution of (44a) is

$$R(\lambda, r) = AJ_v(\lambda r) + BY_v(\lambda r). \tag{48}$$

If we let J_v' denote the derivative of J_v with respect to its argument, that is, if

$$J_v'(x) = \frac{d}{dx}J_v(x),$$

then

$$\frac{d}{dr}J_v(\lambda r) = \lambda J_v'(\lambda r).$$

With this notation, boundary conditions (44b, c) require that

$$-l_1\lambda[AJ_v'(\lambda r_1) + BY_v'(\lambda r_1)] + h_1[AJ_v(\lambda r_1) + BY_v(\lambda r_1)] = 0, \tag{49a}$$

$$l_2\lambda[AJ_v'(\lambda r_2) + BY_v'(\lambda r_2)] + h_2[AJ_v(\lambda r_2) + BY_v(\lambda r_2)] = 0. \tag{49b}$$

From (49b),

$$B = -A\left(\frac{\lambda l_2 J_v'(\lambda r_2) + h_2 J_v(\lambda r_2)}{\lambda l_2 Y_v'(\lambda r_2) + h_2 Y_v(\lambda r_2)}\right),$$

which, substituted into (49a), yields

$$\frac{-\lambda l_1 J_v'(\lambda r_1) + h_1 J_v(\lambda r_1)}{-\lambda l_2 J_v'(\lambda r_2) + h_2 J_v(\lambda r_2)} = \frac{-\lambda l_1 Y_v'(\lambda r_1) + h_1 Y_v(\lambda r_1)}{\lambda l_2 Y_v'(\lambda r_2) + h_2 Y_v(\lambda r_2)}. \tag{50}$$

This is the eigenvalue equation, the equation defining eigenvalues of Sturm-Liouville system (44). Because values of λ will depend on the value of v in differential equation (44a), we denote eigenvalues of (50) by λ_{vn} ($n = 1, 2, \ldots$) [although, in fact, $(\lambda_{vn})^2$ are the eigenvalues of the Sturm-Liouville system]. Corresponding eigenfunctions can be expressed in the form

$$R_{vn}(r) = R(\lambda_{vn}, r) = \frac{1}{N}\left(\frac{J_v(\lambda_{vn}r)}{\lambda_{vn}l_2 J_v'(\lambda_{vn}r_2) + h_2 J_v(\lambda_{vn}r_2)} - \frac{Y_v(\lambda_{vn}r)}{\lambda_{vn}l_2 Y_v'(\lambda_{vn}r_2) + h_2 Y_v(\lambda_{vn}r_2)}\right),$$

(51a)

where the normalizing factor N^{-1} is given by

$$N^2 = \int_{r_1}^{r_2} r\left(\frac{J_v(\lambda_{vn}r)}{\lambda_{vn}l_2 J_v'(\lambda_{vn}r_2) + h_2 J_v(\lambda_{vn}r_2)} - \frac{Y_v(\lambda_{vn}r)}{\lambda_{vn}l_2 Y_v'(\lambda_{vn}r_2) + h_2 Y_v(\lambda_{vn}r_2)}\right)^2 dr. \quad (51b)$$

This integral is evaluated in Exercise 1. We end our discussion of system (44) by noting that according to Theorem 2 in Section 4.2, functions of r can be expressed in terms of the orthonormal eigenfunctions $R_{vn}(r)$. Indeed, when $f(r)$ is piecewise smooth for $r_1 \leq r \leq r_2$, we find that at any point in the open interval $r_1 < r < r_2$,

$$\frac{f(r+) + f(r-)}{2} = \sum_{n=1}^{\infty} c_n R_{vn}(r), \quad (52a)$$

where

$$c_n = \int_{r_1}^{r_2} rf(r)R_{vn}(r)\, dr. \quad (52b)$$

This is often called the Fourier-Bessel series for $f(r)$. It is important to remember that v has been fixed throughout this discussion; that is, for a fixed value of $v \geq 0$, there is a sequence of eigenvalues $\{\lambda_{vn}^2\}$ of (44) together with corresponding orthonormal eigenfunctions $R_{vn}(r)$ and an eigenfunction expansion (52). Changing the value of v results in another set of eigenpairs and a new eigenfunction expansion.

More important for our discussions is singular Sturm-Liouville system (45); we consider it in detail. The system is singular because no boundary condition exists at $r = 0$. Notice also that $q(r) = -v^2/r$ is not continuous at $r = 0$.

We are not really justified in denoting eigenvalues of a singular system by λ^2, since we cannot yet be sure that eigenvalues are nonnegative. However, because we shall show shortly that all eigenvalues must indeed be nonnegative, and because use of λ^2 has the immediate advantage of avoiding square roots in subsequent discussions, it is convenient to adopt this notation. Since the coefficient function of $R'(r)$ vanishes at $r = 0$, the corollary to Theorem 1 in Section 4.1 indicates that a boundary condition at $r = 0$ is unnecessary for that theorem. Examination of the proof of the theorem also indicates that continuity of $q(r)$ at $r = 0$ is unnecessary. Consequently, eigenvalues of this singular system are real and corresponding eigenfunctions are orthogonal. As in the discussion of system (44), the change in independent variable $x = \lambda r$ leads to the general solution

$$R = AJ_v(\lambda r) + BY_v(\lambda r) \quad (53)$$

of (45a). Because $Y_v(\lambda r)$ is unbounded near $r = 0$, B must be set equal to zero, and we take

$$R = AJ_v(\lambda r). \quad (54)$$

Boundary condition (45b) yields the eigenvalue equation

$$l_2 \lambda J_v'(\lambda r_2) + h_2 J_v(\lambda r_2) = 0, \tag{55}$$

where once again the prime in the first term indicates differentiation of J_v with respect to its argument.

Because the Sturm-Liouville system is singular, we cannot quote the results of Theorem 2 in Section 4.2; we must verify that the theorem is indeed valid for this system. We first show that there is an infinity of eigenvalues, all of which are positive (except when $v = h_2 = 0$, in which case zero is also an eigenvalue). We subdivide our discussion into three cases, depending on whether $l_2 = 0$, $h_2 = 0$, or $h_2 l_2 \neq 0$.

Case 1: $l_2 = 0$.
In this case, we set $h_2 = 1$, and from equation (55) eigenvalues are defined by

$$J_v(\lambda r_2) = 0; \tag{56}$$

that is, eigenvalues are the zeros of Bessel function $J_v(x)$ divided by r_2. In Section 8.3 we verified that Bessel functions have an infinity of positive zeros.

Case 2: $h_2 = 0$.
In this case, we set $l_2 = 1$, and eigenvalues are defined by the equation

$$J_v'(\lambda r_2) = 0; \tag{57}$$

that is, eigenvalues are critical values of Bessel function $J_v(x)$ divided by r_2. Since $J_v(x)$ has a continuous first derivative, Rolle's theorem from elementary calculus indicates that between every pair of zeros of $J_v(x)$, there is at least one point at which its derivative vanishes. Hence, (57) has an infinity of positive solutions. [The first few positive critical values of $J_0(x)$ and $J_1(x)$ are shown in Figure 8.2.]

Case 3: $h_2 l_2 \neq 0$.
In this case, eigenvalues are defined by (55). If we set $x = \lambda r_2$, eigenvalues are roots of the equation

$$Q(x) = x J_v'(x) + \frac{r_2 h_2}{l_2} J_v(x) = 0 \tag{58}$$

divided by r_2. When x_j and x_{j+1} are consecutive positive zeros of $J_v(x)$, $Q(x)$ has one sign at x_j and the opposite sign at x_{j+1}. Because $Q(x)$ is continuous, it must have at least one zero between x_j and x_{j+1}. It follows, therefore, that equation (58) must have an infinity of positive solutions.

We have shown that each of the eigenvalue equations (55), (56), and (57) has an infinity of positive solutions λ. These solutions define positive eigenvalues λ^2 of the singular Sturm-Liouville system. To show that the system can have no negative eigenvalues, we set $\lambda = i\phi$ (ϕ real and not equal to zero). Equation (55) with $\lambda = i\phi$ then reads

$$il_2 \phi J_v'(i\phi r_2) + h_2 J_v(i\phi r_2) = 0.$$

If we replace J_v' by J_v and J_{v+1} according to equation (38), this equation becomes

$$[r_2 h_2 + v l_2]J_v(i\phi r_2) - i\phi r_2 l_2 J_{v+1}(i\phi r_2) = 0.$$

We now express $J_\nu(i\phi r_2)$ and $J_{\nu+1}(i\phi r_2)$ in terms of their power series; the result is

$$0 = \left(\frac{i\phi r_2}{2}\right)^\nu \left((r_2 h_2 + \nu l_2) \sum_{n=0}^\infty \frac{1}{n!\,\Gamma(n+\nu+1)}\left(\frac{\phi r_2}{2}\right)^{2n}\right.$$
$$\left. + \frac{\phi^2 r_2^2 l_2}{2} \sum_{n=0}^\infty \frac{1}{n!\,\Gamma(n+\nu+2)}\left(\frac{\phi r_2}{2}\right)^{2n}\right).$$

Because $r_2 h_2 + \nu l_2 \geq 0$ and $l_2 \geq 0$, and both series contain only positive terms, there can be no solution ϕ. Thus, all eigenvalues of (55) must be nonnegative.

We now show that $\lambda = 0$ is an eigenvalue only when $h_2 = \nu = 0$. Since the eigenfunction corresponding to an eigenvalue λ is always $J_\nu(\lambda r)$, it is clear that the eigenfunction will be identically zero if $\lambda = 0$ is an eigenvalue, except when $\nu = 0$ [when $\nu = 0$, the eigenfunction corresponding to $\lambda = 0$ is $J_0(0) = 1$]. Because $J_0(0) \neq 0$ and $J_0'(0) = 0$, it follows that $\lambda = 0$ is an eigenvalue of equation (57) but not of (55) or (56). Thus, there is only one possibility for a zero eigenvalue—both h_2 and ν must be equal to zero.

Only one last point remains to be cleared up. If ν is such that J_ν is defined for negative arguments, then for every positive solution λ of (55), (56), and (57), $-\lambda$ is also a solution. However, the power series expansion for J_ν clearly indicates that the eigenfunction $J_\nu(-\lambda r)$ is, except for a multiplicative constant, identical to $J_\nu(\lambda r)$. Thus, negative solutions of the eigenvalue equations lead to the same eigenvalues λ^2 of the Sturm-Liouville system and the same eigenfunctions.

We have now shown that singular Sturm-Liouville system (45) has an infinity of eigenvalues, all of which are positive (except when $\nu = h_2 = 0$, in which case zero is also an eigenvalue). If we denote these eigenvalues by $\lambda_{\nu n}$ ($n = 1, 2, \ldots$), then from (54), corresponding orthonormal eigenfunctions are

$$R_{\nu n}(r) = R(\lambda_{\nu n}, r) = \frac{1}{N} J_\nu(\lambda_{\nu n} r), \tag{59a}$$

where
$$N^2 = \int_0^{r_2} r[J_\nu(\lambda_{\nu n} r)]^2 \, dr. \tag{59b}$$

To avoid direct integration of J_ν, we note that any function R satisfying differential equation (45) also satisfies

$$0 = 2rR'(rR')' + \left(\lambda^2 r - \frac{\nu^2}{r}\right) 2rRR'$$
$$= \frac{d}{dr}(rR')^2 + (\lambda^2 r^2 - \nu^2)\frac{d}{dr}(R^2).$$

Integration of this equation with respect to r from $r = 0$ to $r = r_2$ gives

$$0 = \{(rR')^2 - \nu^2 R^2\}_0^{r_2} + \lambda^2 \int_0^{r_2} r^2 \frac{d}{dr}(R^2)\,dr$$
$$= \{(rR')^2 - \nu^2 R^2\}_0^{r_2} + \lambda^2 \{r^2 R^2\}_0^{r_2} - \lambda^2 \int_0^{r_2} 2rR^2 \, dr,$$

and when this is solved for the remaining integral,

$$2\lambda^2 \int_0^{r_2} rR^2\, dr = \{(rR')^2 - v^2R^2 + \lambda^2 r^2 R^2\}_0^{r_2}.$$

If we now replace λ with λ_{vn} and R with the corresponding solution $J_v(\lambda_{vn}r)$ of (45a),

$$2\lambda_{vn}^2 \int_0^{r_2} r[J_v(\lambda_{vn}r)]^2\, dr = r_2^2 \lambda_{vn}^2 [J_v'(\lambda_{vn}r_2)]^2 + (\lambda_{vn}^2 r_2^2 - v^2)[J_v(\lambda_{vn}r_2)]^2,$$

from which

$$2N^2 = 2\int_0^{r_2} r[J_v(\lambda_{vn}r)]^2\, dr$$

$$= r_2^2 [J_v'(\lambda_{vn}r_2)]^2 + \left(r_2^2 - \frac{v^2}{\lambda_{vn}^2}\right)[J_v(\lambda_{vn}r_2)]^2$$

$$= r_2^2 \left(\frac{-h_2 J_v(\lambda_{vn}r_2)}{\lambda_{vn}l_2}\right)^2 + \left[r_2^2 - \left(\frac{v}{\lambda_{vn}}\right)^2\right][J_v(\lambda_{vn}r_2)]^2$$

$$= r_2^2 \left[1 - \left(\frac{v}{\lambda_{vn}r_2}\right)^2 + \left(\frac{h_2}{\lambda_{vn}l_2}\right)^2\right][J_v(\lambda_{vn}r_2)]^2.$$

Summarizing our results, orthonormal eigenfunctions of singular Sturm-Liouville system (45) are

$$R_{vn}(r) = \frac{1}{N} J_v(\lambda_{vn}r), \tag{60a}$$

where

$$2N^2 = r_2^2 \left[1 - \left(\frac{v}{\lambda_{vn}r_2}\right)^2 + \left(\frac{h_2}{\lambda_{vn}l_2}\right)^2\right][J_v(\lambda_{vn}r_2)]^2 \tag{60b}$$

and eigenvalues λ_{vn} are defined by the equation

$$l_2\lambda J_v'(\lambda r_2) + h_2 J_v(\lambda r_2) = 0. \tag{60c}$$

There are three possible boundary conditions at $r = r_2$, depending on whether $l_2 = 0$, $h_2 = 0$, or $l_2 h_2 \neq 0$. The results for all three cases are listed in Table 8.1.

Table 8.1   *Eigenpairs for Sturm-Liouville System $(rR')' + (\lambda^2 r - v^2/r)R = 0$, $0 < r < r_2$,*
$l_2 R'(r_2) + h_2 R(r_2) = 0$

Condition at $r = r_2$	Eigenvalue Equation	NR_{vn}	$2N^2$
$h_2 l_2 \neq 0$	$l_2\lambda J_v'(\lambda r_2) + h_2 J_v(\lambda r_2) = 0$	$J_v(\lambda_{vn}r)$	$r_2^2\left\{1 - \left(\dfrac{v}{\lambda_{vn}r_2}\right)^2 + \left(\dfrac{h_2}{\lambda_{vn}l_2}\right)^2\right\}[J_v(\lambda_{vn}r_2)]^2$
$h_2 = 0$	$J_v'(\lambda r_2) = 0$	$J_v(\lambda_{vn}r)$	$r_2^2\left\{1 - \left(\dfrac{v}{\lambda_{vn}r_2}\right)^2\right\}[J_v(\lambda_{vn}r_2)]^2$
$l_2 = 0$	$J_v(\lambda r_2) = 0$	$J_v(\lambda_{vn}r)$	$r_2^2[J_v'(\lambda_{vn}r_2)]^2 = r_2^2[J_{v+1}(\lambda_{vn}r_2)]^2$

According to the following theorem, piecewise smooth functions of r can be expanded in Fourier Bessel series of these eigenfunctions.

Theorem 2

If a function $f(r)$ is piecewise smooth on the interval $0 \le r \le r_2$, then for each r in $0 < r < r_2$,

$$\frac{f(r+) + f(r-)}{2} = \sum_{n=1}^{\infty} c_n R_{vn}(r), \tag{61a}$$

where

$$c_n = \int_0^{r_2} r f(r) R_{vn}(r) \, dr. \tag{61b}$$

Example 3:

Expand the function $f(r) = r^2$ in terms of the eigenfunctions of Sturm-Liouville system (45) when $r_2 = 1$, $l_2 = 0$, $h_2 = 1$, and $v = 0$.

Solution:

Orthonormal eigenfunctions of

$$\frac{d}{dr}\left(r\frac{dR}{dr}\right) + \lambda^2 r R = 0, \qquad 0 < r < 1,$$

$$R(1) = 0$$

are

$$R_n(r) = \frac{\sqrt{2}\, J_0(\lambda_n r)}{J_1(\lambda_n)},$$

where eigenvalues λ_n are solutions of $J_0(\lambda) = 0$. The eigenfunction expansion of r^2 is

$$r^2 = \sum_{n=1}^{\infty} c_n R_n(r),$$

where

$$c_n = \int_0^1 r^3 R_n(r) \, dr = \frac{\sqrt{2}}{J_1(\lambda_n)} \int_0^1 r^3 J_0(\lambda_n r) \, dr.$$

To evaluate this integral, we first set $x = \lambda_n r$, in which case

$$c_n = \frac{\sqrt{2}}{J_1(\lambda_n)} \int_0^{\lambda_n} \left(\frac{x}{\lambda_n}\right)^3 J_0(x) \frac{dx}{\lambda_n} = \frac{\sqrt{2}}{\lambda_n^4 J_1(\lambda_n)} \int_0^{\lambda_n} x^3 J_0(x) \, dx.$$

We now use the reduction formula in Exercise 9 of Section 8.3:

$$c_n = \frac{\sqrt{2}}{\lambda_n^4 J_1(\lambda_n)} \left(\{x^3 J_1(x) + 2x^2 J_0(x)\}_0^{\lambda_n} - 4 \int_0^{\lambda_n} x J_0(x) \, dx \right)$$

$$= \frac{\sqrt{2}}{\lambda_n^4 J_1(\lambda_n)} \left(\lambda_n^3 J_1(\lambda_n) - 4 \int_0^{\lambda_n} \frac{d}{dx}[x J_1(x)] \, dx \right) \quad \text{[see identity (39) with } v = 1\text{]}$$

$$= \frac{\sqrt{2}}{\lambda_n^4 J_1(\lambda_n)} (\lambda_n^3 J_1(\lambda_n) - 4\lambda_n J_1(\lambda_n))$$

$$= \frac{\sqrt{2}(\lambda_n^2 - 4)}{\lambda_n^3}.$$

Consequently,

$$r^2 = \sum_{n=1}^{\infty} \frac{\sqrt{2}(\lambda_n^2 - 4)}{\lambda_n^3} \frac{\sqrt{2}J_0(\lambda_n r)}{J_1(\lambda_n)}$$

$$= 2 \sum_{n=1}^{\infty} \frac{\lambda_n^2 - 4}{\lambda_n^3 J_1(\lambda_n)} J_0(\lambda_n r), \qquad 0 < r < 1. \qquad \blacksquare$$

Exercises 8.4

1. Use the following argument to evaluate the normalizing factor N^{-1} in (51b).

   (a) Show that any solution of (44a) also satisfies

   $$\frac{d}{dr}(rR')^2 + (\lambda^2 r^2 - v^2)\frac{d}{dr}R^2 = 0.$$

   (b) Integrate this equation from r_1 to r_2 to obtain

   $$2\lambda^2 \int_{r_1}^{r_2} rR^2 \, dr = \{(rR')^2 + (\lambda^2 r^2 - v^2)R^2\}_{r_1}^{r_2}.$$

   (c) Use boundary conditions (44b, c) to write this expression in the form

   $$2\lambda^2 \int_{r_1}^{r_2} rR^2 \, dr = [r_2 R(r_2)]^2 \left[\lambda^2 - \left(\frac{v}{r_2}\right)^2 + \left(\frac{h_2}{l_2}\right)^2\right]$$

   $$- [r_1 R(r_1)]^2 \left[\lambda^2 - \left(\frac{v}{r_1}\right)^2 + \left(\frac{h_1}{l_1}\right)^2\right].$$

   (d) Substitute $\lambda = \lambda_{vn}$ and $R = R_{vn}$ [from (51a), without the normalizing factor N^{-1}] to obtain an expression for N^{-1}.

2. Expand the function r^v ($v \geq 1$) in terms of the eigenfunctions of Sturm-Liouville system (45) when (a) $l_2 = 0$ and (b) $h_2 = 0$.

3. Expand the function $f(r) = 1$ in terms of the eigenfunctions of Sturm-Liouville system (45) when $v = 0$.

4. Show that eigenpairs for the singular Sturm-Liouville system

   $$\frac{d}{dr}\left(r\frac{dR}{dr}\right) + \left(\lambda^2 r - \frac{v^2}{r}\right)R = 0, \qquad 0 < r < r_2, \qquad v > 0,$$

   $$l_2 R'(r_2) - h_2 R(r_2) = 0,$$

   where $l_2 > 0$ and $h_2 > 0$, are also given in the first line of Table 8.1 (with h_2 replaced by $-h_2$).

5. The singular Sturm-Liouville system

   $$\frac{d}{dr}\left(r^2\frac{dR}{dr}\right) + \lambda^2 r^2 R = 0, \qquad 0 < r < r_2,$$

   $$R(r_2) = 0$$

   arises when separation of variables is applied to heat conduction problems in a sphere, when temperature is a function of only radial distance r and time.

(a) Use a Frobenius series to obtain the general solution

$$R(r) = \frac{1}{r}(A \cos \lambda r + B \sin \lambda r)$$

of the differential equation.

(b) Find eigenvalues and normalized eigenfunctions of the Sturm-Liouville system.

(c) An alternative way to find eigenfunctions of this Sturm-Liouville system is to make a change of dependent variable $Z(r) = \sqrt{\lambda r} R(r)$. Show that this leads to the differential equation

$$\frac{d}{dr}\left(r\frac{dZ}{dr}\right) + \left(\lambda^2 r - \frac{1/4}{r}\right)Z = 0, \qquad 0 < r < r_2,$$

and the solutions $R(r) = (A \cos \lambda r + B \sin \lambda r)/r$.

6. (a) Show that when the boundary condition in Exercise 5 is $R'(r_2) = 0$, eigenvalues are non-negative solutions of

$$\tan \lambda r_2 = \lambda r_2.$$

(b) Find normalized eigenfunctions.

7. (a) Show that when the boundary condition in Exercise 5 is $l_2 R'(r_2) + h_2 R(r_2) = 0$, eigenvalues are positive solutions of

$$\left(1 - \frac{h_2 r_2}{l_2}\right)\tan \lambda r_2 = \lambda r_2.$$

(b) Find normalized eigenfunctions when $h_2 r_2/l_2 > 1$.

8. Use the technique of Exercise 5(c) to find normalized eigenfunctions of the singular Sturm-Liouville system

$$\frac{d}{dr}\left(r^2 \frac{dR}{dr}\right) + (\lambda^2 r^2 - m(m+1))R = 0, \qquad 0 < r < r_2,$$

$$l_2 R'(r_2) + h_2 R(r_2) = 0,$$

where $m \geq 0$ is an integer and $l_2 \geq 0$ and $h_2 \geq 0$. Tabulate the results for the three cases $l_2 = 0$, $h_2 = 0$, and $l_2 h_2 \neq 0$.

8.5 Legendre Functions

Legendre functions arise when separation of variables is applied to (initial) boundary value problems expressed in spherical coordinates. They are solutions of the linear, homogeneous, second-order differential equation

$$(1 - x^2)\frac{d^2 y}{dx^2} - 2x\frac{dy}{dx} + n(n+1)y = 0, \tag{62}$$

called *Legendre's differential equation*. If we assume a power series solution $y(x) = \sum_{k=0}^{\infty} a_k x^k$ ($x = 0$ being an ordinary point of the differential equation), we obtain arbitrary a_0 and a_1 and the recurrence relation

$$a_k = -\frac{(n-k+2)(n+k-1)}{k(k-1)}a_{k-2}, \qquad k \geq 2. \tag{63}$$

Iteration of this result leads to the general solution

$$y(x) = a_0 \left(1 + \sum_{k=1}^{\infty} (-1)^k \frac{(n-2k+2)\cdots(n-2)n(n+1)(n+3)\cdots(n+2k-1)}{(2k)!} x^{2k} \right)$$
$$+ a_1 \left(x + \sum_{k=1}^{\infty} (-1)^k \frac{(n-2k+1)\cdots(n-3)(n-1)(n+2)(n+4)\cdots(n+2k)}{(2k+1)!} x^{2k+1} \right),$$

$$(64)$$

which converges for $|x| < 1$.

When n is a nonnegative integer, one of these series reduces to a polynomial while the other remains an infinite series. In particular, if n is an even integer, all terms in the first series vanish for $2k > n$, and if n is odd, all terms in the second series vanish for $2k + 1 > n$. Thus, in either case, the solution defines a polynomial of degree n. To express these polynomials compactly, we reverse (63) to write

$$a_{k-2} = -\frac{k(k-1)}{(n-k+2)(n+k-1)} a_k$$

and iterate to obtain

$$a_{n-2k} = \frac{(-1)^k n(n-1)(n-2)\cdots(n-2k+1)}{2^k k! (2n-1)(2n-3)\cdots(2n-2k+1)} a_n.$$ $$(65)$$

When we choose $a_n = (2n)!/[2^n(n!)^2]$, (65) becomes

$$a_{n-2k} = \frac{(-1)^k (2n-2k)!}{2^n k! (n-2k)! (n-k)!}, \qquad k = 1, 2, \dots, [n/2], \qquad (66)$$

where $[n/2]$ denotes the integer part of $n/2$. With this choice for a_n, the particular polynomial solution of (62) is called the *Legendre polynomial of degree n*, denoted by

$$P_n(x) = \sum_{k=0}^{[n/2]} \frac{(-1)^k (2n-2k)!}{2^n k! (n-2k)! (n-k)!} x^{n-2k}. \qquad (67)$$

The first five Legendre polynomials are

$$P_0(x) = 1, \qquad P_1(x) = x, \qquad P_2(x) = \frac{3x^2 - 1}{2},$$

$$P_3(x) = \frac{5x^3 - 3x}{2}, \qquad P_4(x) = \frac{35x^4 - 30x^2 + 3}{8}.$$

The remaining solution of (62) for n a nonnegative integer is in the form of an infinite series valid for $|x| < 1$. When n is even, and a_1 is chosen as $(-1)^{n/2} 2^n [(n/2)!]^2/n!$, the series solution is denoted by

$$Q_n(x) = \frac{(-1)^{n/2} 2^n [(n/2)!]^2}{n!}$$
$$\times \left(x + \sum_{k=1}^{\infty} \frac{(-1)^k (n-2k+1)\cdots(n-3)(n-1)(n+2)(n+4)\cdots(n+2k)}{(2k+1)!} x^{2k+1} \right).$$

$$(68a)$$

When n is odd, and a_0 is set equal to $(-1)^{(n+1)/2}2^{n-1}([(n-1)/2]!)^2/n!$, the series solution is

$$Q_n(x) = \frac{(-1)^{(n+1)/2}2^{n-1}([(n-1)/2]!)^2}{n!}$$
$$\times \left(1 + \sum_{k=1}^{\infty} \frac{(-1)^k(n-2k+2)\cdots(n-2)n(n+1)(n+3)\cdots(n+2k-1)}{(2k)!}x^{2k}\right).$$

(68b)

These solutions are called *Legendre functions of the second kind of order n*. Closed-form representations are discussed in Exercise 10; they are unbounded near $x = \pm 1$.

In summary, the general solution of Legendre's differential equation (62) for n a nonnegative integer is

$$y(x) = AP_n(x) + BQ_n(x),$$

(69)

where A and B are arbitrary constants. Legendre polynomials $P_n(x)$ are given by (67), and Legendre functions $Q_n(x)$ of the second kind are defined by (68). Our discussions concentrate on Legendre polynomials.

Generating Function for Legendre Polynomials

When the binomial expansion is applied to the function $(1 - 2xt + t^2)^{-1/2}$,

$$\frac{1}{(1 - 2xt + t^2)^{1/2}} = 1 + \sum_{m=1}^{\infty} \frac{(1/2)(3/2)\cdots(1/2 + m - 1)}{m!}(2xt - t^2)^m,$$

and the binomial theorem is then used on $(2xt - t^2)^m$:

$$\frac{1}{(1 - 2xt + t^2)^{1/2}} = 1 + \sum_{m=1}^{\infty} \frac{(1)(3)(5)\cdots(2m - 1)}{2^m m!} \sum_{k=0}^{m} (-1)^k \binom{m}{k}(2x)^{m-k}t^{m+k}.$$

Terms in t^n occur when $k + m = n$, and since k ranges from 0 to m, it follows that the coefficient of t^n is

$$\sum_{m=[(n+1)/2]}^{n} \frac{(1)(3)(5)\cdots(2m - 1)}{2^m m!}(-1)^{n-m}\binom{m}{n-m}(2x)^{2m-n}.$$

If we set $k = n - m$ in this summation, the coefficient of t^n is

$$\sum_{k=n-[(n+1)/2]}^{0} \frac{(1)(3)(5)\cdots(2n - 2k - 1)}{2^{n-k}(n-k)!}(-1)^k\binom{n-k}{k}(2x)^{n-2k},$$

and this immediately reduces to

$$\sum_{k=0}^{[n/2]} \frac{(-1)^k(2n - 2k)!}{2^n k!(n - 2k)!(n - k)!}x^{n-2k};$$

that is,

$$\frac{1}{(1 - 2xt + t^2)^{1/2}} = \sum_{n=0}^{\infty} \left(\sum_{k=0}^{[n/2]} \frac{(-1)^k(2n - 2k)!}{2^n k!(n - 2k)!(n - k)!}x^{n-2k}\right)t^n.$$

(70)

The coefficient of t^n is $P_n(x)$, and we say that $(1 - 2xt + t^2)^{-1/2}$ is a generating function for $P_n(x)$:

$$\frac{1}{\sqrt{1 - 2xt + t^2}} = \sum_{n=0}^{\infty} P_n(x)t^n. \tag{71}$$

Recurrence Relations

When we differentiate (71) with respect to t,

$$(1 - 2xt + t^2)^{-3/2}(x - t) = \sum_{n=0}^{\infty} nP_n(x)t^{n-1}, \tag{72}$$

from which

$$(x - t) \sum_{n=0}^{\infty} P_n(x)t^n = (1 - 2xt + t^2) \sum_{n=0}^{\infty} nP_n(x)t^{n-1}.$$

Equating coefficients of like powers of t gives the recurrence relation

$$(n + 1)P_{n+1}(x) - (2n + 1)xP_n(x) + nP_{n-1}(x) = 0, \qquad n \geq 1, \tag{73}$$

which permits evaluation of Legendre polynomials of higher orders in terms of those of lower orders. Useful relations among the derivatives of Legendre polynomials also exist. Differentiation of (71) with respect to x gives

$$\frac{t}{(1 - 2xt + t^2)^{3/2}} = \sum_{n=0}^{\infty} P_n'(x)t^n,$$

which, together with (72), implies that

$$t \sum_{n=0}^{\infty} nP_n(x)t^{n-1} = (x - t) \sum_{n=0}^{\infty} P_n'(x)t^n. \tag{74}$$

Equating coefficients yields

$$xP_n'(x) - P_{n-1}'(x) - nP_n(x) = 0, \qquad n \geq 1. \tag{75}$$

Differentiation of (73) gives

$$(n + 1)P_{n+1}'(x) - (2n + 1)P_n(x) - (2n + 1)xP_n'(x) + nP_{n-1}'(x) = 0, \qquad n \geq 1. \tag{76}$$

Elimination of $P_n'(x)$ between (75) and (76) yields

$$P_{n+1}'(x) - P_{n-1}'(x) = (2n + 1)P_n(x), \qquad n \geq 1 \tag{77}$$

and, in addition,

$$P_{n+1}'(x) - xP_n'(x) = (n + 1)P_n(x), \qquad n \geq 0. \tag{78}$$

We now show that $P_n(x)$ is a constant multiple of $d^n[(x^2 - 1)^n]/dx^n$. We first note that

$$\frac{d}{dx}(x^2 - 1)^n = 2nx(x^2 - 1)^{n-1}$$

or
$$(x^2 - 1)\frac{d}{dx}(x^2 - 1)^n = 2nx(x^2 - 1)^n.$$

Differentiation of this equation $n + 1$ times with Leibniz's rule[†] gives

$$\sum_{k=0}^{n+1}\binom{n+1}{k}\frac{d^k}{dx^k}(x^2-1)\frac{d^{n-k+2}}{dx^{n-k+2}}(x^2-1)^n = 2n\sum_{k=0}^{n+1}\binom{n+1}{k}\frac{d^k}{dx^k}x\frac{d^{n-k+1}}{dx^{n-k+1}}(x^2-1)^n,$$

but only the first three terms on the left and the first two terms on the right do not vanish. When these terms are written out and rearranged,

$$(1-x^2)\frac{d^2}{dx^2}\left(\frac{d^n}{dx^n}(x^2-1)^n\right) - 2x\frac{d}{dx}\left(\frac{d^n}{dx^n}(x^2-1)^n\right) + n(n+1)\left(\frac{d^n}{dx^n}(x^2-1)^n\right) = 0.$$

This equation indicates that the function $d^n[(x^2 - 1)^n]/dx^n$ satisfies Legendre's differential equation (62). Since the function is a polynomial in x, it follows that

$$P_n(x) = A\frac{d^n}{dx^n}(x^2 - 1)^n.$$

To obtain the constant A, we equate coefficients of x^n on each side:

$$\frac{(2n)!}{2^n(n!)^2} = A(2n)(2n-1)\cdots(n+1).$$

Thus, $A = 1/(2^n n!)$, and we obtain Rodrigues' formula,

$$\boxed{P_n(x) = \frac{1}{2^n n!}\frac{d^n}{dx^n}(x^2 - 1)^n.} \tag{79}$$

Rodrigues' formula is useful in the evaluation of definite integrals involving Legendre's polynomials. In addition, it quickly yields values for $P_n(\pm 1)$. With $x^2 - 1$ in factored form, Leibniz's rule gives

$$P_n(\pm 1) = \frac{1}{2^n n!}\left(\frac{d^n}{dx^n}(x^2 - 1)^n\right)_{|x=\pm 1}$$

$$= \frac{1}{2^n n!}\left(\sum_{k=0}^{n}\binom{n}{k}\frac{d^k}{dx^k}(x+1)^n\frac{d^{n-k}}{dx^{n-k}}(x-1)^n\right)_{|x=\pm 1}.$$

The only term in this summation that does not involve $x - 1$ occurs when $k = 0$, and therefore

$$P_n(1) = \frac{\binom{n}{0}2^n n!}{2^n n!} = 1. \tag{80a}$$

[†] Leibniz's rule for the nth derivative of a product is

$$\frac{d^n}{dx^n}[f(x)g(x)] = \sum_{r=0}^{n}\binom{n}{r}\left[\frac{d^r}{dx^r}f(x)\right]\left[\frac{d^{n-r}}{dx^{n-r}}g(x)\right].$$

Similarly, because $k = n$ is the only term without a factor $x + 1$,

$$P_n(-1) = \frac{\binom{n}{n} n!(-2)^n}{2^n n!} = (-1)^n. \tag{80b}$$

Associated Legendre Functions

Legendre's associated differential equation is

$$(1 - x^2)\frac{d^2 y}{dx^2} - 2x\frac{dy}{dx} + \left(n(n+1) - \frac{m^2}{1-x^2}\right)y = 0, \tag{81}$$

where m is some given nonnegative integer. When $m = 0$, it reduces to Legendre's differential equation (62). It is straightforward to show (see Exercise 9) that when $y(x)$ is a solution of (62), $(1 - x^2)^{m/2}d^m y/dx^m$ is a solution of (81). This means that a general solution of (81) is

$$y(x) = (1 - x^2)^{m/2}\left(A\frac{d^m P_n(x)}{dx^m} + B\frac{d^m Q_n(x)}{dx^m}\right), \tag{82}$$

where $P_n(x)$ are Legendre polynomials and $Q_n(x)$ are Legendre functions of the second kind. The functions

$$P_{mn}(x) = (1 - x^2)^{m/2}\frac{d^m P_n(x)}{dx^m} \tag{83a}$$

and

$$Q_{mn}(x) = (1 - x^2)^{m/2}\frac{d^m Q_n(x)}{dx^m} \tag{83b}$$

are called *associated Legendre functions of degree n and order m of the first and second kind*. Since $P_n(x)$ is a polynomial of degree n, it follows that $P_{mn}(x)$ is nonvanishing only when $n \geq m$.

Exercises 8.5

1. Calculate the first seven Legendre polynomials, using (a) equation (79); (b) equation (67).
2. Show that Legendre polynomials $P_n(x)$ are even when n is even and odd when n is odd.
3. Use $P_0(x) = 1$, $P_1(x) = x$, and recurrence relation (73) to obtain $P_2(x)$, $P_3(x)$, $P_4(x)$, $P_5(x)$, and $P_6(x)$.
4. Prove the following:

(a) $P_{2n+1}(0) = 0$

(b) $P_{2n}(0) = \dfrac{(-1)^n(2n)!}{2^{2n}(n!)^2}$

(c) $P'_{2n}(0) = 0$

(d) $P'_{2n+1}(0) = \dfrac{(-1)^n(2n+1)!}{2^{2n}(n!)^2}$

(e) $P'_n(1) = \dfrac{n(n+1)}{2}$

(f) $P'_n(-1) = \dfrac{(-1)^{n-1}n(n+1)}{2}$

5. Verify the following identities for Legendre's polynomials:

   (a) $nP_{n-1}(x) - P'_n(x) + xP'_{n-1}(x) = 0, \quad n > 0$

   Hint: Show that the generating function for $P_n(x)$ satisfies

   $$t\frac{\partial}{\partial t}\left(\frac{t}{\sqrt{1-2xt+t^2}}\right) + (tx-1)\frac{\partial}{\partial x}\left(\frac{1}{\sqrt{1-2xt+t^2}}\right) = 0.$$

   (b) $(1-x^2)P'_n(x) = nP_{n-1}(x) - nxP_n(x), \quad n > 0$

   (c) $nP_n(x) = nxP_{n-1}(x) + (x^2-1)P'_{n-1}(x), \quad n > 0$

6. Verify that when $f(x)$ has continuous derivatives of orders up to and including n,

   $$\int_{-1}^{1} f(x)P_n(x)\,dx = \frac{(-1)^n}{2^n n!}\int_{-1}^{1} f^{(n)}(x)(x^2-1)^n\,dx.$$

7. Verify the following results:

   (a) $\displaystyle\int_{-1}^{1} P_n(x)\,dx = \begin{cases} 2 & n = 0 \\ 0 & n \neq 0 \end{cases}$

   (b) $\displaystyle\int_{-1}^{1} P_m(x)P_n(x)\,dx = \begin{cases} 0 & n \neq m \\ \dfrac{2}{2n+1} & n = m \end{cases}$

   (*Hint:* Use Exercise 6.)

   (c) $\displaystyle\int_{-1}^{1} xP_n(x)P'_n(x)\,dx = \frac{2n}{2n+1}, \quad n \geq 0$

   (d) $\displaystyle\int_{-1}^{1} xP_n(x)P_{n-1}(x)\,dx = \frac{2n}{4n^2-1}, \quad n > 0$

   (e) $\displaystyle\int_{-1}^{1} P_n(x)P'_{n+1}(x)\,dx = 2, \quad n > 0$

   (f) $\displaystyle\int_{-1}^{1} x^m P_n(x)\,dx = \begin{cases} 0 & m < n \\[2mm] \dfrac{2^{n+1}(n!)^2}{(2n+1)!} & m = n \\[3mm] 0 & m-n > 0 \text{ is odd} \\[3mm] \dfrac{2^{n+1}m!\left(\dfrac{m+n}{2}\right)!}{(m+n+1)!\left(\dfrac{m-n}{2}\right)!} & m-n > 0 \text{ is even} \end{cases}$

   (*Hint:* Use Exercise 6.)

8. Verify that

   (a) $\displaystyle\int_{0}^{1} P_n(x)\,dx = \begin{cases} 1 & n = 0 \\[2mm] 0 & n > 0 \text{ even} \\[3mm] \dfrac{(-1)^{(n-1)/2}(n-1)!}{2^n\left(\dfrac{n+1}{2}\right)!\left(\dfrac{n-1}{2}\right)!} & n \text{ odd} \end{cases}$

(b) $\displaystyle\int_0^1 xP_n(x)\,dx = \begin{cases} 0 & n \geq 3 \text{ odd} \\ 1/2 & n = 0 \\ 1/3 & n = 1 \\ \dfrac{(-1)^{(n-2)/2}(n-2)!}{2^n\left(\dfrac{n-2}{2}\right)!\left(\dfrac{n+2}{2}\right)!} & n \geq 2 \text{ even} \end{cases}$

9. Verify that when $y(x)$ is a solution of Legendre's differential equation (62), $(1 - x^2)^{m/2}d^m y/dx^m$ is a solution of Legendre's associated equation (81).

10. **(a)** Use series (68a, b) to show that

$$Q_0(x) = \text{Tanh}^{-1} x = \frac{1}{2}\ln\left(\frac{1+x}{1-x}\right) \quad \text{and} \quad Q_1(x) = xQ_0(x) - 1.$$

(b) Assuming that the $Q_n(x)$ also satisfy recurrence relation (73), express $Q_2(x)$, $Q_3(x)$, and $Q_4(x)$ in terms of $Q_0(x)$.

(c) Express $Q_n(x)$ ($n = 2, 3, 4$) in terms of $Q_0(x)$ and $P_n(x)$.

11. Prove the following recurrence relations for $P_{mn}(x)$:

(a) $P_{m+1,n+1}(x) - P_{m+1,n-1}(x) = (2n + 1)\sqrt{1 - x^2}\,P_{mn}(x)$

(b) $xP_{m+1,n}(x) - P_{m+1,n-1}(x) = (n - m)\sqrt{1 - x^2}\,P_{mn}(x)$

(c) $(n - m + 1)P_{m,n+1}(x) - (2n + 1)xP_{mn}(x) + (n + m)P_{m,n-1}(x) = 0$

8.6 Sturm-Liouville Systems and Legendre's Differential Equation

When separation of variables is applied to (initial) boundary value problems expressed in spherical coordinates, the following singular Sturm-Liouville system often results:

$$\frac{d}{d\phi}\left(\sin\phi\,\frac{d\Phi}{d\phi}\right) + \left(\lambda\sin\phi - \frac{m^2}{\sin\phi}\right)\Phi = 0, \qquad 0 < \phi < \pi, \tag{84}$$

where m is some given nonnegative integer. The system is singular because there are no boundary conditions and also because $q(\phi) = -m^2/\sin\phi$ is not continuous at $\phi = 0$ and $\phi = \pi$. Because the coefficient $\sin\phi$ of $d\Phi/d\phi$ vanishes at $\phi = 0$ and $\phi = \pi$, the corollary to Theorem 1 of Section 4.1 indicates that boundary conditions at $\phi = 0$ and $\phi = \pi$ are unnecessary for that theorem. Examination of the proof of the theorem also indicates that continuity of $q(\phi)$ at $\phi = 0$ and $\phi = \pi$ is not necessary. Consequently, eigenvalues of this singular system are real, and corresponding eigenfunctions are orthogonal.

If we make the change of independent variable $\mu = \cos\phi$, then $d/d\mu = -(\sin\phi)^{-1}d/d\phi$ and (84) is replaced by

$$\frac{d}{d\mu}\left((1 - \mu^2)\frac{d\Phi}{d\mu}\right) + \left(\lambda - \frac{m^2}{1 - \mu^2}\right)\Phi = 0$$

or $\qquad (1 - \mu^2)\dfrac{d^2\Phi}{d\mu^2} - 2\mu\dfrac{d\Phi}{d\mu} + \left(\lambda - \dfrac{m^2}{1 - \mu^2}\right)\Phi = 0, \qquad -1 < \mu < 1, \tag{85}$

Legendre's associated differential equation. When λ is set equal to $n(n + 1)$, where $n \geq m$ is an integer, this equation has general solution

$$\Phi = AP_{mn}(\mu) + BQ_{mn}(\mu), \tag{86}$$

where A and B are arbitrary constants and P_{mn} and Q_{mn} are associated Legendre functions of degree n and order m of the first and second kind. Since $Q_{mn}(\mu)$ is unbounded near $\mu = \pm 1$, bounded solutions are

$$\Phi = AP_{mn}(\mu). \tag{87}$$

In other words, $\lambda_{mn} = n(n + 1)$, where $n \geq m$, are eigenvalues of this singular Sturm-Liouville system, with corresponding orthonormal eigenfunctions

$$\Phi_{mn}(\phi) = \Phi(\lambda_{mn}, \phi) = \frac{1}{N} P_{mn}(\cos \phi), \tag{88a}$$

where
$$N^2 = \int_0^\pi \sin \phi \, [P_{mn}(\cos \phi)]^2 \, d\phi = \int_{-1}^1 [P_{mn}(\mu)]^2 \, d\mu. \tag{88b}$$

To evaluate N, we proceed as follows. Since

$$P_{mn}(\mu) = (1 - \mu^2)^{m/2} \frac{d^m}{d\mu^m} P_n(\mu),$$

where $P_n(\mu)$ is the Legendre polynomial of degree n, differentiation with respect to μ yields

$$\frac{d}{d\mu} P_{mn}(\mu) = -\mu m(1 - \mu^2)^{m/2 - 1} \frac{d^m}{d\mu^m} P_n(\mu) + (1 - \mu^2)^{m/2} \frac{d^{m+1}}{d\mu^{m+1}} P_n(\mu).$$

Multiplication of this result by $(1 - \mu^2)^{1/2}$ gives

$$(1 - \mu^2)^{1/2} \frac{d}{d\mu} P_{mn}(\mu) = \frac{-\mu m(1 - \mu^2)^{m/2}}{(1 - \mu^2)^{1/2}} \frac{d^m}{d\mu^m} P_n(\mu) + (1 - \mu^2)^{(m+1)/2} \frac{d^{m+1}}{d\mu^{m+1}} P_n(\mu)$$

$$= \frac{-\mu m}{(1 - \mu^2)^{1/2}} P_{mn}(\mu) + P_{m+1, n}(\mu).$$

When this equation is solved for $P_{m+1, n}(\mu)$, squared, and integrated between the limits $\mu = \pm 1$,

$$\int_{-1}^1 (P_{m+1, n})^2 \, d\mu = \int_{-1}^1 (1 - \mu^2) \left(\frac{d}{d\mu} P_{mn} \right)^2 d\mu + 2m \int_{-1}^1 \mu P_{mn} \frac{d}{d\mu} P_{mn} \, d\mu + m^2 \int_{-1}^1 \frac{\mu^2}{1 - \mu^2} (P_{mn})^2 \, d\mu.$$

Integration by parts on the first two integrals on the right gives

$$\int_{-1}^1 (P_{m+1, n})^2 \, d\mu = \left\{ (1 - \mu^2) \frac{dP_{mn}}{d\mu} P_{mn} \right\}_{-1}^1 - \int_{-1}^1 P_{mn} \frac{d}{d\mu} \left((1 - \mu^2) \frac{dP_{mn}}{d\mu} \right) d\mu$$

$$+ 2m \left\{ \frac{\mu}{2} (P_{mn})^2 \right\}_{-1}^1 - 2m \int_{-1}^1 \frac{1}{2} (P_{mn})^2 \, d\mu + m^2 \int_{-1}^1 \frac{\mu^2}{1 - \mu^2} (P_{mn})^2 \, d\mu$$

$$= \int_{-1}^1 P_{mn} \left[-\frac{d}{d\mu} \left((1 - \mu^2) \frac{dP_{mn}}{d\mu} \right) - mP_{mn} + \frac{m^2 \mu^2}{1 - \mu^2} P_{mn} \right] d\mu,$$

since $P_{mn}(\pm 1) = 0$ for $m > 0$; $P_{0n}(1) = P_n(1) = 1$; and $P_{0n}(-1) = P_n(-1) = (-1)^n$. Now, using Legendre's associated differential equation (81), we obtain

$$\int_{-1}^{1} (P_{m+1,n})^2 \, d\mu = \int_{-1}^{1} P_{mn} \left[\left(\frac{-m^2}{1-\mu^2} + n(n+1) \right) P_{mn} - m P_{mn} \right.$$

$$\left. + \left(\frac{m^2}{1-\mu^2} - m^2 \right) P_{mn} \right] d\mu$$

$$= \int_{-1}^{1} (P_{mn})^2 \left(n(n+1) - m - m^2 \right) d\mu$$

or

$$\int_{-1}^{1} (P_{mn})^2 \, d\mu = \frac{1}{(n-m)(n+m+1)} \int_{-1}^{1} (P_{m+1,n})^2 \, d\mu.$$

Iteration of this result on m from m to n gives

$$\int_{-1}^{1} (P_{mn})^2 \, d\mu = \frac{(n+m)!}{(n-m)!(2n)!} \int_{-1}^{1} (P_{nn})^2 \, d\mu. \tag{89}$$

Now,

$$P_{nn} = (1-\mu^2)^{n/2} \frac{d^n}{d\mu^n} P_n = (1-\mu^2)^{n/2} \frac{d^n}{d\mu^n} \left(\frac{1}{2^n n!} \frac{d^n}{d\mu^n} (\mu^2 - 1)^n \right)$$

$$= \frac{(1-\mu^2)^{n/2}}{2^n n!} \frac{d^{2n}}{d\mu^{2n}} (\mu^2 - 1)^n = \frac{(2n)!}{2^n n!} (1-\mu^2)^{n/2},$$

and substitution of this into (89) yields

$$\int_{-1}^{1} (P_{mn})^2 \, d\mu = \frac{(n+m)!}{(n-m)!(2n)!} \frac{[(2n)!]^2}{2^{2n}(n!)^2} \int_{-1}^{1} (1-\mu^2)^n \, d\mu.$$

In elementary calculus [see also Exercise 7(a) in Section 8.5], it is shown that

$$\int_{-1}^{1} (1-\mu^2)^n \, d\mu = \frac{2^{2n+1}(n!)^2}{(2n+1)!},$$

and therefore

$$N^2 = \int_{-1}^{1} [P_{mn}(\mu)]^2 \, d\mu = \frac{(n+m)!}{(n-m)!(2n)!} \frac{[(2n)!]^2}{2^{2n}(n!)^2} \frac{2^{2n+1}(n!)^2}{(2n+1)!}$$

$$= \frac{(n+m)!}{(n-m)!} \frac{2}{2n+1}. \tag{90}$$

Summarizing our results, orthonormal eigenfunctions of (84) are

$$\Phi_{mn}(\phi) = \sqrt{\frac{(2n+1)(n-m)!}{2(n+m)!}} \, P_{mn}(\cos \phi), \tag{91}$$

corresponding to eigenvalues $\lambda_{mn} = n(n+1)$, where n is an integer greater than or equal to m.

Because the Sturm-Liouville system is singular, we cannot quote the results of Theorem 2 in Section 4.2. We have already shown that there is an infinite number of eigenvalues, all of which are positive, except when $m = 0$, in which case $\lambda = 0$ is also an eigenvalue. According to the following theorem, piecewise smooth functions can be expanded in terms of these eigenfunctions.

Theorem 3

If a function $f(\phi)$ is piecewise smooth on the interval $0 \le \phi \le \pi$, then for each ϕ in $0 < \phi < \pi$,

$$\frac{f(\phi+) + f(\phi-)}{2} = \sum_{n=m}^{\infty} c_n \Phi_{mn}(\phi), \tag{92a}$$

where

$$c_n = \int_0^{\pi} \sin \phi \, f(\phi) \Phi_{mn}(\phi) \, d\phi. \tag{92b}$$

Example 4:   Expand the function

$$f(\phi) = \begin{cases} 1 & 0 \le \phi < \pi/2 \\ 0 & \phi = \pi/2 \\ -1 & \pi/2 < \phi \le \pi \end{cases}$$

in terms of the eigenfunctions of Sturm-Liouville system (84) when $m = 0$.

Solution: Orthonormal eigenfunctions of

$$\frac{d}{d\phi}\left(\sin \phi \frac{d\Phi}{d\phi} \right) + \lambda \sin \phi \, \Phi = 0, \qquad 0 < \phi < \pi,$$

are Legendre polynomials

$$\Phi_{0n}(\phi) = \sqrt{\frac{2n+1}{2}} \, P_n(\cos \phi), \qquad n \ge 0.$$

The eigenfunction expansion of $f(\phi)$ is

$$f(\phi) = \sum_{n=0}^{\infty} c_n \Phi_{0n}(\phi),$$

where

$$c_n = \int_0^{\pi} \sin \phi \, f(\phi) \Phi_{0n}(\phi) \, d\phi.$$

When we set $\mu = \cos \phi$,

$$\sqrt{\frac{2}{2n+1}} c_n = \int_1^{-1} f[\phi(\mu)] P_n(\mu)(-d\mu)$$

$$= -\int_{-1}^{0} P_n(\mu) \, d\mu + \int_0^1 P_n(\mu) \, d\mu$$

$$= \begin{cases} 0 & n \text{ even} \\ 2\displaystyle\int_0^1 P_n(\mu) \, d\mu & n \text{ odd} \end{cases}$$

$$= \begin{cases} 0 & n \text{ even} \\ \dfrac{(-1)^{(n-1)/2}(n-1)!}{2^{n-1}\left(\dfrac{n+1}{2}\right)!\left(\dfrac{n-1}{2}\right)!} & n \text{ odd} \end{cases}$$

(see Exercise 8 in Section 8.5). Consequently,

$$c_{2n-1} = \sqrt{\frac{4n-1}{2}} \frac{(-1)^{n-1}(2n-2)!}{2^{2n-2}n!(n-1)!}$$

and

$$f(\phi) = \sum_{n=1}^{\infty} \sqrt{\frac{4n-1}{2}} \frac{(-1)^{n-1}(2n-2)!}{2^{2n-2}n!(n-1)!} \sqrt{\frac{4n-1}{2}} P_{2n-1}(\cos\phi)$$

$$= \sum_{n=1}^{\infty} \frac{(-1)^{n-1}(2n-2)!(4n-1)}{2^{2n-1}n!(n-1)!} P_{2n-1}(\cos\phi). \qquad \blacksquare$$

Exercises 8.6

In Exercises 1–4, expand the function in terms of the orthonormal eigenfunctions of Sturm-Liouville system (84) when m = 0.

1. $f(\phi) = \begin{cases} 1 & 0 \le \phi < \pi/2 \\ 0 & \pi/2 < \phi < \pi \end{cases}$

2. $f(\phi) = \cos^4 \phi$

3. $f(\phi) = \begin{cases} \cos\phi & 0 \le \phi \le \pi/2 \\ 0 & \pi/2 < \phi \le \pi \end{cases}$

4. $f(\phi) = \begin{cases} \cos\phi & 0 \le \phi \le \pi/2 \\ -\cos\phi & \pi/2 < \phi \le \pi \end{cases}$

5. Find eigenvalues and orthonormal eigenfunctions of the Sturm-Liouville system

$$\frac{d}{d\phi}\left(\sin\phi \frac{d\Phi}{d\phi}\right) + \lambda \sin\phi\, \Phi = 0, \qquad 0 < \phi < \pi/2,$$

$$\Phi\left(\frac{\pi}{2}\right) = 0.$$

6. Repeat Exercise 5 if the boundary condition is $\Phi'(\pi/2) = 0$.

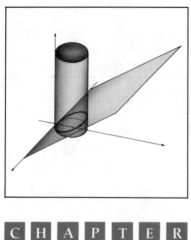

Problems in Polar, Cylindrical, and Spherical Coordinates

9.1 Homogeneous Problems in Polar, Cylindrical, and Spherical Coordinates

In Section 5.3, separation of variables was used to solve homogeneous boundary value problems expressed in polar coordinates. With the results of Chapter 8, we are in a position to tackle boundary value problems in cylindrical and spherical coordinates and initial boundary value problems in all three coordinate systems. Homogeneous problems are discussed in this section; nonhomogeneous problems are discussed in Section 9.2.

We begin with the following heat conduction problem.

Example 1: An infinitely long cylinder of radius r_2 is initially at temperature $f(r) = r_2^2 - r^2$, and for time $t > 0$, the boundary $r = r_2$ is insulated. Find the temperature in the cylinder for $t > 0$.

320

Solution: The initial boundary value problem for $U(r, t)$ is

$$\frac{\partial U}{\partial t} = k\left(\frac{\partial^2 U}{\partial r^2} + \frac{1}{r}\frac{\partial U}{\partial r}\right), \qquad 0 < r < r_2, \qquad t > 0, \tag{1a}$$

$$\frac{\partial U(r_2, t)}{\partial r} = 0, \qquad t > 0, \tag{1b}$$

$$U(r, 0) = r_2^2 - r^2, \qquad 0 < r < r_2. \tag{1c}$$

When a function $U(r, t) = R(r)T(t)$ with variables separated is substituted into PDE (1a) and the equation is divided by kRT, there results

$$\frac{T'}{kT} = \frac{R''}{R} + \frac{R'}{rR} = \alpha = \text{constant independent of } r \text{ and } t.$$

This equation and boundary condition (1b) yield the Sturm-Liouville system

$$(rR')' - \alpha rR = 0, \qquad 0 < r < r_2, \tag{2a}$$

$$R'(r_2) = 0. \tag{2b}$$

This singular system was discussed in Section 8.4 (see Table 8.1 with $v = 0$). If we set $\alpha = -\lambda^2$, eigenvalues are defined by the equation $J_1(\lambda r_2) = 0$, and normalized eigenfunctions are

$$R_n(r) = \frac{\sqrt{2}\,J_0(\lambda_n r)}{r_2 J_0(\lambda_n r_2)}, \qquad n \geq 0. \tag{3}$$

(For simplicity of notation, we have dropped the zero subscript on R_{0n} and λ_{0n}.)
The differential equation

$$T' + k\lambda_n^2 T = 0 \tag{4}$$

has general solution

$$T(t) = Ce^{-k\lambda_n^2 t}. \tag{5}$$

In order to satisfy initial condition (1c), we superpose separated functions and take

$$U(r, t) = \sum_{n=0}^{\infty} C_n e^{-k\lambda_n^2 t} R_n(r), \tag{6}$$

where the C_n are constants. Condition (1c) requires these constants to satisfy

$$r_2^2 - r^2 = \sum_{n=0}^{\infty} C_n R_n(r), \qquad 0 < r < r_2. \tag{7}$$

Thus, the C_n are coefficients in the Fourier Bessel series of $r_2^2 - r^2$, and, according to equation (61b) in Chapter 8,

$$C_n = \int_0^{r_2} r(r_2^2 - r^2) R_n(r)\, dr = \frac{\sqrt{2}}{r_2 J_0(\lambda_n r_2)} \int_0^{r_2} r(r_2^2 - r^2) J_0(\lambda_n r)\, dr.$$

To evaluate this integral when $n > 0$, we set $u = \lambda_n r$, in which case

$$C_n = \frac{\sqrt{2}}{r_2 J_0(\lambda_n r_2)} \int_0^{\lambda_n r_2} \left(\frac{r_2^2 u}{\lambda_n} - \frac{u^3}{\lambda_n^3} \right) J_0(u) \frac{du}{\lambda_n}$$

$$= \frac{\sqrt{2}}{\lambda_n^4 r_2 J_0(\lambda_n r_2)} \int_0^{\lambda_n r_2} (r_2^2 \lambda_n^2 u - u^3) J_0(u) \, du.$$

For the term involving u^3, we use the reduction formula in Exercise 9 of Section 8.3:

$$C_n = \frac{\sqrt{2}}{\lambda_n^4 r_2 J_0(\lambda_n r_2)} \left(r_2^2 \lambda_n^2 \int_0^{\lambda_n r_2} u J_0(u) \, du - \{u^3 J_1(u)\}_0^{\lambda_n r_2} \right.$$

$$\left. - \{2u^2 J_0(u)\}_0^{\lambda_n r_2} + 4 \int_0^{\lambda_n r_2} u J_0(u) \, du \right).$$

If we recall the eigenvalue equation $J_1(\lambda r_2) = 0$, and equation (39) in Section 8.3 with $\nu = 1$, we may write

$$C_n = \frac{\sqrt{2}}{\lambda_n^4 r_2 J_0(\lambda_n r_2)} \left(-2\lambda_n^2 r_2^2 J_0(\lambda_n r_2) + (r_2^2 \lambda_n^2 + 4) \int_0^{\lambda_n r_2} \frac{d}{du} [u J_1(u)] \, du \right)$$

$$= \frac{\sqrt{2}}{\lambda_n^4 r_2 J_0(\lambda_n r_2)} \left(-2\lambda_n^2 r_2^2 J_0(\lambda_n r_2) + (r_2^2 \lambda_n^2 + 4) \{u J_1(u)\}_0^{\lambda_n r_2} \right)$$

$$= \frac{-2\sqrt{2} r_2}{\lambda_n^2}.$$

When $n = 0$, $R_0(r) = \sqrt{2}/r_2$, and

$$C_0 = \int_0^{r_2} r(r_2^2 - r^2) R_0(r) \, dr = \frac{\sqrt{2}}{r_2} \left(\frac{r_2^2 r^2}{2} - \frac{r^4}{4} \right)_0^{r_2} = \frac{\sqrt{2} r_2^3}{4}.$$

The solution of problem (1) is therefore

$$U(r, t) = \frac{\sqrt{2} r_2^3}{4} \left(\frac{\sqrt{2}}{r_2} \right) + \sum_{n=1}^{\infty} \frac{-2\sqrt{2} r_2}{\lambda_n^2} e^{-k\lambda_n^2 t} \frac{\sqrt{2} J_0(\lambda_n r)}{r_2 J_0(\lambda_n r_2)}$$

$$= \frac{r_2^2}{2} - 4 \sum_{n=1}^{\infty} \frac{e^{-k\lambda_n^2 t}}{\lambda_n^2} \frac{J_0(\lambda_n r)}{J_0(\lambda_n r_2)}. \tag{8}$$

Notice that for large t, the limit of this solution is $r_2^2/2$, and this is the average value of $r_2^2 - r^2$ over the circle $r \leq r_2$. ∎

In the following heat conduction problem, we add angular dependence to the temperature function.

Example 2: An infinitely long rod with semicircular cross section is initially ($t = 0$) at a constant nonzero temperature throughout. For $t > 0$, its flat side is held at temperature $0°C$ while its round side is insulated. Find temperature in the rod for $t > 0$.

Solution: Temperature in that half of the rod for which $x < 0$ in Figure 9.1 is identical to that in the half for which $x \geq 0$; no heat crosses the $x = 0$ plane. As a result, the temperature function $U(r, \theta, t)$ (and it is independent of z) must satisfy the initial boundary value problem

$$\frac{\partial U}{\partial t} = k\left(\frac{\partial^2 U}{\partial r^2} + \frac{1}{r}\frac{\partial U}{\partial r} + \frac{1}{r^2}\frac{\partial^2 U}{\partial \theta^2}\right), \quad 0 < r < r_2, \quad 0 < \theta < \frac{\pi}{2}, \quad t > 0, \tag{9a}$$

$$U(r,0,t) = 0, \qquad 0 < r < r_2, \qquad t > 0, \tag{9b}$$

$$U_\theta\left(r,\frac{\pi}{2},t\right) = 0, \qquad 0 < r < r_2, \qquad t > 0, \tag{9c}$$

$$U_r(r_2,\theta,t) = 0, \qquad 0 < \theta < \frac{\pi}{2}, \qquad t > 0, \tag{9d}$$

$$U(r,\theta,0) = U_0, \qquad 0 < r < r_2, \qquad 0 < \theta < \frac{\pi}{2}. \tag{9e}$$

[In Exercise 4, the problem is solved for $0 < \theta < \pi$ with the condition $U(r,\pi,t) = 0$ in place of (9c).]

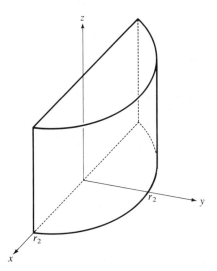

Figure 9.1

When a function with variables separated, $U(r,\theta,t) = R(r)H(\theta)T(t)$, is substituted into PDE (9a),

$$RHT' = k(R''HT + r^{-1}R'HT + r^{-2}RH''T)$$

or $\qquad -\dfrac{H''}{H} = \dfrac{r^2R''}{R} + \dfrac{rR'}{R} - \dfrac{r^2T'}{kT} = \alpha = $ constant independent of r, θ, and t.

When boundary conditions (9b, c) are imposed on the separated function, a Sturm-Liouville system in $H(\theta)$ results:

$$H'' + \alpha H = 0, \qquad 0 < \theta < \frac{\pi}{2}, \tag{10a}$$

$$H(0) = 0 = H'\left(\frac{\pi}{2}\right). \tag{10b}$$

This system was discussed in Section 4.2. If we set $\alpha = v^2$, then, according to Table 4.1, eigenvalues are $v_m^2 = (2m - 1)^2$ $(m = 1, 2, \ldots)$, with orthonormal eigenfunctions

$$H_m(\theta) = \frac{2}{\sqrt{\pi}} \sin(2m - 1)\theta. \tag{11}$$

Continued separation of the equation in $R(r)$ and $T(t)$ gives

$$\frac{R'' + r^{-1}R'}{R} - \frac{v_m^2}{r^2} = \frac{T'}{kT} = \beta = \text{constant independent of } r \text{ and } t.$$

Boundary condition (9d) leads to the Sturm-Liouville system

$$(rR')' + \left(-\beta r - \frac{(2m - 1)^2}{r}\right)R = 0, \qquad 0 < r < r_2, \tag{12a}$$

$$R'(r_2) = 0. \tag{12b}$$

This is Sturm-Liouville system (45) of Section 8.4. If we set $\beta = -\lambda^2$, eigenvalues are defined by the equation

$$J'_{2m-1}(\lambda r_2) = 0 \tag{13}$$

with corresponding eigenfunctions

$$R_{mn}(r) = \frac{1}{N} J_{2m-1}(\lambda_{mn} r), \tag{14a}$$

where

$$2N^2 = r_2^2 \left[1 - \left(\frac{2m - 1}{\lambda_{mn} r_2}\right)^2\right] [J_{2m-1}(\lambda_{mn} r_2)]^2. \tag{14b}$$

The differential equation

$$T' = -k\lambda_{mn}^2 T \tag{15}$$

has general solution

$$T(t) = Ce^{-k\lambda_{mn}^2 t}. \tag{16}$$

To satisfy initial condition (9e), we superpose separated functions and take

$$U(r, \theta, t) = \sum_{m=1}^{\infty} \sum_{n=1}^{\infty} C_{mn} e^{-k\lambda_{mn}^2 t} R_{mn}(r) H_m(\theta), \tag{17}$$

where c_{mn} are constants. Initial condition (9e) requires these constants to satisfy

$$U_0 = \sum_{m=1}^{\infty} \sum_{n=1}^{\infty} C_{mn} R_{mn}(r) H_m(\theta), \qquad 0 < r < r_2, \qquad 0 < \theta < \frac{\pi}{2}. \tag{18}$$

If we multiply this equation by $H_i(\theta)$ and integrate with respect to θ from $\theta = 0$ to $\theta = \pi/2$, orthogonality of the eigenfunctions in θ gives

$$\sum_{n=1}^{\infty} C_{in} R_{in}(r) = \int_0^{\pi/2} U_0 H_i(\theta)\, d\theta = U_0 \int_0^{\pi/2} \frac{2}{\sqrt{\pi}} \sin(2i - 1)\theta\, d\theta$$

$$= \frac{2U_0}{\sqrt{\pi}} \left\{\frac{-1}{2i - 1} \cos(2i - 1)\theta\right\}_0^{\pi/2} = \frac{2U_0}{(2i - 1)\sqrt{\pi}}.$$

But this equation implies that the C_{in} are Fourier Bessel coefficients for the function $2U_0/[(2i-1)\sqrt{\pi}]$, that is,

$$C_{in} = \int_0^{r_2} \frac{2U_0}{(2i-1)\sqrt{\pi}} rR_{in}(r)\,dr.$$

Thus, the solution of (9) for $0 \le \theta \le \pi/2$ is (17), where

$$C_{mn} = \frac{2U_0}{(2m-1)\sqrt{\pi}} \int_0^{r_2} rR_{mn}(r)\,dr. \qquad (19)$$

For an angle θ between $\pi/2$ and π, we should evaluate $U(r, \pi - \theta, t)$. Since

$$H_m(\pi-\theta) = \frac{2}{\sqrt{\pi}}\sin(2m-1)(\pi-\theta) = \frac{2}{\sqrt{\pi}}\sin(2m-1)\theta,$$

it follows that $U(r, \pi-\theta, t) = U(r, \theta, t)$. Hence, solution (17) is valid for $0 \le \theta \le \pi$. ■

Our next example is a vibration problem.

Example 3:   Solve the initial boundary value problem

$$\frac{\partial^2 z}{\partial t^2} = c^2\left(\frac{\partial^2 z}{\partial r^2} + \frac{1}{r}\frac{\partial z}{\partial r} + \frac{1}{r^2}\frac{\partial^2 z}{\partial \theta^2}\right), \quad 0 < r < r_2, \quad -\pi < \theta \le \pi, \quad t > 0, \qquad (20a)$$

$$z(r_2, \theta, t) = 0, \qquad -\pi < \theta \le \pi, \qquad t > 0, \qquad (20b)$$

$$z(r, \theta, 0) = f(r, \theta), \qquad 0 < r < r_2, \qquad -\pi < \theta \le \pi, \qquad (20c)$$

$$z_t(r, \theta, 0) = 0, \qquad 0 < r < r_2, \qquad -\pi < \theta \le \pi. \qquad (20d)$$

Physically described is a membrane stretched over the circle $r \le r_2$ that has an initial displacement $f(r, \theta)$ and zero initial velocity. Boundary condition (20b) states that the edge of the membrane is fixed on the xy-plane.

Solution: When a function $z(r, \theta, t)$, separated in the form $z(r, \theta, t) = R(r)H(\theta)T(t)$, is substituted into PDE (20a),

$$RHT'' = c^2(R''HT + r^{-1}R'HT + r^{-2}RH''T)$$

or $-\dfrac{H''}{H} = r^2\left(\dfrac{R'' + r^{-1}R'}{R} - \dfrac{T''}{c^2T}\right) = \alpha = \text{constant independent of } r, \theta, \text{ and } t.$

Since the solution and its first derivative with respect to θ must be 2π-periodic in θ, it follows that $H(\theta)$ must satisfy the periodic Sturm-Liouville system

$$H'' + \alpha H = 0, \qquad -\pi < \theta \le \pi, \qquad (21a)$$

$$H(-\pi) = H(\pi), \qquad (21b)$$

$$H'(-\pi) = H'(\pi). \qquad (21c)$$

This system was discussed in Chapter 4 [Example 2 and equation (21)]. The eigenvalues are $\alpha = m^2$, m a nonnegative integer, with orthonormal eigenfunctions

$$\frac{1}{\sqrt{2\pi}}, \qquad \frac{1}{\sqrt{\pi}}\sin m\theta, \qquad \frac{1}{\sqrt{\pi}}\cos m\theta. \qquad (22)$$

Continued separation of the equation in $R(r)$ and $T(t)$ gives

$$\frac{R'' + r^{-1}R'}{R} - \frac{m^2}{r^2} = \frac{T''}{c^2 T} = \beta = \text{constant independent of } r \text{ and } t.$$

When boundary condition (20b) is imposed on the separated function, a Sturm-Liouville system in $R(r)$ results:

$$(rR')' + \left(-\beta r - \frac{m^2}{r}\right)R = 0, \qquad 0 < r < r_2, \tag{23a}$$

$$R(r_2) = 0. \tag{23b}$$

This is, once again, singular system (45) in Section 8.4. If we set $\beta = -\lambda^2$, eigenvalues λ_{mn} are defined by

$$J_m(\lambda r_2) = 0, \tag{24}$$

with corresponding orthonormal eigenfunctions

$$R_{mn}(r) = \frac{\sqrt{2}\, J_m(\lambda_{mn}r)}{r_2 J_{m+1}(\lambda_{mn}r_2)} \tag{25}$$

(see Table 8.1).

The differential equation

$$T'' + (c\lambda_{mn})^2 T = 0 \tag{26}$$

has general solution

$$T(t) = d\cos c\lambda_{mn}t + b\sin c\lambda_{mn}t, \tag{27}$$

where d and b are constants. Initial condition (20d) implies that $b = 0$, and hence

$$T(t) = d\cos c\lambda_{mn}t. \tag{28}$$

In order to satisfy the final initial condition (20c), we superpose separated functions and take

$$z(r, \theta, t) = \sum_{n=1}^{\infty} d_{0n}\frac{R_{0n}(r)}{\sqrt{2\pi}}\cos c\lambda_{0n}t$$

$$+ \sum_{m=1}^{\infty}\sum_{n=1}^{\infty} R_{mn}(r)\left(d_{mn}\frac{\cos m\theta}{\sqrt{\pi}} + f_{mn}\frac{\sin m\theta}{\sqrt{\pi}}\right)\cos c\lambda_{mn}t, \tag{29}$$

where d_{mn} and f_{mn} are constants. Condition (20c) requires these constants to satisfy

$$f(r, \theta) = \sum_{n=1}^{\infty} d_{0n}\frac{R_{0n}(r)}{\sqrt{2\pi}} + \sum_{m=1}^{\infty}\sum_{n=1}^{\infty} R_{mn}(r)\left(d_{mn}\frac{\cos m\theta}{\sqrt{\pi}} + f_{mn}\frac{\sin m\theta}{\sqrt{\pi}}\right) \tag{30}$$

for $0 < r < r_2$, $-\pi < \theta \leq \pi$. If we multiply this equation by $(1/\sqrt{\pi})\cos i\theta$ and integrate with respect to θ from $\theta = -\pi$ to $\theta = \pi$, orthogonality of the eigenfunctions in θ gives

$$\int_{-\pi}^{\pi} f(r, \theta)\frac{\cos i\theta}{\sqrt{\pi}}\, d\theta = \sum_{n=1}^{\infty} d_{in} R_{in}(r).$$

Multiplication of this equation by $rR_{ij}(r)$ and integration with respect to r from $r = 0$ to $r = r_2$ yields (because of orthogonality of the R_{ij} for fixed i)

$$\int_0^{r_2} \int_{-\pi}^{\pi} rf(r, \theta) R_{ij} \frac{\cos i\theta}{\sqrt{\pi}} \, d\theta \, dr = d_{ij};$$

that is,

$$d_{mn} = \int_{-\pi}^{\pi} \int_0^{r_2} rR_{mn} \frac{\cos m\theta}{\sqrt{\pi}} f(r, \theta) \, dr \, d\theta. \tag{31a}$$

Similarly,

$$f_{mn} = \int_{-\pi}^{\pi} \int_0^{r_2} rR_{mn} \frac{\sin m\theta}{\sqrt{\pi}} f(r, \theta) \, dr \, d\theta \tag{31b}$$

and

$$d_{0n} = \int_{-\pi}^{\pi} \int_0^{r_2} rR_{0n}(r) \frac{f(r, \theta)}{\sqrt{2\pi}} \, dr \, d\theta. \tag{31c}$$

The solution of (20) is therefore (29), where d_{mn} and f_{mn} are defined by (31).   ∎

Coefficients d_{mn} and f_{mn} in this example were calculated by first using orthogonality of the trigonometric eigenfunctions and then using orthogonality of the $R_{mn}(r)$. An alternative procedure is to determine the multidimensional eigenfunctions for problem (20). This approach is discussed in Exercise 23.

Our final example on separation is a potential problem.

Example 4:   Find the electrostatic potential interior to a sphere when the potential is given on the sphere.

Solution: The boundary value problem for the potential $V(r, \theta, \phi)$ is

$$\frac{\partial^2 V}{\partial r^2} + \frac{2}{r} \frac{\partial V}{\partial r} + \frac{1}{r^2 \sin \phi} \frac{\partial}{\partial \phi} \left(\sin \phi \frac{\partial V}{\partial \phi} \right) + \frac{1}{r^2 \sin^2 \phi} \frac{\partial^2 V}{\partial \theta^2} = 0,$$

$$0 < r < r_2, \qquad -\pi < \theta \leq \pi, \qquad 0 < \phi < \pi, \tag{32a}$$

$$V(r_2, \theta, \phi) = f(\theta, \phi), \qquad -\pi < \theta \leq \pi, \qquad 0 \leq \phi \leq \pi. \tag{32b}$$

When a function with variables separated, $V(r, \theta, \phi) = R(r) H(\theta) \Phi(\phi)$, is substituted into (32a),

$$R'' H\Phi + \frac{2}{r} R' H\Phi + \frac{1}{r^2 \sin \phi} \frac{\partial}{\partial \phi} (\sin \phi \, RH\Phi') + \frac{RH''\Phi}{r^2 \sin^2 \phi} = 0$$

or

$$r^2 \sin^2 \phi \left(\frac{R''}{R} + \frac{2R'}{rR} + \frac{1}{r^2 \sin \phi \, \Phi} \frac{d}{d\phi} (\sin \phi \, \Phi') \right) = -\frac{H''}{H}$$

$$= \alpha = \text{constant independent of } r, \phi, \text{ and } \theta.$$

Because $V(r, \theta, \phi)$ must be 2π-periodic in θ, as must its first derivative with respect to θ, it follows that $H(\theta)$ must satisfy the periodic Sturm-Liouville system

$$H'' + \alpha H = 0, \qquad -\pi < \theta \leq \pi, \tag{33a}$$

$$H(-\pi) = H(\pi), \tag{33b}$$

$$H'(-\pi) = H'(\pi). \tag{33c}$$

This is Sturm-Liouville system (21) with eigenvalues $\alpha = m^2$ and orthonormal eigenfunctions

$$\frac{1}{\sqrt{2\pi}} \quad \text{and} \quad \frac{1}{\sqrt{\pi}} \cos m\theta, \qquad \frac{1}{\sqrt{\pi}} \sin m\theta.$$

Continued separation of the equation in $R(r)$ and $\Phi(\phi)$ gives

$$\frac{r^2 R''}{R} + \frac{2rR'}{R} = \frac{m^2}{\sin^2 \phi} - \frac{1}{\Phi \sin \phi} \frac{d}{d\phi}(\sin \phi \, \Phi') = \beta = \text{constant independent of } r \text{ and } \phi.$$

Thus, $\Phi(\phi)$ must satisfy the singular Sturm-Liouville system

$$\frac{d}{d\phi}\left(\sin \phi \frac{d\Phi}{d\phi}\right) + \left(\beta \sin \phi - \frac{m^2}{\sin \phi}\right)\Phi = 0, \qquad 0 < \phi < \pi. \tag{34}$$

According to the results of Section 8.6, eigenvalues are $\beta = n(n+1)$, where $n \geq m$ is an integer, with orthonormal eigenfunctions

$$\Phi_{mn}(\phi) = \sqrt{\frac{(2n+1)(n-m)!}{2(n+m)!}} \, P_{mn}(\cos \phi). \tag{35}$$

The remaining differential equation,

$$r^2 R'' + 2rR' - n(n+1)R = 0, \tag{36}$$

is a Cauchy-Euler equation that can be solved by setting $R(r) = r^s$, s an unknown constant. This results in the general solution

$$R(r) = \frac{C}{r^{n+1}} + Ar^n. \tag{37}$$

For $R(r)$ to remain bounded as r approaches zero, we must set $C = 0$. Superposition of separated functions now yields

$$V(r, \theta, \phi) = \sum_{n=0}^{\infty} \frac{1}{\sqrt{2\pi}} A_{0n} r^n \Phi_{0n}(\phi) + \sum_{m=1}^{\infty} \sum_{n=m}^{\infty} r^n \Phi_{mn}(\phi)\left(A_{mn} \frac{\cos m\theta}{\sqrt{\pi}} + B_{mn} \frac{\sin m\theta}{\sqrt{\pi}}\right), \tag{38}$$

where A_{mn} and B_{mn} are constants. Boundary condition (32b) requires these constants to satisfy

$$f(\theta, \phi) = \sum_{n=0}^{\infty} \frac{1}{\sqrt{2\pi}} A_{0n} r_2^n \Phi_{0n}(\phi) + \sum_{m=1}^{\infty} \sum_{n=m}^{\infty} r_2^n \Phi_{mn}(\phi)\left(A_{mn} \frac{\cos m\theta}{\sqrt{\pi}} + B_{mn} \frac{\sin m\theta}{\sqrt{\pi}}\right) \tag{39}$$

for $-\pi < \theta \leq \pi$, $0 \leq \phi \leq \pi$. Because of orthogonality of eigenfunctions in θ and ϕ, multiplication by $(1/\sqrt{2\pi}) \sin \phi \, \Phi_{0j}(\phi)$ and integration with respect to θ and ϕ give

$$A_{0j} = \frac{1}{r_2^n} \int_0^\pi \int_{-\pi}^\pi f(\theta, \phi) \frac{1}{\sqrt{2\pi}} \sin \phi \, \Phi_{0j}(\phi) \, d\theta \, d\phi. \tag{40a}$$

Similarly,

$$A_{mn} = \frac{1}{r_2^n} \int_0^\pi \int_{-\pi}^\pi f(\theta, \phi) \frac{\cos m\theta}{\sqrt{\pi}} \sin \phi \, \Phi_{mn}(\phi) \, d\theta \, d\phi \tag{40b}$$

and

$$B_{mn} = \frac{1}{r_2^n} \int_0^\pi \int_{-\pi}^\pi f(\theta, \phi) \frac{\sin m\theta}{\sqrt{\pi}} \sin \phi \, \Phi_{mn}(\phi) \, d\theta \, d\phi. \tag{40c}$$

Notice that the potential at the center of the sphere is

$$V(0, \theta, \phi) = \frac{1}{\sqrt{2\pi}} A_{00} \Phi_{00}(\phi)$$

$$= \frac{1}{\sqrt{2\pi}} \left(\int_0^\pi \int_{-\pi}^\pi f(\theta, \phi) \frac{1}{\sqrt{2\pi}} \sin \phi \, \Phi_{00}(\phi) \, d\theta \, d\phi \right) \Phi_{00}(\phi).$$

Since $\Phi_{00}(\phi) = 1/\sqrt{2}$,

$$V(0, \theta, \phi) = \frac{1}{4\pi} \int_0^\pi \int_{-\pi}^\pi f(\theta, \phi) \sin \phi \, d\theta \, d\phi$$

$$= \frac{1}{4\pi r_2^2} \int_0^\pi \int_{-\pi}^\pi f(\theta, \phi) r_2^2 \sin \phi \, d\theta \, d\phi,$$

and this is the average value of $f(\theta, \phi)$ over the sphere. ∎

Exercises 9.1

Part A—Heat Conduction

1. (a) The initial temperature of an infinitely long cylinder of radius r_2 is $f(r)$. If, for time $t > 0$, the outer surface is held at $0°C$, find the temperature in the cylinder.

   (b) Simplify the solution in (a) when $f(r)$ is a constant U_0.

   (c) Find the solution when $f(r) = r_2^2 - r^2$.

2. A long cylinder of radius r_2 is initially at temperature $f(r)$ and, for time $t > 0$, the boundary $r = r_2$ is insulated.

   (a) Find the temperature $U(r, t)$ in the cylinder.

   (b) What is the limit of $U(r, t)$ for large t?

3. A thin circular plate of radius r_2 is insulated top and bottom. At time $t = 0$ its temperature is $f(r, \theta)$. If the temperature of its edge is held at $0°C$ for $t > 0$, find its interior temperature for $t > 0$.

4. Solve Example 2 using the boundary condition $U(r, \pi, t) = 0$ in place of $\partial U(r, \pi/2, t)/\partial \theta = 0$.

5. A flat plate is in the form of a sector of a circle of radius 1 and angle α. At time $t = 0$, the temperature of the plate increases linearly from $0°C$ at $r = 0$ to a constant value $\bar{U}$ at $r = 1$ (and is therefore independent of θ). If, for $t > 0$, the rounded edge is insulated and the straight edges are held at temperature $0°C$, find the temperature in the plate for $t > 0$. Prove that heat never crosses the line $\theta = \alpha/2$.

6. Find the temperature in the plate of Exercise 5 if the initial temperature is $f(r)$, the straight sides are insulated, and the curved edge is held at temperature $0°C$.

7. Repeat Exercise 6 if the initial temperature is a function of r and θ, $f(r, \theta)$.

8. A cylinder occupies the region $r \leq r_2$, $0 \leq z \leq L$. It has temperature $f(r, z)$ at time $t = 0$. For $t > 0$, its end $z = 0$ is insulated, and the remaining two surfaces are held at temperature $0°C$. Find the temperature in the cylinder.

9. Solve Exercise 1(a), (b) if heat is transferred at $r = r_2$ according to Newton's law of cooling to an environment at temperature zero.

10. (a) A sphere of radius r_2 is initially at temperature $f(r)$ and, for time $t > 0$, the boundary $r = r_2$ is held at temperature zero. Find the temperature in the sphere for $t > 0$. (You will need the results of Exercise 5 in Section 8.4.)

    (b) Simplify the solution when $f(r) = U_0$, a constant.

11. Repeat Exercise 10 if the surface of the sphere is insulated. (See Exercise 6 in Section 8.4.) What is the temperature for large t?

12. Repeat Exercise 10 if the surface transfers heat to an environment at temperature zero according to Newton's law of cooling; that is, take as boundary condition

$$\kappa \frac{\partial U(r_2, t)}{\partial r} + \mu U(r_2, t) = 0, \qquad t > 0.$$

(Assume that $\mu r_2 > \kappa$ and see Exercise 7 in Section 8.4.)

13. Repeat Exercise 10(a) if the initial temperature is also a function of ϕ. (You will need the results of Exercise 8 in Section 8.4.)

14. (a) Repeat Exercise 10(a) if the initial temperature is also a function of ϕ and the surface of the sphere is insulated. (You will need the results of Exercise 8 in Section 8.4.)

    (b) What is the limit of the solution for large t?

15. The result of this exercise is analogous to that in Exercise 9 of Section 5.4. Show that the solution of the homogeneous heat conduction problem

$$\frac{\partial U}{\partial t} = k \left(\frac{\partial^2 U}{\partial r^2} + \frac{1}{r} \frac{\partial U}{\partial r} + \frac{\partial^2 U}{\partial z^2} \right), \qquad 0 < r < r_2, \qquad 0 < z < L, \qquad t > 0,$$

$$-l_1 \frac{\partial U}{\partial z} + h_1 U = 0, \qquad z = 0, \qquad 0 < r < r_2, \qquad t > 0,$$

$$l_2 \frac{\partial U}{\partial z} + h_2 U = 0, \qquad z = L, \qquad 0 < r < r_2, \qquad t > 0,$$

$$l_3 \frac{\partial U}{\partial r} + h_3 U = 0, \qquad r = r_2, \qquad 0 < z < L, \qquad t > 0,$$

$$U(r, z, 0) = f(r)g(z), \qquad 0 < r < r_2, \qquad 0 < z < L,$$

where the initial temperature is the product of a function of r and a function of z, is the product of the solutions of the problems

$$\frac{\partial U}{\partial t} = k \left(\frac{\partial^2 U}{\partial r^2} + \frac{1}{r} \frac{\partial U}{\partial r} \right), \qquad 0 < r < r_2, \qquad t > 0,$$

$$l_3 \frac{\partial U(r_2, t)}{\partial r} + h_3 U(r_2, t) = 0, \qquad t > 0,$$

$$U(r, 0) = f(r), \qquad 0 < r < r_2$$

and
$$\frac{\partial U}{\partial t} = k\frac{\partial^2 U}{\partial z^2}, \qquad 0 < z < L, \qquad t > 0,$$

$$-l_1\frac{\partial U(0,t)}{\partial z} + h_1 U(0,t) = 0, \qquad t > 0,$$

$$l_2\frac{\partial U(L,t)}{\partial z} + h_2 U(L,t) = 0, \qquad t > 0,$$

$$U(z,0) = g(z), \qquad 0 < z < L.$$

16. Solve the heat conduction problem

$$\frac{\partial U}{\partial t} = k\left(\frac{\partial^2 U}{\partial r^2} + \frac{1}{r}\frac{\partial U}{\partial r} + \frac{\partial^2 U}{\partial z^2}\right), \qquad 0 < r < r_2, \qquad 0 < z < L, \qquad t > 0,$$

$$U_z(r,0,t) = 0, \qquad 0 < r < r_2, \qquad t > 0,$$
$$U(r,L,t) = 0, \qquad 0 < r < r_2, \qquad t > 0,$$
$$U_r(r_2,z,t) = 0, \qquad 0 < z < L, \qquad t > 0,$$
$$U(r,z,0) = (r_2^2 - r^2)(L - z), \qquad 0 < r < r_2, \qquad 0 < z < L,$$

(a) by using the results of Exercise 15 and Example 1 in this section and that of Exercise 1(a) in Section 5.2.

(b) by separation of variables.

Part B—Vibrations

17. (a) A vibrating circular membrane of radius r_2 is given an initial displacement that is a function only of r, namely, $f(r)$, $0 \le r \le r_2$, and zero initial velocity. Show that subsequent displacements of the membrane, if its edge $r = r_2$ is fixed on the xy-plane, are of the form

$$z(r,t) = \frac{\sqrt{2}}{r_2}\sum_{n=1}^{\infty} A_n \cos c\lambda_n t\,\frac{J_0(\lambda_n r)}{J_1(\lambda_n r_2)}.$$

What is A_n?

(b) The first term in the series in (a), called the *fundamental mode of vibration* for the membrane, is

$$H_1(r,t) = \frac{\sqrt{2}}{r_2} A_1 \cos c\lambda_1 t\,\frac{J_0(\lambda_1 r)}{J_1(\lambda_1 r_2)}.$$

Simplify and describe this mode when $r_2 = 1$. Does $H_1(r,t)$ have nodal curves?

(c) Repeat part (b) for the second mode of vibration.

(d) Are frequencies of modes of vibration for a circular membrane integer multiples of the frequency of the fundamental mode? Were they for a vibrating string with fixed ends?

18. A circular membrane of radius r_2 has its edge fixed on the xy-plane. In addition, a clamp holds the membrane on the xy-plane along a radial line from the center to the circumference. If the membrane is released from rest at a displacement $f(r,\theta)$, find subsequent displacements. [For consistency, we would require $f(r,\theta)$ to vanish along the clamped radial line.]

19. Simplify the solution in part (a) of Exercise 17 when $f(r) = r_2^2 - r^2$. (See Example 1.)

20. All points in a circular membrane of radius r_2 are given the same initial velocity v_0 but no initial displacement (except points on the edge). If its edge is, fixed on the xy-plane, find subsequent displacements of points in the membrane.

21. Equation (29) with coefficients defined in (31) describes displacements of a circular membrane with fixed edge when oscillations are initiated from rest at some prescribed displacement. In this exercise we examine nodal curves for various modes of vibration.

(a) The first mode of vibration is the term $(d_{01}/\sqrt{2\pi})R_{01}(r)\cos c\lambda_{01}t$. Show that this mode has no nodal curves.

(b) Show that the mode $(d_{02}/\sqrt{2\pi})R_{02}(r)\cos c\lambda_{02}t$ has one nodal curve, a circle.

(c) Show that the mode $(d_{03}/\sqrt{2\pi})R_{03}(r)\cos c\lambda_{03}t$ has two circular nodal curves.

(d) On the basis of (a), (b), and (c), what are the nodal curves for the mode $(d_{0n}/\sqrt{2\pi})R_{0n}(r)\cos c\lambda_{0n}t$?

(e) Corresponding to $n = m = 1$ there are two modes of vibration, $(d_{11}/\sqrt{\pi})R_{11}(r)\cos c\lambda_{11}t\cos\theta$ and $(f_{11}/\sqrt{\pi})R_{11}(r)\cos c\lambda_{11}t\sin\theta$. Show that each of these modes has only one nodal curve, a straight line.

(f) Find nodal curves for the modes $(d_{12}/\sqrt{\pi})R_{12}(r)\cos c\lambda_{12}t\cos\theta$ and $(f_{12}/\sqrt{\pi})R_{12}(r)\cos c\lambda_{12}t\sin\theta$.

(g) Find nodal curves for the modes $(d_{22}/\sqrt{\pi})R_{22}(r)\cos c\lambda_{22}t\cos 2\theta$ and $(f_{22}/\sqrt{\pi})R_{22}(r)\cos c\lambda_{22}t\sin 2\theta$.

(h) On the basis of (e), (f), and (g), what are the nodal curves for the modes $(d_{mn}/\sqrt{\pi})R_{mn}(r)\cos c\lambda_{mn}t\cos m\theta$ and $(f_{mn}/\sqrt{\pi})R_{mn}(r)\cos c\lambda_{mn}t\sin m\theta$?

22. The initial boundary value problem for small horizontal displacements of a suspended cable when gravity is the only force acting on the cable is

$$\frac{\partial^2 y}{\partial t^2} = -g\frac{\partial}{\partial x}\left(x\frac{\partial y}{\partial x}\right), \qquad 0 < x < L, \qquad t > 0,$$

$$y(L, t) = 0, \qquad t > 0,$$

$$y(x, 0) = f(x), \qquad 0 < x < L,$$

$$y_t(x, 0) = h(x), \qquad 0 < x < L$$

(see Exercise 20 in Section 1.3).

(a) Show that when a new independent variable $z = \sqrt{-4x/g}$ is introduced, $y(z, t)$ must satisfy

$$\frac{\partial^2 y}{\partial t^2} = \frac{1}{z}\frac{\partial}{\partial z}\left(z\frac{\partial y}{\partial z}\right), \qquad 0 < z < M, \qquad t > 0,$$

$$y(M, t) = 0, \qquad t > 0,$$

$$y(z, 0) = f\left(\frac{-gz^2}{4}\right), \qquad 0 < z < M,$$

$$y_t(z, 0) = h\left(\frac{-gz^2}{4}\right), \qquad 0 < z < M,$$

where $M = \sqrt{-4L/g}$.

(b) Solve this problem by separation of variables, and hence find $y(x, t)$.

23. Multidimensional eigenfunctions for problem (20) are solutions of the two-dimensional eigenvalue problem

$$\frac{\partial^2 W}{\partial r^2} + \frac{1}{r}\frac{\partial W}{\partial r} + \frac{1}{r^2}\frac{\partial^2 W}{\partial \theta^2} + \lambda^2 W = 0, \qquad 0 < r < r_2, \qquad -\pi < \theta \le \pi,$$

$$W(r_2, \theta) = 0, \qquad -\pi < \theta \le \pi.$$

(a) Find eigenfunctions (normalized with respect to the unit weight function over the circle $r \le r_2$).

(b) Use the eigenfunctions in (a) to solve problem (20).

Part C—Potential, Steady-State Heat Conduction, Static Deflections of Membranes

24. (a) Solve the following boundary value problem associated with the Helmholtz equation on a circle

$$\nabla^2 V + k^2 V = 0, \qquad 0 < r < r_2, \qquad -\pi < \theta \le \pi \quad (k > 0 \text{ a constant})$$

$$V(r_2, \theta) = f(\theta), \qquad -\pi < \theta \le \pi.$$

(b) Is $V(0, \theta)$ the average value of $f(\theta)$ on $r = r_2$?

(c) What is the solution when $f(\theta) = 1$?

25. Solve the following problem for potential in a cylinder:

$$\frac{\partial^2 V}{\partial r^2} + \frac{1}{r}\frac{\partial V}{\partial r} + \frac{\partial^2 V}{\partial z^2} = 0, \qquad 0 < r < r_2, \qquad 0 < z < L,$$

$$V(r_2, z) = 0, \qquad 0 < z < L,$$

$$V(r, 0) = 0, \qquad 0 < r < r_2,$$

$$V(r, L) = f(r), \qquad 0 < r < r_2.$$

26. Find the potential inside a cylinder of length L and radius r_2 when potential on the curved surface is zero and potentials on the flat ends are nonzero.

27. (a) Find the steady-state temperature in a cylinder of radius r_2 and length L if the end $z = 0$ is maintained at temperature $f(r)$, the end $z = L$ is kept at temperature zero, and heat is transferred on $r = r_2$ to a medium at temperature zero according to Newton's law of cooling.

(b) Simplify the solution when $f(r) = U_0$, a constant.

28. Find the potential inside a hemisphere $r \le r_2, z \ge 0$ when the potential on $z = 0$ is zero and that on $r = r_2$ is a function of ϕ only. (*Hint:* See the results of Exercise 5 in Section 8.6.)

29. Find the potential interior to a sphere of radius r_2 when the potential on the upper half is a constant V_0 and the potential on the lower half is zero.

30. Use the result of Exercise 29 to find the potential inside a sphere of radius r_2 when potentials on the top and bottom halves are constant values V_0 and V_1, respectively.

31. Find the potential in the region between two concentric spheres when the potential on each sphere is a function only of ϕ.

32. What is the potential exterior to a sphere when the potential is given on the sphere, if the potential must vanish at infinity?

33. Consider the following boundary value problem for steady-state temperature inside a cylinder of length L and radius r_2 when temperatures of its ends are zero:

$$\frac{\partial^2 U}{\partial r^2} + \frac{1}{r}\frac{\partial U}{\partial r} + \frac{\partial^2 U}{\partial z^2} = 0, \qquad 0 < r < r_2, \qquad 0 < z < L,$$

$$U(r, 0) = 0, \qquad 0 < r < r_2,$$

$$U(r, L) = 0, \qquad 0 < r < r_2,$$

$$U(r_2, z) = f(z), \qquad 0 < z < L.$$

(a) Verify that separation of variables $U(r, z) = R(r)Z(z)$ leads to a Sturm-Liouville system in $Z(z)$ and the following differential equation in $R(r)$:

$$r\frac{d^2 R}{dr^2} + \frac{dR}{dr} - \lambda^2 r R = 0, \qquad 0 < r < r_2.$$

(b) Show that the change of variable $x = \lambda r$ leads to Bessel's modified differential equation of order zero,

$$x\frac{d^2 R}{dx^2} + \frac{dR}{dx} - xR = 0.$$

(See Exercise 10 in Section 8.3.)

(c) Find functions $R_n(r)$ corresponding to eigenvalues λ_n, and use superposition to solve the boundary value problem.

(d) Simplify the solution in (c) in the case that $f(z)$ is a constant value U_0.

34. Solve the boundary value problem in Exercise 33 if the ends of the cylinder are insulated.

35. (a) A charge Q is distributed uniformly around a thin ring of radius a in the xy-plane with center at the origin (Figure 9.2). Show that the potential at every point on the z-axis due to this charge is

$$V = \frac{Q}{4\pi\varepsilon_0 \sqrt{a^2 + r^2}}.$$

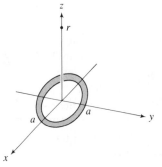

Figure 9.2

(b) The potential at other points in space must be independent of the spherical coordinate θ. Show that $V(r, \phi)$ must be of the form

$$V(r, \phi) = \sum_{n=0}^{\infty} \left(A_n r^n + \frac{B_n}{r^{n+1}} \right) \sqrt{\frac{2n + 1}{2}} \, P_n(\cos \phi).$$

What does this result predict for potential at points on the positive z-axis?

(c) Equate expressions from (a) and (b) for V on the positive z-axis and expand $1/\sqrt{a^2 + r^2}$ in powers of r/a and a/r to find $V(r, \phi)$.

36. Repeat Exercise 35 in the case that charge Q is distributed uniformly over a disc of radius a in the xy-plane with center at the origin (Figure 9.3).

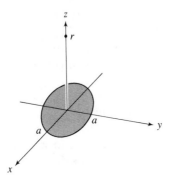

Figure 9.3

9.2 Nonhomogeneous Problems in Polar, Cylindrical, and Spherical Coordinates

Nonhomogeneities in problems expressed in polar, cylindrical, or spherical coordinates can be treated in the same way that they were treated in Cartesian coordinates—separate off "steady-state" or "static deflection" solutions, or use eigenfunction expansions or finite Fourier transforms. We begin our discussions with finite Fourier transforms.

With each of the Sturm-Liouville systems in Sections 8.4 and 8.6 we associate a finite Fourier transform. In particular, for the singular system

$$(rR')' + \left(\lambda^2 r - \frac{v^2}{r}\right) R = 0, \qquad 0 < r < r_2, \tag{41a}$$

$$l_2 R'(r_2) + h_2 R(r_2) = 0, \tag{41b}$$

with eigenvalues and eigenfunctions in Table 8.1, we define the transform

$$\tilde{f}(\lambda_{vn}) = \int_0^{r_2} r f(r) R_{vn}(r)\, dr, \tag{42a}$$

called the finite *Hankel* transform. It associates with a function $f(r)$, the sequence $\{\tilde{f}(\lambda_{vn})\}$ of coefficients in the eigenfunction expansion of $f(r)$ in terms of the $R_{vn}(r)$. The inverse transform of (42a) is this eigenfunction expansion,

$$f(r) = \sum_{n=1}^{\infty} \tilde{f}(\lambda_{vn}) R_{vn}(r), \qquad 0 < r < r_2, \tag{42b}$$

[provided, of course, that $f(r)$ is defined as the average of right and left limits at any point of discontinuity]. The finite Hankel transform is used to eliminate the r-variable from initial boundary value problems in polar, cylindrical, and spherical coordinates.

With the singular Sturm-Liouville system

$$(\sin\phi\,\Phi')' + \left(\lambda\sin\phi - \frac{m^2}{\sin\phi}\right)\Phi = 0, \qquad 0 < \phi < \pi \tag{43}$$

($m \geq 0$ an integer) is associated the *Legendre* transform,

$$\tilde{f}(m, n) = \int_0^\pi \sin\phi f(\phi)\Phi_{mn}(\phi)\,d\phi, \tag{44a}$$

where eigenvalues are $\lambda_{mn} = n(n + 1)$ ($n \geq m$ an integer), and Φ_{mn} are normalized associated Legendre functions of the first kind [see equation (91) in Section 8.6]. The inverse transform is

$$f(\phi) = \sum_{n=m}^\infty \tilde{f}(m, n)\Phi_{mn}(\phi). \tag{44b}$$

This transform removes the ϕ-variable from problems in spherical coordinates.

To complete the set of finite Fourier transforms, we associate a transform with the periodic Sturm-Liouville system

$$H'' + \lambda^2 H = 0, \qquad -\pi < \theta \leq \pi, \tag{45a}$$

$$H(-\pi) = H(\pi), \tag{45b}$$

$$H'(-\pi) = H'(\pi), \tag{45c}$$

which arises in so many of our problems. Eigenvalues of this system are $\lambda_m^2 = m^2$, m a nonnegative integer, with orthonormal eigenfunctions

$$\frac{1}{\sqrt{2\pi}} \longleftrightarrow \lambda_0 = 0; \qquad \frac{1}{\sqrt{\pi}}\cos m\theta, \quad \frac{1}{\sqrt{\pi}}\sin m\theta \longleftrightarrow \lambda_m, \qquad m > 0.$$

Periodic functions $f(\theta)$ may be expressed in terms of these eigenfunctions as ordinary trigonometric Fourier series:

$$f(\theta) = \frac{a_0}{\sqrt{2\pi}} + \sum_{m=1}^\infty \left(a_m \frac{\cos m\theta}{\sqrt{\pi}} + b_m \frac{\sin m\theta}{\sqrt{\pi}}\right), \tag{46a}$$

where
$$a_0 = \int_{-\pi}^\pi \frac{f(\theta)}{\sqrt{2\pi}}\,d\theta, \qquad a_m = \int_{-\pi}^\pi f(\theta)\frac{\cos m\theta}{\sqrt{\pi}}\,d\theta,$$

$$b_m = \int_{-\pi}^\pi f(\theta)\frac{\sin m\theta}{\sqrt{\pi}}\,d\theta. \tag{46b}$$

The complex representation of this series in Exercise 27 of Section 2.1 provides the finite Fourier transform. We may rewrite (46) in the form

$$f(\theta) = \frac{1}{2\pi}\sum_{m=-\infty}^\infty C_m e^{im\theta}, \tag{47a}$$

where
$$C_m = \int_{-\pi}^\pi f(\theta)e^{-im\theta}\,d\theta. \tag{47b}$$

[We took the liberty in Exercise 27 of Section 2.1 of incorporating the 2π-factor into the series rather than the coefficient C_m. The series representation of $f(\theta)$ is the same in either case.] Associated with this representation is the finite Fourier transform of 2π-periodic functions

$$\tilde{f}(m) = \int_{-\pi}^{\pi} f(\theta)e^{-im\theta}\,d\theta \qquad \text{(48a)}$$

and its inverse,

$$f(\theta) = \frac{1}{2\pi} \sum_{m=-\infty}^{\infty} \tilde{f}(m)e^{im\theta}. \qquad \text{(48b)}$$

[The exponentials in equations (48) could be interchanged to give an alternative transform; this uses the complex representation of equation (16) in Section 2.1.] The similarity between this finite Fourier transform and Fourier transform (23) in Chapter 7 is unmistakable.

The following examples illustrate how these transforms facilitate the solution of (initial) boundary value problems that are nonhomogeneous.

Example 5: A circular plate of radius r_2 is insulated at its top and bottom. At time $t = 0$, its temperature is $0°C$ throughout. If, for $t > 0$, all points on the edge of the plate have the same temperature $\bar{U}$, find the temperature in the plate for $t > 0$.

Solution: The initial boundary value problem for $U(r,t)$ is

$$\frac{\partial U}{\partial t} = k\left(\frac{\partial^2 U}{\partial r^2} + \frac{1}{r}\frac{\partial U}{\partial r}\right), \qquad 0 < r < r_2, \qquad t > 0, \qquad \text{(49a)}$$

$$U(r_2,t) = \bar{U}, \qquad t > 0, \qquad \text{(49b)}$$

$$U(r,0) = 0, \qquad 0 < r < r_2. \qquad \text{(49c)}$$

To eliminate r from the problem, we use the finite Hankel transform

$$\tilde{f}(\lambda_n) = \int_0^{r_2} rf(r)R_n(r)\,dr, \qquad \text{(50)}$$

where $R_n(r) = \sqrt{2}\,J_0(\lambda_n r)/[r_2 J_1(\lambda_n r_2)]$ are eigenfunctions of the Sturm-Liouville system

$$(rR')' + \lambda^2 rR = 0, \qquad 0 < r < r_2, \qquad \text{(51a)}$$

$$R(r_2) = 0. \qquad \text{(51b)}$$

(This is the system that would result were separation of variables applied to the corresponding homogeneous problem.) Application of the transform to PDE (49a) gives

$$\int_0^{r_2} r\frac{\partial U}{\partial t} R_n\,dr = k\int_0^{r_2} r\left(\frac{\partial^2 U}{\partial r^2} + \frac{1}{r}\frac{\partial U}{\partial r}\right) R_n\,dr.$$

An interchange of differentiation with respect to t and integration with respect to r on the left, and integration by parts on the right, yield

$$\frac{\partial \tilde{U}}{\partial t} = k\left\{r\frac{\partial U}{\partial r}R_n\right\}_0^{r_2} + k\int_0^{r_2}\frac{\partial U}{\partial r}\left(-\frac{d}{dr}(rR_n) + R_n\right)dr$$

$$= -k\int_0^{r_2} r\frac{\partial U}{\partial r}R'_n\,dr \quad\text{[because of (51b)]}$$

$$= -k\left\{UrR'_n\right\}_0^{r_2} + k\int_0^{r_2} U(rR'_n)'\,dr \quad\text{(by a second integration by parts)}$$

$$= -kr_2 R'_n(r_2)\bar{U} + k\int_0^{r_2} U[-\lambda_n^2 rR_n]\,dr \quad\text{[from (49b) and (51a)]}$$

$$= -k\bar{U}r_2 R'_n(r_2) - k\lambda_n^2 \tilde{U}.$$

Thus, $\tilde{U}(\lambda_n, t)$ must satisfy the ODE

$$\frac{d\tilde{U}}{dt} + k\lambda_n^2 \tilde{U} = -k\bar{U}r_2 R'_n(r_2) \tag{52a}$$

subject to the transform of initial condition (49c),

$$\tilde{U}(\lambda_n, 0) = 0. \tag{52b}$$

Since the solution of (52) is

$$\tilde{U}(\lambda_n, t) = \frac{\bar{U}r_2 R'_n(r_2)}{\lambda_n^2}\left(-1 + e^{-k\lambda_n^2 t}\right), \tag{53}$$

we obtain

$$U(r, t) = \sum_{n=1}^{\infty} \tilde{U}(\lambda_n, t)R_n(r)$$

$$= \sum_{n=1}^{\infty} \frac{\bar{U}r_2\sqrt{2}\,\lambda_n J'_0(\lambda_n r_2)}{r_2 J_1(\lambda_n r_2)\lambda_n^2}\left(e^{-k\lambda_n^2 t} - 1\right)\frac{\sqrt{2}\,J_0(\lambda_n r)}{r_2 J_1(\lambda_n r_2)}$$

$$= \frac{2\bar{U}}{r_2}\sum_{n=1}^{\infty}\frac{-J_1(\lambda_n r_2)}{\lambda_n[J_1(\lambda_n r_2)]^2}\left(e^{-k\lambda_n^2 t} - 1\right)J_0(\lambda_n r)$$

$$= \frac{2\bar{U}}{r_2}\sum_{n=1}^{\infty}\frac{1}{\lambda_n J_1(\lambda_n r_2)}\left(1 - e^{-k\lambda_n^2 t}\right)J_0(\lambda_n r). \tag{54}$$

The limit of this temperature function for large t is

$$\lim_{t\to\infty} U(r, t) = \frac{2\bar{U}}{r_2}\sum_{n=1}^{\infty}\frac{J_0(\lambda_n r)}{\lambda_n J_1(\lambda_n r_2)}.$$

The transform $\tilde{1}$ of the function $f(r) \equiv 1$ is

$$\tilde{1} = \int_0^{r_2} r\frac{\sqrt{2}\,J_0(\lambda_n r)}{r_2 J_1(\lambda_n r_2)}\,dr = \frac{\sqrt{2}}{r_2 J_1(\lambda_n r_2)}\int_0^{\lambda_n r_2}\left(\frac{u}{\lambda_n}\right)J_0(u)\left(\frac{du}{\lambda_n}\right)$$

$$= \frac{\sqrt{2}}{r_2 \lambda_n^2 J_1(\lambda_n r_2)} \int_0^{\lambda_n r_2} \frac{d}{du}[uJ_1(u)] \, du \quad \text{[see identity (39) in Section 8.3 with } v = 1]$$

$$= \frac{\sqrt{2}}{r_2 \lambda_n^2 J_1(\lambda_n r_2)} \left\{ uJ_1(u) \right\}_0^{\lambda_n r_2}$$

$$= \frac{\sqrt{2}}{\lambda_n}.$$

Consequently,

$$1 = \sum_{n=1}^{\infty} \frac{\sqrt{2}}{\lambda_n} \frac{\sqrt{2} J_0(\lambda_n r)}{r_2 J_1(\lambda_n r_2)} = \frac{2}{r_2} \sum_{n=1}^{\infty} \frac{J_0(\lambda_n r)}{\lambda_n J_1(\lambda_n r_2)}, \tag{55}$$

and it follows that

$$\lim_{t \to \infty} U(r, t) = \bar{U},$$

as expected. Furthermore, this suggests that we write $U(r, t)$ in the form

$$U(r, t) = \bar{U} - \frac{2\bar{U}}{r_2} \sum_{n=1}^{\infty} \frac{1}{\lambda_n J_1(\lambda_n r_2)} e^{-k\lambda_n^2 t} J_0(\lambda_n r). \tag{56}$$

Because the nonhomogeneity in boundary condition (49b) is independent of time, we could have begun by separating off the steady-state solution; that is, we could set $U(r, t) = V(r, t) + \psi(r)$, where $\psi(r)$ is the solution of

$$\frac{d^2\psi}{dr^2} + \frac{1}{r}\frac{d\psi}{dr} = 0, \qquad 0 < r < r_2, \tag{57a}$$

$$\psi(r_2) = \bar{U}. \tag{57b}$$

The only bounded solution of this system is $\psi(r) = \bar{U}$. With this steady-state solution, $V(r, t)$ must satisfy the homogeneous problem

$$\frac{\partial V}{\partial t} = k\left(\frac{\partial^2 V}{\partial r^2} + \frac{1}{r}\frac{\partial V}{\partial r}\right), \qquad 0 < r < r_2, \qquad t > 0, \tag{58a}$$

$$V(r_2, t) = 0, \qquad t > 0, \tag{58b}$$

$$V(r, 0) = -\bar{U}, \qquad 0 < r < r_2. \tag{58c}$$

Separation $V(r, t) = R(r)T(t)$ leads to Sturm-Liouville system (51) in $R(r)$ and the ODE

$$T' + k\lambda^2 T = 0, \qquad t > 0. \tag{59}$$

Eigenvalues are defined by $J_0(\lambda r_2) = 0$, and normalized eigenfunctions are $R_n(r) = \sqrt{2} J_0(\lambda_n r)/[r_2 J_1(\lambda_n r_2)]$. Corresponding solutions of (59) are

$$T(t) = Ce^{-k\lambda_n^2 t}. \tag{60}$$

Superposition of separated functions yields

$$V(r, t) = \sum_{n=1}^{\infty} C_n e^{-k\lambda_n^2 t} R_n(r), \tag{61}$$

and initial condition (58c) requires that

$$-\bar{U} = \sum_{n=1}^{\infty} C_n R_n(r). \tag{62}$$

The C_n are therefore Fourier coefficients in the eigenfunction expansion of the function $-\bar{U}$; that is,

$$C_n = \int_0^{r_2} r(-\bar{U}) R_n(r)\, dr = -\bar{U} \int_0^{r_2} r \frac{\sqrt{2} J_0(\lambda_n r)}{r_2 J_1(\lambda_n r_2)}\, dr = \frac{-\sqrt{2}\,\bar{U}}{\lambda_n}.$$

(This integral was evaluated in the above transform solution.) Consequently,

$$U(r,t) = \bar{U} + \sum_{n=1}^{\infty} \frac{-\sqrt{2}\,\bar{U}}{\lambda_n} e^{-k\lambda_n^2 t} \frac{\sqrt{2} J_0(\lambda_n r)}{r_2 J_1(\lambda_n r_2)}$$

$$= \bar{U} - \frac{2\bar{U}}{r_2} \sum_{n=1}^{\infty} \frac{1}{\lambda_n J_1(\lambda_n r_2)} e^{-k\lambda_n^2 t} J_0(\lambda_n r),$$

the same solution as that obtained by finite Fourier transforms. ∎

Our next example is a vibration problem.

Example 6: A circular membrane of radius r_2 has an initial displacement at time $t = 0$ described by the function $f(r, \theta)$, $0 \le r \le r_2$, $-\pi < \theta \le \pi$, but no initial velocity. For time $t > 0$, its edge $r = r_2$ is forced to undergo periodic oscillations described by $A \sin \omega t$, A a constant. [For consistency, we assume that $f(r_2, \theta) = 0$.] Find its displacement as a function of r, θ, and t.

Solution: The initial boundary value problem for $z(r, \theta, t)$ is

$$\frac{\partial^2 z}{\partial t^2} = c^2 \left(\frac{\partial^2 z}{\partial r^2} + \frac{1}{r}\frac{\partial z}{\partial r} + \frac{1}{r^2}\frac{\partial^2 z}{\partial \theta^2} \right), \quad 0 < r < r_2, \quad -\pi < \theta \le \pi, \quad t > 0, \tag{63a}$$

$$z(r_2, \theta, t) = A \sin \omega t, \qquad -\pi < \theta \le \pi, \qquad t > 0, \tag{63b}$$

$$z(r, \theta, 0) = f(r, \theta), \qquad 0 < r < r_2, \qquad -\pi < \theta \le \pi, \tag{63c}$$

$$z_t(r, \theta, 0) = 0, \qquad 0 < r < r_2, \qquad -\pi < \theta \le \pi. \tag{63d}$$

To remove θ from the problem, we apply transform (48a) to PDE (63a):

$$\int_{-\pi}^{\pi} \frac{\partial^2 z}{\partial t^2} e^{-im\theta}\, d\theta = c^2 \int_{-\pi}^{\pi} \left(\frac{\partial^2 z}{\partial r^2} + \frac{1}{r}\frac{\partial z}{\partial r} + \frac{1}{r^2}\frac{\partial^2 z}{\partial \theta^2} \right) e^{-im\theta}\, d\theta.$$

Integrations with respect to θ and differentiations with respect to t and r may be interchanged, with the result that

$$\frac{\partial^2 \tilde{z}}{\partial t^2} - c^2 \left(\frac{\partial^2 \tilde{z}}{\partial r^2} + \frac{1}{r}\frac{\partial \tilde{z}}{\partial r} \right) = \frac{c^2}{r^2} \int_{-\pi}^{\pi} \frac{\partial^2 z}{\partial \theta^2} e^{-im\theta}\, d\theta.$$

Integration by parts on the remaining integral gives

$$\int_{-\pi}^{\pi} \frac{\partial^2 z}{\partial \theta^2} e^{-im\theta}\, d\theta = \left\{ \frac{\partial z}{\partial \theta} e^{-im\theta} \right\}_{-\pi}^{\pi} + \int_{-\pi}^{\pi} im \frac{\partial z}{\partial \theta} e^{-im\theta}\, d\theta$$

$$= \frac{\partial z(r, \pi, t)}{\partial \theta} \cos(-m\pi) - \frac{\partial z(r, -\pi, t)}{\partial \theta} \cos m\pi + im \int_{-\pi}^{\pi} \frac{\partial z}{\partial \theta} e^{-im\theta}\, d\theta.$$

Because $\partial z/\partial\theta$ must be 2π-periodic, it follows that $\partial z(r,\pi,t)/\partial\theta = \partial z(r,-\pi,t)/\partial\theta$, and therefore

$$\int_{-\pi}^{\pi} \frac{\partial^2 z}{\partial\theta^2} e^{-im\theta}\, d\theta = im \int_{-\pi}^{\pi} \frac{\partial z}{\partial\theta} e^{-im\theta}\, d\theta$$

$$= im\{ze^{-im\theta}\}_{-\pi}^{\pi} + im \int_{-\pi}^{\pi} imze^{-im\theta}\, d\theta$$

$$= im\big(z(r,\pi,t)\cos(-m\pi) - z(r,-\pi,t)\cos m\pi\big) - m^2 \int_{-\pi}^{\pi} ze^{-im\theta}\, d\theta$$

$$= -m^2\tilde{z},$$

since $z(r,0,t)$ must also be 2π-periodic. Consequently, $\tilde{z}(r,m,t)$ must satisfy the PDE

$$\frac{\partial^2 \tilde{z}}{\partial t^2} = c^2\left(\frac{\partial^2 \tilde{z}}{\partial r^2} + \frac{1}{r}\frac{\partial \tilde{z}}{\partial r} - \frac{m^2}{r^2}\tilde{z}\right), \qquad 0 < r < r_2, \qquad t > 0 \tag{64a}$$

subject to the transforms of (63b–d),

$$\tilde{z}(r_2,m,t) = A\sin\omega t\, \tilde{1}, \qquad t > 0, \tag{64b}$$

$$\tilde{z}(r,m,0) = \tilde{f}(r,m), \qquad 0 < r < r_2, \tag{64c}$$

$$\tilde{z}_t(r,m,0) = 0, \qquad 0 < r < r_2, \tag{64d}$$

where

$$\tilde{1} = \int_{-\pi}^{\pi} e^{-im\theta}\, d\theta = \begin{cases} 2\pi & m = 0 \\ 0 & m \neq 0 \end{cases}. \tag{64e}$$

To eliminate r from problem (64), we use the finite Hankel transform

$$\tilde{f}(\lambda_{mn}) = \int_0^{r_2} rf(r)R_{mn}(r)\, dr, \tag{65}$$

where $R_{mn}(r)$ are the orthonormal eigenfunctions of the Sturm-Liouville system

$$(rR')' + \left(\lambda^2 r - \frac{m^2}{r}\right)R = 0, \qquad 0 < r < r_2, \tag{66a}$$

$$R(r_2) = 0 \tag{66b}$$

[the system that would result were separation performed on problem (64) with the homogeneous version of (64b)]. Application of (65) to (64a) and integration by parts give

$$\frac{\partial^2 \tilde{\tilde{z}}}{\partial t^2} = c^2 \int_0^{r_2} r\left(\frac{\partial^2 \tilde{z}}{\partial r^2} + \frac{1}{r}\frac{\partial \tilde{z}}{\partial r} - \frac{m^2}{r^2}\tilde{z}\right) R_{mn}\, dr$$

$$= c^2\left\{rR_{mn}\frac{\partial \tilde{z}}{\partial r}\right\}_0^{r_2} + c^2 \int_0^{r_2}\left(-\frac{\partial \tilde{z}}{\partial r}(rR_{mn})' + \frac{\partial \tilde{z}}{\partial r}R_{mn} - \frac{m^2}{r}\tilde{z}R_{mn}\right) dr$$

$$= c^2 \int_0^{r_2}\left(-r\frac{\partial \tilde{z}}{\partial r}R'_{mn} - \frac{m^2}{r}\tilde{z}R_{mn}\right) dr \quad \text{[since } R_{mn}(r_2) = 0\text{]}$$

$$= c^2\{-r\tilde{z}R'_{mn}\}_0^{r_2} + c^2 \int_0^{r_2}\left(\tilde{z}(rR'_{mn})' - \frac{m^2}{r}\tilde{z}R_{mn}\right) dr$$

$$= -r_2 c^2 A \sin \omega t \, \tilde{1} R'_{mn}(r_2) + c^2 \int_0^{r_2} \tilde{z} \left((rR'_{mn})' - \frac{m^2}{r} R_{mn} \right) dr \quad \text{[by (64b)]}$$

$$= -r_2 c^2 A \tilde{1} R'_{mn}(r_2) \sin \omega t + c^2 \int_0^{r_2} \tilde{z}(-\lambda_{mn}{}^2 r) R_{mn} \, dr \quad \text{[by (66a)]}$$

$$= -r_2 c^2 A \tilde{1} R'_{mn}(r_2) \sin \omega t - c^2 \lambda_{mn}^2 \tilde{z}.$$

Thus, $\tilde{\tilde{z}}(\lambda_{mn}, m, t)$ must satisfy the ODE

$$\frac{d^2 \tilde{\tilde{z}}}{dt^2} + c^2 \lambda_{mn}^2 \tilde{\tilde{z}} = -r_2 c^2 A \tilde{1} R'_{mn}(r_2) \sin \omega t \tag{67a}$$

subject to

$$\tilde{\tilde{z}}(\lambda_{mn}, m, 0) = \tilde{\tilde{f}}(\lambda_{mn}, m), \tag{67b}$$

$$\tilde{\tilde{z}}_t(\lambda_{mn}, m, 0) = 0. \tag{67c}$$

The general solution of (67a) is

$$\tilde{\tilde{z}}(\lambda_{mn}, m, t) = \begin{cases} B_{0n} \cos c\lambda_{0n} t + D_{0n} \sin c\lambda_{0n} t + \dfrac{2\pi r_2 c^2 A R'_{0n}(r_2) \sin \omega t}{\omega^2 - c^2 \lambda_{0n}^2} & m = 0 \\[4mm] B_{mn} \cos c\lambda_{mn} t + D_{mn} \sin c\lambda_{mn} t & m \neq 0 \end{cases} \tag{68}$$

provided $\omega \neq c\lambda_{0n}$ for any n. Discussion of this special case is given in Exercise 18. Initial conditions (67b, c) yield

$$\tilde{\tilde{z}}(\lambda_{mn}, m, t) = \begin{cases} \tilde{\tilde{f}}(\lambda_{0n}, 0) \cos c\lambda_{0n} t + \dfrac{2\pi A r_2 c R'_{0n}(r_2)}{\lambda_{0n}(\omega^2 - c^2 \lambda_{0n}^2)} (c\lambda_{0n} \sin \omega t - \omega \sin c\lambda_{0n} t) & m = 0 \\[4mm] \tilde{\tilde{f}}(\lambda_{mn}, m) \cos c\lambda_{mn} t & m \neq 0 \end{cases}$$

$$\tag{69}$$

The inverse transform now yields

$$z(r, \theta, t) = \frac{1}{2\pi} \sum_{m=-\infty}^{\infty} \sum_{n=1}^{\infty} \tilde{\tilde{z}}(\lambda_{mn}, m, t) R_{mn}(r) e^{im\theta}$$

$$= \frac{1}{2\pi} \sum_{n=1}^{\infty} \left(\tilde{\tilde{f}}(\lambda_{0n}, 0) \cos c\lambda_{0n} t + \frac{2\pi A r_2 c R'_{0n}(r_2)}{\lambda_{0n}(\omega^2 - c^2 \lambda_{0n}^2)} (c\lambda_{0n} \sin \omega t - \omega \sin c\lambda_{0n} t) \right) R_{0n}(r)$$

$$+ \frac{1}{2\pi} \sum_{\substack{m=-\infty \\ m \neq 0}}^{\infty} \sum_{n=1}^{\infty} \tilde{\tilde{f}}(\lambda_{mn}, m) \cos c\lambda_{mn} t \, R_{mn}(r) e^{im\theta}. \tag{70}$$

We can reduce the second double summation by noting that $\lambda_{-mn} = \lambda_{mn}$, $R_{-mn}(r) = R_{mn}(r)$, and $\tilde{\tilde{f}}(\lambda_{-mn}, -m) = \overline{\tilde{\tilde{f}}(\lambda_{mn}, m)}$ [the complex conjugate of $\tilde{\tilde{f}}(\lambda_{mn}, m)$]. Then

$$z(r, \theta, t) = \frac{1}{2\pi} \sum_{n=1}^{\infty} \left(\tilde{\tilde{f}}(\lambda_{0n}, 0) \cos c\lambda_{0n} t + \frac{2\pi A r_2 c R'_{0n}(r_2)}{\lambda_{0n}(\omega^2 - c^2 \lambda_{0n}^2)} (c\lambda_{0n} \sin \omega t - \omega \sin c\lambda_{0n} t) \right) R_{0n}(r)$$

$$+ \frac{1}{2\pi} \sum_{m=1}^{\infty} \sum_{n=1}^{\infty} \left(\tilde{\tilde{f}}(\lambda_{mn}, m) e^{im\theta} + \overline{\tilde{\tilde{f}}(\lambda_{mn}, m)} e^{-im\theta} \right) \cos c\lambda_{mn} t \, R_{mn}(r)$$

or

$$z(r, \theta, t) = \frac{1}{2\pi} \sum_{n=1}^{\infty} \left(\tilde{\tilde{f}}(\lambda_{0n}, 0) \cos c\lambda_{0n} t + \frac{2\pi A r_2 c R'_{0n}(r_2)}{\lambda_{0n}(\omega^2 - c^2 \lambda_{0n}^2)} (c\lambda_{0n} \sin \omega t - \omega \sin c\lambda_{0n} t) \right) R_{0n}(r)$$

$$+ \frac{1}{2\pi} \sum_{m=1}^{\infty} \sum_{n=1}^{\infty} 2 \operatorname{Re}[\tilde{\tilde{f}}(\lambda_{mn}, m) e^{im\theta}] \cos c\lambda_{mn} t \, R_{mn}(r). \qquad \blacksquare \quad (71)$$

Our final example is a potential problem.

Example 7:   Find the potential inside a sphere if the potential on the sphere is only a function $g(\phi)$ of angle ϕ and the region contains a constant charge with density σ.

Solution: The boundary value problem is

$$\frac{\partial^2 V}{\partial r^2} + \frac{2}{r} \frac{\partial V}{\partial r} + \frac{1}{r^2 \sin \phi} \frac{\partial}{\partial \phi} \left(\sin \phi \frac{\partial V}{\partial \phi} \right) = -\frac{\sigma}{\varepsilon}, \qquad 0 < r < r_2, \qquad 0 < \phi < \pi, \quad (72a)$$

$$V(r_2, \phi) = g(\phi), \qquad 0 < \phi < \pi. \qquad (72b)$$

To remove ϕ from the problem, we use the Legendre transform

$$\tilde{f}(n) = \int_0^\pi \sin \phi \, f(\phi) \Phi_n(\phi) \, d\phi, \qquad (73)$$

where $\Phi_n(\phi) = \sqrt{(2n + 1)/2} P_n(\cos \phi)$ are orthonormal eigenfunctions of the Sturm-Liouville system

$$(\sin \phi \, \Phi')' + n(n + 1) \sin \phi \, \Phi = 0, \qquad 0 < \phi < \pi \qquad (74)$$

[the system that would result were separation of variables applied to the homogeneous version of (72a)]. Application of (73) to (72a) and integration by parts give

$$\frac{d^2\tilde{V}}{dr^2} + \frac{2}{r} \frac{d\tilde{V}}{dr} + \frac{\sigma}{\varepsilon} \tilde{1} = \frac{-1}{r^2} \int_0^\pi \frac{\partial}{\partial \phi} \left(\sin \phi \frac{\partial V}{\partial \phi} \right) \Phi_n(\phi) \, d\phi$$

$$= \frac{-1}{r^2} \left(\left\{ \sin \phi \frac{\partial V}{\partial \phi} \Phi_n \right\}_0^\pi - \int_0^\pi \sin \phi \frac{\partial V}{\partial \phi} \Phi'_n \, d\phi \right)$$

$$= \frac{1}{r^2} \left(\left\{ \sin \phi \, V \Phi'_n \right\}_0^\pi - \int_0^\pi V(\sin \phi \, \Phi'_n)' \, d\phi \right)$$

$$= \frac{-1}{r^2} \int_0^\pi V[-n(n + 1) \sin \phi \, \Phi_n] \, d\phi \qquad [\text{by (74)}]$$

$$= \frac{n(n + 1)}{r^2} \tilde{V}.$$

Thus, $\tilde{V}(r, n)$ must satisfy the ODE

$$\frac{d^2\tilde{V}}{dr^2} + \frac{2}{r} \frac{d\tilde{V}}{dr} - \frac{n(n + 1)}{r^2} \tilde{V} = -\frac{\sigma}{\varepsilon} \tilde{1}, \qquad (75a)$$

where

$$\tilde{1} = \int_0^\pi \sin \phi \, \Phi_n \, d\phi = \begin{cases} \sqrt{2}, & n = 0 \\ 0 & n > 0 \end{cases} \qquad (75b)$$

subject to

$$\tilde{V}(r_2, n) = \tilde{g}(n). \tag{75c}$$

The general solution of (75a) is

$$\tilde{V}(r, n) = \begin{cases} A_0 + \dfrac{B_0}{r} - \dfrac{\sqrt{2}\,\sigma r^2}{6\varepsilon} & n = 0 \\[3mm] A_n r^n + \dfrac{B_n}{r^{n+1}}, & n > 0 \end{cases}. \tag{76}$$

The only bounded solution satisfying (75c) is

$$\tilde{V}(r, n) = \begin{cases} \tilde{g}(0) + \dfrac{\sqrt{2}\,\sigma}{6\varepsilon}(r_2^2 - r^2) & n = 0 \\[3mm] \dfrac{\tilde{g}(n)}{r_2^n} r^n & n > 0 \end{cases}, \tag{77}$$

and therefore

$$V(r, \phi) = \sum_{n=0}^{\infty} \tilde{V}(r, n)\Phi_n(\phi)$$

$$= \frac{\tilde{g}(0)}{\sqrt{2}} + \frac{\sigma}{6\varepsilon}(r_2^2 - r^2) + \sum_{n=1}^{\infty}\left(\frac{r}{r_2}\right)^n \tilde{g}(n)\Phi_n(\phi)$$

$$= \frac{\sigma}{6\varepsilon}(r_2^2 - r^2) + \sum_{n=0}^{\infty}\left(\frac{r}{r_2}\right)^n \tilde{g}(n)\Phi_n(\phi). \tag{78}$$

In retrospect, notice that $\sigma(r_2^2 - r^2)/(6\varepsilon)$ satisfies (72a) and a homogeneous (72b), while the series part of $V(r, \phi)$ satisfies (72b) and a homogeneous (72a).   ∎

Exercises 9.2

Part A—Heat Conduction

1. Solve Example 5 if the temperature of the edge $r = r_2$ is a function $f(t)$ of time.

2. (a) Solve Example 5 if heat is transferred to the plate along its edge $r = r_2$ at a rate $f_1(t)$ W/m^2 equally all around.
   (b) Simplify the solution when $f_1(t) = Q$, a constant.

3. (a) A very long cylinder of radius r_2 is initially at temperature $f(r)$. For time $t > 0$, its edge $r = r_2$ is held at 0°C. If heat generation within the cylinder is $g(r, t)$, find the temperature for $0 \le r < r_2$ and $t > 0$.
   (b) Simplify the solution in (a) when $f(r) \equiv 0$ and $g(r, t)$ is constant.
   (c) Solve the problem in (b) by separating off the steady-state solution.

4. Repeat Exercise 3(a) and (b) if the boundary $r = r_2$ is insulated.

5. Repeat Exercise 3 if heat is transferred at $r = r_2$ to a medium at constant temperature U_m according to Newton's law of cooling.

6. (a) A sphere of radius r_2 is initially at temperature $f(r)$. For $t > 0$, its surface is held at temperature $f_1(t)$, and heat is generated at a rate $g(r, t)$. Find the temperature in the sphere. (See Exercise 5 in Section 8.4 for the appropriate finite Fourier transform.)

   (b) Simplify the solution when $f(r) \equiv 0$, $f_1(t) \equiv 0$, and $g(r, t)$ is constant.

   (c) Simplify the solution when $f(r) \equiv 0$, $g(r, t) \equiv 0$, and $f_1(t)$ is constant.

7. (a) A sphere of radius r_2 is initially at temperature $f(r)$. For $t > 0$, heat is added to its surface at a rate $f_1(t)$ W/m², and heat is generated at a rate $g(r, t)$ W/m³. Find the temperature in the sphere. (See Exercise 6 in Section 8.4 for the appropriate finite Fourier transform.)

   (b) Simplify the solution when $f(r) \equiv 0$, $g(r, t) \equiv 0$, and $f_1(t)$ is constant.

8. A cylinder of length L and radius r_2 is initially at temperature $f(r, z)$, $0 \le r \le r_2$, $0 \le z \le L$. For time $t > 0$, the face $z = 0$ is insulated, face $z = L$ has a time-dependent temperature $f_1(t)$, and the round surface $r = r_2$ has temperature $f_2(t)$. Find the temperature of the cylinder for $t > 0$.

9. A hemisphere $x^2 + y^2 + z^2 \le r_2^2$, $z \ge 0$, is initially at temperature zero throughout. For time $t > 0$, its base $z = 0$ continues to be held at temperature zero, but the surface of the hemisphere has a time-dependent temperature $f_1(t)$. Find a series representation for temperature inside the hemisphere. (*Hint:* You will need the eigenfunctions from Exercise 8 in Section 8.4.)

10. Solve Example 5 if the constant temperature on $r = r_2$ is replaced by $f(\theta) = \sin\theta$.

11. (a) Solve Example 5 when the initial temperature of the plate is $f(r, \theta)$.

    (b) Does the solution reduce to that of Example 5 when $f(r, \theta) = 0$?

12. Solve Exercise 2 when the initial temperature of the plate is $f(r, \theta)$.

13. Solve Example 5 if heat is exchanged with a constant-temperature environment along the edge $r = r_2$ according to Newton's law of cooling and the initial temperature of the plate is $f(r, \theta)$.

Part B—Vibrations

14. (a) Find the displacement of a circular membrane of radius r_2 that is initially $(t = 0)$ at rest but is displaced according to $f(r, \theta)$, the boundary of which is displaced permanently according to $f_1(\theta)$.

    (b) Simplify the solution when $f(r, \theta)$ and $f_1(\theta)$ are independent of θ.

15. Solve the following nonhomogeneous version of Exercise 22 in Section 9.1:

$$\frac{\partial^2 y}{\partial t^2} = -g\frac{\partial}{\partial x}\left(x\frac{\partial y}{\partial x}\right) + \frac{F(x, t)}{\rho}, \qquad 0 < x < L, \qquad t > 0,$$

$$y(L, t) = 0, \qquad t > 0,$$

$$y(x, 0) = f(x), \qquad 0 < x < L,$$

$$y_t(x, 0) = h(x), \qquad 0 < x < L.$$

16. A circular membrane of radius r_2 is initially at rest on the xy-plane. For time $t > 0$, its edge is forced to undergo periodic oscillations described by $A \sin\omega t$, A a constant. Use finite Fourier transforms to find its displacement as a function of r and t. Include a discussion of resonance.

17. A circular membrane of radius r_2 is initially at rest on the xy-plane. For time $t > 0$, a periodic vertical force per unit area $A \sin\omega t$ (A a constant) acts at every point in the membrane. If its edge $r = r_2$ is fixed on the xy-plane, find its displacement.

18. Discuss the solution of Example 6 when $\omega = c\lambda_{0k}$ for some k.

19. Do the solutions of Example 6 and Exercise 18 reduce to those of Exercise 16 when $f(r, \theta) \equiv 0$?

Part C—Potential, Steady-State Heat Conduction, and Static Deflections of Membranes

20. A solid cylinder is bounded by the planes $\theta = 0$ and $\theta = \beta$ and the curved surface $r = r_0$ $(0 \le \theta \le \beta)$. A constant charge density σ exists inside the cylinder. If the three bounding surfaces are all held at potential zero, find the potential interior to the cylinder. Special consideration is required for the cases $\beta = \pi/2$, π, and $3\pi/2$.

21. An infinite cylinder of radius r_2 has charge density kr^n, $k > 0$ and $n > 0$ constants. If the surface of the cylinder has potential $f(\theta)$, what is the interior potential?

22. A hemisphere $x^2 + y^2 + z^2 \le r_2^2, z \ge 0$, has a constant charge σ throughout. If potentials on the rounded and flat surfaces are both specified constants, but different ones, find the potential inside. (You will need the results of Exercise 5 in Section 8.6 and Exercise 8 in Section 8.5.)

23. A thin plate is in the shape of a sector of a circle bounded by the lines $\theta = 0$ and $\theta = \beta < \pi$ and the arc $r = r_2, 0 \le \theta \le \beta$. Edge $\theta = \beta$ is insulated, as are the top and bottom of the plate. Heat is removed from the plate along the edge $\theta = 0$ at a constant rate $q > 0$ W/m². Along the curved edge $r = r_2$, heat is also removed at a constant rate $Q > 0$ W/m². Heat is being generated at each point in the plate at a uniform rate of g W/m³.

    (a) Formulate the boundary value problem for steady-state temperature in the plate. (See Exercises 16 and 17 in Section 1.2 for the boundary conditions along $\theta = 0$ and $r = r_2$.) What condition must q, Q, and g satisfy?

    (b) Solve the problem in (a).

9.3   Hankel Transforms

Fourier transforms have been used to remove Cartesian coordinates on infinite intervals from (initial) boundary value problems; Fourier sine and cosine transforms are applicable to Cartesian coordinates on semi-infinite intervals. For problems in polar and cylindrical coordinates wherein the radial coordinate has range $r \ge 0$, the Hankel transform is prominent. It is based on Bessel's differential equation

$$\frac{d}{dr}\left(r\frac{dR}{dr}\right) + \left(\lambda^2 r - \frac{v^2}{r}\right)R = 0, \qquad r > 0, \qquad v \ge 0. \tag{79}$$

We have already seen that solutions of this differential equation that are bounded near $r = 0$ are multiples of

$$R(r) = J_v(\lambda r). \tag{80}$$

In order to associate a transform with $J_v(\lambda r)$, we must be aware of the behavior of Bessel functions for large r. It is shown in the theory of asymptotics that $J_v(r)$ may be approximated for large r by

$$J_v(r) \approx \sqrt{\frac{2}{\pi r}} \cos\left(r - \frac{\pi}{4} - \frac{v\pi}{2}\right), \tag{81}$$

the approximation being better the larger the value of r. This means that for large r, $J_v(r)$ is oscillatory with an amplitude that decays at the same rate as $1/\sqrt{r}$.

    Corresponding to the corollary of Theorem 1 in Section 7.2, we have the following *Hankel integral formula*.

Theorem 1

If $\sqrt{r}f(r)$ is absolutely integrable on $0 < r < \infty$, and $f(r)$ is piecewise smooth on every finite interval, then for $0 < r < \infty$,

$$\frac{f(r+) + f(r-)}{2} = \int_0^\infty \lambda A(\lambda) J_v(\lambda r) \, d\lambda \tag{82a}$$

where

$$A(\lambda) = \int_0^\infty rf(r) J_v(\lambda r) \, dr. \tag{82b}$$

In view of the asymptotic behavior of $J_v(r)$ in expression (81), it is clear that absolute integrability of $\sqrt{r}f(r)$ guarantees convergence of (82b). Associated with this integral formula is the Hankel transform $\tilde{f}_v(\lambda)$ of a function $f(r)$,

$$\tilde{f}_v(\lambda) = \int_0^\infty rf(r) J_v(\lambda r) \, dr, \tag{83a}$$

and its inverse,

$$f(r) = \int_0^\infty \lambda \tilde{f}_v(\lambda) J_v(\lambda r) \, d\lambda, \tag{83b}$$

where it is understood in (83b) that $f(r)$ is defined as the average of left and right limits at points of discontinuity. We place a subscript v on $\tilde{f}_v(\lambda)$ to remind ourselves that the Hankel transform is dependent on the choice of v in (79); changing v changes the transform.

Example 8:   Find the Hankel transform $\tilde{f}_v(\lambda)$ of

$$f(r) = \begin{cases} r^v & 0 < r < a \\ 0 & r > a \end{cases}.$$

Solution: By definition (83a),

$$\tilde{f}_v(\lambda) = \int_0^\infty r^{v+1} J_v(\lambda r) \, dr = \int_0^a r^{v+1} J_v(\lambda r) \, dr.$$

If we set $u = \lambda r$, then

$$\tilde{f}_v(\lambda) = \int_0^{\lambda a} \left(\frac{u}{\lambda}\right)^{v+1} J_v(u) \frac{du}{\lambda} = \frac{1}{\lambda^{v+2}} \int_0^{\lambda a} u^{v+1} J_v(u) \, du$$

$$= \frac{1}{\lambda^{v+2}} \int_0^{\lambda a} \frac{d}{du} [u^{v+1} J_{v+1}(u)] \, du \quad \text{[see equation (39) in Section 8.3]}$$

$$= \frac{1}{\lambda} a^{v+1} J_{v+1}(\lambda a).$$

The inverse Hankel transform (83b) then gives

$$\int_0^\infty \lambda \left(\frac{1}{\lambda} a^{v+1} J_{v+1}(\lambda a)\right) J_v(\lambda r) \, d\lambda = \begin{cases} r^v & 0 < r < a \\ a^v/2 & r = a, \\ 0 & r > a \end{cases}$$

and from this we obtain the following useful integration formula:

$$\int_0^\infty J_{v+1}(\lambda a)J_v(\lambda r)\,d\lambda = \begin{cases} \dfrac{1}{a}\left(\dfrac{r}{a}\right)^v & 0 < r < a \\ 1/(2a) & r = a. \\ 0 & r > a \end{cases}$$ ■

Example 9:   Use the Hankel transform to find an integral representation for the solution of the heat conduction problem

$$\frac{\partial U}{\partial t} = k\left(\frac{\partial^2 U}{\partial r^2} + \frac{1}{r}\frac{\partial U}{\partial r}\right), \qquad r > 0, \qquad t > 0, \tag{84a}$$

$$U(r,0) = f(r), \qquad r > 0. \tag{84b}$$

Solution: Because the Bessel function $J_0(r)$ results when separation of variables is performed on the PDE, we apply the Hankel transform associated with $J_0(r)$, namely,

$$\tilde{f}(\lambda) = \int_0^\infty rf(r)J_0(\lambda r)\,dr,$$

where we have suppressed the zero subscript on $\tilde{f}(\lambda)$. Application of this transform to the PDE gives

$$\frac{d\tilde{U}}{dt} = k\int_0^\infty r\left(\frac{\partial^2 U}{\partial r^2} + \frac{1}{r}\frac{\partial U}{\partial r}\right)J_0(\lambda r)\,dr$$

$$= k\left\{r\frac{\partial U}{\partial r}J_0(\lambda r)\right\}_0^\infty - k\int_0^\infty \frac{\partial U}{\partial r}\left(\frac{d}{dr}[rJ_0(\lambda r)] - J_0(\lambda r)\right)dr$$

$$= -k\int_0^\infty \frac{\partial U}{\partial r}r\frac{d}{dr}[J_0(\lambda r)]\,dr \qquad \left(\text{provided } \lim_{r\to\infty}\sqrt{r}\,\frac{\partial U}{\partial r} = 0\right)$$

$$= -k\left\{Ur\frac{d}{dr}[J_0(\lambda r)]\right\}_0^\infty + k\int_0^\infty U\frac{d}{dr}\left(r\frac{dJ_0(\lambda r)}{dr}\right)dr$$

$$= k\int_0^\infty U(-\lambda^2 rJ_0(\lambda r))\,dr \qquad \left(\text{provided } \lim_{r\to\infty}\sqrt{r}\,U = 0\right)$$

$$= -k\lambda^2\tilde{U}.$$

Thus, $\tilde{U}(\lambda, t)$ must satisfy the ODE

$$\frac{d\tilde{U}}{dt} + k\lambda^2\tilde{U} = 0 \tag{85a}$$

subject to the transform of (84b),

$$\tilde{U}(\lambda, 0) = \tilde{f}(\lambda) = \int_0^\infty rf(r)J_0(\lambda r)\,dr. \tag{85b}$$

The solution of this problem is

$$\tilde{U}(\lambda, t) = \tilde{f}(\lambda)e^{-k\lambda^2 t}, \tag{86}$$

and therefore

$$U(r, t) = \int_0^\infty \lambda \tilde{f}(\lambda)e^{-k\lambda^2 t} J_0(\lambda r)\, d\lambda. \qquad \blacksquare \tag{87}$$

Exercises 9.3

Part A—Heat Conduction

1. Heat is generated at a constant rate g W/m^2 inside the cylinder $0 < r < a$ for time $t > 0$. If the temperature of space is zero at time $t = 0$, find the temperature at all points for $t > 0$.

2. An infinite wedge is bounded by the straight edges $\theta = 0$ and $\theta = \alpha\,(0 < \alpha < 2\pi)$. At time $t = 0$, its temperature is zero throughout, and for $t > 0$, its edges $\theta = 0$ and $\theta = \alpha$ are held at constant temperature $\bar{U}$. Find the temperature in the wedge for $t > 0$. *Hint:* Apply a finite Fourier transform with respect to θ and a Hankel transform with respect to r. You will need the result that

$$\int_0^\infty \frac{J_\nu(x)}{x}\, dx = \frac{1}{\nu}.$$

Part B—Vibrations

3. (a) A very large membrane is given an initial displacement that is only a function $f(r)$ of distance r from some fixed point but has no initial velocity. Find an integral representation for its subsequent displacement.

   (b) Use the result that

   $$\int_0^\infty e^{-a\lambda} J_0(\lambda r)\, d\lambda = \frac{1}{\sqrt{r^2 + a^2}}$$

   to simplify the solution when $f(r) = A/\sqrt{1 + (r/a)^2}$, a and A positive constants, to

   $$z(r, t) = aA \int_0^\infty e^{-a\lambda} \cos c\lambda t\, J_0(\lambda r)\, d\lambda.$$

   (c) By expressing $\cos c\lambda t$ as the real part of $e^{ic\lambda t}$, show that the solution can be expressed in the form

   $$z(r, t) = \frac{aA\sqrt{\sqrt{(r^2 + a^2 - c^2 t^2)^2 + 4a^2 c^2 t^2} + (r^2 + a^2 - c^2 t^2)}}{\sqrt{2}\sqrt{(r^2 + a^2 - c^2 t^2)^2 + 4a^2 c^2 t^2}}.$$

4. Repeat part (a) of Exercise 3 when $f(r)$ is the initial velocity of the membrane and it has no initial displacement.

Part C—Potential, Steady-State Heat Conduction, and Static Deflections of Membranes

5. A disc $0 \leq r < a$ in the xy-plane emits heat into the region $z > 0$ at a constant rate Q W/m^2. If the remainder $(r > a)$ of the plane is insulated, the steady-state temperature in $z > 0$ must satisfy

$$\frac{\partial^2 U}{\partial r^2} + \frac{1}{r}\frac{\partial U}{\partial r} + \frac{\partial^2 U}{\partial z^2} = 0, \qquad r > 0, \qquad z > 0,$$

$$\frac{\partial U(r,0)}{\partial z} = \begin{cases} -Q/\kappa & 0 \leq r < a \\ 0 & r > a \end{cases}.$$

Find $U(r, z)$.

6. Repeat Exercise 5 if the disc is held at constant temperature $\bar{U}$ and the remainder of the xy-plane is held at temperature zero.

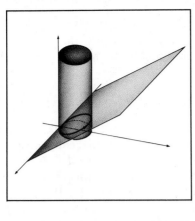

T   E   N

Laplace Transforms

10.1 Introduction

The Laplace transform is a mathematical operation, like the Fourier transform, that replaces differentiation problems with algebraic ones, an essential simplification for ordinary and partial differential equations. Fourier transforms are associated with space variables; the Laplace transform is associated with time. In this section we give a brief review of the transform and its simple properties; the complex inversion integral is developed in Section 10.3, and the transform is applied to initial boundary value problems in Sections 10.2, 10.4, and 10.5.

The Laplace transform $\tilde{f}(s)$ of a function $f(t)$ is defined by

$$\tilde{f}(s) = \mathscr{L}\{f(t)\} = \int_0^\infty e^{-st}f(t)\,dt, \tag{1}$$

provided the improper integral converges. When $f(t)$ is piecewise continuous on every finite interval $0 \le t \le T$, and $f(t)$ is of exponential order[†] α, its Laplace transform exists for $s > \alpha$.

[†] A function $f(t)$ is said to be of exponential order α, written $O(e^{\alpha t})$, if there exist constants T and M such that $|f(t)| < Me^{\alpha t}$ for all $t > T$. For example, e^{2t} is $O(e^{2t})$, $\sin t$ is $O(e^{0t})$, and t^n, n a nonnegative integer, is $O(e^{\varepsilon t})$ for arbitrarily small $\varepsilon > 0$.

351

When $\tilde{f}(s)$ is the Laplace transform of $f(t)$, we call $f(t)$ the *inverse Laplace transform of* $\tilde{f}(s)$ and write

$$f(t) = \mathscr{L}^{-1}\{\tilde{f}(s)\}. \qquad (2)$$

The Laplace transforms contained in Table 10.1 are fundamental to applications of the transform to ordinary and partial differential equations; more extensive tables are contained in such references as *Tables of Integral Transforms*, Vol. 1, by Erdelyi, Magnus, Oberhettinger, and Tricomi (New York: McGraw-Hill, 1954). All but the last entry are straightforward applications of definition (1). The transform of $t^{-1/2}$ requires the improper integral of e^{-t^2} over the interval $0 \le t < \infty$, an integral that was evaluated in Exercise 24 of Section 7.2.

Table 10.1

$f(t)$	$\tilde{f}(s)$	$f(t)$	$\tilde{f}(s)$
t^n	$\dfrac{n!}{s^{n+1}}$	$\sinh at$	$\dfrac{a}{s^2 - a^2}$
e^{at}	$\dfrac{1}{s-a}$	$\cosh at$	$\dfrac{s}{s^2 - a^2}$
$\sin at$	$\dfrac{a}{s^2 + a^2}$	$t \sinh at$	$\dfrac{2as}{(s^2 - a^2)^2}$
$\cos at$	$\dfrac{s}{s^2 + a^2}$	$t \cosh at$	$\dfrac{s^2 + a^2}{(s^2 - a^2)^2}$
$t \sin at$	$\dfrac{2as}{(s^2 + a^2)^2}$	$\dfrac{1}{\sqrt{t}}$	$\sqrt{\dfrac{\pi}{s}}$
$t \cos at$	$\dfrac{s^2 - a^2}{(s^2 + a^2)^2}$		

Because the Laplace transform is an integral transform, $\tilde{f}(s)$ is unique for given $f(t)$, but there exist many functions $f(t)$ having the same transform $\tilde{f}(s)$. For example, the functions

$$f(t) = t^2 \quad \text{and} \quad g(t) = \begin{cases} 0 & t = 1 \\ t^2 & t \ne 1, 2, \\ 0 & t = 2 \end{cases}$$

which are identical except for their values at $t = 1$ and $t = 2$, both have the same transform $2/s^3$. What we are saying is that because the Laplace transform is not a one-to-one operation, the inverse transform $\mathscr{L}^{-1}\{\tilde{f}(s)\}$ in (2) cannot be a true inverse. In Section 10.3 we derive a formula for calculating inverse transforms, and this formula always yields a continuous function $f(t)$, if this is possible. In the event that this is not possible, the formula gives a piecewise continuous function whose value is the average of right and left limits at discontinuities, namely, $[f(t+) + f(t-)]/2$. This is reminiscent of equation (14a) in Chapter 4 for Fourier series and equation (6) in Chapter 7 for Fourier integrals. The importance, then, of this formula is that it defines $f(t) = \mathscr{L}^{-1}\{\tilde{f}(s)\}$ in a unique way. Other functions that have the same transform $\tilde{f}(s)$

differ from $f(t)$ only in their values at isolated points; they cannot differ from $f(t)$ over an entire interval $a \le t \le b$. In compliance with this anticipated formula, we adopt the procedure in this section and the next of always choosing a continuous function $\mathcal{L}^{-1}\{\tilde{f}(s)\}$ for given $\tilde{f}(s)$ or, when this is not possible, a piecewise continuous function.

The Laplace transform and its inverse are linear operators. Some of their simple properties are summarized below.

One of two shifting properties is

$$\mathcal{L}\left(e^{at}f(t)\right) = \tilde{f}(s - a), \tag{3a}$$

$$\mathcal{L}^{-1}\{\tilde{f}(s - a)\} = e^{at}f(t) \tag{3b}$$

(see Exercise 1). It states that multiplication by an exponential e^{at} in the time domain is equivalent to a translation in the s domain. For example, since $\mathcal{L}\{\cos 2t\} = s/(s^2 + 4)$, (3a) implies that

$$\mathcal{L}(e^{3t}\cos 2t) = \frac{s - 3}{(s - 3)^2 + 4}.$$

The other shifting property is

$$\mathcal{L}\{f(t - a)H(t - a)\} = e^{-as}\tilde{f}(s) \tag{4a}$$

and

$$\mathcal{L}^{-1}\left(e^{-as}\tilde{f}(s)\right) = f(t - a)H(t - a), \tag{4b}$$

where $H(t - a)$ is the Heaviside unit step function. It has value 0 when $t < a$ and value 1 when $t > a$. (See Exercise 2 for a proof of these properties.) These properties imply that multiplication by an exponential e^{-as} in the s domain is equivalent to a translation in the time domain. Graphs of $f(t)$ and $f(t - a)H(t - a)$ are shown in Figure 10.1.

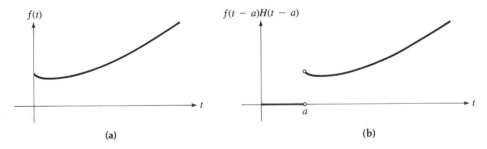

$f(t)$

$f(t - a)H(t - a)$

Figure 10.1

(a)

(b)

The following property is often called the *change of scale* property:

$$\mathcal{L}\{f(at)\} = a^{-1}\tilde{f}\left(\frac{s}{a}\right), \tag{5a}$$

$$\mathcal{L}^{-1}\{\tilde{f}(as)\} = a^{-1}f\left(\frac{t}{a}\right) \tag{5b}$$

(see Exercise 3). For instance, since $\mathcal{L}^{-1}\{1/(s^2 + 2)\} = (1/\sqrt{2})\sin\sqrt{2}\,t$, (5b) implies that

$$\mathcal{L}^{-1}\left(\frac{1}{4s^2 + 2}\right) = \mathcal{L}^{-1}\left(\frac{1}{(2s)^2 + 2}\right) = \frac{1}{2}\left(\frac{1}{\sqrt{2}}\right)\sin\left(\frac{\sqrt{2}\,t}{2}\right) = \frac{1}{2\sqrt{2}}\sin\left(\frac{t}{\sqrt{2}}\right).$$

When a function is periodic with period P, the improper integral in (1) may be replaced by an integral over $0 \le t \le P$:

$$\mathscr{L}\{f(t)\} = \frac{1}{1 - e^{-sP}} \int_0^P e^{-st}f(t)\,dt \tag{6}$$

(see Exercise 4).

The following theorem and its corollary eliminate much of the work when Laplace transforms are applied to initial boundary value problems.

Theorem 1

Suppose $f(t)$ is continuous with a piecewise continuous first derivative on every finite interval $0 \le t \le T$. If $f(t)$ is $O(e^{\alpha t})$, then $\mathscr{L}\{f'(t)\}$ exists for $s > \alpha$ and

$$\mathscr{L}\{f'(t)\} = s\tilde{f}(s) - f(0). \tag{7a}$$

Proof: If $t_j, j = 1,\dots,n$ denote the discontinuities of $f'(t)$ in $0 \le t \le T$, then

$$\int_0^T e^{-st}f'(t)\,dt = \sum_{j=0}^n \int_{t_j}^{t_{j+1}} e^{-st}f'(t)\,dt,$$

where $t_0 = 0$ and $t_{n+1} = T$. Since $f'(t)$ is continuous on each subinterval, we may integrate by parts on each subinterval:

$$\int_0^T e^{-st}f'(t)\,dt = \sum_{j=0}^n \left(\{e^{-st}f(t)\}_{t_j}^{t_{j+1}} + s \int_{t_j}^{t_{j+1}} e^{-st}f(t)\,dt \right).$$

Because $f(t)$ is continuous, $f(t_j+) = f(t_j-), j = 1,\dots,n$, and therefore

$$\int_0^T e^{-st}f'(t)\,dt = -f(0) + e^{-sT}f(T) + s \int_0^T e^{-st}f(t)\,dt.$$

Thus, $$\mathscr{L}\{f'(t)\} = \int_0^\infty e^{-st}f'(t)\,dt = \lim_{T \to \infty} \int_0^T e^{-st}f'(t)\,dt$$

$$= \lim_{T \to \infty} \left(-f(0) + e^{-sT}f(T) + s \int_0^T e^{-st}f(t)\,dt \right)$$

$$= s\tilde{f}(s) - f(0) + \lim_{T \to \infty} e^{-sT}f(T),$$

provided the limit on the right exists. Since $f(t)$ is $O(e^{\alpha t})$, there exist M and $\bar{T}$ such that for $t > \bar{T}$, $|f(t)| < Me^{\alpha t}$. Thus, for $T > \bar{T}$,

$$e^{-sT}|f(T)| < e^{-sT}Me^{\alpha T} = Me^{(\alpha - s)T},$$

which approaches zero as T approaches infinity (provided $s > \alpha$). Consequently, $\mathscr{L}\{f'(t)\} = s\tilde{f}(s) - f(0)$.   ∎

This result is easily extended to second-order derivatives. The extension is stated in the following corollary and is verified in Exercise 5. For extensions when $f(t)$ is only piecewise continuous, see Exercise 35.

Corollary	Suppose $f(t)$ and $f'(t)$ are continuous and $f''(t)$ is piecewise continuous on every finite interval $0 \le t \le T$. If $f(t)$ and $f'(t)$ are $O(e^{\alpha t})$, then $\mathscr{L}\{f''(t)\}$ exists for $s > \alpha$, and

$$\mathscr{L}\{f''(t)\} = s^2\tilde{f}(s) - sf(0) - f'(0). \tag{7b}$$

The following examples use these properties and at the same time indicate how Laplace transforms reduce ordinary differential equations to algebraic problems.

Example 1:   Solve the differential equation

$$y'' - 2y' + y = 2e^t, \qquad y(0) = y'(0) = 0.$$

Solution: When we take Laplace transforms of both sides of the differential equation and use linearity of the operator,

$$\mathscr{L}\{y''\} - 2\mathscr{L}\{y'\} + \mathscr{L}\{y\} = 2\mathscr{L}\{e^t\}.$$

Properties (7a, b) yield

$$[s^2\tilde{y}(s) - sy(0) - y'(0)] - 2[s\tilde{y}(s) - y(0)] + \tilde{y}(s) = \frac{2}{s-1}.$$

We now use the initial conditions $y(0) = y'(0) = 0$,

$$s^2\tilde{y} - 2s\tilde{y} + \tilde{y} = \frac{2}{s-1}$$

and solve this equation for $\tilde{y}(s)$:

$$\tilde{y}(s) = \frac{2}{(s-1)^3}.$$

The required function $y(t)$ can now be obtained by taking the inverse transform of $\tilde{y}(s)$:

$$y(t) = \mathscr{L}^{-1}\left(\frac{2}{(s-1)^3}\right) = 2\mathscr{L}^{-1}\left(\frac{1}{(s-1)^3}\right) \quad \text{(by linearity)}$$

$$= 2e^t\mathscr{L}^{-1}\left(\frac{1}{s^3}\right) \quad \text{[by (3b)]}$$

$$= 2e^t\left(\frac{t^2}{2}\right) \quad \text{(from Table 10.1)}$$

$$= t^2e^t. \qquad\qquad\blacksquare$$

Example 2:   Solve the differential equation

$$y'' + 4y = 3\cos 2t, \qquad y(0) = 1, \qquad y'(0) = 0.$$

Solution: When we take the Laplace transforms of the differential equation and use the initial conditions,

$$[s^2\tilde{y} - s(1) - 0] + 4\tilde{y} = \frac{3s}{s^2+4}.$$

The solution of this equation for $\tilde{y}(s)$ is

$$\tilde{y}(s) = \frac{3s}{(s^2 + 4)^2} + \frac{s}{s^2 + 4},$$

and Table 10.1 gives

$$y(t) = 3\left(\frac{t}{4}\sin 2t\right) + \cos 2t. \qquad \blacksquare$$

When solving ordinary differential equations by means of Laplace transforms, considerable emphasis is placed on partial fraction decompositions of transform functions $\tilde{y}(s)$, and rightly so, because for ODEs, transform functions are often rational functions of s. Once the transform is decomposed into constituent fractions, and provided the decomposition is not too complicated, inverse transforms of individual terms can be located in tables. Unfortunately, transforms arising from PDEs are seldom rational functions, and there is therefore little point in our giving a detailed discussion of partial fractions.

It is often necessary in applications to find the inverse transform of the product of two functions $\tilde{f}(s)\tilde{g}(s)$ when inverse transforms of $\tilde{f}(s)$ and $\tilde{g}(s)$ are known. Recalling that convolutions were introduced for precisely the same problem associated with Fourier transforms, it should not be surprising that convolutions are defined for Laplace transforms. The convolution of two functions $f(t)$ and $g(t)$ is defined as

$$f * g = \int_0^t f(u)g(t - u)\, du. \tag{8}$$

It has the same properties as convolution (32) in Chapter 7 [see equations (36) in Exercises 7.3], and its importance lies in the following theorem.

Theorem 2

If $f(t)$ and $g(t)$ are $O(e^{\alpha t})$ and piecewise continuous on every finite interval $0 \le t \le T$, then

$$\mathscr{L}\{f * g\} = \mathscr{L}\{f(t)\}\mathscr{L}\{g(t)\}, \qquad s > \alpha. \tag{9a}$$

Proof: If $\tilde{f}(s) = \mathscr{L}\{f(t)\}$ and $\tilde{g}(s) = \mathscr{L}\{g(t)\}$, then

$$\tilde{f}(s)\tilde{g}(s) = \int_0^\infty e^{-su}f(u)\, du \int_0^\infty e^{-s\tau}g(\tau)\, d\tau$$

$$= \int_0^\infty \int_0^\infty e^{-s(u+\tau)}f(u)g(\tau)\, d\tau\, du.$$

Suppose we change variables of integration in the inner integral with respect to τ by setting $t = u + \tau$. Then

$$\tilde{f}(s)\tilde{g}(s) = \int_0^\infty \int_u^\infty e^{-st}f(u)g(t - u)\, dt\, du.$$

Now, $g(t)$ is defined only for $t \geq 0$. If we set $g(t) = 0$ for $t < 0$, we may write

$$\tilde{f}(s)\tilde{g}(s) = \lim_{T \to \infty} \int_0^T \int_0^\infty e^{-st} f(u)g(t-u)\,dt\,du.$$

We would like to interchange orders of integration, but to do so requires that the inner integral converge uniformly with respect to u. To verify that this is indeed the case, we note that since $f(t)$ and $g(t)$ are $O(e^{\alpha t})$ and piecewise continuous on every finite interval $0 \leq t \leq T$, there exists a constant M such that for all $t \geq 0$, $|f(t)| \leq Me^{\alpha t}$ and $|g(t)| \leq Me^{\alpha t}$. For each $u \geq 0$, we therefore have $|e^{-st} f(u)g(t-u)| < M^2 e^{-st} e^{\alpha u} e^{\alpha(t-u)} = M^2 e^{-t(s-\alpha)}$. Thus,

$$\left| \int_0^\infty e^{-st} f(u)g(t-u)\,dt \right| < M^2 \int_0^\infty e^{-t(s-\alpha)}\,dt = M^2 \left\{ \frac{e^{-t(s-\alpha)}}{\alpha - s} \right\}_0^\infty = \frac{M^2}{s-\alpha},$$

provided $s > \alpha$ and the improper integral is uniformly convergent with respect to u. The order of integration in the expression for $\tilde{f}(s)\tilde{g}(s)$ may therefore be interchanged, and we obtain

$$\tilde{f}(s)\tilde{g}(s) = \lim_{T \to \infty} \int_0^\infty e^{-st} \int_0^T f(u)g(t-u)\,du\,dt$$

$$= \lim_{T \to \infty} \left(\int_0^T e^{-st} \int_0^T f(u)g(t-u)\,du\,dt + \int_T^\infty e^{-st} \int_0^T f(u)g(t-u)\,du\,dt \right).$$

Since

$$\left| \int_T^\infty e^{-st} \int_0^T f(u)g(t-u)\,du\,dt \right| < \int_T^\infty \int_0^T M^2 e^{-t(s-\alpha)}\,du\,dt$$

$$= M^2 T \left\{ \frac{e^{-t(s-\alpha)}}{\alpha - s} \right\}_T^\infty = \frac{M^2 T e^{-T(s-\alpha)}}{s-\alpha},$$

provided $s > \alpha$, it follows that

$$\lim_{T \to \infty} \int_T^\infty e^{-st} \int_0^T f(u)g(t-u)\,du\,dt = 0.$$

Further, due to the fact that $g(t-u) = 0$ for $u > t$, we may write, for $T > t$,

$$\int_0^T e^{-st} \int_0^T f(u)g(t-u)\,du\,dt = \int_0^T e^{-st} \int_0^t f(u)g(t-u)\,du\,dt = \int_0^T e^{-st} f * g\,dt.$$

Thus,

$$\tilde{f}(s)\tilde{g}(s) = \lim_{T \to \infty} \int_0^T e^{-st} f * g\,dt = \mathscr{L}\{f * g\}.$$ ∎

More important in practice is the inverse of (9a).

Corollary

If $\mathscr{L}^{-1}\{\tilde{f}(s)\} = f(t)$ and $\mathscr{L}^{-1}\{\tilde{g}(s)\} = g(t)$, where $f(t)$ and $g(t)$ are $O(e^{\alpha t})$ and piecewise continuous on every finite interval, then

$$\mathscr{L}^{-1}\{\tilde{f}(s)\tilde{g}(s)\} = \int_0^t f(u)g(t-u)\,du. \tag{9b}$$

As an example to illustrate this corollary, consider finding $\mathcal{L}^{-1}\{2/[s^2(s^2+4)]\}$. Since $\mathcal{L}^{-1}\{2/(s^2+4)\} = \sin 2t$ and $\mathcal{L}^{-1}\{1/s^2\} = t$, we can state that the inverse transform of $2/[s^2(s^2+4)]$ is

$$\mathcal{L}^{-1}\left(\frac{2}{s^2(s^2+4)}\right) = \int_0^t u \sin 2(t-u)\,du$$

$$= \left\{\frac{u}{2}\cos 2(t-u) + \frac{1}{4}\sin 2(t-u)\right\}_0^t$$

$$= \frac{t}{2} - \frac{1}{4}\sin 2t.$$

Convolutions are particularly important in ODEs that contain unspecified forcing functions.

Example 3:

Find the solution of the problem

$$y'' + 2y' - y = f(t), \qquad y(0) = A, \qquad y'(0) = B$$

for arbitrary constants A and B and an arbitrary function $f(t)$.

Solution:

When we take Laplace transforms,

$$[s^2\tilde{y} - As - B] + 2[s\tilde{y} - A] - \tilde{y} = \tilde{f}(s),$$

and solve for $\tilde{y}$,

$$\tilde{y}(s) = \frac{\tilde{f}(s)}{s^2 + 2s - 1} + \frac{As + B + 2A}{s^2 + 2s - 1}.$$

To find the inverse transform of this function, we first note that

$$\mathcal{L}^{-1}\left(\frac{1}{s^2+2s-1}\right) = \mathcal{L}^{-1}\left(\frac{1}{(s+1)^2-2}\right) = e^{-t}\mathcal{L}^{-1}\left(\frac{1}{s^2-2}\right) = \frac{1}{\sqrt{2}}e^{-t}\sinh\sqrt{2}\,t.$$

Convolution property (9b) on the first term of $\tilde{y}(s)$ now yields

$$y(t) = \int_0^t f(u)\frac{1}{\sqrt{2}}e^{-(t-u)}\sinh\sqrt{2}\,(t-u)\,du + \mathcal{L}^{-1}\left(\frac{A(s+1)+(B+A)}{(s+1)^2-2}\right)$$

$$= \frac{1}{\sqrt{2}}\int_0^t f(u)e^{-(t-u)}\sinh\sqrt{2}\,(t-u)\,du + e^{-t}\mathcal{L}^{-1}\left(\frac{As+(B+A)}{s^2-2}\right)$$

$$= \frac{1}{\sqrt{2}}\int_0^t f(u)e^{-(t-u)}\sinh\sqrt{2}\,(t-u)\,du + e^{-t}\left(A\cosh\sqrt{2}\,t + \frac{B+A}{\sqrt{2}}\sinh\sqrt{2}\,t\right).$$

∎

Exercises 10.1

1. (a) Verify shifting property (3).

   (b) Use (3a) and Table 10.1 to calculate Laplace transforms for the following:
      (i) $f(t) = t^3 e^{-5t}$ (ii) $f(t) = e^{-t}\cos 2t + e^{3t}\sin 2t$
      (iii) $f(t) = e^{at}\cosh 4t - e^{-at}\sinh 4t$

(c) Use (3b) and Table 10.1 to calculate inverse Laplace transforms for the following:

(i) $\tilde{f}(s) = 1/(s^2 - 2s + 5)$ (ii) $\tilde{f}(s) = 1/\sqrt{s + 3}$

(iii) $\tilde{f}(s) = s/(s^2 + 4s + 1)$

2. (a) Verify shifting property (4).

(b) Use (4a) and Table 10.1 to calculate Laplace transforms for the following:

(i) $f(t) = \begin{cases} 0 & 0 < t < 3 \\ t - 2 & t > 3 \end{cases}$ (ii) $f(t) = \begin{cases} 0 & 0 < t < a \\ 1 & t > a \end{cases}$

(iii) $f(t) = \begin{cases} 1 & 0 < t < a \\ 0 & t > a \end{cases}$ (iv) $f(t) = \begin{cases} 0 & 0 < t < a \\ 1 & a < t < b \\ 0 & t > b \end{cases}$

(c) Use (4b) and Table 10.1 to calculate inverse Laplace transforms for the following:

(i) $\tilde{f}(s) = e^{-2s}/s^2$ (ii) $\tilde{f}(s) = e^{-3s}/(s^2 + 1)$

(iii) $\tilde{f}(s) = se^{-5s}/(s^2 - 2)$

3. (a) Verify change of scale property (5).

(b) Use (5a) and Table 10.1 to calculate Laplace transforms for the following:

(i) $f(t) = 4t^2 + \sinh 2t$ (ii) $f(t) = e^{4t} \cos 4t$

(c) Use (5b) and Table 10.1 to calculate inverse Laplace transforms for the following:

(i) $\tilde{f}(s) = s/(9s^2 + 2)$ (ii) $\tilde{f}(s) = \dfrac{1}{4s^2 - 6s - 5}$

4. (a) Verify equation (6).

(b) Find Laplace transforms for the following functions:

(i) $f(t) = t, \quad 0 < t < a, \quad f(t + a) = f(t)$

(ii) $f(t) = \begin{cases} 1 & 0 < t < a \\ -1 & a < t < 2a \end{cases}, \quad f(t + 2a) = f(t)$

(iii) $f(t) = |\sin at|$

5. Verify equation (7b).

In Exercises 6–9, use convolutions to find the inverse transform for the function.

6. $\tilde{f}(s) = \dfrac{1}{s(s + 1)}$ 7. $\tilde{f}(s) = \dfrac{1}{(s^2 + 1)(s^2 + 4)}$

8. $\tilde{f}(s) = \dfrac{s}{(s + 4)(s^2 - 2)}$ 9. $\tilde{f}(s) = \dfrac{s}{(s^2 - 4)(s^2 - 9)}$

In Exercises 10–15, find the Laplace transform of the function.

10. $f(t) = \begin{cases} 2t & 0 \le t \le 1 \\ t & t > 1 \end{cases}$ 11. $f(t) = \begin{cases} t^2 & 0 \le t \le 1 \\ 2t & t > 1 \end{cases}$

12. $f(t) = \begin{cases} t & 0 < t < a \\ 2a - t & a < t < 2a \end{cases}, \quad f(t + 2a) = f(t)$

13. $f(t) = \begin{cases} 1 & 0 < t < a \\ 0 & a < t < 2a \end{cases}, \quad f(t + 2a) = f(t)$

14. $f(t) = \begin{cases} 0 & 0 < t < a \\ 1 & t > a \end{cases}$ 15. $f(t) = \begin{cases} 0 & 0 < t < a \\ 1 & a < t < a + 1 \\ 0 & t > a + 1 \end{cases}$

In Exercises 16–25, find the inverse Laplace transform for the function.

16. $\tilde{f}(s) = \dfrac{s}{s^2 - 3s + 2}$

17. $\tilde{f}(s) = \dfrac{4s + 1}{(s^2 + s)(4s^2 - 1)}$

18. $\tilde{f}(s) = \dfrac{e^{-3s}}{s + 5}$

19. $\tilde{f}(s) = \dfrac{e^{-2s}}{s^2 + 3s + 2}$

20. $\tilde{f}(s) = \dfrac{1}{s^3 + 1}$

21. $\tilde{f}(s) = \dfrac{5s - 2}{3s^2 + 4s + 8}$

22. $\tilde{f}(s) = \dfrac{e^{-s}(1 - e^{-s})}{s(s^2 + 1)}$

23. $\tilde{f}(s) = \dfrac{s}{(s + 1)^5}$

24. $\tilde{f}(s) = \dfrac{s^2 + 2s + 3}{(s^2 + 2s + 2)(s^2 + 2s + 5)}$

25. $\tilde{f}(s) = \dfrac{s^2}{(s^2 - 4)^2}$

In Exercises 26–32, solve the differential equation.

26. $y'' + 2y' - y = e^t, \quad y(0) = 1, \quad y'(0) = 2$

27. $y'' + y = 2e^{-t}, \quad y(0) = y'(0) = 0$

28. $y'' + 2y' + y = t, \quad y(0) = 0, \quad y'(0) = 1$

29. $y''' - 3y'' + 3y' - y = t^2 e^t, \quad y(0) = 1, \quad y'(0) = 0, \quad y''(0) = -2$

30. $y'' + 9y = \cos 2t, \quad y(0) = 1, \quad y(\pi/2) = -1$

31. $y''' - 3y'' + 3y' - y = t^2 e^t$

32. $y'' - a^2 y = f(t)$

33. Verify that the Laplace transform of a function $f(t)$ that is piecewise continuous on every finite interval $0 \le t \le T$ and is $O(e^{\alpha t})$ exists for $s > \alpha$.

34. (a) Prove that when n is a nonnegative integer, t^n is $O(e^{\varepsilon t})$ for every $\varepsilon > 0$.

(b) Prove that when $f(t)$ is $O(e^{\alpha t})$, $t^n f(t)$ is $O[e^{(\alpha + \varepsilon)t}]$ for every $\varepsilon > 0$.

35. (a) Let $f(t)$ be $O(e^{\alpha t})$ and be continuous for $t \ge 0$ except for a finite discontinuity at $t = t_0 > 0$; and let $f'(t)$ be piecewise continuous on every finite interval $0 \le t \le T$. Show that

$$\mathcal{L}\{f'(t)\} = s\tilde{f}(s) - f(0) - e^{-st_0}[f(t_0+) - f(t_0-)].$$

(b) What is the result in (a) if $t_0 = 0$?

36. Let $f(t)$ and $f'(t)$ be $O(e^{\alpha t})$, let $f'(t)$ be piecewise continuous on every finite interval $0 \le t \le T$, and let $f(t)$ have only a finite number of finite discontinuities for $t \ge 0$. Verify the "initial value theorem,"

$$\lim_{s \to \infty} s\tilde{f}(s) = \lim_{t \to 0^+} f(t).$$

Assume the result that

$$\lim_{s \to \infty} \tilde{f}(s) = 0$$

for functions that are piecewise continuous and of exponential order.

10.2 Laplace Transform Solutions for Problems on Unbounded Domains

In this section we illustrate the use of Laplace transforms on problems over unbounded domains. Such problems do not require the complex inversion formula of Section 10.3. We begin with a heat conduction problem on a semi-infinite interval.

Example 4:   Solve the heat conduction problem

$$\frac{\partial U}{\partial t} = k\frac{\partial^2 U}{\partial x^2}, \qquad x > 0, \qquad t > 0, \tag{10a}$$

$$U(0, t) = U_0, \qquad t > 0, \tag{10b}$$

$$U(x, 0) = 0, \qquad x > 0, \tag{10c}$$

for temperature in a semi-infinite rod that is initially at temperature $0°C$. For time $t > 0$, its end at $x = 0$ is held at constant temperature U_0. (This problem was solved by Fourier sine transforms in Exercise 2 of Section 7.4.)

Solution: When we take Laplace transforms of PDE (10a) and use initial condition (10c), we obtain

$$s\tilde{U} = k\mathscr{L}\left(\frac{\partial^2 U}{\partial x^2}\right).$$

Since the integration with respect to t in the Laplace transform and the differentiation with respect to x are independent, we interchange the order of operations on the right:

$$s\tilde{U} = k\frac{\partial^2 \tilde{U}}{\partial x^2}.$$

Because only derivatives with respect to x remain, we replace the partial derivative with an ordinary derivative:

$$\frac{d^2\tilde{U}}{dx^2} - \frac{s}{k}\tilde{U} = 0, \qquad x > 0. \tag{11a}$$

This ordinary differential equation is subject to the transform of (10b),

$$\tilde{U}(0, s) = \frac{U_0}{s}. \tag{11b}$$

For problems on finite domains, we have found it convenient to express general solutions of equations like (11a) in terms of hyperbolic functions. On infinite and semi-infinite intervals, it is advantageous to use the exponential formulation,

$$\tilde{U}(x, s) = Ae^{\sqrt{s/k}x} + Be^{-\sqrt{s/k}x}. \tag{12}$$

Because $U(x, t)$ must remain bounded as x becomes infinite, so also must $\tilde{U}(x, s)$. We must therefore set $A = 0$, in which case (11b) requires that $B = U_0/s$. Thus,

$$\tilde{U}(x, s) = \frac{U_0}{s}e^{-\sqrt{s/k}x}. \tag{13}$$

The inverse Laplace transform of this function is found in tables:

$$U(x, t) = U_0\mathscr{L}^{-1}\left(\frac{e^{-\sqrt{s/k}x}}{s}\right) = U_0\,\text{erfc}\left(\frac{x}{2\sqrt{kt}}\right), \tag{14}$$

where $\text{erfc}(x)$ is the complementary error function

$$\text{erfc}(x) = 1 - \text{erf}(x) = \frac{2}{\sqrt{\pi}}\int_x^\infty e^{-u^2}\,du. \tag{15}$$

Notice that for any $x > 0$ and any $t > 0$, temperature $U(x, t)$ is positive. This indicates that the abrupt change in temperature at the end $x = 0$ from $0°C$ to U_0 is felt instantaneously at every point in the rod. In other words, energy is "transmitted" infinitely fast along the rod, a property of the heat equation that we mentioned in Section 5.6. ∎

When $U(0, t)$ is a function of time in this example, say $U(0, t) = f_1(t)$, transform (13) is replaced by

$$\tilde{U}(x, s) = \tilde{f}_1(s)e^{-\sqrt{s/k}x}. \tag{16}$$

Because $\mathcal{L}^{-1}\{e^{-a\sqrt{s}}\} = [a/(2\sqrt{\pi t^3})]e^{-a^2/(4t)}$, it follows by convolution property (9b) that

$$U(x, t) = \int_0^t f_1(t - u)\frac{x}{2\sqrt{k\pi u^3}}e^{-x^2/(4ku)}\, du \tag{17a}$$

$$= \frac{x}{2\sqrt{k\pi}}\int_0^t u^{-3/2}f_1(t - u)e^{-x^2/(4ku)}\, du$$

or, alternatively, that

$$U(x, t) = \frac{x}{2\sqrt{k\pi}}\int_0^t (t - u)^{-3/2}f_1(u)e^{-x^2/[4k(t-u)]}\, du. \tag{17b}$$

In the next example we illustrate how a semi-infinite string falling under gravity reacts to one end being fixed.

Example 5:   A semi-infinite string is supported from below so that it lies motionless on the x-axis. At time $t = 0$, the support is removed and gravity is permitted to act on the string. If the end $x = 0$ is fixed at the origin, find the displacement of the string.

Solution: The initial boundary value problem is

$$\frac{\partial^2 y}{\partial t^2} = c^2\frac{\partial^2 y}{\partial x^2} + g, \qquad x > 0, \qquad t > 0, \tag{18a}$$

$$y(0, t) = 0, \qquad t > 0, \tag{18b}$$

$$y(x, 0) = 0, \qquad x > 0, \tag{18c}$$

$$y_t(x, 0) = 0, \qquad x > 0, \tag{18d}$$

where $g = -9.81$. When we apply the Laplace transform to the PDE and use the initial conditions,

$$s^2\tilde{y} = c^2\frac{d^2\tilde{y}}{dx^2} + \frac{g}{s}.$$

Thus, $\tilde{y}(x, s)$ must satisfy the ODE

$$\frac{d^2\tilde{y}}{dx^2} - \frac{s^2}{c^2}\tilde{y} = -\frac{g}{c^2 s}, \qquad x > 0, \tag{19a}$$

subject to the transform of (18b),

$$\tilde{y}(0, s) = 0. \tag{19b}$$

The general solution of (19a) is

$$\tilde{y}(x, s) = Ae^{sx/c} + Be^{-sx/c} + \frac{g}{s^3}.$$

For this function to remain bounded as $x \to \infty$, we must set $A = 0$, in which case boundary condition (19b) requires that $B = -g/s^3$. Hence,

$$\tilde{y}(x, s) = \frac{g}{s^3}(1 - e^{-sx/c}). \tag{20}$$

The inverse transform of this function is

$$y(x, t) = \frac{gt^2}{2} - \frac{g}{2}\left(t - \frac{x}{c}\right)^2 H\left(t - \frac{x}{c}\right), \tag{21}$$

where $H(t - x/c)$ is the Heaviside unit step function. What this says is that a point x in the string falls freely under gravity for $0 < t < x/c$, after which it falls with constant velocity gx/c [since for $t > x/c$, $y(x, t) = -(g/2)(-2xt/c + x^2/c^2)$]. A picture of the string at any given time t_0 is shown in Figure 10.2. It is parabolic for $0 < x < ct_0$ and horizontal for $x > ct_0$. As t_0 increases, the parabolic portion lengthens and the horizontal section drops.

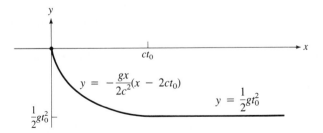

Figure 10.2

It is worthwhile noting that this problem cannot be solved by Fourier sine transforms because a constant function (g in this case) is not absolutely integrable on $0 \le x < \infty$.

Exercises 10.2

Part A—Heat Conduction

1. Solve Exercise 3 in Section 7.4.

2. Show that every solution $U(x, t)$ of the one-dimensional heat conduction equation

$$\frac{\partial U}{\partial t} = k\frac{\partial^2 U}{\partial x^2} + \frac{k}{\kappa}g(x, t),$$

which at time $t = 0$ has value $U(x, 0) = f(x)$, must have a Laplace transform of the form

$$\tilde{U}(x, s) = Ae^{\sqrt{s/k}x} + Be^{-\sqrt{s/k}x} - \sqrt{\frac{k}{s}} \int_0^x \left(\frac{f(u)}{k} + \frac{\tilde{g}(x, u)}{\kappa} \right) \sinh \sqrt{\frac{s}{k}}(x - u) \, du,$$

where A and B are independent of x. In Exercises 3–6 we use this result to solve various heat conduction problems on infinite and semi-infinite intervals.

3. (a) Use the result of Exercise 2 to solve the heat conduction problem

$$\frac{\partial U}{\partial t} = k \frac{\partial^2 U}{\partial x^2}, \qquad x > 0, \qquad t > 0,$$

$$U(0, t) = f_1(t), \qquad t > 0,$$

$$U(x, 0) = U_0 = \text{constant}, \qquad x > 0.$$

(b) Simplify the solution when $f_1(t) = \bar{U} = \text{constant}$. [See also Exercises 4(b) and (c) in Section 7.4.]

4. (a) Use the result of Exercise 2 to solve the heat conduction problem

$$\frac{\partial U}{\partial t} = k \frac{\partial^2 U}{\partial x^2}, \qquad x > 0, \qquad t > 0,$$

$$\frac{\partial U(0, t)}{\partial x} = -\frac{f_1(t)}{\kappa}, \qquad t > 0,$$

$$U(x, 0) = U_0 = \text{constant}, \qquad x > 0.$$

(b) Simplify the solution when $f_1(t) = Q_0 = \text{constant}$. [See also Exercises 5(b) and (c) in Section 7.4.]

5. (a) Use the result of Exercise 2 to solve the heat conduction problem

$$\frac{\partial U}{\partial t} = k \frac{\partial^2 U}{\partial x^2}, \qquad x > 0, \qquad t > 0,$$

$$-\kappa \frac{\partial U(0, t)}{\partial x} + \mu U(0, t) = \mu f_1(t), \qquad t > 0,$$

$$U(x, 0) = 0, \qquad x > 0.$$

(b) Simplify the solution when $f_1(t) = U_m = \text{constant}$. [See also Exercise 6 in Section 7.4.]

6. (a) Use the result of Exercise 2, and the fact that the transform must remain bounded as $x \to \pm\infty$, to show that the transform of the function satisfying the heat conduction problem

$$\frac{\partial U}{\partial t} = k \frac{\partial^2 U}{\partial x^2}, \qquad -\infty < x < \infty, \qquad t > 0,$$

$$U(x, 0) = U_0 H(x), \qquad -\infty < x < \infty,$$

must be of the form

$$\tilde{U}(x, s) = \begin{cases} Ae^{\sqrt{s/k}x} & x < 0 \\ Be^{-\sqrt{s/k}x} + \dfrac{U_0}{2s}(2 - e^{-\sqrt{s/k}x}) & x > 0 \end{cases}.$$

(b) By demanding that the expression for $\tilde{U}(x, s)$ and its first derivative with respect to x agree at $x = 0$, show that

$$\tilde{U}(x, s) = \frac{U_0}{2s} \begin{cases} e^{\sqrt{s/k}\,x} & x < 0 \\ 2 - e^{-\sqrt{s/k}\,x} & x \geq 0 \end{cases}.$$

(c) Find the inverse transform $U(x, t)$. [See also Case 2 for solution (47b) in Section 7.4.]

Part B—Vibrations

7. Show that every solution $y(x, t)$ of the one-dimensional wave equation

$$\frac{\partial^2 y}{\partial t^2} = c^2 \frac{\partial^2 y}{\partial x^2} + \frac{F(x, t)}{\rho}$$

that also satisfies the initial conditions

$$y(x, 0) = f(x), \qquad y_t(x, 0) = g(x)$$

must have a Laplace transform of the form

$$\bar{y}(x, s) = Ae^{sx/c} + Be^{-sx/c} - \frac{1}{cs} \int_0^x \left(sf(u) + g(u) + \frac{\tilde{F}(u, s)}{\rho} \right) \sinh \frac{s}{c}(x - u)\, du,$$

where A and B are independent of x. In Exercises 8 and 9 we use this result to solve vibration problems on semi-infinite intervals.

8. At time $t = 0$ a semi-infinite taut string lies motionless along the positive x-axis. If its left end is subjected to vertical motion described by $f_1(t)$ for $t > 0$, find its subsequent displacements. (See also Example 11 in Section 7.4.)

9. Solve Exercise 8 if $f_1(t)$ represents a force on the end $x = 0$ of the string; that is, replace the Dirichlet condition with the Neumann condition $\partial y(0, t)/\partial x = -\tau^{-1} f_1(t)$. (See also Exercise 8 in Section 7.4.)

10.3 The Complex Inversion Integral

Finding the inverse Laplace transform in Section 10.1 was a matter of organization and tables; we used properties (3b), (4b), (5b) (and partial fractions) to organize a given transform $\tilde{f}(s)$ into a form for which the inverse transform can be found in tables. In Section 10.2, for PDEs on infinite and semi-infinite intervals, tables and convolutions were once again prominent. For PDEs on finite domains, however, the situation is different; transform functions are so complicated that they can seldom be found in tables. What we need, then, is a direct method for inverting the Laplace transform. In this section we use the theory of functions of a complex variable to derive such a formula.

We first note that the results in equations (3)–(9) remain valid when s is complex; the complex derivation may be somewhat different from its real counterpart, but each result is valid when s is complex.

The following theorem shows that Laplace transforms are analytic functions of the complex variable s.

Theorem 3

If $f(t)$ is $O(e^{\alpha t})$ and piecewise continuous on every finite interval $0 \le t \le T$, the Laplace transform $\tilde{f}(s) = \tilde{f}(x + iy)$ of $f(t)$ is an analytic function of s in the half-plane $x > \alpha$.

Proof:

If the real and imaginary parts of $\tilde{f}(s)$ are denoted by $u(x, y)$ and $v(x, y)$,

$$\tilde{f}(s) = u + iv = \int_0^\infty e^{-(x+iy)t} f(t)\, dt,$$

then
$$u(x, y) = \int_0^\infty e^{-xt} \cos yt\, f(t)\, dt, \qquad v(x, y) = \int_0^\infty -e^{-xt} \sin yt\, f(t)\, dt.$$

To verify the analyticity of $\tilde{f}(s)$, we show that $u(x, y)$ and $v(x, y)$ have continuous first partial derivatives that satisfy the Cauchy-Riemann equations when $x > \alpha$. Now,

$$\left\{ \begin{matrix} |e^{-xt} \cos yt\, f(t)| \\ |e^{-xt} \sin yt\, f(t)| \end{matrix} \right\} \le e^{-xt} |f(t)|,$$

and since $f(t)$ is $O(e^{\alpha t})$, there exist constants M and T such that for all $t > T$, $|f(t)| < Me^{\alpha t}$. Consequently, whenever $x \ge \alpha' > \alpha$ and $t > T$,

$$\left\{ \begin{matrix} |e^{-xt} \cos yt\, f(t)| \\ |e^{-xt} \sin yt\, f(t)| \end{matrix} \right\} < e^{-xt} Me^{\alpha t} \le Me^{(\alpha - \alpha')t}$$

and
$$\left\{ \begin{matrix} |u(x, y)| \\ |v(x, y)| \end{matrix} \right\} < \int_0^T e^{-xt} |f(t)|\, dt + \int_T^\infty Me^{(\alpha - \alpha')t}\, dt$$

$$\le \int_0^T e^{-\alpha't} |f(t)|\, dt + M\left\{ \frac{e^{(\alpha - \alpha')t}}{\alpha - \alpha'} \right\}_0^\infty$$

$$= \int_0^T e^{-\alpha't} |f(t)|\, dt + \frac{M}{\alpha' - \alpha}.$$

Thus, the integrals representing u and v converge absolutely and uniformly with respect to x and y in the half-plane $x \ge \alpha' > \alpha$. Since $f(t)$ is piecewise continuous, u and v are continuous functions for $x \ge \alpha'$. Now,

$$\int_0^\infty \frac{\partial}{\partial x}(e^{-xt} \cos yt\, f(t))\, dt = \int_0^\infty -te^{-xt} \cos yt\, f(t)\, dt$$

and
$$\int_0^\infty \frac{\partial}{\partial y}(-e^{-xt} \sin yt\, f(t))\, dt = \int_0^\infty -te^{-xt} \cos yt\, f(t)\, dt.$$

Since $tf(t)$ is $O[e^{(\alpha + \varepsilon)t}]$ for any $\varepsilon > 0$ and is piecewise continuous on every finite interval $0 \le t \le T$, a similar argument to that above shows that this integral is absolutely and uniformly convergent with respect to x and y for $x \ge \alpha' > \alpha$. Because $\alpha' > \alpha$ is arbitrary, it follows that this integral converges to a continuous function that is equal to both $\partial u/\partial x$ and $\partial v/\partial y$ for $x > \alpha$. We have shown, then, that the first of the Cauchy-Riemann equations $\partial u/\partial x = \partial v/\partial y$ is satisfied for $x > \alpha$. In a similar way, we can show that $\partial u/\partial y = -\partial v/\partial x$, and therefore $\tilde{f}(s)$ is analytic for $x > \alpha$. ∎

To obtain the complex inversion integral for $L^{-1}\{\tilde{f}(s)\}$, we use the extension of Cauchy's integral formula contained in the following theorem.

Theorem 4

Let $f(z)$ be a complex function analytic in a domain containing the half-plane $x \geq \gamma$ (Figure 10.3), and let $f(z)$ be $0(z^{-k})^{\dagger}$ $(k > 0)$ as $|z| \to \infty$ in that half-plane. Then, if z_0 is any complex number with real part greater than γ,

$$f(z_0) = -\frac{1}{2\pi i} \lim_{\beta \to \infty} \int_{\gamma - i\beta}^{\gamma + i\beta} \frac{f(z)}{z - z_0}\, dz. \tag{22}$$

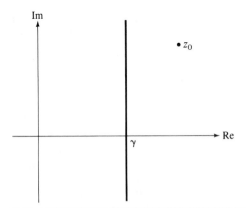

Figure 10.3

When a function $f(t)$ is $O(e^{\alpha t})$, we know that its transform $\tilde{f}(s)$ is analytic for $x > \alpha$ (see Theorem 3). It follows from (22) that when $\tilde{f}(s)$ is $O(s^{-k})$ in a half-plane $x \geq \gamma > \alpha$, we can write $\tilde{f}(s)$ in the form

$$\tilde{f}(s) = -\frac{1}{2\pi i} \lim_{\beta \to \infty} \int_{\gamma - i\beta}^{\gamma + i\beta} \frac{\tilde{f}(z)}{z - s}\, dz$$

for $x > \gamma$. If we formally take inverse transforms of both sides of this equation and interchange the order of integration and $\mathscr{L}^{-1}$, we obtain

$$f(t) = -\frac{1}{2\pi i} \lim_{\beta \to \infty} \int_{\gamma - i\beta}^{\gamma + i\beta} -\tilde{f}(z)\mathscr{L}^{-1}\left(\frac{1}{s - z}\right) dz = \frac{1}{2\pi i} \lim_{\beta \to \infty} \int_{\gamma - i\beta}^{\gamma + i\beta} e^{zt}\tilde{f}(z)\, dz.$$

This expression,

$$\boxed{f(t) = \frac{1}{2\pi i} \lim_{\beta \to \infty} \int_{\gamma - i\beta}^{\gamma + i\beta} e^{st}\tilde{f}(s)\, ds,} \tag{23}$$

---

† A function $f(z)$ is said to be $0(z^{-k})$ as $|z| \to \infty$ if there exist constants M and r such that $|f(z)z^k| < M$ for $|z| > r$.

is called the *complex inversion integral* for the Laplace transformation. Although it is an integral in the complex plane along the line $x = \gamma$, it can be written as a complex combination of real improper integrals. But even for very simple functions $\tilde{f}(s)$, the integrations involved in this real form are usually very difficult (see Exercise 17). Fortunately, in Theorem 7 we prove that residues of $e^{st}\tilde{f}(s)$ may be used to evaluate the integral. First, however, we give conditions on a function $\tilde{f}(s)$ sufficient to guarantee that a function $f(t)$ exists whose transform is $\tilde{f}(s)$ and that $f(t)$ is given by this inversion integral.

Theorem 5

Let $\tilde{f}(s)$ be any function of the complex variable s that is analytic and $O(s^{-k})$, $k > 1$, for all $s = x + iy$ in a half-plane $x \geq \alpha$. Let also $\tilde{f}(x)$ be real when $x \geq \alpha$. Then the inversion integral of $\tilde{f}(s)$ along any line $x = \gamma (\gamma \geq \alpha)$ converges to a real-valued function $f(t)$ that is independent of γ and whose Laplace transform is $\tilde{f}(s)$ for $x > \alpha$. Furthermore, $f(t)$ is $O(e^{\alpha t})$, it is continuous, and $f(t) = 0$ for $t \leq 0$.

The conditions on $\tilde{f}(s)$ in this theorem are severe. They are not, for instance, satisfied by $\tilde{f}(s) = 1/s$, since this function is $O(s^{-1})$. By qualifying the function $f(t)$ instead of $\tilde{f}(s)$, it is possible to relax conditions on the inversion integral formula.

Theorem 6

If $\tilde{f}(s)$ is the Laplace transform of any function $f(t)$ of $O(e^{\alpha t})$, which is piecewise smooth on every finite interval $0 \leq t \leq T$, then the inversion integral of $\tilde{f}(s)$ along any line $x = \gamma > \alpha$ exists and represents $f(t)$. At any point of discontinuity of $f(t)$, the inversion integral represents $[f(t+) + f(t-)]/2$, and if $t = 0$, it represents $f(0+)/2$.

Proof: Define a function

$$g(t) = \begin{cases} 0 & t < 0 \\ e^{-\gamma t} f(t) & t > 0 \end{cases} \qquad \text{where } \gamma > \alpha.$$

Then $g(t)$ is piecewise smooth on every finite interval $0 \leq t \leq T$, and if T is such that $|f(t)| < Me^{\alpha t}$ for $t > T$,

$$\int_{-\infty}^{\infty} |g(t)|\, dt = \int_{0}^{\infty} e^{-\gamma t}|f(t)|\, dt \leq \int_{0}^{T} e^{-\gamma t}|f(t)|\, dt + \int_{T}^{\infty} e^{-\gamma t} Me^{\alpha t}\, dt$$

$$= \int_{0}^{T} e^{-\gamma t}|f(t)|\, dt + \frac{Me^{-(\gamma - \alpha)T}}{\gamma - \alpha};$$

that is, $g(t)$ is absolutely integrable on $-\infty < t < \infty$. Consequently, $g(t)$ may be represented by Fourier's integral formula [see equation (6) in Chapter 7]:

$$\frac{g(t+) + g(t-)}{2} = \int_{0}^{\infty} \left[\left(\frac{1}{\pi} \int_{-\infty}^{\infty} g(x) \cos \lambda x\, dx \right) \cos \lambda t \right.$$

$$\left. + \left(\frac{1}{\pi} \int_{-\infty}^{\infty} g(x) \sin \lambda x\, dx \right) \sin \lambda t \right] d\lambda$$

$$= \frac{1}{\pi} \int_{0}^{\infty} \int_{-\infty}^{\infty} g(x) \cos \lambda(t - x)\, dx\, d\lambda. \tag{24}$$

But because $\cos \lambda(x - t)$ and $\sin \lambda(x - t)$ are even and odd functions of λ, respectively, it follows that

$$\int_{-\infty}^{0} \int_{-\infty}^{\infty} g(x) \cos \lambda(t - x) \, dx \, d\lambda = \int_{0}^{\infty} \int_{-\infty}^{\infty} g(x) \cos \lambda(t - x) \, dx \, d\lambda$$

and

$$\int_{-\infty}^{0} \int_{-\infty}^{\infty} g(x) \sin \lambda(t - x) \, dx \, d\lambda = -\int_{0}^{\infty} \int_{-\infty}^{\infty} g(x) \sin \lambda(t - x) \, dx \, d\lambda.$$

This means that we can replace (24) with

$$\frac{g(t+) + g(t-)}{2} = \frac{1}{2\pi} \int_{-\infty}^{\infty} \int_{-\infty}^{\infty} g(x) \cos \lambda(t - x) \, dx \, d\lambda$$

$$+ \frac{i}{2\pi} \int_{-\infty}^{\infty} \int_{-\infty}^{\infty} g(x) \sin \lambda(t - x) \, dx \, d\lambda$$

$$= \frac{1}{2\pi} \int_{-\infty}^{\infty} \int_{-\infty}^{\infty} g(x) e^{i\lambda(t - x)} \, dx \, d\lambda$$

$$= \frac{1}{2\pi} \lim_{\beta \to \infty} \int_{-\beta}^{\beta} e^{i\lambda t} \int_{-\infty}^{\infty} g(x) e^{-i\lambda x} \, dx \, d\lambda.$$

Because $g(x)$ vanishes for $x < 0$ and is equal to $e^{-\gamma x} f(x)$ for $x > 0$, we may write

$$\frac{g(t+) + g(t-)}{2} = \frac{1}{2\pi} \lim_{\beta \to \infty} \int_{-\beta}^{\beta} e^{i\lambda t} \int_{0}^{\infty} e^{-(\gamma + i\lambda)x} f(x) \, dx \, d\lambda$$

$$= \frac{1}{2\pi} \lim_{\beta \to \infty} \int_{-\beta}^{\beta} e^{i\lambda t} \tilde{f}(\gamma + i\lambda) \, d\lambda.$$

We now regard this integral as an integral along the line $x = \gamma$ in the complex plane by setting $s = \gamma + i\lambda$ and $ds = i \, d\lambda$. Multiplying both sides of the equation by $e^{\gamma t}$, we obtain

$$e^{\gamma t} \left(\frac{g(t+) + g(t-)}{2} \right) = \frac{1}{2\pi i} \lim_{\beta \to \infty} \int_{\gamma - i\beta}^{\gamma + i\beta} e^{st} \tilde{f}(s) \, ds.$$

But from the definition of $g(t)$, we see that when $t > 0$, $e^{\gamma t}[g(t+) + g(t-)]/2 = [f(t+) + f(t-)]/2$, and when $t = 0$, $e^{\gamma t}[g(t+) + g(t-)]/2 = f(0+)/2$. Thus,

$$\frac{f(t+) + f(t-)}{2} = \frac{1}{2\pi i} \lim_{\beta \to \infty} \int_{\gamma - i\beta}^{\gamma + i\beta} e^{st} \tilde{f}(s) \, ds. \qquad \blacksquare$$

One might argue that Theorem 6 is of little use in applications since we do not know $f(t)$; it is precisely $f(t)$ that is the unknown in the problem. For instance, suppose the Laplace transform was applied to an ODE (or a PDE) in $y(t)$ and some analysis was performed, leading to an expression for $\tilde{y}(s)$. It now remains to apply the inverse transform to find $y(t)$. But how then can we use Theorem 6? What we do is ignore the conditions of the theorem and simply apply the inversion integral to $\tilde{y}(s)$ to obtain a function $y(t)$, a function that we hope is both the inverse transform of $\tilde{y}(s)$ and a solution to our differential equation. To verify that this is indeed the case, we can proceed in two ways. First, we can take the Laplace transform of $y(t)$, and if we obtain $\tilde{y}(s)$, there is no question that $y(t)$ is the inverse transform of $\tilde{y}(s)$. Alternatively, we can set aside Laplace transforms completely and verify that $y(t)$ is a solution of the differential equation with which we began.

As we have already mentioned, the inversion integral is seldom used to find inverse transforms; it is circumvented with residues of the complex function $e^{st}\tilde{y}(s)$. The main argument of the method is contained in the following theorem, wherein $\tilde{f}(s)$ is assumed to satisfy conditions like those of Theorem 5 or Theorem 6.

Theorem 7

Let $\tilde{f}(s)$ be a function for which the inversion integral along a line $x = \gamma$ represents the inverse function $f(t)$, and let $\tilde{f}(s)$ be analytic except for isolated singularities $s_n(n = 1,\dots)$ in the half-plane $x < \gamma$. Then the series of residues of $e^{st}\tilde{f}(s)$ at $s = s_n$ converges to $f(t)$ for each positive t,

$$f(t) = \text{sum of residues of } e^{st}\tilde{f}(s) \text{ at its singularities,}$$

provided a sequence C_n of contours can be found that satisfies the following properties:

(1) C_n consists of the straight line $x = \gamma$ from $\gamma - i\beta_n$ to $\gamma + i\beta_n$ and some curve Γ_n beginning at $\gamma + i\beta_n$, ending at $\gamma - i\beta_n$, and lying in $x \leq \gamma$;

(2) C_n encloses $s_1, s_2, \dots, s_n$;

(3) $\lim_{n\to\infty} \beta_n = \infty$; and

(4) $\lim_{n\to\infty} \int_{\Gamma_n} e^{st}\tilde{f}(s)\,ds = 0$ (Figure 10.4).

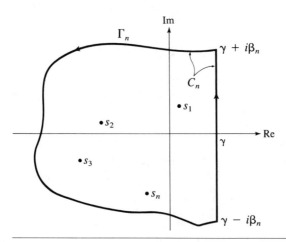

Figure 10.4

Proof: Since $e^{st}\tilde{f}(s)$ is analytic in C_n except at $s_1, \dots, s_n$, the residue theorem states that

$$\left(\begin{array}{c}\text{Sum of residues of}\\ e^{st}\tilde{f}(s) \text{ at } s_1, \dots, s_n\end{array}\right) = \frac{1}{2\pi i}\oint_{C_n} e^{st}\tilde{f}(s)\,ds$$

$$= \frac{1}{2\pi i}\int_{\gamma - i\beta_n}^{\gamma + i\beta_n} e^{st}\tilde{f}(s)\,ds + \frac{1}{2\pi i}\int_{\Gamma_n} e^{st}\tilde{f}(s)\,ds.$$

When we take limits on n [and use conditions (3) and (4) in the theorem],

$$\left(\begin{array}{c}\text{Sum of residues of}\\ e^{st}\tilde{f}(s)\text{ at }s_1,\ldots,s_n,\ldots\end{array}\right) = \frac{1}{2\pi i}\lim_{n\to\infty}\int_{\gamma-i\beta_n}^{\gamma+i\beta_n}e^{st}\tilde{f}(s)\,ds = f(t). \qquad \blacksquare$$

It is not essential, as condition (2) requires, that C_n contain precisely n of the singularities of $\tilde{f}(s)$. In fact, this could be very difficult to accomplish, depending on how the singularities are enumerated. What is essential is that as n increases, the C_n expand to enclose eventually all singularities of $\tilde{f}(s)$.

As a result of Theorem 7, finding the inverse transform of a function $\tilde{f}(s)$ is now a matter of calculating residues of the function $e^{st}\tilde{f}(s)$ at its singularities. When s_0 is a singularity of $e^{st}\tilde{f}(s)$, the residue at s_0 is defined as the coefficient of $(s-s_0)^{-1}$ in the Laurent expansion of $e^{st}\tilde{f}(s)$ about s_0. It can be found in one of two ways:

(1) Find the Laurent expansion of $e^{st}\tilde{f}(s)$ about s_0, or at least enough of it to identify the coefficient of $(s-s_0)^{-1}$.

(2) When it is known that s_0 is a pole of order m, the following formula yields the residue of $e^{st}\tilde{f}(s)$ at s_0:

$$\text{Res}[e^{st}\tilde{f}(s),s_0] = \lim_{s\to s_0}\left[\frac{1}{(m-1)!}\frac{d^{m-1}}{ds^{m-1}}\left((s-s_0)^m e^{st}\tilde{f}(s)\right)\right]. \qquad (25)$$

Example 6: Use Theorem 5 to find inverse transforms when $\tilde{f}(s)$ is equal to (a) $\dfrac{1}{s^m}$, $m\geq 2$ an integer;

(b) $1/(s^2+9)$; (c) $s^2/(s^2+1)^2$.

Solution: (a) The function $\tilde{f}(s)=1/s^m$ has a pole of order m at $s=0$, as does $e^{st}\tilde{f}(s)$. According to equation (25), the residue there is

$$\lim_{s\to 0}\frac{1}{(m-1)!}\frac{d^{m-1}}{ds^{m-1}}\left(s^m e^{st}\tilde{f}(s)\right) = \frac{1}{(m-1)!}\lim_{s\to 0}\frac{d^{m-1}}{ds^{m-1}}\left(e^{st}\right) = \frac{t^{m-1}}{(m-1)!}.$$

The contours Γ_n in Figure 10.5 clearly satisfy conditions (1) and (3) in Theorem 7. Furthermore, on Γ_n,

$$\left|\frac{e^{st}}{s^m}\right| = \left|\frac{e^{(x+iy)t}}{n^m e^{im\theta}}\right| = \frac{e^{xt}}{n^m} \leq \frac{e^t}{n^m}.$$

Thus,

$$\left|\int_{\Gamma_n}\frac{e^{st}}{s^m}\,ds\right| < \frac{2\pi n e^t}{n^m} = \frac{2\pi e^t}{n^{m-1}},^\dagger$$

and this expression approaches zero as $n\to\infty$. Consequently, the Γ_n satisfy condition (4) of Theorem 7, and by this theorem,

$$\mathscr{L}^{-1}\left\{\frac{1}{s^m}\right\} = \frac{t^{m-1}}{(m-1)!}.$$

---

† We have used the following result to arrive at this inequality. When $|f(z)|\leq M$ on a curve C of finite length L,

$$\left|\int_C f(z)\,dz\right| \leq ML.$$

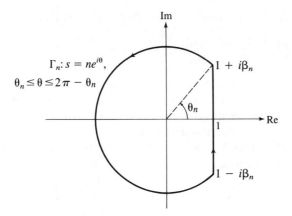

$\Gamma_n: s = ne^{i\theta},$

$\theta_n \le \theta \le 2\pi - \theta_n$

Figure 10.5

(b) The function $\tilde{f}(s) = 1/(s^2 + 9)$ has poles of order 1 at $s = \pm 3i$, as does $e^{st}\tilde{f}(s)$. The residue at $3i$ is

$$\text{Res}[e^{st}\tilde{f}(s), 3i] = \lim_{s \to 3i} \frac{(s - 3i)e^{st}}{(s + 3i)(s - 3i)} = \frac{e^{3it}}{6i} = -\frac{i}{6}e^{3it}.$$

Similarly, $\text{Res}[e^{st}\tilde{f}(s), -3i] = (i/6)e^{-3it}$. On the contour Γ_n ($n \ge 4$) in Figure 10.5,

$$\left| \frac{e^{st}}{s^2 + 9} \right| \le \frac{|e^{(x + iy)t}|}{|s|^2 - 9} = \frac{e^{xt}}{n^2 - 9} \le \frac{e^t}{n^2 - 9}.$$

Thus,

$$\left| \int_{\Gamma_n} \frac{e^{st}}{s^2 + 9} ds \right| < \frac{2\pi n e^t}{n^2 - 9},$$

and this expression approaches zero as $n \to \infty$. By Theorem 7, then,

$$\mathscr{L}^{-1}\left(\frac{1}{s^2 + 9} \right) = -\frac{i}{6}e^{3it} + \frac{i}{6}e^{-3it} = \frac{1}{3}\sin 3t.$$

(c) The function $\tilde{f}(s) = s^2/(s^2 + 1)^2$ has poles of order 2 at $s = \pm i$, as does $e^{st}\tilde{f}(s)$. The residue at i is

$$\text{Res}[e^{st}\tilde{f}(s), i] = \lim_{s \to i} \frac{d}{ds}\left(\frac{(s - i)^2 e^{st} s^2}{(s + i)^2 (s - i)^2} \right)$$

$$= \lim_{s \to i} \left(\frac{(s + i)^2 (2se^{st} + ts^2 e^{st}) - s^2 e^{st}(2)(s + i)}{(s + i)^4} \right)$$

$$= \frac{1}{4}e^{it}(t - i).$$

Similarly, $\text{Res}[e^{st}\tilde{f}(s), -i] = (1/4)e^{-it}(t + i)$. On the contour Γ_n ($n \ge 2$) in Figure 10.5,

$$\left| \frac{s^2 e^{st}}{(s^2 + 1)^2} \right| \le \frac{|s|^2 e^{xt}}{(|s|^2 - 1)^2} \le \frac{n^2 e^t}{(n^2 - 1)^2}.$$

Thus,

$$\left| \int_{\Gamma_n} \frac{s^2 e^{st}}{(s^2 + 1)^2} ds \right| < \frac{2\pi n^3 e^t}{(n^2 - 1)^2},$$

and this expression approaches zero as $n \to \infty$. By Theorem 7, then,

$$\mathcal{L}^{-1}\left(\frac{s^2}{(s^2+1)^2}\right) = \frac{1}{4}e^{it}(t-i) + \frac{1}{4}e^{-it}(t+i) = \frac{t}{2}\cos t + \frac{1}{2}\sin t. \qquad \blacksquare$$

More complicated illustrations of Theorem 7 are contained in Example 7. This example is more typical of problems encountered in Section 10.4, where Laplace transforms are used to solve initial boundary value problems.

Example 7:   Find inverse transforms for the following:

$$\text{(a) } \tilde{f}(s) = \frac{\sinh\sqrt{s}\,x}{s\sinh\sqrt{s}}; \qquad \text{(b) } \tilde{f}(s) = \frac{1}{s^3}(1-\cosh sx) + \frac{\sinh s \sinh sx}{s^3\cosh s}.$$

Solutions: (a) The function $\tilde{f}(s)$ has singularities at the zeros of $\sinh\sqrt{s}$; that is, when $\sqrt{s} = n\pi i$ or $s = -n^2\pi^2$, $n \geq 0$ an integer. To determine the nature of the singularity at $s = 0$, we find the Laurent expansion of $\tilde{f}(s)$ about $s = 0$. We do this with expansions of the hyperbolic functions:

$$\tilde{f}(s) = \frac{1}{s}\left(\frac{\sqrt{s}\,x + \frac{1}{3!}(\sqrt{s}\,x)^3 + \cdots}{\sqrt{s} + \frac{1}{3!}(\sqrt{s})^3 + \cdots}\right) = \frac{1}{s}\left(x + \frac{s}{6}(x^3 - x) + \cdots\right).$$

Consequently, $\tilde{f}(s)$ has a pole of order 1 at $s = 0$, as does $e^{st}\tilde{f}(s)$. The following expansion shows that the residue of $e^{st}\tilde{f}(s)$ at this pole is x:

$$e^{st}\tilde{f}(s) = \left(1 + st + \frac{(st)^2}{2!} + \cdots\right)\left(\frac{1}{s}\right)\left(x + \frac{s}{6}(x^3 - x) + \cdots\right)$$

$$= \frac{1}{s}\left(x + \frac{s}{6}(6xt + x^3 - x) + \cdots\right).$$

Because the derivative of $\sinh\sqrt{s}$ does not vanish at the remaining singularities $s = -n^2\pi^2$ $(n > 0)$, these are also poles of order 1, and the residues of $e^{st}\tilde{f}(s)$ at these poles are given by limit (25):

$$\lim_{s\to -n^2\pi^2}(s + n^2\pi^2)e^{st}\frac{\sinh\sqrt{s}\,x}{s\sinh\sqrt{s}} = e^{-n^2\pi^2 t}\frac{\sinh n\pi xi}{-n^2\pi^2}\lim_{s\to -n^2\pi^2}\frac{s + n^2\pi^2}{\sinh\sqrt{s}}.$$

L'Hôpital's rule can be used to evaluate this limit, which, combined with the facts that $\sinh i\theta = i\sin\theta$ and $\cosh i\theta = \cos\theta$, gives, for these residues,

$$-\frac{i}{n^2\pi^2}e^{-n^2\pi^2 t}\sin n\pi x \lim_{s\to -n^2\pi^2}\frac{1}{\frac{1}{2\sqrt{s}}\cosh\sqrt{s}}$$

$$= -\frac{2i}{n^2\pi^2}e^{-n^2\pi^2 t}\sin n\pi x\frac{n\pi i}{\cosh n\pi i}$$

$$= \frac{2}{n\pi}e^{-n^2\pi^2 t}\sin n\pi x\frac{1}{\cos n\pi} = \frac{2(-1)^n}{n\pi}e^{-n^2\pi^2 t}\sin n\pi x.$$

Thus, the sum of the residues of $e^{st}\tilde{f}(s)$ at its singularities is

$$f(t) = x + \frac{2}{\pi}\sum_{n=1}^{\infty}\frac{(-1)^n}{n}e^{-n^2\pi^2 t}\sin n\pi x.$$

Verification that this function is the inverse of $\tilde{f}(s)$ still requires the establishment of a sequence of contours satisfying the conditions of Theorem 7. We omit this part of the argument. Transforms of this type arise in heat conduction problems.

(b) This transform has singularities at $s = 0$ and $s = (2n-1)\pi i/2$, n an integer (the zeros of cosh s). The Laurent expansion of $\tilde{f}(s)$ about $s = 0$ can be found by expanding the hyperbolic functions in Maclaurin series:

$$\tilde{f}(s) = \frac{1}{s^3}\left(1 - 1 - \frac{s^2 x^2}{2!} - \frac{s^4 x^4}{4!} - \cdots\right)$$

$$+ \frac{1}{s^3}\left(\frac{s + \dfrac{s^3}{3!} + \dfrac{s^5}{5!} + \cdots}{1 + \dfrac{s^2}{2!} + \dfrac{s^4}{4!} + \cdots}\right)\left(sx + \frac{s^3 x^3}{3!} + \cdots\right)$$

$$= \left(-\frac{x^2}{2s} - \frac{x^4 s}{24} - \cdots\right) + \left(s - \frac{s^3}{3} + \cdots\right)\left(\frac{x}{s^2} + \frac{x^3}{6} + \cdots\right)$$

$$= \frac{x}{2s}(2 - x) + \frac{xs}{24}(-x^3 + 4x^2 - 8) + \cdots.$$

Consequently, $\tilde{f}(s)$ has a pole of order 1 at $s = 0$, as does $e^{st}\tilde{f}(s)$. Multiplication of this series by the Maclaurin series for e^{st} gives

$$e^{st}\tilde{f}(s) = \left(1 + st + \frac{(st)^2}{2!} + \cdots\right)\left(\frac{x}{2s}(2 - x) + \frac{xs}{24}(-x^3 + 4x^2 - 8) + \cdots\right)$$

$$= \frac{x}{2s}(2 - x) + \frac{xt}{2}(2 - x) + \cdots,$$

and therefore the residue of $e^{st}\tilde{f}(s)$ at $s = 0$ is $x(2 - x)/2$.

Because the derivative of $\cosh s$ does not vanish at $s = (2n-1)\pi i/2$, these singularities are also poles of order 1, and the residues of $e^{st}\tilde{f}(s)$ at these poles are given by the limits

$$\lim_{s\to(2n-1)\pi i/2}\left(s - \frac{(2n-1)\pi i}{2}\right)e^{st}\left(\frac{1}{s^3}(1 - \cosh sx) + \frac{\sinh s \sinh sx}{s^3 \cosh s}\right)$$

$$= \frac{e^{(2n-1)\pi t i/2}}{-(2n-1)^3\pi^3 i/8}\sinh\frac{(2n-1)\pi i}{2}\sinh\frac{(2n-1)\pi x i}{2}\lim_{s\to(2n-1)\pi i/2}\frac{s - (2n-1)\pi i/2}{\cosh s}$$

$$= \frac{8e^{(2n-1)\pi t i/2}}{(2n-1)^3\pi^3 i}\sin\frac{(2n-1)\pi}{2}\sin\frac{(2n-1)\pi x}{2}\lim_{s\to(2n-1)\pi i/2}\frac{1}{\sinh s}$$

$$\left(\text{using l'Hôpital's} \atop \text{rule}\right)$$

$$= \frac{8(-1)^{n+1}e^{(2n-1)\pi ti/2}}{(2n-1)^3\pi^3 i}\sin\frac{(2n-1)\pi x}{2}\cdot\frac{1}{\sinh\dfrac{(2n-1)\pi i}{2}}$$

$$= -\frac{8e^{(2n-1)\pi ti/2}}{(2n-1)^3\pi^3}\sin\frac{(2n-1)\pi x}{2}.$$

The sum of the residues of $e^{st}\tilde{f}(s)$ at its singularities is therefore

$$f(t) = \frac{x}{2}(2-x) - \frac{8}{\pi^3}\sum_{n=-\infty}^{\infty}\frac{e^{(2n-1)\pi ti/2}}{(2n-1)^3}\sin\frac{(2n-1)\pi x}{2}.$$

To simplify this expression, we separate it into two summations, one over positive n and the other over nonpositive n, and in the latter we set $m = 1 - n$:

$$f(t) = \frac{x}{2}(2-x) - \frac{8}{\pi^3}\sum_{n=1}^{\infty}\frac{e^{(2n-1)\pi ti/2}}{(2n-1)^3}\sin\frac{(2n-1)\pi x}{2}$$

$$\quad - \frac{8}{\pi^3}\sum_{n=0}^{-\infty}\frac{e^{(2n-1)\pi ti/2}}{(2n-1)^3}\sin\frac{(2n-1)\pi x}{2}$$

$$= \frac{x}{2}(2-x) - \frac{8}{\pi^3}\sum_{n=1}^{\infty}\frac{e^{(2n-1)\pi ti/2}}{(2n-1)^3}\sin\frac{(2n-1)\pi x}{2}$$

$$\quad - \frac{8}{\pi^3}\sum_{m=1}^{\infty}\frac{e^{[2(1-m)-1]\pi ti/2}}{[2(1-m)-1]^3}\sin\frac{[2(1-m)-1]\pi x}{2}.$$

If we now replace m by n in the second summation and combine it with the first,

$$f(t) = \frac{x}{2}(2-x) - \frac{8}{\pi^3}\sum_{n=1}^{\infty}\frac{e^{(2n-1)\pi ti/2}}{(2n-1)^3}\sin\frac{(2n-1)\pi x}{2}$$

$$\quad - \frac{8}{\pi^3}\sum_{n=1}^{\infty}\frac{e^{-(2n-1)\pi ti/2}}{(2n-1)^3}\sin\frac{(2n-1)\pi x}{2}$$

$$= \frac{x}{2}(2-x) - \frac{8}{\pi^3}\sum_{n=1}^{\infty}\frac{e^{(2n-1)\pi ti/2} + e^{-(2n-1)\pi ti/2}}{(2n-1)^3}\sin\frac{(2n-1)\pi x}{2}$$

$$= \frac{x}{2}(2-x) - \frac{16}{\pi^3}\sum_{n=1}^{\infty}\frac{1}{(2n-1)^3}\cos\frac{(2n-1)\pi t}{2}\sin\frac{(2n-1)\pi x}{2}.$$

Once again, we omit verification of existence of a sequence of contours satisfying Theorem 7. Transforms of this type occur in vibration problems. ∎

Exercises 10.3

In Exercises 1–16, use residues to find the inverse Laplace transform of the given function. In Exercises 1–5, verify the existence of contours satisfying the requirements of Theorem 7; in Exercises 6–16, neglect this verification.

1. $\tilde{f}(s) = s/(s-1)^3$

2. $\tilde{f}(s) = s/(s^2+4)^2$

3. $\tilde{f}(s) = \dfrac{1}{s^2(s+3)}$

4. $\tilde{f}(s) = \dfrac{s^2+2}{(s+1)^2(s-3)^3}$

5. $\tilde{f}(s) = \dfrac{s^2}{(s^2 + 1)(s^2 + 4)}$

6. $\tilde{f}(s) = \dfrac{s}{s^2 - 1}$

7. $\tilde{f}(s) = \dfrac{s^3}{(s^2 - 4)^3}$

8. $\tilde{f}(s) = \dfrac{1}{(s^2 - 2s + 2)^2}$

9. $\tilde{f}(s) = \dfrac{s - 1}{(s^2 - 2s + 2)^2}$

10. $\tilde{f}(s) = \dfrac{s^2}{(s^2 - 2s + 2)^2}$

11. $\tilde{f}(x, s) = \dfrac{1}{s}\left(x - \dfrac{\sinh\sqrt{s}\,x}{\sinh\sqrt{s}}\right)$

12. $\tilde{f}(x, u, s) = \dfrac{\sinh sx \sinh s(1 - u)}{s \sinh s}$

13. $\tilde{f}(x, s) = \dfrac{2\sinh sx}{s^3 \sinh s}(1 - \cosh s) + \dfrac{2}{s^3}(\cosh sx - 1) + \dfrac{x}{s}(1 - x)$

14. $\tilde{f}(x, s) = \dfrac{1}{s^3} + \dfrac{\cosh sx}{s^2 \sinh s}$

15. $\tilde{f}(x, s) = \dfrac{\sinh sx}{(4s^2 + \pi^2)\sinh s}$

16. $\tilde{f}(x, s) = \dfrac{\sinh sx}{(s^2 + \pi^2)\sinh s}$

17. We have claimed that to use inversion integral (23) directly is usually impossible. Set up the complex combination of real improper integrals for (23) when $\tilde{f}(s) = 1/s^2$; that is, express (23) in the form

$$\mathscr{L}^{-1}\left\{\dfrac{1}{s^2}\right\} = I_1 + iI_2,$$

where I_1 and I_2 are real, improper integrals. Use the line $\gamma = 1$.

10.4 Applications to Partial Differential Equations on Bounded Domains

Laplace transforms can be used to eliminate the time variable from initial boundary value problems. This reduces the PDE to an ODE or a PDE with one fewer variable. We illustrate with the following examples.

Example 8:   Solve the heat conduction problem

$$\dfrac{\partial U}{\partial t} = k\dfrac{\partial^2 U}{\partial x^2}, \qquad 0 < x < L, \qquad t > 0, \tag{26a}$$

$$U(0, t) = 0, \qquad t > 0, \tag{26b}$$

$$U(L, t) = 0, \qquad t > 0, \tag{26c}$$

$$U(x, 0) = x, \qquad 0 < x < L. \tag{26d}$$

Solution: When we take Laplace transforms with respect to t on both sides of PDE (26a) and use property (7a),

$$s\tilde{U}(x, s) - x = k\dfrac{\partial^2 \tilde{U}}{\partial x^2}.$$

Thus, $\tilde{U}(x, s)$ must satisfy the ODE

$$\frac{d^2\tilde{U}}{dx^2} - \frac{s}{k}\tilde{U} = -\frac{x}{k} \tag{27a}$$

subject to the transforms of (26b, c),

$$\tilde{U}(0, s) = 0, \tag{27b}$$

$$\tilde{U}(L, s) = 0. \tag{27c}$$

The general solution of ODE (27a) is

$$\tilde{U}(x, s) = C_1 \cosh\sqrt{\frac{s}{k}}x + C_2 \sinh\sqrt{\frac{s}{k}}x + \frac{x}{s},$$

and boundary conditions (27b, c) require that

$$0 = C_1, \qquad 0 = C_1 \cosh\sqrt{\frac{s}{k}}L + C_2 \sinh\sqrt{\frac{s}{k}}L + \frac{L}{s}.$$

From these,

$$\tilde{U}(x, s) = \frac{1}{s}\left(x - \frac{L\sinh\sqrt{s/k}x}{\sinh\sqrt{s/k}L}\right). \tag{28}$$

It remains now to find the inverse transform of $\tilde{U}(x, s)$. We do this by calculating the residues of $e^{st}\tilde{U}(x, s)$ at its singularities. To discover the nature of the singularity at $s = 0$, we expand $\tilde{U}(x, s)$ in a Laurent series around $s = 0$:

$$\tilde{U}(x, s) = \frac{1}{s}\left(x - \frac{L[\sqrt{s/k}x + (\sqrt{s/k}x)^3/3! + \cdots]}{\sqrt{s/k}L + (\sqrt{s/k}L)^3/3! + \cdots}\right)$$

$$= \frac{1}{s}\left(x - \frac{x + sx^3/(6k) + \cdots}{1 + sL^2/(6k) + \cdots}\right)$$

$$= \frac{1}{s}\left(\frac{sx(L^2 - x^2)}{6k} + \cdots\right) = \frac{x(L^2 - x^2)}{6k} + \text{terms in } s, s^2, \ldots.$$

It follows that $\tilde{U}(x, s)$ has a removable singularity at $s = 0$.

The remaining singularities of $\tilde{U}(x, s)$ occur at the zeros of $\sinh\sqrt{s/k}L$; that is, when $\sqrt{s/k}L = n\pi i$ or $s = -n^2\pi^2 k/L^2$, n a positive integer. Because the derivative of $\sinh\sqrt{s/k}L$ does not vanish at $s = -n^2\pi^2 k/L^2$, this function has zeros of order 1 at $s = -n^2\pi^2 k/L^2$. It follows that $\tilde{U}(x, s)$ has poles of order 1 at these singularities, and, according to formula (25), the residue of $e^{st}\tilde{U}(x, s)$ at $s = -n^2\pi^2 k/L^2$ is

$$\lim_{s \to -n^2\pi^2 k/L^2}\left(s + \frac{n^2\pi^2 k}{L^2}\right)\frac{e^{st}}{s}\left(x - \frac{L\sinh\sqrt{s/k}x}{\sinh\sqrt{s/k}L}\right)$$

$$= -\frac{e^{-n^2\pi^2 kt/L^2}}{-n^2\pi^2 k/L^2}L\,\sinh\frac{n\pi xi}{L}\lim_{s \to -n^2\pi^2 k/L^2}\frac{s + n^2\pi^2 k/L^2}{\sinh\sqrt{s/k}L}.$$

L'Hôpital's rule, together with the facts that $\sinh i\theta = i\sin\theta$ and $\cosh i\theta = \cos\theta$, yields

$$\frac{iL^3}{n^2\pi^2 k}e^{-n^2\pi^2 kt/L^2}\sin\frac{n\pi x}{L}\lim_{s\to -n^2\pi^2 k/L^2}\frac{1}{\dfrac{L}{2\sqrt{ks}}\cosh\sqrt{s/k}\,L}$$

$$=\frac{2iL^2}{n^2\pi^2 k}e^{-n^2\pi^2 kt/L^2}\sin\frac{n\pi x}{L}\frac{1}{\dfrac{L}{n\pi ki}\cosh n\pi i}$$

$$=\frac{2L}{n\pi}(-1)^{n+1}e^{-n^2\pi^2 kt/L^2}\sin\frac{n\pi x}{L}.$$

We sum these residues to find the inverse Laplace transform of $\tilde{U}(x,s)$:

$$U(x,t)=\frac{2L}{\pi}\sum_{n=1}^{\infty}\frac{(-1)^{n+1}}{n}e^{-n^2\pi^2 kt/L^2}\sin\frac{n\pi x}{L}. \qquad (29)\quad\blacksquare$$

Before proceeding to further problems, some general comments are appropriate:

(1) In the above example, the Laplace transform was applied to the time variable t to eliminate the time derivative from the PDE and obtain an ODE in $\tilde{U}(x,s)$. The Laplace transform cannot be applied to the space variable x, because the range of x is only $0\le x\le L$. It is the power of finite Fourier transforms to eliminate the space variable, not the Laplace transform. This is why Laplace transforms are applied to initial boundary value problems and not boundary value problems.

(2) The Laplace transform immediately incorporates the initial condition into the solution, and boundary conditions on $U(x,t)$ become boundary conditions for $\tilde{U}(x,s)$. Contrast this with finite Fourier transforms, which immediately incorporate boundary conditions and use the initial condition on $U(x,t)$ as an initial condition for $\tilde{U}(\lambda_n, t)$.

(3) Mathematically, the solution is not complete because the existence of a sequence of contours satisfying the properties of Theorem 7 has not been established, but we omit this part of the problem. We could circumvent this difficulty by now verifying that function (29) does indeed satisfy initial boundary value problem (26).

Problems with arbitrary initial conditions are more difficult to handle. This is illustrated in the next example.

Example 9:   Solve the vibration problem

$$\frac{\partial^2 y}{\partial t^2}=c^2\frac{\partial^2 y}{\partial x^2}, \qquad 0<x<L, \qquad t>0, \qquad (30a)$$

$$y(0,t)=0, \qquad t>0, \qquad (30b)$$

$$y(L,t)=0, \qquad t>0, \qquad (30c)$$

$$y(x, 0) = f(x), \qquad 0 < x < L, \tag{30d}$$

$$y_t(x, 0) = 0, \qquad 0 < x < L \tag{30e}$$

[see Exercise 10 in Section 3.2, with $g(x) = 0$].

Solution: When we take Laplace transforms of (30a) with respect to t and use initial conditions (30d, e) in property (7b),

$$s^2 \tilde{y} - s f(x) = c^2 \frac{\partial^2 \tilde{y}}{\partial x^2}.$$

Thus, $\tilde{y}(x, s)$ must satisfy the ODE

$$\frac{d^2 \tilde{y}}{dx^2} - \frac{s^2}{c^2} \tilde{y} = -\frac{s}{c^2} f(x) \tag{31a}$$

subject to the transforms of (30b, c),

$$\tilde{y}(0, s) = 0, \qquad \tilde{y}(L, s) = 0. \tag{31b}$$

Variation of parameters (see Section 3.3) leads to the following form for the general solution of (31a):

$$\tilde{y}(x, s) = C_1 \cosh \frac{sx}{c} + C_2 \sinh \frac{sx}{c} - \frac{1}{c} \int_0^x f(u) \sinh \frac{s}{c}(x - u)\, du.$$

Boundary conditions (31b) on $\tilde{y}(x, s)$ require that

$$0 = C_1, \qquad 0 = C_1 \cosh \frac{sL}{c} + C_2 \sinh \frac{sL}{c} - \frac{1}{c} \int_0^L f(u) \sinh \frac{s}{c}(L - u)\, du,$$

from which

$$\tilde{y}(x, s) = \frac{\sinh \dfrac{sx}{c}}{c \sinh \dfrac{sL}{c}} \int_0^L f(u) \sinh \frac{s}{c}(L - u)\, du - \frac{1}{c} \int_0^x f(u) \sinh \frac{s}{c}(x - u)\, du$$

$$= \int_0^L f(u) \tilde{p}(x, u, s)\, du - \frac{1}{c} \int_0^x f(u) \sinh \frac{s}{c}(x - u)\, du, \tag{32a}$$

where

$$\tilde{p}(x, u, s) = \frac{\sinh \dfrac{sx}{c} \sinh \dfrac{s}{c}(L - u)}{c \sinh \dfrac{sL}{c}}. \tag{32b}$$

To obtain $y(x, t)$ by residues requires the singularities of $\tilde{y}(x, s)$. Provided $f(x)$ is piecewise continuous, integration with respect to u in (32a) and any differentiation with respect to s can be interchanged, and therefore the second integral in (32a) has no singularities. Singularities of the first integral are determined by those of $\tilde{p}(x, u, s)$. For the singularity at $s = 0$, we note that

$$\tilde{p}(x, u, s) = \frac{1}{c} \sinh \frac{s}{c}(L - u) \left(\frac{\sinh \dfrac{sx}{c}}{\sinh \dfrac{sL}{c}} \right)$$

$$= \frac{1}{c} \left(\frac{s}{c}(L - u) + \frac{s^3}{3!c^3}(L - u)^3 + \cdots \right) \left(\frac{\dfrac{sx}{c} + \dfrac{1}{3!}\left(\dfrac{sx}{c}\right)^3 + \cdots}{\dfrac{sL}{c} + \dfrac{1}{3!}\left(\dfrac{sL}{c}\right)^3 + \cdots} \right)$$

$$= \left(\frac{s}{c^2}(L - u) + \frac{s^3}{6c^4}(L - u)^3 + \cdots \right) \left(\frac{x + \dfrac{x^3 s^2}{6c^2} + \cdots}{L + \dfrac{L^3 s^2}{6c^2} + \cdots} \right)$$

$$= \frac{s}{c^2}(L - u)\frac{x}{L} + \text{terms in } s^2, s^3, \ldots,$$

and therefore $\tilde{p}(x, u, s)$ has a removable singularity at $s = 0$. The remaining singularities of $\tilde{p}(x, u, s)$ are $s = n\pi ci/L$, n a nonzero integer. Because the derivative of $\sinh (sL/c)$ does not vanish at $s = n\pi ci/L$, these singularities are poles of order 1. According to formula (25), the residue of $\tilde{p}(x, u, s)$ at $s = n\pi ci/L$ is

$$\lim_{s \to n\pi ci/L} \left(s - \frac{n\pi ci}{L} \right) \tilde{p}(x, u, s)$$

$$= \lim_{s \to n\pi ci/L} \left(s - \frac{n\pi ci}{L} \right) \frac{\sinh \dfrac{sx}{c} \sinh \dfrac{s}{c}(L - u)}{c \sinh \dfrac{sL}{c}}$$

$$= \sinh \frac{n\pi xi}{L} \sinh \frac{n\pi i(L - u)}{L} \lim_{s \to n\pi ci/L} \frac{s - \dfrac{n\pi ci}{L}}{c \sinh \dfrac{sL}{c}}$$

$$= -\sin \frac{n\pi x}{L} \sin \frac{n\pi}{L}(L - u) \lim_{s \to n\pi ci/L} \frac{1}{L \cosh \dfrac{sL}{c}} \quad \text{(by l'Hôpital's rule)}$$

$$= \frac{(-1)^n}{L} \sin \frac{n\pi x}{L} \sin \frac{n\pi u}{L} \frac{1}{\cosh n\pi i}$$

$$= \frac{1}{L} \sin \frac{n\pi x}{L} \sin \frac{n\pi u}{L}.$$

The residue of e^{st} times the first integral in (32a) at $s = n\pi ci/L$ is now

$$\lim_{s \to n\pi ci/L} \left(s - \frac{n\pi ci}{L}\right) e^{st} \int_0^L f(u)\tilde{p}(x, u, s)\, du.$$

When we interchange the limit on s with the integration with respect to u, the residue becomes

$$\int_0^L \lim_{s \to n\pi ci/L} \left[e^{st} \left(s - \frac{n\pi ci}{L}\right) f(u)\tilde{p}(x, u, s) \right] du$$

$$= \int_0^L e^{n\pi cti/L} f(u) \frac{1}{L} \sin \frac{n\pi x}{L} \sin \frac{n\pi u}{L}\, du$$

$$= \frac{1}{L} e^{n\pi cti/L} \sin \frac{n\pi x}{L} \int_0^L f(u) \sin \frac{n\pi u}{L}\, du.$$

The inverse transform of $\tilde{y}(x, s)$ is the sum of all such residues:

$$y(x, t) = \frac{1}{L} \sum_{\substack{n=-\infty \\ n \neq 0}}^{\infty} e^{n\pi cti/L} \sin \frac{n\pi x}{L} \int_0^L f(u) \sin \frac{n\pi u}{L}\, du. \tag{33}$$

To simplify this summation, we divide it into two parts,

$$y(x, t) = \frac{1}{L} \sum_{n=1}^{\infty} e^{n\pi cti/L} \sin \frac{n\pi x}{L} \int_0^L f(u) \sin \frac{n\pi u}{L}\, du$$

$$+ \frac{1}{L} \sum_{n=-\infty}^{-1} e^{n\pi cti/L} \sin \frac{n\pi x}{L} \int_0^L f(u) \sin \frac{n\pi u}{L}\, du,$$

and replace n by $-n$ in the second term:

$$y(x, t) = \frac{1}{L} \sum_{n=1}^{\infty} e^{n\pi cti/L} \sin \frac{n\pi x}{L} \int_0^L f(u) \sin \frac{n\pi u}{L}\, du$$

$$+ \frac{1}{L} \sum_{n=1}^{\infty} e^{-n\pi cti/L} \sin \left(\frac{-n\pi x}{L}\right) \int_0^L f(u) \sin \left(\frac{-n\pi u}{L}\right) du$$

$$= \frac{1}{L} \sum_{n=1}^{\infty} \sin \frac{n\pi x}{L} (e^{n\pi cti/L} + e^{-n\pi cti/L}) \int_0^L f(u) \sin \frac{n\pi u}{L}\, du$$

$$= \frac{1}{L} \sum_{n=1}^{\infty} 2 \sin \frac{n\pi x}{L} \cos \frac{n\pi ct}{L} \int_0^L f(u) \sin \frac{n\pi u}{L}\, du$$

$$= \sum_{n=1}^{\infty} a_n \cos \frac{n\pi ct}{L} \sin \frac{n\pi x}{L}, \tag{34a}$$

where

$$a_n = \frac{2}{L} \int_0^L f(u) \sin \frac{n\pi u}{L}\, du. \tag{34b}$$

This is identical to the solution obtained by separation of variables in Exercise 10 of Section 3.2 when $g(x)$ is set equal to zero. ∎

Examples 8 and 9 were homogeneous problems. Convolutions can be used to handle problems with nonhomogeneities.

Example 10: Solve Example 8 if the end $x = 0$ of the rod has a prescribed temperature $f(t)$ and the initial temperature is zero throughout. Compare the solution with that obtained by eigenfunction expansions and finite Fourier transforms.

Solution: The initial boundary value problem in this case is

$$\frac{\partial U}{\partial t} = k\frac{\partial^2 U}{\partial x^2}, \qquad 0 < x < L, \qquad t > 0, \tag{35a}$$

$$U(0, t) = f(t), \qquad t > 0, \tag{35b}$$

$$U(L, t) = 0, \qquad t > 0, \tag{35c}$$

$$U(x, 0) = 0, \qquad 0 < x < L. \tag{35d}$$

When the Laplace transform is applied to PDE (35a) and initial temperature (35d) is used, the transform function $\tilde{U}(x, s)$ must satisfy the ODE

$$\frac{d^2\tilde{U}}{dx^2} - \frac{s}{k}\tilde{U} = 0, \qquad 0 < x < L, \tag{36a}$$

$$\tilde{U}(0, s) = \tilde{f}(s), \tag{36b}$$

$$\tilde{U}(L, s) = 0. \tag{36c}$$

The solution of this system is

$$\tilde{U}(x, s) = \frac{\tilde{f}(s)\sinh\sqrt{s/k}(L - x)}{\sinh\sqrt{s/k}L}. \tag{37}$$

To find the inverse transform of this function, we first find the inverse of $\tilde{p}(x, s) = \sinh\sqrt{s/k}(L - x)/\sinh\sqrt{s/k}L$. This function has singularities when $\sqrt{s/k}L = n\pi i$ or $s = -n^2\pi^2 k/L^2$, n a nonnegative integer. Expansion of $\tilde{p}(x, s)$ in a Laurent series around $s = 0$ immediately shows that $\tilde{p}(x, s)$ has a removable singularity at $s = 0$. The remaining singularities are poles of order 1, and the residue of $e^{st}\tilde{p}(x, s)$ at $s = -n^2\pi^2 k/L^2$ is

$$\lim_{s \to -n^2\pi^2 k/L^2} \left(s + \frac{n^2\pi^2 k}{L^2}\right) e^{st} \frac{\sinh\sqrt{s/k}(L - x)}{\sinh\sqrt{s/k}L}$$

$$= e^{-n^2\pi^2 kt/L^2} \sinh\frac{n\pi i(L - x)}{L} \lim_{s \to -n^2\pi^2 k/L^2} \frac{s + n^2\pi^2 k/L^2}{\sinh\sqrt{s/k}L}$$

$$= ie^{-n^2\pi^2 kt/L^2} \sin\frac{n\pi(L - x)}{L} \lim_{s \to -n^2\pi^2 k/L^2} \frac{1}{\frac{L}{2\sqrt{ks}}\cosh\sqrt{s/k}L}$$

$$= ie^{-n^2\pi^2 kt/L^2}(-1)^{n+1} \sin\frac{n\pi x}{L} \frac{2nk\pi i}{L^2\cosh n\pi i}$$

$$= \frac{2nk\pi}{L^2} e^{-n^2\pi^2 kt/L^2} \sin\frac{n\pi x}{L}.$$

Convolutions can now be used to invert $\tilde{U}(x, s)$ in (37):

$$U(x, t) = \mathscr{L}^{-1}[\tilde{f}(s)\tilde{p}(x, s)] = \int_0^t f(u)p(x, t - u)\, du$$

$$= \int_0^t f(u)\left(\frac{2k\pi}{L^2} \sum_{n=1}^{\infty} n e^{-n^2\pi^2 k(t-u)/L^2} \sin\frac{n\pi x}{L}\right) du$$

$$= \frac{2k\pi}{L^2} \sum_{n=1}^{\infty} c_n(t) \sin\frac{n\pi x}{L}, \tag{38a}$$

where

$$c_n(t) = n \int_0^t f(u)e^{-n^2\pi^2 k(t-u)/L^2}\, du. \tag{38b}$$

With eigenfunction expansions (from Section 3.3), the dependent variable is changed to $V(x, t) = U(x, t) - f(t)(1 - x/L)$, resulting in a problem with homogeneous boundary conditions for $V(x, t)$,

$$\frac{\partial V}{\partial t} = k\frac{\partial^2 V}{\partial x^2} - f'(t)\left(1 - \frac{x}{L}\right), \qquad 0 < x < L, \qquad t > 0,$$

$$V(0, t) = 0, \qquad t > 0,$$

$$V(L, t) = 0, \qquad t > 0,$$

$$V(x, 0) = -f(0)\left(1 - \frac{x}{L}\right) = 0, \qquad 0 < x < L,$$

provided we assume that $f(0) = 0$. [The $f(0) \neq 0$ situation is discussed in Exercise 14.] An eigenfunction expansion

$$V(x, t) = \sum_{n=1}^{\infty} a_n(t) \sin\frac{n\pi x}{L}$$

leads to

$$a_n(t) = \frac{-2}{n\pi} \int_0^t f'(u)e^{-n^2\pi^2 k(t-u)/L^2}\, du,$$

and therefore

$$U(x, t) = f(t)\left(1 - \frac{x}{L}\right) - \frac{2}{\pi} \sum_{n=1}^{\infty} \left(\frac{1}{n}\int_0^t f'(u)e^{-n^2\pi^2 k(t-u)/L^2}\, du\right) \sin\frac{n\pi x}{L}. \tag{39}$$

That this is identical to (38) is verified by integrating (38b) by parts,

$$c_n(t) = n\left\{\frac{L^2}{n^2\pi^2 k} f(u)e^{-n^2\pi^2 k(t-u)/L^2}\right\}_0^t$$

$$- n\int_0^t \frac{L^2}{n^2\pi^2 k} f'(u)e^{-n^2\pi^2 k(t-u)/L^2}\, du$$

$$= \frac{L^2}{nk\pi^2} f(t) - \frac{L^2}{n\pi^2 k} \int_0^t f'(u)e^{-n^2\pi^2 k(t-u)/L^2}\, du,$$

and substituting into (38a):

$$U(x,t) = \frac{2k\pi}{L^2} \sum_{n=1}^{\infty} \left(\frac{L^2}{nk\pi^2} f(t) - \frac{L^2}{nk\pi^2} \int_0^t f'(u)e^{-n^2\pi^2 k(t-u)/L^2}\, du \right) \sin\frac{n\pi x}{L}$$

$$= f(t) \sum_{n=1}^{\infty} \frac{2}{n\pi} \sin\frac{n\pi x}{L} - \frac{2}{\pi} \sum_{n=1}^{\infty} \left(\frac{1}{n} \int_0^t f'(u)e^{-n^2\pi^2 k(t-u)/L^2}\, du \right) \sin\frac{n\pi x}{L}.$$

This is identical to (39) when we notice that the coefficients in the Fourier sine series of $1 - x/L$ are $2/(n\pi)$.

The finite Fourier transform

$$\tilde{f}(\lambda_n) = \int_0^L f(x)\sqrt{\frac{2}{L}} \sin\frac{n\pi x}{L}\, dx$$

applied to problem (35) gives the solution in form (38).   ∎

When we write solution (38) for problem (35) in the form

$$U(x,t) = \frac{2k\pi}{L^2} \sum_{n=1}^{\infty} b_n e^{-n^2\pi^2 kt/L^2} \sin\frac{n\pi x}{L}, \tag{40a}$$

where

$$b_n = n \int_0^t f(u)e^{n^2\pi^2 ku/L^2}\, du, \tag{40b}$$

we see that the exponentials in (40a) enhance convergence for large values of t. For instance, if the temperature of the left end is maintained at 100°C for $t > 0$, temperature function (40) reduces to

$$U(x,t) = \frac{200}{\pi} \sum_{n=1}^{\infty} \frac{1}{n}(1 - e^{-n^2\pi^2 kt/L^2}) \sin\frac{n\pi x}{L}, \tag{41}$$

which can also be expressed in the form

$$U(x,t) = 100\left(1 - \frac{x}{L}\right) - \frac{200}{\pi} \sum_{n=1}^{\infty} \frac{1}{n} e^{-n^2\pi^2 kt/L^2} \sin\frac{n\pi x}{L}. \tag{42}$$

Suppose the rod is 1/5 m in length and is made from stainless steel with thermal diffusivity $k = 3.87 \times 10^{-6}$ m²/s. Consider finding the temperature at the midpoint $x = 1/10$ of the rod at the four times $t = 2, 5, 30$, and 100 min. Series (42) gives

$$U\left(\frac{1}{10}, 120\right) = 100\left(1 - \frac{1}{2}\right) - \frac{200}{\pi} \sum_{n=1}^{\infty} \frac{1}{n} e^{-0.1145861 n^2} \sin\frac{n\pi}{2}$$

$$= 0.10°C;$$

$$U\left(\frac{1}{10}, 300\right) = 100\left(1 - \frac{1}{2}\right) - \frac{200}{\pi} \sum_{n=1}^{\infty} \frac{1}{n} e^{-0.28646526 n^2} \sin\frac{n\pi}{2}$$

$$= 3.80°C;$$

$$U\left(\frac{1}{10}, 1800\right) = 100\left(1 - \frac{1}{2}\right) - \frac{200}{\pi} \sum_{n=1}^{\infty} \frac{1}{n} e^{-1.7187915 n^2} \sin\frac{n\pi}{2}$$

$$= 38.6°C;$$

$$U\left(\frac{1}{10}, 6000\right) = 100\left(1 - \frac{1}{2}\right) - \frac{200}{\pi} \sum_{n=1}^{\infty} \frac{1}{n} e^{-5.7293052n^2} \sin\frac{n\pi}{2}$$

$$= 49.8°C.$$

To obtain these temperatures, we required only four nonzero terms from the first series, three from the second, and one each from the third and fourth. This substantiates our claim that as t increases, fewer and fewer terms in series (42) are required for accurate calculations of temperature.

Laplace transforms can be used to give a completely different representation for the temperature in the rod when $f(t) = 100$. To find this representation, we return to expression (37) for the Laplace transform $\tilde{U}(x, s)$ of $U(x, t)$ and set $\tilde{f}(s) = 100/s$, the transform of $f(t) = 100$:

$$\tilde{U}(x, s) = \frac{100 \sinh\sqrt{s/k}(L - x)}{s \sinh\sqrt{s/k}L} = \frac{100}{s} \frac{e^{\sqrt{s/k}(L-x)} - e^{-\sqrt{s/k}(L-x)}}{e^{\sqrt{s/k}L} - e^{-\sqrt{s/k}L}}$$

$$= \frac{100}{s} \frac{e^{-\sqrt{s/k}L}(e^{\sqrt{s/k}(L-x)} - e^{-\sqrt{s/k}(L-x)})}{1 - e^{-2\sqrt{s/k}L}}.$$

If we regard $1/(1 - e^{-2\sqrt{s/k}L})$ as the sum of an infinite geometric series with common ratio $e^{-2\sqrt{s/k}L}$, we may write

$$\tilde{U}(x, s) = \frac{100}{s}(e^{-\sqrt{s/k}x} - e^{-\sqrt{s/k}(2L - x)}) \sum_{n=0}^{\infty} e^{-2n\sqrt{s/k}L}$$

$$= 100 \sum_{n=0}^{\infty} \left(\frac{e^{-\sqrt{s/k}(2nL + x)}}{s} - \frac{e^{-\sqrt{s/k}[2(n+1)L - x]}}{s}\right). \tag{43}$$

Tables of Laplace transforms indicate that

$$\mathcal{L}^{-1}\left(\frac{e^{-a\sqrt{s}}}{s}\right) = \operatorname{erfc}\left(\frac{a}{2\sqrt{t}}\right),$$

where erfc(x) is the complementary error function in equation (15). Hence, $U(x, t)$ may be expressed as a series of complementary error functions,

$$U(x, t) = 100 \sum_{n=0}^{\infty} \left[\operatorname{erfc}\left(\frac{2nL + x}{2\sqrt{kt}}\right) - \operatorname{erfc}\left(\frac{2(n+1)L - x}{2\sqrt{kt}}\right)\right]$$

$$= 100 \sum_{n=0}^{\infty} \left[\operatorname{erf}\left(\frac{2(n+1)L - x}{2\sqrt{kt}}\right) - \operatorname{erf}\left(\frac{2nL + x}{2\sqrt{kt}}\right)\right], \tag{44}$$

where we have used the fact that erfc(x) = $1 - $ erf(x). This representation of $U(x, t)$ is valuable for small values of t [as opposed to (42), which converges rapidly for large t]. To understand this, consider temperature at the midpoint of the above stainless steel rod at $t = 300$ s:

$$U\left(\frac{1}{10}, 300\right) = 100 \sum_{n=0}^{\infty} \left[\operatorname{erf}\left(\frac{2(n+1)/5 - 1/10}{2\sqrt{3.87 \times 10^{-6}(300)}}\right) - \operatorname{erf}\left(\frac{2n/5 + 1/10}{2\sqrt{3.87 \times 10^{-6}(300)}}\right)\right].$$

For $n > 0$, all terms in this series essentially vanish, and

$$U\left(\frac{1}{10}, 300\right) = 100[\text{erf}(4.40) - \text{erf}(1.467)] = 3.80°C.$$

For $t = 1800$,

$$U\left(\frac{1}{10}, 1800\right) = 100 \sum_{n=0}^{\infty} \left[\text{erf}\left(\frac{2(n+1)/5 - 1/10}{2\sqrt{3.87 \times 10^{-6}(1800)}}\right) - \text{erf}\left(\frac{2n/5 + 1/10}{2\sqrt{3.87 \times 10^{-6}(1800)}}\right) \right].$$

Once again, only the $n = 0$ term is required; it yields

$$U\left(\frac{1}{10}, 1800\right) = 38.6°C.$$

Finally, for $t = 6000$,

$$U\left(\frac{1}{10}, 6000\right) = 100 \sum_{n=0}^{\infty} \left[\text{erf}\left(\frac{2(n+1)/5 - 1/10}{2\sqrt{3.87 \times 10^{-6}(6000)}}\right) - \text{erf}\left(\frac{2n/5 + 1/10}{2\sqrt{3.87 \times 10^{-6}(6000)}}\right) \right].$$

In this case, the $n = 0$ and $n = 1$ terms give

$$U\left(\frac{1}{10}, 6000\right) = 49.9°C.$$

For larger values of t, more and more terms of (44) are required.

The error function representation in (44) once again substantiates our claim in Section 5.6 that heat propagates with infinite speed. Because the error function is an increasing function of its argument, and the argument $(2nL + 2L - x)/(2\sqrt{kt})$ of the first error function in (44) is greater than the second argument, $(2nL + x)/(2\sqrt{kt})$, it follows that each term in (44) is positive. Since this is true for every x in $0 < x < L$ and every $t > 0$, the temperature at every point in the rod for every $t > 0$ is positive. This means that the effect of changing the temperature of the end $x = 0$ of the rod from 0°C to 100°C at time $t = 0$ is instantaneously felt at every point in the rod. The amount of heat transmitted to other parts of the rod may be minute, but nonetheless, heat is transmitted instantaneously to all parts of the rod.

Exercises 10.4

Use Laplace transforms to solve all problems in this set of exercises.

Part A—Heat Conduction

1. A homogeneous, isotropic rod with insulated sides has temperature $\sin m\pi x/L$ (m an integer) at time $t = 0$. For time $t > 0$, its ends ($x = 0$ and $x = L$) are held at temperature 0°C. Find a formula for temperature $U(x, t)$ in the rod for $0 < x < L$ and $t > 0$.

2. Solve Example 1 in Section 3.2 when the initial temperature is $U_0 = $ constant.

3. Repeat Exercise 1 if the initial temperature is 10°C throughout.

4. Solve Exercise 8 in Section 3.3.

5. Repeat Exercise 4 if $g(x,t) = e^{-\alpha t}$. Assume that $\alpha \neq n^2\pi^2 k/L^2$ for any integer n.

6. (a) Repeat Exercise 5 if the initial temperature at time $t = 0$ is $10°C$ throughout.

   (b) Compare the solution with that obtained in Exercise 9 of Section 3.3.

7. Solve Exercise 2 in Section 3.2.

8. Solve Example 1 in Section 3.2 when the initial temperature is $f(x)$ (in place of x).

9. A homogeneous, isotropic rod with insulated sides is initially ($t = 0$) at temperature $0°C$ throughout. For time $t > 0$, its left end, $x = 0$, is kept at $0°C$ and its right end, $x = L$, is kept at constant temperature $U_L°C$. Find two expressions for temperature in the rod, one in terms of exponentials in time and the other in terms of error functions.

10. A homogeneous, isotropic rod with insulated sides is initially ($t = 0$) at constant temperature $U_0°C$ throughout. For $t > 0$, its end $x = 0$ is insulated, and heat is added to the end $x = L$ at a constant rate Q W/m². Find the temperature in the rod for $0 < x < L$ and $t > 0$.

11. (a) A homogeneous, isotropic rod with insulated sides has, for time $t > 0$, its ends at $x = 0$ and $x = L$ kept at temperature zero. Initially its temperature is Ax, where A is constant. Show that temperature in the rod can be expressed in two ways:

$$U(x,t) = \frac{2AL}{\pi} \sum_{n=1}^{\infty} \frac{(-1)^{n+1}}{n} e^{-n^2\pi^2 kt/L^2} \sin\frac{n\pi x}{L}$$

and $U(x,t) = A\left(x - L\sum_{n=0}^{\infty}\left[\text{erf}\left(\frac{(2n+1)L+x}{2\sqrt{kt}}\right) - \text{erf}\left(\frac{(2n+1)L-x}{2\sqrt{kt}}\right)\right]\right)$.

   (b) Which of the two solutions do you expect to converge more quickly for small t? For large t?

   (c) Verify your conjecture in (b) by calculating the temperature at the midpoint of a stainless steel rod ($k = 3.87 \times 10^{-6}$) of length $1/5$ m when $A = 500$ and

   (i) $t = 30$ s   (ii) $t = 5$ min.   (iii) $t = 100$ min.

12. A homogeneous, isotropic rod with insulated sides is initially ($t = 0$) at temperature $0°C$ throughout. For $t > 0$, its left end, $x = 0$, is kept at $0°C$ and heat is added to the end $x = L$ at a constant rate $Q > 0$ W/m². Find two series representations for $U(x,t)$, one in terms of error functions and one in terms of time exponentials.

13. Solve Exercise 13 in Section 6.2.

14. Show that the Laplace transform solution and the eigenfunction expansion solution to the problem in Example 10 are identical when $f(0) \neq 0$.

15. A homogeneous, isotropic rod with insulated sides has initial temperature distribution $U_L x/L$, $0 \leq x \leq L$ (U_L a constant). For time $t > 0$, its ends $x = 0$ and $x = L$ are held at temperatures $0°C$ and $U_L°C$, respectively. Find the temperature distribution in the rod for $t > 0$.

16. Repeat Exercise 15 if the initial temperature distribution is $f(x) = x$, $0 \leq x \leq L$, and the ends $x = 0$ and $x = L$ are held at constant temperatures $U_0°C$ and $0°C$, respectively, for $t > 0$.

17. Solve Exercise 5 in Section 3.3. (See also Exercise 8 in Section 6.2.)

Part B—Vibrations

18. A taut string has its ends fixed at $x = 0$ and $x = L$ on the x-axis. If it is given an initial displacement (at time $t = 0$) of $f(x) = kx(L - x)$ (k a constant) and zero initial velocity, find its subsequent displacement.

19. Solve Exercise 8 in Section 3.2.

20. Repeat Exercise 18 for zero initial displacement and an unspecified initial velocity $g(x)$.

21. Solve Exercise 33(a) in Section 6.2.

22. Solve Exercise 23 in Section 6.2. Assume that $\omega \neq n\pi c/L$ for any integer n.

23. A taut string has its ends fixed at $x = 0$ and $x = L$ on the x-axis. An external force (per unit x-length) $F = -ky$ $(k > 0)$ acts at each point on the string. Assuming an initial displacement $f(x)$ and a velocity $g(x)$, find subsequent displacements of the string.

For Exercises 24–29, solve Exercises 26–31 in Section 6.2.

30. Repeat Example 9 if gravity is taken into account. See also Exercise 37 in Section 6.2.

31. Solve Exercise 24 in Section 6.2.

32. Show that Laplace transforms lead to the solution in part (b) for the problem in Exercise 21 of Section 6.2.

33. (a) Find a series solution for displacements in the bar of Exercise 21 of Section 6.2 if the constant force per unit area F is replaced by an impulse force $F = F_0 \delta(t)$. Use the fact that

$$\int_0^\infty f(t)\delta(t)\, dt = f(0+).$$

(b) Show that the displacement of the end $x = L$ is $cF_0/(AE)$ times the square wave function

$$M_{2L/c}(t) = \begin{cases} 1 & 0 < t < 2L/c \\ -1 & 2L/c < t < 4L/c \end{cases},$$

$$M_{2L/c}(t + 4L/c) = M_{2L/c}(t).$$

34. Solve Exercise 38 in Section 6.2.

35. A taut string of length L is initially at rest along the x-axis. For time $t > 0$, its ends are subjected to prescribed displacements

$$y(0, t) = f_1(t), \qquad y(L, t) = f_2(t).$$

Find its displacement for $0 < x < L$ and $t > 0$.

36. (a) Show that the Laplace transform of the displacement function $y(x, t)$ for the vibrations in Exercise 41 of Section 6.2 is

$$\tilde{y}(x, s) = \frac{F_0 \omega c \sinh(sx/c)}{s(s^2 + \omega^2)[AE \cosh(sL/c) + mcs \sinh(sL/c)]}.$$

(b) Resonance occurs if either of the zeros $s = \pm i\omega$ of $s^2 + \omega^2$ coincides with a zero of

$$h(s) = AE \cosh\left(\frac{sL}{c}\right) + mcs \sinh\left(\frac{sL}{c}\right).$$

By expressing zeros of $h(s)$ in the form $s = c(\mu + i\lambda)$, show that

$$\tanh 2\mu L = \frac{-2AEmc^2\mu}{A^2E^2 + m^2c^4(\mu^2 + \lambda^2)}$$

and that therefore $\mu = 0$. Verify that resonance occurs if $\omega = c\lambda$ where λ is a root of the equation

$$\tan \lambda L = \frac{AE}{mc^2\lambda}.$$

37. Solve Example 3 in Section 3.2, but with an unspecified initial displacement $f(x)$. [*Hint:* Replace s by icq^2 in the ODE for $\tilde{y}(x, s)$.]

38. (a) The top of the bar in Exercise 21 is attached to a spring with constant k. If $x = 0$ corresponds to the top end of the bar when the spring is unstretched, show that the Laplace transform of the displacement function for cross sections of the bar is

$$\tilde{y}(x, s) = \frac{g}{s^3} - \frac{kgc \cosh\left[s(L - x)/c\right]}{s^3[AEs \sinh(sL/c) + kc \cosh(sL/c)]}.$$

(b) Verify that $\tilde{y}(x, s)$ has a pole of order 1 at $s = 0$. What is the residue of $e^{st}\tilde{y}(x, s)$ at $s = 0$?

(c) By setting $s = c(\mu + i\lambda)$ to obtain zeros of

$$h(s) = AEs \sinh\left(\frac{sL}{c}\right) + kc \cosh\left(\frac{sL}{c}\right),$$

show that μ must be zero and that λ must satisfy

$$\tan \lambda L = \frac{k}{AE\lambda}.$$

(d) Find $y(x, t)$. (See also Exercise 34 in Section 6.2.)

39. (a) An unstrained elastic bar falls vertically under gravity with its axis in the vertical position (Figure 10.6). When its velocity is $v > 0$, it strikes a solid object and remains in contact with it thereafter. Show that the Laplace transform of displacements $y(x, t)$ of cross sections of the bar is

$$\tilde{y}(x, s) = \left(\frac{v}{s^2} + \frac{g}{s^3}\right)\left(1 - \frac{\cosh(sx/c)}{\cosh(sL/c)}\right).$$

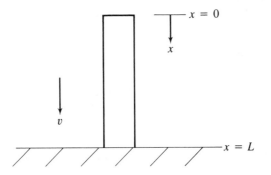

Figure 10.6

(b) Use residues to find

$$y(x, t) = \frac{g(L^2 - x^2)}{2c^2} + \frac{8Lv}{\pi^2 c} \sum_{n=1}^{\infty} \frac{(-1)^{n+1}}{(2n - 1)^2} \sin\frac{(2n - 1)\pi ct}{2L} \cos\frac{(2n - 1)\pi x}{2L}$$

$$+ \frac{16L^2 g}{\pi^3 c^2} \sum_{n=1}^{\infty} \frac{(-1)^n}{(2n - 1)^3} \cos\frac{(2n - 1)\pi ct}{2L} \cos\frac{(2n - 1)\pi x}{2L}.$$

(c) Verify that the second series in (b) may be expressed in the form

$$-\frac{g}{4c^2}\left(K(x + ct) + K(x - ct)\right),$$

where $K(x)$ is the even, odd-harmonic extension of $L^2 - x^2$, $0 \le x \le L$, to a function of period $4L$. (See Exercise 22 in Section 2.2 for the definition of an even, odd-harmonic function.)

(d) Verify that the first series in (b) may be expressed in the form

$$\frac{v}{2c}\left(M_L(x + ct) - M_L(x - ct)\right),$$

where $M_L(x)$ is the odd, odd-harmonic extension of x, $0 \le x \le L$, to a function of period $4L$. (See Exercise 21 in Section 2.2 for the definition of an odd, odd-harmonic function.)

(e) Find an expression for the force $F(t)$ due to the bar on the cross section at $x = L$. Sketch graphs of $F(t)$ when $v < 2Lg/c$ and $v > 2Lg/c$.

40. A bar 1/4 m long is falling as in Exercise 39 when it strikes an object squarely. Use the result of Exercise 39 to find a formula for the length of time of contact of the bar with the object. Use this formula to find the contact time for a steel bar with $\rho = 7.8 \times 10^3$ kg/m^3 and $E = 2.1 \times 10^{11}$ kg/m^2 when $v = 2$ m/s.

10.5 Laplace Transform Solutions to Problems in Polar, Cylindrical, and Spherical Coordinates

Laplace transforms can also be used to solve problems in polar, cylindrical, and spherical coordinates, but calculations are sometimes more difficult. We illustrate with the following examples.

Example 11:   An infinitely long cylinder of radius r_2 is initially at temperature $f(r) = r_2^2 - r^2$, and for time $t > 0$, the boundary $r = r_2$ is insulated. Find the temperature in the cylinder for $t > 0$. (This problem was solved by separation of variables in Example 1 of Section 9.1.)

Solution: The initial boundary value problem for $U(r, t)$ is

$$\frac{\partial U}{\partial t} = k\left(\frac{\partial^2 U}{\partial r^2} + \frac{1}{r}\frac{\partial U}{\partial r}\right), \qquad 0 < r < r_2, \qquad t > 0, \tag{45a}$$

$$\frac{\partial U(r_2, t)}{\partial r} = 0, \qquad t > 0, \tag{45b}$$

$$U(r, 0) = r_2^2 - r^2, \qquad 0 < r < r_2. \tag{45c}$$

When we take Laplace transforms of (45a) and use (45c),

$$s\tilde{U}(r, s) - (r_2^2 - r^2) = k\left(\frac{\partial^2 \tilde{U}}{\partial r^2} + \frac{1}{r}\frac{\partial \tilde{U}}{\partial r}\right);$$

that is, $\tilde{U}(r, s)$ must satisfy the ODE

$$r\frac{d^2\tilde{U}}{dr^2} + \frac{d\tilde{U}}{dr} - \frac{sr}{k}\tilde{U} = \frac{r^3 - r_2^2 r}{k}, \qquad 0 < r < r_2 \tag{46a}$$

subject to the transform of boundary condition (45b),

$$\tilde{U}'(r_2, s) = 0. \tag{46b}$$

The change of independent variable $u = i\sqrt{s/kr}$ replaces the homogeneous equation

$$r\frac{d^2\tilde{U}}{dr^2} + \frac{d\tilde{U}}{dr} - \frac{sr}{k}\tilde{U} = 0 \tag{47}$$

with

$$u\frac{d^2\tilde{U}}{du^2} + \frac{d\tilde{U}}{du} + u\tilde{U} = 0. \tag{48}$$

This is Bessel's differential equation of order zero, with general solution

$$AJ_0(u) + BY_0(u).$$

Thus, the general solution of (47) is

$$AJ_0\left(i\sqrt{\frac{s}{k}}r\right) + BY_0\left(i\sqrt{\frac{s}{k}}r\right). \tag{49}$$

When the particular solution $-r^2/s + (r_2^2 s - 4k)/s^2$ of (46a) is added to (49), the general solution of (46a) is

$$\tilde{U}(r,s) = AJ_0\left(i\sqrt{\frac{s}{k}}r\right) + BY_0\left(i\sqrt{\frac{s}{k}}r\right) - \frac{4k}{s^2} + \frac{r_2^2 - r^2}{s}. \tag{50}$$

Because $U(r,t)$ must remain bounded as r approaches zero, so also must $\tilde{U}(r,s)$. This implies that B must vanish, in which case boundary condition (46b) requires that

$$i\sqrt{\frac{s}{k}}AJ_0'\left(i\sqrt{\frac{s}{k}}r_2\right) - \frac{2r_2}{s} = 0.$$

When this equation is solved for A and the result is substituted into (50),

$$\tilde{U}(r,s) = \frac{2r_2 J_0(i\sqrt{s/k}r)}{i\sqrt{s^3/k}J_0'(i\sqrt{s/k}r_2)} - \frac{4k}{s^2} + \frac{r_2^2 - r^2}{s}. \tag{51}$$

This function has singularities at $s = 0$ and values of s satisfying $J_0'(i\sqrt{s/k}r_2) = 0$. If we set $\sqrt{s/k}i = \lambda_n$, singularities occur for $s = -k\lambda_n^2$ where $J_0'(\lambda_n r_2) = 0$. Power series (15) in Section 8.3 can be used to expand $\tilde{U}(r,s)$ about $s = 0$:

$$\tilde{U}(r,s) = \frac{2\sqrt{k}r_2}{is^{3/2}} \left| \frac{1 - \dfrac{(i\sqrt{s/k}r)^2}{4} + \dfrac{(i\sqrt{s/k}r)^4}{64} - \cdots}{-\dfrac{(i\sqrt{s/k}r_2)}{2} + \dfrac{(i\sqrt{s/k}r_2)^3}{16} - \cdots} \right| - \frac{4k}{s^2} + \frac{r_2^2 - r^2}{s}$$

$$= \frac{2\sqrt{k}r_2}{is^{3/2}}\left[-\frac{2}{i\sqrt{s/k}r_2} - \frac{i\sqrt{s/k}}{r_2}\left(\frac{r_2^2}{4} - \frac{r^2}{2}\right) + \cdots\right] - \frac{4k}{s^2} + \frac{r_2^2 - r^2}{s}$$

$$= \frac{r_2^2}{2s} + \cdots.$$

When this result is multiplied by e^{st},

$$e^{st}\tilde{U}(r,s) = \left(1 + st + \frac{s^2 t^2}{2} + \cdots\right)\left(\frac{r_2^2}{2s} + \cdots\right),$$

it is clear that the residue of $e^{st}\tilde{U}(r, s)$ at $s = 0$ is $r_2^2/2$. Because the derivative of J_0' does not vanish at its zeros, the remaining singularities at $s = -k\lambda_n^2$ are poles of order 1, and the residues of $e^{st}\tilde{U}(r, s)$ at these poles are

$$\lim_{s \to -k\lambda_n^2} (s + k\lambda_n^2)e^{st}\left(\frac{2r_2 J_0(i\sqrt{s/k}\, r)}{i\sqrt{s^3/k}\, J_0'(i\sqrt{s/k}\, r_2)} - \frac{4k}{s^2} + \frac{r_2^2 - r^2}{s}\right)$$

$$= \frac{2r_2}{-k\lambda_n^3} e^{-k\lambda_n^2 t} J_0(\lambda_n r) \lim_{s \to -k\lambda_n^2} \frac{s + k\lambda_n^2}{J_0'(i\sqrt{s/k}\, r_2)}$$

$$= \frac{-2r_2}{k\lambda_n^3} e^{-k\lambda_n^2 t} J_0(\lambda_n r) \lim_{s \to -k\lambda_n^2} \frac{1}{\dfrac{ir_2}{2\sqrt{ks}} J_0''(i\sqrt{s/k}\, r_2)} \qquad \text{(by l'Hôpital's rule)}$$

$$= \frac{-4}{k\lambda_n^3} e^{-k\lambda_n^2 t} J_0(\lambda_n r)\frac{1}{\dfrac{-1}{k\lambda_n} J_0''(\lambda_n r_2)}$$

$$= \frac{4}{\lambda_n^2 J_0''(\lambda_n r_2)} e^{-k\lambda_n^2 t} J_0(\lambda_n r).$$

But, because $J_0(\lambda_n r)$ satisfies equation (47) when $s = -k\lambda_n^2$,

$$r\frac{d^2 J_0(\lambda_n r)}{dr^2} + \frac{dJ_0(\lambda_n r)}{dr} + \lambda_n^2 r J_0(\lambda_n r) = 0$$

or $\qquad\qquad \lambda_n^2 r J_0''(\lambda_n r) + \lambda_n J_0'(\lambda_n r) + \lambda_n^2 r J_0(\lambda_n r) = 0.$

When we set $r = r_2$ in this equation and note that $J_0'(\lambda_n r_2) = 0$, we obtain

$$J_0''(\lambda_n r_2) = -J_0(\lambda_n r_2).$$

Residues of $e^{st}\tilde{U}(r, s)$ at $s = -k\lambda_n^2$ can therefore be expressed as

$$\frac{-4}{\lambda_n^2 J_0(\lambda_n r_2)} e^{-k\lambda_n^2 t} J_0(\lambda_n r).$$

The sum of the residues at $s = 0$ and $s = -k\lambda_n^2$ yields the temperature function

$$U(r, t) = \frac{r_2^2}{2} - 4 \sum_{n=1}^{\infty} \frac{e^{-k\lambda_n^2 t} J_0(\lambda_n r)}{\lambda_n^2 J_0(\lambda_n r_2)}. \qquad\qquad \blacksquare \quad \textbf{(52)}$$

The following vibration problem has a nonhomogeneous boundary condition.

Example 12:   A circular membrane of radius r_2 is initially at rest on the xy-plane. Find its displacement for time $t > 0$ if its edge is forced to undergo periodic oscillations described by $A \sin \omega t$, A a constant.

Solution: The initial boundary value problem for displacements $z(r, t)$ of the membrane is

$$\frac{\partial^2 z}{\partial t^2} = c^2\left(\frac{\partial^2 z}{\partial r^2} + \frac{1}{r}\frac{\partial z}{\partial r}\right), \qquad 0 < r < r_2, \qquad t > 0, \qquad \text{(53a)}$$

$$z(r_2, t) = A \sin \omega t, \qquad t > 0, \qquad\qquad\qquad \text{(53b)}$$

$$z(r, 0) = 0, \qquad 0 < r < r_2, \tag{53c}$$

$$z_t(r, 0) = 0, \qquad 0 < r < r_2. \tag{53d}$$

When we apply the Laplace transform to PDE (53a) and use initial conditions (53c, d),

$$s^2 \bar{z} = c^2 \left(\frac{d^2 \bar{z}}{dr^2} + \frac{1}{r} \frac{d\bar{z}}{dr} \right);$$

that is, $\bar{z}(r, s)$ must satisfy

$$r \frac{d^2 \bar{z}}{dr^2} + \frac{d\bar{z}}{dr} - \frac{s^2 r}{c^2} \bar{z} = 0 \tag{54a}$$

subject to

$$\bar{z}(r_2, s) = \frac{A\omega}{s^2 + \omega^2}. \tag{54b}$$

The change of independent variable $u = isr/c$ replaces this equation with

$$u \frac{d^2 \bar{z}}{du^2} + \frac{d\bar{z}}{du} + u\bar{z} = 0, \tag{55}$$

Bessel's differential equation of order zero. Since the general solution of (55) is $BJ_0(u) + DY_0(u)$, it follows that

$$\bar{z}(r, s) = BJ_0 \left(\frac{isr}{c} \right) + DY_0 \left(\frac{isr}{c} \right). \tag{56}$$

Because $z(r, t)$ must remain bounded as r approaches zero, so also must $\bar{z}(r, s)$. This implies that D must vanish, in which case boundary condition (54b) requires that

$$\frac{A\omega}{s^2 + \omega^2} = BJ_0 \left(\frac{isr_2}{c} \right).$$

When this equation is solved for B and the result is substituted into (56),

$$\bar{z}(r, s) = \frac{A\omega}{s^2 + \omega^2} \frac{J_0(isr/c)}{J_0(isr_2/c)}. \tag{57}$$

This function has singularities at $s = \pm i\omega$ and values of s satisfying $J_0(isr_2/c) = 0$. If we set $is/c = \lambda_n$, singularities occur for $s = -ic\lambda_n$ where $J_0(\lambda_n r_2) = 0$. (For every positive value of λ_n satisfying this equation, $\lambda_{-n} = -\lambda_n$ is also a solution.) Provided $\omega \neq c\lambda_n$ for any n, all singularities are poles of order 1. The residue of $e^{st}\bar{z}(r, s)$ at $s = i\omega$ is

$$\lim_{s \to i\omega} (s - i\omega)e^{st}\bar{z}(r, s) = \lim_{s \to i\omega} (s - i\omega) \frac{A\omega e^{st}}{(s + i\omega)(s - i\omega)} \frac{J_0(isr/c)}{J_0(isr_2/c)}$$

$$= \frac{A\omega e^{i\omega t}}{2i\omega} \frac{J_0(-\omega r/c)}{J_0(-\omega r_2/c)}$$

$$= -\frac{i}{2} A e^{i\omega t} \frac{J_0(\omega r/c)}{J_0(\omega r_2/c)}.$$

Similarly, the residue of $e^{st}\bar{z}(r,s)$ at $s=-i\omega$ is

$$\frac{i}{2}Ae^{-i\omega t}\frac{J_0(\omega r/c)}{J_0(\omega r_2/c)}.$$

The residues of $e^{st}\bar{z}(r,s)$ at $s=-ic\lambda_n$ are

$$\lim_{s\to -ic\lambda_n}(s+ic\lambda_n)e^{st}\frac{A\omega}{s^2+\omega^2}\frac{J_0(isr/c)}{J_0(isr_2/c)}$$

$$=\frac{A\omega}{\omega^2-c^2\lambda_n^2}e^{-ic\lambda_n t}J_0(\lambda_n r)\lim_{s\to -ic\lambda_n}\frac{s+ic\lambda_n}{J_0(isr_2/c)}$$

$$=\frac{A\omega}{\omega^2-c^2\lambda_n^2}e^{-ic\lambda_n t}J_0(\lambda_n r)\lim_{s\to -ic\lambda_n}\frac{1}{\dfrac{ir_2}{c}J_0'(isr_2/c)}\qquad\text{(by l'Hôpital's rule)}$$

$$=\frac{-iA\omega ce^{-ic\lambda_n t}}{r_2(\omega^2-c^2\lambda_n^2)}J_0(\lambda_n r)\frac{1}{J_0'(\lambda_n r_2)}=\frac{iA\omega ce^{-ic\lambda_n t}}{r_2(\omega^2-c^2\lambda_n^2)}\frac{J_0(\lambda_n r)}{J_1(\lambda_n r_2)}.$$

The sum of the residues at $s=\pm i\omega$ and $s=-ic\lambda_n$ yields the displacement of the membrane,

$$z(r,t)=-\frac{i}{2}Ae^{i\omega t}\frac{J_0(\omega r/c)}{J_0(\omega r_2/c)}+\frac{i}{2}Ae^{-i\omega t}\frac{J_0(\omega r/c)}{J_0(\omega r_2/c)}+\sum_{\substack{n=-\infty\\ n\neq 0}}^{\infty}\frac{iA\omega ce^{-ic\lambda_n t}}{r_2(\omega^2-c^2\lambda_n^2)}\frac{J_0(\lambda_n r)}{J_1(\lambda_n r_2)}$$

$$=A\frac{J_0(\omega r/c)}{J_0(\omega r_2/c)}\left(\frac{e^{i\omega t}-e^{-i\omega t}}{2i}\right)+\sum_{n=1}^{\infty}\frac{iA\omega ce^{-ic\lambda_n t}}{r_2(\omega^2-c^2\lambda_n^2)}\frac{J_0(\lambda_n r)}{J_1(\lambda_n r_2)}$$

$$+\sum_{n=-1}^{-\infty}\frac{iA\omega ce^{-ic\lambda_n t}}{r_2(\omega^2-c^2\lambda_n^2)}\frac{J_0(\lambda_n r)}{J_1(\lambda_n r_2)}$$

$$=A\frac{J_0(\omega r/c)}{J_0(\omega r_2/c)}\sin\omega t+\frac{iA\omega c}{r_2}\sum_{n=1}^{\infty}\frac{e^{-ic\lambda_n t}}{\omega^2-c^2\lambda_n^2}\frac{J_0(\lambda_n r)}{J_1(\lambda_n r_2)}$$

$$+\frac{iA\omega c}{r_2}\sum_{n=1}^{\infty}\frac{e^{-ic\lambda_{-n} t}}{\omega^2-c^2(\lambda_{-n})^2}\frac{J_0(\lambda_{-n} r)}{J_1(\lambda_{-n} r_2)}.$$

Since $\lambda_{-n}=-\lambda_n$, and J_0 and J_1 are even and odd functions, respectively, it follows that

$$z(r,t)=A\sin\omega t\frac{J_0(\omega r/c)}{J_0(\omega r_2/c)}-\frac{iA\omega c}{r_2}\sum_{n=1}^{\infty}\frac{e^{ic\lambda_n t}-e^{-ic\lambda_n t}}{\omega^2-c^2\lambda_n^2}\frac{J_0(\lambda_n r)}{J_1(\lambda_n r_2)}$$

$$=A\sin\omega t\frac{J_0(\omega r/c)}{J_0(\omega r_2/c)}+\frac{2A\omega c}{r_2}\sum_{n=1}^{\infty}\frac{1}{\omega^2-c^2\lambda_n^2}\frac{J_0(\lambda_n r)}{J_1(\lambda_n r_2)}\sin c\lambda_n t.\qquad(58)$$

The solution of this problem, obtained by finite Fourier transforms in Exercise 16 of Section 9.2, is

$$z(r,t)=-\frac{2Ac}{r_2}\sum_{n=1}^{\infty}\frac{c\lambda_n\sin\omega t-\omega\sin c\lambda_n t}{(\omega^2-c^2\lambda_n^2)J_1(\lambda_n r_2)}J_0(\lambda_n r).$$

The Laplace transform solution is preferable; it expresses part of the finite Fourier transform solution in closed form.   ∎

Exercises 10.5

Part A—Heat Conduction

1. Solve Exercise 1(b) in Section 9.1.

2. Solve Exercise 1(c) in Section 9.1.

3. Laplace transforms do not handle problems in polar coordinates efficiently when initial conditions contain unspecified functions. To illustrate this, find the Laplace transform of the PDE for Exercise 1(a) in Section 9.1. How difficult is it to solve the ODE in $\tilde{U}(r, s)$?

4. Solve Example 5 in Section 9.2.

5. (a) An infinitely long cylinder of radius r_2 is initially at temperature $0°C$ throughout. If the surface $r = r_2$ has variable temperature $f(t)$ for $t > 0$, find the temperature inside the cylinder.

   (b) Simplify the solution when $f(t) = \bar{U}$, a constant. Do you obtain the solution to Exercise 4?

6. Solve Exercise 2(b) in Section 9.2.

7. (a) A cylinder occupying the region $0 \le r \le r_2, 0 \le z \le L$, is initially at constant temperature $U_0°C$ throughout. What is the initial boundary value problem for temperature in the cylinder if its surface is held at $0°C$ for $t > 0$?

   (b) If a finite Fourier transform is used to remove the z-variable from the problem in $U(r, z, t)$, what is the initial boundary value problem for $\tilde{U}(r, \mu_m, t)$ (where $\mu_m = m\pi/L$ are eigenvalues associated with this transform)?

   (c) Show that when the Laplace transform is applied to the PDE in $\tilde{U}(r, \mu_m, t)$, the transform function $\tilde{\tilde{U}}(r, \mu_m, s)$ must satisfy

   $$r\frac{d^2\tilde{\tilde{U}}}{dr^2} + \frac{d\tilde{\tilde{U}}}{dr} - r\left(\frac{s}{k} + \mu_m^2\right)\tilde{\tilde{U}} = -\frac{rU_0\tilde{1}}{k}, \qquad 0 < r < r_2,$$

   $$\tilde{\tilde{U}}(r_2, \mu_m, s) = 0,$$

   where $\tilde{1} = \sqrt{2L}[1 + (-1)^{n+1}]/(m\pi)$ is the finite Fourier transform of the unity function.

   (d) Verify that the solution for $\tilde{\tilde{U}}(r, \mu_m, s)$ is

   $$\tilde{\tilde{U}}(r, \mu_m, s) = \frac{U_0\tilde{1}}{s + k\mu_m^2}\left(1 - \frac{J_0(i\sqrt{\mu_m^2 + s/k}\, r)}{J_0(i\sqrt{\mu_m^2 + s/k}\, r_2)}\right).$$

   (e) Prove that $\tilde{\tilde{U}}(r, \mu_m, s)$ has a removable singularity at $s = -k\mu_m^2$ and poles of order 1 at $s = -k(\lambda_n^2 + \mu_m^2)$ where $J_0(\lambda_n r_2) = 0$. Show that the residues of $e^{st}\tilde{\tilde{U}}(r, \mu_m, s)$ at these poles are

   $$\frac{2U_0\tilde{1}}{r_2\lambda_n}e^{-k(\lambda_n^2 + \mu_m^2)t}\frac{J_0(\lambda_n r)}{J_1(\lambda_n r_2)}.$$

   (f) Finally, invert the Laplace transform and the finite Fourier transform to find $U(r, z, t)$.

Part B—Vibrations

8. Solve Exercise 19 in Section 9.1.

9. Solve Exercise 20 in Section 9.1.

10. Solve Exercise 17 in Section 9.2 in the nonresonance case.

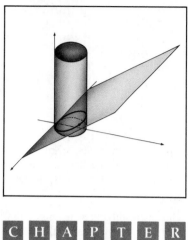

Green's Functions
for Ordinary Differential Equations

11.1 Generalized Functions

To solve many physical problems, we create mathematical idealizations called "point" entities—point charges, point masses, point heat sources, and point forces, to name a few. For example, suppose a 1-N force is applied to the midpoint of a taut string (of negligible mass) as shown in Figure 11.1. The boundary value problem that describes static deflections of the string is

$$-\tau \frac{d^2 y}{dx^2} = F(x), \qquad 0 < x < L, \tag{1a}$$

$$y(0) = 0 = y(L), \tag{1b}$$

where τ is the constant tension in the string and $F(x)$ is the force per unit x-length on the string due to the applied force. Although it would seem to be a simple procedure to integrate the differential equation twice and apply the boundary conditions (for determination of constants of integration), integration of $F(x)$ presents a problem. If we use

$$F(x) = \begin{cases} 0 & 0 < x < L/2 \\ 1 & x = L/2 \\ 0 & L/2 < x < L \end{cases} \qquad \text{(2)}$$

as the definition of $F(x)$, antidifferentiation gives

$$y(x) = \begin{cases} Ax + B & 0 < x < L/2 \\ Cx + D & L/2 < x < L \end{cases}.$$

(Recall from elementary calculus that we antidifferentiate only over an interval, not at a point; hence the absence of an antiderivative "at" $x = L/2$.) If we now apply boundary conditions (1b) and demand that $y(x)$ be continuous at $x = L/2$, we obtain

$$y(x) = \begin{cases} Ax & 0 \le x \le L/2 \\ -A(x - L) & L/2 \le x \le L \end{cases}.$$

But how do we calculate A? Certainly the size of the force (1 N here) and the tension τ in the string must determine A, but there seems to be no way to use this information. The problem must be representation (2) for a point force concentrated at $x = L/2$. Perhaps what we should do is distribute this force along the string, solve the problem, and then take a limit as the distributed force approaches a concentrated force. There is a multitude of ways that $F(x)$ might be defined, but clearly each must satisfy the condition

$$\int_0^L F(x)\, dx = 1. \qquad \text{(3)}$$

Two possibilities, which are symmetric, are shown in Figure 11.2.

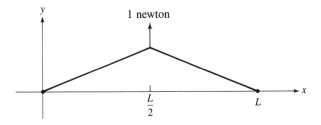

Figure 11.1

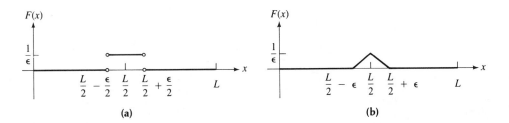

Figure 11.2   **(a)**   **(b)**

Suppose we solve the boundary value problem for $y(x)$ using the distribution in Figure 11.2(a). Then

$$\frac{d^2y}{dx^2} = -\frac{1}{\tau}\begin{cases} 0 & 0 < x < (L-\varepsilon)/2 \\ 1/\varepsilon & (L-\varepsilon)/2 < x < (L+\varepsilon)/2. \\ 0 & (L+\varepsilon)/2 < x < L \end{cases}$$

Integration leads to

$$y(x) = -\frac{1}{\tau}\begin{cases} Ax + B & 0 < x < (L-\varepsilon)/2 \\ x^2/(2\varepsilon) + Cx + D & (L-\varepsilon)/2 < x < (L+\varepsilon)/2. \\ Ex + F & (L+\varepsilon)/2 < x < L \end{cases}$$

If we apply boundary conditions (1b) and demand that $y(x)$ and $y'(x)$ be continuous at $x = (L-\varepsilon)/2$ and $x = (L+\varepsilon)/2$, we find that

$$y(x) = \frac{1}{\tau}\begin{cases} \dfrac{x}{2} & 0 \le x \le (L-\varepsilon)/2 \\ -\dfrac{x^2}{2\varepsilon} + \dfrac{Lx}{2\varepsilon} - \dfrac{1}{8\varepsilon}(L-\varepsilon)^2 & (L-\varepsilon)/2 \le x \le (L+\varepsilon)/2, \\ \dfrac{L-x}{2} & (L+\varepsilon)/2 \le x \le L \end{cases} \qquad (4)$$

the graph of which is shown in Figure 11.3. To obtain the solution of (1) for a concentrated force, we now let ε approach zero. Geometrically, the parabolic section becomes smaller and smaller in width, and in the limit the two straight-line sections meet at $x = L/2$ (Figure 11.4). This implies that the displacement at $L/2$ is $L/(4\tau)$ and the displacement function for the unit point force in Figure 11.1 is that in Figure 11.4, defined algebraically by

$$y(x) = \begin{cases} x/(2\tau) & 0 \le x \le L/2 \\ (L-x)/(2\tau) & L/2 \le x \le L \end{cases}. \qquad (5)$$

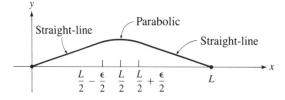

Figure 11.3

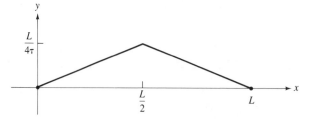

Figure 11.4

In Exercise 7, displacement $y(x)$ for the distributed load in Figure 11.2(b) is calculated. Although it is different from (4), its limit as ε approaches zero is once again (5).

We have attempted to illustrate with this one example that problems containing point sources can be solved with distributed sources and limits. This example and other physical situations in the exercises make it abundantly clear, however, that the method is extremely cumbersome. It is the purpose of this chapter and the next to develop representations for concentrated sources that are effective in solving ordinary and partial differential equations.

When we solve linear, second-order differential equations

$$P(x)\frac{d^2y}{dx^2} + Q(x)\frac{dy}{dx} + R(x)y = f(x),$$

where $P(x)$, $Q(x)$, and $R(x)$ are continuous and $f(x)$ is piecewise continuous, the solution should be continuous and have a continuous first derivative. In fact, for the distributed load of Figure 11.2(a) we actually imposed these conditions at $x = (L \pm \varepsilon)/2$ to obtain displacement (4). But notice that limit function (5), shown in Figure 11.4, has a discontinuity in $y'(x)$ at $x = L/2$. In other words, when "point" sources influence second-order boundary value problems, we cannot expect solutions to have continuous first derivatives.

To begin our search for representations of concentrated sources, suppose that we have a time-independent one-dimensional problem along the x-axis (perhaps static deflections of a string, or steady-state heat conduction in a rod, or potential). We wish to define a function, which we denote by $\delta(x - c)$, to represent a unit point source at $x = c$. Based on the above example (where the unit force was distributed over an interval on the x-axis), it might seem reasonable to define $\delta(x - c)$ as the limit as $\varepsilon \to 0$ of the unit pulse function $P_\varepsilon(x, c)$ in Figure 11.5, that is, define

$$\delta(x - c) = \lim_{\varepsilon \to 0} P_\varepsilon(x, c). \tag{6}$$

Because the area under $P_\varepsilon(x, c)$ is unity for any $\varepsilon > 0$, this definition appears to preserve the "unit" character of the source. But, from the point of view of a function as a mapping from domain to range, definition (6) is unacceptable. It maps all values $x \neq c$ onto zero, and the value of $\delta(x - c)$ at $x = c$ is somehow "infinite." What we are saying is that $\delta(x - c)$ cannot be defined in a pointwise sense; functions that represent point sources require a completely new approach.

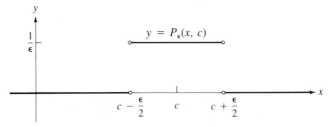

Figure 11.5

To introduce this approach, recall that when $y_n(x)$ are normalized eigenfunctions of a Sturm-Liouville system on an interval $a \leq x \leq b$, and $f(x)$ is suitably behaved, the finite Fourier transform of $f(x)$ is

$$\tilde{f}(\lambda_n) = \int_a^b p(x)f(x)y_n(x)\,dx$$

$[p(x)$ is the weight function of the Sturm-Liouville system]. By this definition, each eigenfunction $y_n(x)$ associates with a function $f(x)$ its nth Fourier coefficient $\tilde{f}(\lambda_n)$,

$$f(x) \xrightarrow{\;y_n(x)\;} \tilde{f}(\lambda_n).$$

We have, then, an infinity of mappings $y_n(x)$. Each maps functions onto reals, and the real numbers are calculated by means of integrals. Such mappings are not restricted to eigenfunctions arising from Sturm-Liouville systems, however. We can associate such a mapping with any continuous function whatsoever. Indeed, if $g(x)$ is continuous on an interval $a \leq x \leq b$, we can associate an integral mapping with $g(x)$ according to

$$f(x) \xrightarrow{\;g(x)\;} \int_a^b f(x)g(x)\,dx;$$

that is, $g(x)$ is a *functional*, or *operator*, which maps functions $f(x)$ onto real numbers, and these numbers are defined by integrals. It is this view of an ordinary function as a functional or operator that we adopt to define $\delta(x - c)$. The "generalized" function[†] $\delta(x - c)$, called the *(Dirac)[‡] delta function*, is the functional that maps a function $f(x)$, continuous at $x = c$, onto its value at $x = c$,

$$f(x) \xrightarrow{\;\delta(x-c)\;} f(c).$$

For example,

$$x^2 + 2x - 3 \xrightarrow{\;\delta(x-2)\;} 5$$

and

$$(x + 1)^2 \cos x \xrightarrow{\;\delta(x)\;} 1.$$

In order that the delta functional have an integral representation, we write

$$f(x) \xrightarrow{\;\delta(x-c)\;} f(c) = \int_{-\infty}^{\infty} f(x)\delta(x - c)\,dx. \tag{7}$$

But because $\delta(x - c)$ cannot be regarded pointwise, the multiplication in this integral, and the integral itself, are symbolic. When we encounter an integral such as that in (7), we interpret it as the action of the functional $\delta(x - c)$ operating on $f(x)$ and immediately write $f(c)$. For example,

$$\int_{-\infty}^{\infty} \left(x^2 + \frac{2}{x - 1} \right) \delta(x)\,dx = -2$$

[†] A complete treatment of generalized functions can be found in M. J. Lighthill, *Introduction to Fourier Analysis and Generalized Functions* (Cambridge, England: Cambridge University Press, 1958).
[‡] After the mathematical physicist Paul Dirac.

and
$$\int_{-\infty}^{\infty} \delta(x+2)\,dx = 1$$

[since the left side of the latter integral is interpreted as the delta function $\delta(x+2)$ operating on the function $f(x) \equiv 1$].

Because $\delta(x-c)$ picks out the value of a function at $x=c$, we write

$$\int_a^b f(x)\delta(x-c)\,dx = f(c) \tag{8a}$$

as long as $a < c < b$; that is, the limits on the integral need not be $\pm\infty$. Furthermore, if $x=c$ is not between a and b, we set

$$\int_a^b f(x)\delta(x-c)\,dx = 0. \tag{8b}$$

For instance,

$$\int_{-2}^6 \sqrt{x+5}\,\delta(x)\,dx = \sqrt{5}$$

and
$$\int_2^3 (x^2 + 2x - 4)\delta(x+1)\,dx = 0.$$

From a functional point of view, it is not at all clear that the delta function $\delta(x-c)$ represents a point source at $x=c$. Our first evidence of this appears in the next section.

Exercises 11.1

In Exercises 1–6, evaluate the integral.

1. $\displaystyle\int_{-\infty}^{\infty} (x^2 - 2x + 4)\delta(x-1)\,dx$

2. $\displaystyle\int_{-8}^{3} \sin(3x+1)\delta(x)\,dx$

3. $\displaystyle\int_{-4}^{20} (e^x + x^2)\delta(x+3)\,dx$

4. $\displaystyle\int_{3}^{\infty} (x^2 + 1/x)\delta(x)\,dx$

5. $\displaystyle\int_{-\infty}^{\infty} (2x^2 + x^3 + 4)\delta(x-4)\,dx$

6. $\displaystyle\int_{-\infty}^{\infty} (1 + 4x - \cos x)\delta(x+10)\,dx$

7. Solve problem (1) when $F(x)$ is defined as in Figure 11.2(b), and sketch the displacement function. Show that the displacement of Figure 11.4 is obtained in the limit as $\varepsilon \to 0^+$.

8. Define your own distributed force function $F(x)$ [subject to condition (3)] and solve problem (1), taking limits as $F(x)$ approaches a point force. Do you obtain the result in Figure 11.4?

9. Calculate the displacement of a taut string (of negligible mass and length L) when two unit point masses are attached at distances $L/3$ from each end. Use distribution functions like that in Figure 11.2(a) for each mass.

10. A beam of length L and negligible weight is subjected to a unit load at its midpoint. If the left end of the beam $(x=0)$ is fixed horizontally and the right end $(x=L)$ is free, use a distributed load like that of Figure 11.2(a) and limits as $\varepsilon \to 0^+$ to find the static deflection of the beam. Sketch the graph of the displacement function. Are $y'(x)$, $y''(x)$, and $y'''(x)$ continuous?

11. Find deflections of the beam in Exercise 10 if the point load is placed at the end $x = L$.

12. The displacement of a mass M from its equilibrium position at the end of a spring with constant k is described by the differential equation

$$M\frac{d^2y}{dt^2} + ky = F(t)$$

when viscous damping is negligible. In this exercise we determine the displacement $y(t)$ due to an instantaneous unit force $F(t)$ applied at time T,

$$F(t) = \begin{cases} 0 & 0 < t < T \\ 1 & t = T, \\ 0 & t > T \end{cases}$$

called a *unit impulse*. We do this by distributing the unit impulse in two ways.

(a) First, distribute $F(t)$ over a time interval of length ε around T according to

$$F_1(t) = \begin{cases} 0 & 0 < t < T - \varepsilon/2 \\ 1/\varepsilon & T - \varepsilon/2 < t < T + \varepsilon/2. \\ 0 & t > T + \varepsilon/2 \end{cases}$$

[Notice that the units of $F_1(t)$ are units of force per unit of time, so the total area "under" the $F_1(t)$ curve is unity.] Solve the differential equation with $F(t)$ replaced by $F_1(t)$ subject to the initial conditions $y(0) = y'(0) = 0$. Find and sketch the limit function as $\varepsilon \to 0^+$.

(b) Repeat (a) with the unit impulse $F(t)$ distributed over the time interval $T < t < T + \varepsilon$ according to

$$F_2(t) = \begin{cases} 0 & 0 < t < T \\ 1/\varepsilon & T < t < T + \varepsilon. \\ 0 & t > T + \varepsilon \end{cases}$$

13. Show that the same function as that in Exercise 12 is obtained if we assume that $y(t) = 0$ for $t < T$ and that for $t \geq T$, $y(t)$ satisfies

$$M\frac{d^2y}{dt^2} + ky = 0, \qquad t > T,$$

$$y(T) = 0, \qquad y'(T) = \frac{1}{M}.$$

Distributing point sources for multidimensional boundary value problems is more complex. The remaining exercises give examples.

14. A square membrane stretched tightly over the region $0 \leq x, y \leq L$ has its edges fixed on the xy-plane. Distribute a unit load at the midpoint of the membrane according to

$$F(x, y) = \begin{cases} -1/\varepsilon^2 & (L - \varepsilon)/2 < x, y < (L + \varepsilon)/2 \\ 0 & \text{otherwise} \end{cases}.$$

(a) Find the static deflection of the membrane due to this load by using the finite Fourier transform associated with the x-variable, or an eigenfunction expansion

$$z(x, y) = \sum_{n=1}^{\infty} a_n(y) \sqrt{\frac{2}{L}} \sin\frac{n\pi x}{L}.$$

(b) Take the limit of the function $z(x, y)$ in (a) as $\varepsilon \to 0^+$ to find the static deflection of the membrane under a unit concentrated load at its center.

(c) Is the result in (b) defined at $(L/2, L/2)$?

15. Repeat Exercise 14 for a circular membrane of radius R. Distribute the unit load at the midpoint of the membrane according to

$$F(r, \theta) = \begin{cases} -1/(\pi\varepsilon^2) & 0 \le r < \varepsilon \\ 0 & \text{otherwise} \end{cases}.$$

11.2 Introductory Example

In this section we use a very simple example to illustrate the essential features of a Green's function. The example also helps justify our hopes that the delta function of Section 11.1 can be used to represent concentrated sources. The boundary value problem

$$-\tau \frac{d^2 y}{dx^2} = F(x), \tag{9a}$$

$$y(0) = y(L) = 0 \tag{9b}$$

describes static deflections of a taut string of negligible mass, tension τ, and length L due to a load $F(x)$ (Figure 11.6). We can solve this problem by using variation of parameters on the general solution $Ax + B$ of the associated homogeneous equation (see Section 3.3). Derivatives of $A(x)$ and $B(x)$ must satisfy

$$A'x + B' = 0,$$

$$A' = -\frac{F(x)}{\tau}.$$

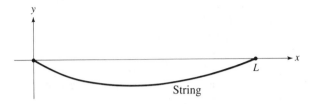

Figure 11.6

String

Solutions of these equations may be expressed as definite integrals

$$A(x) = \int_0^x -\tau^{-1} F(X)\, dX + C,$$

$$B(x) = \int_0^x \tau^{-1} X F(X)\, dX + D,$$

and hence $\qquad y(x) = x\left(\displaystyle\int_0^x -\tau^{-1}F(X)\,dX + C \right) + \displaystyle\int_0^x \tau^{-1}XF(X)\,dX + D$

$$= \tau^{-1}\int_0^x (X - x)F(X)\,dX + Cx + D.$$

Boundary conditions (9b) require the constants C and D to satisfy

$$0 = y(0) = D,$$

$$0 = y(L) = \tau^{-1}\int_0^L (X - L)F(X)\,dX + CL + D,$$

and therefore

$$y(x) = \tau^{-1}\int_0^x (X - x)F(X)\,dX + (L\tau)^{-1}x\int_0^L (L - X)F(X)\,dX$$

$$= \tau^{-1}\int_0^x \big((X - x) + L^{-1}x(L - X)\big)F(X)\,dX + (L\tau)^{-1}x\int_x^L (L - X)F(X)\,dX$$

$$= (L\tau)^{-1}\int_0^x X(L - x)F(X)\,dX + (L\tau)^{-1}x\int_x^L (L - X)F(X)\,dX$$

or $\qquad\qquad\qquad\qquad y(x) = \displaystyle\int_0^L g(x; X)F(X)\,dX, \qquad\qquad\qquad$ **(10a)**

where $\qquad\qquad g(x; X) = \begin{cases} \dfrac{X(L - x)}{L\tau} & 0 \le X \le x \\[3mm] \dfrac{x(L - X)}{L\tau} & x \le X \le L \end{cases}.$ $\qquad\qquad$ **(10b)**

The solution of problem (9) has therefore been expressed in integral form—the integral of the nonhomogeneity $F(x)$ multiplied by the function $g(x; X)$. The function $g(x; X)$ is called the Green's function for boundary value problem (9). It does not depend on $F(x)$; it depends only on the differential operator and the boundary conditions. Once $g(x; X)$ is known, the solution for any $F(x)$ can be represented in the form of a definite integral involving $g(x; X)$ and $F(x)$, and this integral representation clearly displays how the solution depends on $F(x)$. In addition, we shall see that when the boundary conditions are nonhomogeneous, representation of the solution in terms of the Green's function also indicates the nature of the dependence on these nonhomogeneities. Finally, it should be clear that formulation of the solution as a definite integral is a distinct advantage in numerical analysis.

The representation of $g(x; X)$ in (10b) regards X as the independent variable and x as a parameter. By interchanging the two expressions, we obtain a representation wherein X is the parameter and x is the independent variable:

$$g(x; X) = \begin{cases} \dfrac{x(L - X)}{L\tau} & 0 \le x \le X \\[3mm] \dfrac{X(L - x)}{L\tau} & X \le x \le L \end{cases}. \qquad\qquad \textbf{(10c)}$$

With representation (10c), it is straightforward to illustrate three properties of this Green's function that are shared by all Green's functions. First,

$$g(x; X) \text{ is continuous for all } x \text{ (including } x = X).\tag{11a}$$

Second, the derivative of $g(x; X)$ with respect to x is continuous for all $x \neq X$, and

$$\lim_{x \to X^+} \frac{dg}{dx} - \lim_{x \to X^-} \frac{dg}{dx} = \left(\frac{-X}{L\tau}\right) - \left(\frac{L-X}{L\tau}\right) = -\frac{1}{\tau}.\tag{11b}$$

This jump is the reciprocal of the coefficient of d^2y/dx^2 in differential equation (9a). Finally, it is straightforward to check that at every $x \neq X$,

$$\begin{array}{l} g(x; X) \text{ satisfies the homogeneous version of the} \\ \text{differential equation from which it was derived.} \end{array}\tag{11c}$$

As we said, properties (11a–c) are shared by all Green's functions associated with ordinary differential equations. In fact, we shall use them to characterize Green's functions in Section 11.3.

In Section 11.1 we defined the delta function in hopes that it would represent a concentrated source. Let us see what happens if we set $F(x) = \delta(x - L/2)$ in (10):

$$\begin{aligned} y(x) &= \int_0^L g(x; X)\delta\left(X - \frac{L}{2}\right) dX \\ &= \int_0^x \frac{X(L-x)}{L\tau}\delta\left(X - \frac{L}{2}\right) dX + \int_x^L \frac{x(L-X)}{L\tau}\delta\left(X - \frac{L}{2}\right) dX. \end{aligned}$$

Since the first integral vanishes when $x < L/2$ and the second is zero when $x > L/2$, we separate the solution into two parts,

$$y(x) = \begin{cases} \dfrac{x}{L\tau}\left(\dfrac{L}{2}\right) & 0 \leq x < L/2 \\[2mm] \dfrac{1}{L\tau}\left(\dfrac{L}{2}\right)(L - x) & L/2 < x \leq L \end{cases}$$

$$= \begin{cases} \dfrac{x}{2\tau} & 0 \leq x \leq L/2 \\[2mm] \dfrac{1}{2\tau}(L - x) & L/2 \leq x \leq L \end{cases}$$

(provided we demand continuity of the solution at $L/2$). But this is solution (5) to problem (1) for displacement due to a unit force concentrated at $x = L/2$. In other words, the delta function $\delta(x - L/2)$ appears to be a valid representation for a point force of magnitude unity at $x = L/2$.

Exercises 11.2

1. Consider the boundary value problem

$$\frac{d^2y}{dx^2} + y = F(x), \qquad 0 < x < L,$$

$$y(0) = 0 = y'(L).$$

(a) Use variation of parameters to show that the solution can be expressed in the form

$$y(x) = \int_0^L g(x; X)F(X)\,dX,$$

where $g(x; X)$ is the Green's function of the problem defined by

$$g(x; X) = \frac{-1}{\cos L} \begin{cases} \sin X \cos(L - x) & 0 \le X \le x \\ \sin x \cos(L - X) & x \le X \le L \end{cases}.$$

(b) Show that $g(x; X)$ satisfies properties (11a–c).

11.3 Green's Functions

In this section we associate Green's functions with linear, second-order ordinary differential equations

$$P(x)\frac{d^2y}{dx^2} + Q(x)\frac{dy}{dx} + R(x)y = f(x), \qquad \alpha < x < \beta. \tag{12}$$

Functions $P(x)$, $Q(x)$, and $R(x)$ are assumed continuous for $\alpha \le x \le \beta$, but no assumption is yet made on the behavior of $f(x)$. Provided $P(x)$ does not vanish on the interval $\alpha \le x \le \beta$, multiplication of (12) by $e^{\int(Q/P)\,dx}$ gives

$$\frac{d}{dx}\left(e^{\int(Q/P)\,dx}\frac{dy}{dx}\right) + \frac{R}{P}e^{\int(Q/P)\,dx}\,y = \frac{1}{P}e^{\int(Q/P)\,dx}f(x).$$

When we set $a(x) = e^{\int(Q/P)\,dx}$, $c(x) = RP^{-1}e^{\int(Q/P)\,dx}$, and $F(x) = P^{-1}e^{\int(Q/P)\,dx}f(x)$, the equation takes on a more pleasing appearance:

$$\frac{d}{dx}\left(a(x)\frac{dy}{dx}\right) + c(x)y = F(x), \qquad \alpha < x < \beta. \tag{13a}$$

In other words, every linear, second-order differential equation for which $P(x) \ne 0$ can be expressed in form (13a), where $a(x) > 0$. This is called the *self-adjoint* form of the differential equation. We shall often find it convenient to denote the differential operator on the left side of (13a) by L, in which case the differential equation is expressed more compactly as

$$Ly = F(x), \qquad \alpha < x < \beta. \tag{13b}$$

To obtain a unique solution of (13), it is necessary to specify two boundary conditions. For the most part, we consider conditions of the form

$$B_1 y = -l_1 y'(\alpha) + h_1 y(\alpha) = m_1, \tag{14a}$$

$$B_2 y = l_2 y'(\beta) + h_2 y(\beta) = m_2, \tag{14b}$$

where $l_1, l_2, h_1, h_2, m_1,$ and m_2 are given constants. They are called *unmixed* boundary conditions because one condition is at $x = \alpha$ and the other is at $x = \beta$. On occasion, however, we shall consider conditions of the form

$$y(\alpha) = y(\beta), \tag{15a}$$

$$y'(\alpha) = y'(\beta), \tag{15b}$$

called *periodic* boundary conditions. They arise only when $a(\alpha) = a(\beta)$, and they are always homogeneous. We have seen both types of conditions many times throughout the first ten chapters.

For the moment, we concentrate only on the operator L in (13), not on the differential equation or the boundary conditions. When $u(x)$ and $v(x)$ are continuously differentiable functions on $\alpha \le x \le \beta$ with piecewise continuous second derivatives, it is straightforward to show that

$$uLv - vLu = \frac{d}{dx} J(u, v) = \frac{d}{dx} \big(a(uv' - vu') \big). \tag{16}$$

This equation is known as *Lagrange's identity*; $J(u, v)$ is called the *conjunct* of u and v. The identity is valid at every point except discontinuities of the second derivatives of u and v. Because such discontinuities must be finite, (16) may be integrated between any two values of x in the interval $\alpha \le x \le \beta$:

$$\int_{x_1}^{x_2} (uLv - vLu)\, dx = \{J(u, v)\}_{x_1}^{x_2}. \tag{17}$$

This result is called *Green's formula on the interval* $x_1 \le x \le x_2$. When $x_1 = \alpha$ and $x_2 = \beta$, we obtain Green's formula on $\alpha \le x \le \beta$,

$$\boxed{\int_{\alpha}^{\beta} (uLv - vLu)\, dx = \{J(u, v)\}_{\alpha}^{\beta}.} \tag{18}$$

Identities (16)–(18) were based on the operator L in differential equation (13), but not on the differential equation itself; that is, $F(x)$ was not introduced. Nor were boundary conditions used in the derivation. In other words, (16)–(18) are properties of the operator L.

When $u(x)$ and $v(x)$ satisfy the homogeneous version of (13), it is obvious that their conjunct is constant. This result is sufficiently important that we state it in the form of a theorem.

Theorem 1

If $u(x)$ and $v(x)$ satisfy the homogeneous differential equation $Ly = 0$, then $J(u, v)$ is a constant (independent of x).

The constant value vanishes only if $u(x)$ and $v(x)$ are linearly dependent.

With these preliminaries out of the way, we are prepared to define Green's functions for boundary value problems of the form

$$Ly = \frac{d}{dx}\left(a(x)\frac{dy}{dx}\right) + c(x)y = F(x), \qquad \alpha < x < \beta, \tag{19a}$$

$$B_1 y = m_1, \tag{19b}$$

$$B_2 y = m_2, \tag{19c}$$

where $a(x)$ is continuously differentiable and does not vanish for $\alpha \leq x \leq \beta$ and $c(x)$ is continuous therein. (If the boundary conditions are periodic, they are also homogeneous, $m_1 = m_2 = 0$.) Solutions of (19) are called classical when $F(x)$ is piecewise continuous. A solution $y(x)$ is *classical* if it is continuously differentiable, has a piecewise continuous second derivative, satisfies the boundary conditions (19b, c), and is such that Ly and $F(x)$ are identical at every point of continuity of $F(x)$. We mention this fact because Green's functions do not turn out to be classical solutions. The Green's function $g(x; X)$ for problem (19), if it exists, is defined as the solution of

$$Lg = \delta(x - X), \tag{20a}$$

$$B_1 g = 0, \tag{20b}$$

$$B_2 g = 0. \tag{20c}$$

It is the solution of the same problem, with two changes. The source function $F(x)$ is replaced by a concentrated unit source, and the boundary conditions are made homogeneous. Because $\delta(x - X)$ is not piecewise continuous, Green's function cannot be called a classical solution of (20). It is, however, an ordinary function (as opposed to a generalized function). This is established in Schwartz's theory of distributions, wherein it is also shown that solutions of differential equation (20a) have the following properties analogous to those in (11):

(1) $g(x; X)$ is continuous for $\alpha \leq x \leq \beta$; (21a)

(2) $dg(x; X)/dx$ is continuous except for a discontinuity at $x = X$ of magnitude $1/a(X)$; that is,

$$\lim_{x \to X^+} \frac{dg}{dx} - \lim_{x \to X^-} \frac{dg}{dx} = \frac{1}{a(X)}; \tag{21b}$$

(3) for all $x \neq X$,

$$Lg = 0. \tag{21c}$$

These properties, along with boundary conditions (20b, c), completely characterize Green's functions; in fact, we now use them to derive formulas for Green's functions.

Condition (21c) implies that $g(x; X)$ must be of the form

$$g(x; X) = \begin{cases} Eu(x) + Bv(x) & \alpha \leq x < X \\ Du(x) + Gv(x) & X < x \leq \beta, \end{cases} \qquad (22)$$

where $u(x)$ and $v(x)$ are continuously differentiable solutions of $Ly = 0$. Inclusion of $x = \alpha$ and $x = \beta$ is a result of continuity condition (21a). Continuity at $x = X$ requires that

$$Eu(X) + Bv(X) = Du(X) + Gv(X),$$

and condition (21b) for the jump in dg/dx at $x = X$ implies that

$$Du'(X) + Gv'(X) - Eu'(X) - Bv'(X) = \frac{1}{a(X)}.$$

When these equations are solved for B and D in terms of E and G and substituted into (22), the result is

$$g(x; X) = \begin{cases} Eu(x) + Gv(x) - \dfrac{u(X)v(x)}{J(u, v)} & \alpha \leq x \leq X \\ Eu(x) + Gv(x) - \dfrac{v(X)u(x)}{J(u, v)} & X \leq x \leq \beta \end{cases}.$$

The Heaviside unit step function can be used to combine these two expressions into one:

$$g(x; X) = Eu(x) + Gv(x) - \frac{1}{J(u, v)}\big(u(X)v(x)H(X - x) + v(X)u(x)H(x - X)\big)$$

$$= Eu(x) + Gv(x) - \frac{1}{J(u, v)}\big(u(X)v(x)[1 - H(x - X)]$$

$$+ v(X)u(x)[1 - H(X - x)]\big)$$

$$= \left(E - \frac{v(X)}{J(u, v)}\right)u(x) + \left(G - \frac{u(X)}{J(u, v)}\right)v(x)$$

$$+ \frac{1}{J(u, v)}\big(u(x)v(X)H(X - x) + u(X)v(x)H(x - X)\big)$$

$$= Au(x) + Cv(x) + \frac{1}{J(u, v)}\big(u(x)v(X)H(X - x) + u(X)v(x)H(x - X)\big). \qquad (23)$$

We understand that terms involving the step function are regarded in the limit sense $(x \to X)$ at $x = X$.

The remaining unknowns A and C are evaluated using boundary conditions (20b, c). They require that

$$0 = B_1 g = AB_1 u + CB_1 v + B_1 r, \qquad (24a)$$

$$0 = B_2 g = AB_2 u + CB_2 v + B_2 r, \qquad (24b)$$

where $r = J^{-1}[u(x)v(X)H(X - x) + u(X)v(x)H(x - X)]$. These are algebraic equations for A and C that have a unique solution provided

$$\begin{vmatrix} B_1 u & B_1 v \\ B_2 u & B_2 v \end{vmatrix} \neq 0. \tag{25}$$

Thus, when condition (25) is satisfied, $g(x; X)$ is defined by (23), where A and C are chosen so that $g(x; X)$ satisfies (20b, c).

We briefly examine here the significance of a vanishing determinant and deal with it more fully in Section 11.5. A vanishing determinant is equivalent to the existence of a constant $\lambda \neq 0$ such that

$$B_1 u = \lambda B_1 v \quad \text{and} \quad B_2 u = \lambda B_2 v \tag{26a}$$

or
$$B_1(u - \lambda v) = 0 \quad \text{and} \quad B_2(u - \lambda v) = 0. \tag{26b}$$

Since $u(x)$ and $v(x)$ are linearly independent, we can say that the determinant vanishes if and only if there is a nontrivial solution $u - \lambda v$ of the homogeneous boundary value problem

$$\frac{d}{dx}\left(a(x)\frac{dy}{dx}\right) + c(x)y = 0, \qquad \alpha < x < \beta, \tag{27a}$$

$$B_1 y = 0, \tag{27b}$$

$$B_2 y = 0. \tag{27c}$$

We summarize these results in the following theorem.

Theorem 2

When homogeneous system (27) has only the trivial solution, the Green's function for problem (19) is uniquely given by

$$\boxed{g(x; X) = Au(x) + Cv(x) + \frac{1}{J(u, v)}\left(u(x)v(X)H(X - x) + u(X)v(x)H(x - X)\right),} \tag{28}$$

where $u(x)$ and $v(x)$ are linearly independent solutions of (27a) and A and C are chosen so that $g(x; X)$ satisfies (20b, c).

When the boundary conditions are unmixed, determination of $g(x; X)$ can be simplified further.

Corollary

When homogeneous system (27) has only the trivial solution and boundary conditions are unmixed, the Green's function for problem (19) is uniquely given by

$$\boxed{g(x; X) = \frac{1}{J(u, v)}\left(u(x)v(X)H(X - x) + u(X)v(x)H(x - X)\right),} \tag{29}$$

where $u(x)$ and $v(x)$ are linearly independent solutions of (27a) satisfying $B_1 u = 0$ and $B_2 v = 0$.

Proof: Certainly this function satisfies (20a) [since the function in (28) does]. In addition, when $x < X$, $g(x; X)$ reduces to $J^{-1}u(x)v(X)$, which, as a function of x, satisfies $B_1 g = 0$. Similarly, because $B_2 v = 0$, we must have $B_2 g = 0$.   ∎

Once again, we point out that due to the step functions, expressions for $g(x; X)$ in (28) and (29) are not defined for $x = X$. However, continuity of $g(x; X)$ at $x = X$ implies that $g(x; X)$ must be given by either of the limits $\lim_{x \to X^+} g(x; X) = \lim_{x \to X^-} g(x; X)$, and we implicitly understand this when we write (28) and (29).

Notice that for unmixed boundary conditions, $g(x; X)$ is symmetric in x and X. That this is also true for periodic boundary conditions is verified in Theorem 5 of this section.

Example 1:   Use formula (29) to find the Green's function for problem (9).

Solution: Solutions of $y'' = 0$ satisfying $y(0) = 0$ and $y(L) = 0$, respectively, are $u(x) = x$ and $v(x) = L - x$. With $J(u, v) = a(uv' - vu') = -\tau[(x)(-1) - (1)(L - x)] = L\tau$, (29) gives

$$g(x; X) = \frac{1}{L\tau}\big(x(L - X)H(X - x) + X(L - x)H(x - X)\big),$$

and this is (10c).   ∎

Example 2:   Find the Green's function for the boundary value problem

$$\frac{d^2 y}{dx^2} + 4y = F(x), \qquad \alpha < x < \beta,$$

$$y(\alpha) = m_1, \qquad y'(\beta) = m_2.$$

Solution: Since solutions of $y'' + 4y = 0$ are of the form $A \sin 2(x + \phi)$ or $A \cos 2(x + \phi)$, solutions that satisfy $y(\alpha) = 0$ and $y'(\beta) = 0$, respectively, are $u(x) = \sin 2(x - \alpha)$ and $v(x) = \cos 2(\beta - x)$. With

$$J(u, v) = uv' - vu'$$
$$= 2\sin 2(x - \alpha)\sin 2(\beta - x) - 2\cos 2(x - \alpha)\cos 2(\beta - x)$$
$$= -2\cos 2(\beta - \alpha),$$

formula (29) gives

$$g(x; X) = \frac{1}{-2\cos 2(\beta - \alpha)}\big(\sin 2(x - \alpha)\cos 2(\beta - X)H(X - x)$$
$$+ \sin 2(X - \alpha)\cos 2(\beta - x)H(x - X)\big).$$ ∎

Example 3:   Find the Green's function for

$$\frac{d^2 y}{dx^2} + 2\frac{dy}{dx} + 10y = F(x), \qquad 0 < x < \frac{\pi}{2},$$

$$y'(0) = 5, \qquad y\left(\frac{\pi}{2}\right) = 2.$$

Solution: Solutions of $y'' + 2y' + 10y = 0$ are always of the form $e^{-x}(A \sin 3x + B \cos 3x)$. Solutions that satisfy $y'(0) = 0$ and $y(\pi/2) = 0$, respectively, are

$$u(x) = e^{-x}(\sin 3x + 3\cos 3x) \quad \text{and} \quad v(x) = e^{-x}\cos 3x.$$

To find the conjunct of u and v, we express the differential equation in self-adjoint form by multiplying by e^{2x}:

$$e^{2x}\frac{d^2y}{dx^2} + 2e^{2x}\frac{dy}{dx} + 10e^{2x}y = e^{2x}F(x)$$

or

$$\frac{d}{dx}\left(e^{2x}\frac{dy}{dx}\right) + 10e^{2x}y = e^{2x}F(x).$$

With $a(x)$ identified as e^{2x},

$$
\begin{aligned}
J(u,v) &= e^{2x}\big(e^{-x}(\sin 3x + 3\cos 3x)(-e^{-x}\cos 3x - 3e^{-x}\sin 3x) \\
&\quad - e^{-x}\cos 3x(-10e^{-x}\sin 3x)\big) \\
&= -3,
\end{aligned}
$$

and therefore

$$
\begin{aligned}
g(x;X) = &-\frac{1}{3}\big(e^{-(x+X)}\cos 3X\,(\sin 3x + 3\cos 3x)H(X-x) \\
&+ e^{-(x+X)}\cos 3x\,(\sin 3X + 3\cos 3X)H(x-X)\big).
\end{aligned}
$$
∎

Example 4:

Find the Green's function for the problem

$$\frac{d^2y}{dx^2} + y = F(x), \qquad 0 < x < 1,$$

$$y(0) - y(1) = 0, \qquad y'(0) - y'(1) = 0.$$

Solution:

Since $u(x) = \sin x$ and $v(x) = \cos x$ are solutions of $y'' + y = 0$, we may take [according to (28)]

$$
\begin{aligned}
g(x;X) = &A\sin x + C\cos x + \frac{1}{J(\sin x,\cos x)}(\sin x\cos X\,H(X-x) \\
&+ \sin X\cos x\,H(x-X)),
\end{aligned}
$$

where $J(\sin x,\cos x) = \sin x(-\sin x) - \cos x(\cos x) = -1$. The boundary conditions must also be satisfied by $g(x;X)$, and therefore

$$C - A\sin 1 - C\cos 1 + \sin X\cos 1 = 0,$$

$$A - \cos X - A\cos 1 + C\sin 1 - \sin X\sin 1 = 0.$$

These can be solved for A and C:

$$A = \frac{\cos X - \cos(1+X)}{2(1-\cos 1)}, \qquad C = \frac{\sin X + \sin(1-X)}{2(1-\cos 1)}$$

and

$$
\begin{aligned}
g(x;X) = &\frac{1}{2(1-\cos 1)}(\sin x\,[\cos X - \cos(1+X)] + \cos x[\sin X + \sin(1-X)]) \\
&-\sin x\cos X\,H(X-x) - \sin X\cos x\,H(x-X).
\end{aligned}
$$
∎

The importance of Green's functions is contained in the following theorem.

Theorem 3

When $g(x; X)$ is the Green's function for the boundary value problem

$$Ly = \frac{d}{dx}\left(a(x)\frac{dy}{dx}\right) + c(x)y = F(x), \qquad \alpha < x < \beta, \tag{30a}$$

$$B_1 y = 0, \tag{30b}$$

$$B_2 y = 0, \tag{30c}$$

the solution of the problem is

$$y(x) = \int_\alpha^\beta g(x; X)F(X)\,dX. \tag{31}$$

Notice that the boundary conditions are homogeneous; nonhomogeneous boundary conditions are discussed in Section 11.4.

Proof: The Green's function for (30a) satisfies equations (20). If we substitute (31) into (30a) and reverse orders of integration with respect to X and differentiations with respect to x,

$$\begin{aligned}
Ly &= L\int_\alpha^\beta g(x; X)F(X)\,dX \\
&= \int_\alpha^\beta [Lg(x; X)]F(X)\,dX \\
&= \int_\alpha^\beta \delta(x - X)F(X)\,dX \quad [\text{by (20a)}] \\
&= F(x).
\end{aligned}$$

Furthermore, because $g(x; X)$ satisfies (20b, c), $y(x)$ must satisfy (30b, c).   ∎

As a result of this theorem, once we know the Green's function for a boundary value problem, the solution for any source function $F(x)$ can be obtained by integration. Think of the integral as a superposition. Because the Green's function is the solution of problem (30) due to a unit point source at X, we interpret $g(x; X)F(X)\,dX$ as the effect due to that part $F(X)\,dX$ of the source over the interval dX of the x-axis, and the integral adds over all sources from $x = \alpha$ to $x = \beta$. Were the source composed of both a distributed portion $F(x)$ and n concentrated parts of magnitudes F_j at points x_j, the solution of (30) would be

$$\begin{aligned}
y(x) &= \int_\alpha^\beta g(x; X)\left(F(X) + \sum_{j=1}^n F_j\delta(X - x_j)\right)dX \\
&= \int_\alpha^\beta g(x; X)F(X)\,dX + \sum_{j=1}^n F_j g(x; x_j). \tag{32}
\end{aligned}$$

Before considering examples of Theorem 3 (in Section 11.4), we extend Green's formula to encompass delta functions. One of these extensions immediately implies that $g(x; X)$ is symmetric. Through the other, we see how Green's functions handle nonhomogeneous boundary conditions.

Theorem 4

Let L be the differential operator of problem (30). When $v(x; X)$ is a solution of $Lv = \delta(x - X)$ and $u(x)$ is continuously differentiable with a piecewise continuous second derivative,

$$\int_\alpha^\beta (uLv - vLu)\,dx = \{a(uv' - vu')\}_\alpha^\beta. \tag{33}$$

Proof: Suppose $u(x)$ has a discontinuity in its second derivative at a point $\bar{X} < X$. [Similar discussions can be made if $u(x)$ has more than one such point or if $\bar{X} > X$.] Then

$$\int_\alpha^\beta (uLv - vLu)\,dx = \int_\alpha^{\bar{X}} (uLv - vLu)\,dx + \int_{\bar{X}}^{X-\varepsilon} (uLv - vLu)\,dx$$

$$+ \int_{X-\varepsilon}^{X+\varepsilon} (uLv - vLu)\,dx + \int_{X+\varepsilon}^\beta (uLv - vLu)\,dx,$$

where $\varepsilon > 0$ is some small number. Green's formula (17) can be applied to the first, second, and fourth of these integrals since $Lv = 0$ therein [see condition (21c)]:

$$\int_\alpha^\beta (uLv - vLu)\,dx = \{a(uv' - vu')\}_\alpha^{\bar{X}} + \{a(uv' - vu')\}_{\bar{X}}^{X-\varepsilon}$$

$$+ \int_{X-\varepsilon}^{X+\varepsilon} \left(u\delta(x - X) - vLu\right) dx + \{a(uv' - vu')\}_{X+\varepsilon}^\beta.$$

Because a, u, u', v, and v' are all continuous at $\bar{X}$, terms in $\bar{X}$ vanish, and the expression on the right reduces to

$$\int_\alpha^\beta (uLv - vLu)\,dx = \{a(uv' - vu')\}_\alpha^\beta + a(X - \varepsilon)[u(X - \varepsilon)v'(X - \varepsilon; X)$$

$$- v(X - \varepsilon; X)u'(X - \varepsilon)] - a(X + \varepsilon)[u(X + \varepsilon)v'(X + \varepsilon; X)$$

$$- v(X + \varepsilon; X)u'(X + \varepsilon)] + u(X) - \int_{X-\varepsilon}^{X+\varepsilon} vLu\,dx.$$

We now take limits as $\varepsilon \to 0^+$. Since v, u, u', and u'' are continuous on $X - \varepsilon \le x \le X + \varepsilon$, the final integral vanishes in the limit, and the remaining terms give

$$\int_\alpha^\beta (uLv - vLu)\,dx = \{a(uv' - vu')\}_\alpha^\beta + a(X)[u(X)v'(X-; X) - v(X; X)u'(X)]$$

$$- a(X)[u(X)v'(X+; X) - v(X; X)u'(X)] + u(X)$$

$$= \{a(uv' - vu')\}_\alpha^\beta + a(X)u(X)[v'(X-; X) - v'(X+; X)] + u(X)$$

$$= \{a(uv' - vu')\}_\alpha^\beta$$

[because v satisfies condition (21b)]. ∎

A similar proof leads to the following extension of Green's formula.

Theorem 5

Let L be the differential operator of problem (30). When u and v satisfy $Lu = \delta(x - X)$ and $Lv = \delta(x - Y)$,

$$\int_\alpha^\beta (uLv - vLu)\, dx = \{a(uv' - vu')\}_\alpha^\beta. \tag{34}$$

In this case, the integral of $uLv - vLu$ over the interval $\alpha \leq x \leq \beta$ is subdivided into five integrals over the intervals

$$\alpha \leq x \leq X - \varepsilon, \qquad X - \varepsilon \leq x \leq X + \varepsilon, \qquad X + \varepsilon \leq x \leq Y - \varepsilon,$$
$$Y - \varepsilon \leq x \leq Y + \varepsilon, \qquad Y + \varepsilon \leq x \leq \beta$$

(for $X < Y$), and Green's formula (17) is applied to the first, third, and fifth. Details are given in Exercise 20.

Formula (29) indicates that Green's functions for problems with unmixed boundary conditions are symmetric. That this is true for periodic boundary conditions as well is proved in the next theorem.

Theorem 6

When boundary conditions in problem (30) are unmixed or periodic, Green's function $g(x; X)$ is symmetric:

$$g(x; X) = g(X; x). \tag{35}$$

Proof: When we set $u = g(x; X)$ and $v = g(x; Y)$ in version (34) of Green's formula, the result is

$$\int_\alpha^\beta [g(x; X)Lg(x; Y) - g(x; Y)Lg(x; X)]\, dx$$

$$= \left\{ a(x)\left(g(x; X)\frac{dg(x; Y)}{dx} - g(x; Y)\frac{dg(x; X)}{dx} \right) \right\}_\alpha^\beta.$$

It is straightforward to show that when $g(x; X)$ satisfies unmixed boundary conditions (14) or periodic conditions (15), the right side of this equation must vanish, and therefore

$$0 = \int_\alpha^\beta [g(x; X)\delta(x - Y) - g(x; Y)\delta(x - X)]\, dx = g(Y; X) - g(X; Y). \qquad\blacksquare$$

It is interesting to interpret this symmetry physically, say, in string problem (9) of Section 11.2. Green's function $g(x; X)$ for this problem is the deflection of the string due to a unit force at position X. Symmetry of $g(x; X)$ means that the deflection at x due to a unit force at X is identical to the deflection at X due to a unit force at x. This is often referred to as *Maxwell's reciprocity* and is illustrated in Figure 11.7.

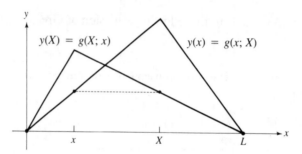

Figure 11.7

Exercises 11.3

In Exercises 1–5, write the differential equation in self-adjoint form.

1. $x\dfrac{d^2y}{dx^2} + \dfrac{dy}{dx} + 3y = F(x)$

2. $\dfrac{d^2y}{dx^2} + \dfrac{dy}{dx} - 2y = F(x)$

3. $x^2\dfrac{d^2y}{dx^2} + 2x\dfrac{dy}{dx} - (x+1)y = F(x)$

4. $x^2\dfrac{d^2y}{dx^2} - x\dfrac{dy}{dx} - (x+1)y = F(x)$

5. $\dfrac{d^2y}{dx^2} + 4\dfrac{dy}{dx} = F(x)$

In Exercises 6–14, find the Green's function for the boundary value problem.

6. $\dfrac{d^2y}{dx^2} = F(x)$, $0 < x < 2$, $y(0) = 0$, $y'(2) = 0$

7. $\dfrac{d^2y}{dx^2} + y = F(x)$, $0 < x < 1$, $y(0) = 0$, $y'(1) = 0$

8. $\dfrac{d^2y}{dx^2} + k^2 y = F(x)$, $0 < x < \pi$ ($k > 0$ a constant, but not an integer), $y(0) = 0$, $y(\pi) = 0$

9. $\dfrac{d^2y}{dx^2} = F(x)$, $0 < x < 1$, $y(0) = y'(0)$, $y'(1) = 0$

10. $\dfrac{d^2y}{dx^2} - 3\dfrac{dy}{dx} - 4y = F(x)$, $0 < x < 2$, $y(0) = 0$, $y'(2) = 0$

11. $\dfrac{d^2y}{dx^2} + 2\dfrac{dy}{dx} + 5y = F(x)$, $0 < x < \pi/2$, $y'(0) = 0$, $y(\pi/2) = 0$

12. $x^2\dfrac{d^2y}{dx^2} + 2x\dfrac{dy}{dx} - 6y = F(x)$, $1 < x < 2$, $y(2) = y'(2)$, $y'(1) = 0$

13. $\dfrac{d^2y}{dx^2} + k^2 y = F(x)$, $\alpha < x < \beta$ ($k > 0$ a constant), $y(\alpha) = y(\beta)$, $y'(\alpha) = y'(\beta)$. Would you place any restrictions on k?

14. $x\dfrac{d^2y}{dx^2} + \dfrac{dy}{dx} + xy = F(x)$, $0 < \alpha < x < \beta$, $y(\alpha) = 0$, $y(\beta) = 0$

15. The boundary value problem for static deflections of a beam subjected to a distributed force

$F(x)$ is

$$EI\frac{d^4y}{dx^4} = F(x), \qquad 0 < x < L,$$

Boundary conditions at $x = 0$ and $x = L$,

where E and I are constants. The Green's function $g(x; X)$ for this fourth-order problem satisfies

$$EI\frac{d^4y}{dx^4} = \delta(x - X),$$

Homogeneous boundary conditions at $x = 0$ and $x = L$.

Thus, it is the solution of the problem due to a unit concentrated force at X (with homogeneous boundary conditions). Solutions of the differential equation are characterized by the following properties:

(i) $g(x; X)$, $dg(x; X)/dx$, and $d^2g(x; X)/dx^2$ are continuous for $0 \leq x \leq L$ except for a removable discontinuity at $x = X$.

(ii) $d^3g(x; X)/dx^3$ is continuous except for a discontinuity at $x = X$ of magnitude $(EI)^{-1}$; that is,

$$\lim_{x \to X^+} \frac{d^3g}{dx^3} - \lim_{x \to X^-} \frac{d^3g}{dx^3} = \frac{1}{EI}.$$

(iii) for any $x \neq X$,

$$EI\frac{d^4g(x; X)}{dx^4} = 0.$$

Use the characterization in (i), (ii), and (iii) to show that $g(x; X)$ can be expressed in the form

$$g(x; X) = \frac{1}{6EI}(x - X)^3 H(x - X) + Ax^3 + Bx^2 + Cx + D,$$

where A, B, C, and D are constants. (The constants are evaluated using the homogeneous boundary conditions.)

In Exercises 16–19, use the result of Exercise 15 to find the Green's function for static deflections of a beam of length L ($0 \leq x \leq L$), where the boundary conditions are as given.

16. $y(0) = y'(0) = 0 = y''(L) = y'''(L)$ (cantilevered)

17. $y(0) = y''(0) = 0 = y(L) = y''(L)$ (simply supported at both ends)

18. $y(0) = y'(0) = 0 = y(L) = y'(L)$ (clamped at both ends)

19. $y(0) = y'(0) = 0 = y(L) = y''(L)$ (clamped at one end, simply supported at the other)

20. Prove Theorem 5.

21. When the boundary conditions in (19) are unmixed, it is sometimes advantageous to represent the Green's function of the problem in terms of orthonormal eigenfunctions of the corresponding Sturm-Liouville system:

$$\frac{d}{dx}\left(a(x)\frac{dy}{dx}\right) + [c(x) + \lambda p(x)]y = 0, \qquad \alpha < x < \beta,$$

$$B_1 y = 0, \qquad B_2 y = 0.$$

[Notice that the weight function $p(x)$ is unspecified, but normally there is only one choice of $p(x)$ for which the differential equation gives rise to standard functions.] Show that when $y_n(x)$ are normalized eigenfunctions corresponding to eigenvalues λ_n, Green's function $g(x; X)$ can be expressed in the form

$$g(x; X) = \sum_{n=1}^{\infty} \frac{y_n(X) y_n(x)}{-\lambda_n}.$$

[*Hint:* Use Green's formula (33) with $u = y_n(x)$ and $v = g(x; X)$.]

22. Find an eigenfunction expansion for the Green's function of the boundary value problem

$$\frac{d^2 y}{dx^2} = F(x), \qquad 0 < x < L,$$

$$y(0) = 0, \qquad y(L) = 0.$$

11.4 Solutions of Boundary Value Problems Using Green's Functions

In this section we show how easy it is to solve boundary value problems once the Green's function for the problem is known. Theorem 3 in Section 11.3 yields solutions to problems with homogeneous boundary conditions; we give two illustrative examples. Nonhomogeneous boundary conditions are handled either by superposition or by Green's formula.

Problems with Homogeneous Boundary Conditions

In Section 11.3 we defined the Green's function for the boundary value problem

$$Ly = \frac{d}{dx}\left(a(x)\frac{dy}{dx}\right) + c(x)y = F(x), \qquad \alpha < x < \beta, \tag{36a}$$

$$B_1 y = 0, \tag{36b}$$

$$B_2 y = 0 \tag{36c}$$

as the solution of

$$Lg = \delta(x - X), \tag{37a}$$

$$B_1 g = 0, \tag{37b}$$

$$B_2 g = 0. \tag{37c}$$

The solution of (36) is then given by the definite integral

$$y(x) = \int_{\alpha}^{\beta} g(x; X) F(X) \, dX \tag{38}$$

(see Theorem 3).

Example 5: A taut string of length L has its ends fixed at $x = 0$ and $x = L$ on the x-axis. A concentrated mass of M kg is attached to the string at $x = L/3$ [Figure 11.8(a)]. Find the deflections in the string if gravity is also taken into account.

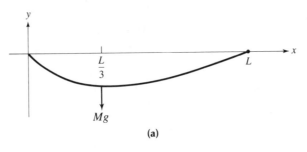

(a)

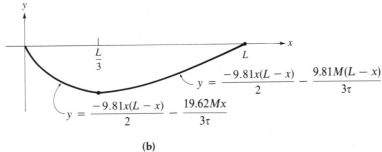

$$y = \frac{-9.81x(L-x)}{2} - \frac{9.81M(L-x)}{3\tau}$$

$$y = \frac{-9.81x(L-x)}{2} - \frac{19.62Mx}{3\tau}$$

Figure 11.8 (b)

Solution: The boundary value problem for deflections in the string is

$$-\tau\frac{d^2y}{dx^2} = -9.81 - 9.81M\delta\left(x - \frac{L}{3}\right),$$

$$y(0) = 0 = y(L).$$

According to equation (10c) and Example 1, the Green's function for this problem is

$$g(x; X) = \frac{1}{L\tau}\left(x(L - X)H(X - x) + X(L - x)H(x - X)\right).$$

The solution is therefore defined by integral (38):

$$y(x) = \int_0^L g(x; X)\left[-9.81 - 9.81M\delta\left(X - \frac{L}{3}\right)\right]dX$$

$$= -9.81\int_0^L g(x; X)\,dX - 9.81Mg\left(x; \frac{L}{3}\right)$$

$$= \frac{-9.81}{L\tau}\int_0^x X(L - x)\,dX - \frac{9.81}{L\tau}\int_x^L x(L - X)\,dX$$

$$- \frac{9.81M}{L\tau}\left[x\left(L - \frac{L}{3}\right)H\left(\frac{L}{3} - x\right) + \left(\frac{L}{3}\right)(L - x)H\left(x - \frac{L}{3}\right)\right]$$

$$= \frac{-9.81}{L\tau}(L - x)\left(\frac{x^2}{2}\right) - \frac{9.81}{L\tau}\frac{x(L - x)^2}{2}$$

$$- \frac{9.81M}{L\tau}\left[\frac{2Lx}{3}H\left(\frac{L}{3} - x\right) + \left(\frac{L}{3}\right)(L - x)H\left(x - \frac{L}{3}\right)\right]$$

$$= \frac{-9.81x(L - x)}{2\tau} - \frac{9.81M}{3\tau}\begin{cases}2x & 0 \le x \le L/3 \\ L - x & L/3 \le x \le L\end{cases}.$$

This is superposition of the displacement due to gravity (the first term) and that due to the concentrated load (the second term) [Figure 11.8(b)]. ∎

Example 6:   Solve the boundary value problem

$$\frac{d^2y}{dx^2} + 4y = F(x), \qquad 0 < x < 3,$$

$$y(0) = 0 = y'(3)$$

when (a) $F(x) = 2x$ and (b) $F(x) = H(x - 1) - H(x - 2)$.

Solution: The Green's function for this problem can be obtained from Example 2 by setting $\alpha = 0$ and $\beta = 3$:

$$g(x; X) = \frac{-1}{2\cos 6}(\sin 2x \cos(6 - 2X)H(X - x) + \sin 2X \cos(6 - 2x)H(x - X)).$$

With source function $F(x)$, the solution of the boundary value problem is

$$y(x) = \int_0^3 g(x; X)F(X)\,dX.$$

(a) When $F(x) = 2x$,

$$y(x) = \int_0^3 2X g(x; X)\,dX$$

$$= \frac{-1}{2\cos 6}\int_0^x 2X \sin 2X \cos(6 - 2x)\,dX$$

$$- \frac{1}{2\cos 6}\int_x^3 2X \sin 2x \cos(6 - 2X)\,dX$$

$$= \frac{-\cos(6 - 2x)}{\cos 6}\left\{\frac{-X\cos 2X}{2} + \frac{\sin 2X}{4}\right\}_0^x$$

$$- \frac{\sin 2x}{\cos 6}\left\{\frac{-X\sin(6 - 2X)}{2} + \frac{\cos(6 - 2X)}{4}\right\}_x^3$$

$$= \frac{x}{2} - \frac{\sin 2x}{4\cos 6}.$$

(This solution could also be derived very simply by finding the general solution of $y'' + 4y = 2x$ and using boundary conditions to evaluate arbitrary constants.)

(b) For $F(x) = H(x - 1) - H(x - 2)$, the solution is

$$y(x) = \int_0^3 [H(X - 1) - H(X - 2)]g(x; X)\,dX$$

$$= \int_1^2 g(x; X)\,dX.$$

When $x \leq 1$,

$$y(x) = \int_1^2 \frac{-1}{2\cos 6} \sin 2x \cos(6 - 2X)\,dX$$

$$= \frac{\sin 2x}{2\cos 6} \left\{ \frac{\sin(6 - 2X)}{2} \right\}_1^2$$

$$= \frac{\sin 2x(\sin 2 - \sin 4)}{4\cos 6};$$

when $1 < x < 2$,

$$y(x) = \int_1^x \frac{-1}{2\cos 6} \sin 2X \cos(6 - 2x)\,dX + \int_x^2 \frac{-1}{2\cos 6} \sin 2x \cos(6 - 2X)\,dX$$

$$= \frac{\cos(6 - 2x)}{2\cos 6} \left\{ \frac{\cos 2X}{2} \right\}_1^x + \frac{\sin 2x}{2\cos 6} \left\{ \frac{\sin(6 - 2X)}{2} \right\}_x^2$$

$$= \frac{1}{4} + \frac{1}{4\cos 6}[\sin 2x \sin 2 - \cos(6 - 2x)\cos 2];$$

and when $2 \leq x < 3$,

$$y(x) = \int_1^2 \frac{-1}{2\cos 6} \sin 2X \cos(6 - 2x)\,dX = \frac{\cos(6 - 2x)}{2\cos 6} \left\{ \frac{\cos 2X}{2} \right\}_1^2$$

$$= \frac{\cos(6 - 2x)(\cos 4 - \cos 2)}{4\cos 6}.$$

This solution is not so easily produced using methods from elementary differential equations. It requires integration of the differential equation on three separate intervals and matching of the solution and its first derivative at $x = 1$ and $x = 2$.   ∎

Problems with Nonhomogeneous Boundary Conditions

Suppose now that boundary conditions (36b, c) are not homogeneous, in which case problem (36) becomes

$$Ly = \frac{d}{dx}\left(a(x)\frac{dy}{dx}\right) + c(x)\,y = F(x), \qquad \alpha < x < \beta, \tag{39a}$$

$$B_1 y = m_1, \tag{39b}$$

$$B_2 y = m_2. \tag{39c}$$

(Only nonhomogeneous unmixed boundary conditions are considered; periodic conditions are always homogeneous.) There are two ways to solve this problem; one is to use superposition, and the other is to use Green's formula. Both methods use Green's function for the associated problem with homogeneous boundary conditions:

$$Ly = \frac{d}{dx}\left(a(x)\frac{dy}{dx}\right) + c(x)y = F(x), \qquad \alpha < x < \beta, \tag{40a}$$

$$B_1 y = 0, \tag{40b}$$

$$B_2 y = 0. \tag{40c}$$

In the superposition method, we note that

$$y_1(x) = \int_\alpha^\beta g(x; X)F(X)\,dX,$$

where $g(x; X)$ is the associated Green's function, is a solution of (40). A solution of (39) will therefore be $y = y_1 + y_2$ if y_2 satisfies

$$Ly = 0, \qquad \alpha < x < \beta, \tag{41a}$$

$$B_1 y = m_1, \tag{41b}$$

$$B_2 y = m_2. \tag{41c}$$

In ODEs it is often quite straightforward to obtain $y_2(x)$—apply boundary conditions (41b, c) to a general solution of (41a). We illustrate with the following example.

Example 7:   Solve the boundary value problem

$$-\tau \frac{d^2 y}{dx^2} = F(x), \qquad 0 < x < L,$$

$$y(0) = m_1, \qquad y(L) = m_2.$$

Solution: In Section 11.2 we derived the solution

$$y_1(x) = \int_0^L g(x; X)F(X)\,dX = \frac{L - x}{L\tau}\int_0^x XF(X)\,dX + \frac{x}{L\tau}\int_x^L (L - X)F(X)\,dX$$

for the associated problem with homogeneous boundary conditions. To this we must add the solution of

$$\frac{d^2 y}{dx^2} = 0, \qquad y(0) = m_1, \qquad y(L) = m_2.$$

Since every solution of this differential equation must be of the form $y_2(x) = Ax + B$, to satisfy the boundary conditions we require that

$$m_1 = B, \qquad m_2 = AL + B.$$

Thus,

$$y_2(x) = (m_2 - m_1)\frac{x}{L} + m_1$$

and
$$y(x) = y_1(x) + y_2(x) = (m_2 - m_1)\frac{x}{L} + m_1 + \frac{L - x}{L\tau}\int_0^x XF(X)\,dX$$

$$+ \frac{x}{L\tau}\int_x^L (L - X)F(X)\,dX. \qquad \blacksquare$$

This superposition method works well for ODEs but fails to generalize to PDEs; it is not usually possible to produce general solutions of homogeneous PDEs and apply nonhomogeneous boundary conditions to determine arbitrary functions. An alternative approach, which does generalize to PDEs, is to use Green's formula (33). This method also illustrates how the solution depends on the nonhomogeneities in the boundary conditions.

If $y(x)$ is the required solution of (39) and $v(x)$ is the Green's function $g(x; X)$ for the problem, (33) becomes

$$\int_\alpha^\beta yLg(x; X)\,dx - \int_\alpha^\beta g(x; X)Ly\,dx = \left\{a(x)\left[y(x)\frac{\partial g(x; X)}{\partial x} - g(x; X)y'(x)\right]\right\}_\alpha^\beta.$$

Because $Ly = F(x)$ and $Lg(x; X) = \delta(x - X)$, we may write

$$\int_\alpha^\beta y(x)\delta(x - X)\,dx - \int_\alpha^\beta g(x; X)F(x)\,dx = \left\{a(x)\left[y(x)\frac{\partial g(x; X)}{\partial x} - g(x; X)y'(x)\right]\right\}_\alpha^\beta$$

or
$$y(X) - \int_\alpha^\beta g(x; X)F(x)\,dx = a(\beta)\left(y(\beta)\frac{\partial g(\beta; X)}{\partial x} - g(\beta; X)y'(\beta)\right)$$

$$- a(\alpha)\left(y(\alpha)\frac{\partial g(\alpha; X)}{\partial x} - g(\alpha; X)y'(\alpha)\right). \qquad (42)$$

If we now substitute from the boundary conditions

$$B_1 y = -l_1 y'(\alpha) + h_1 y(\alpha) = m_1, \qquad (43a)$$

$$B_2 y = l_2 y'(\beta) + h_2 y(\beta) = m_2, \qquad (43b)$$

$$y(X) - \int_\alpha^\beta g(x; X)F(x)\,dx = a(\beta)\left[y(\beta)\frac{\partial g(\beta; X)}{\partial x} - g(\beta; X)\left(\frac{m_2}{l_2} - \frac{h_2}{l_2}y(\beta)\right)\right]$$

$$- a(\alpha)\left[y(\alpha)\frac{\partial g(\alpha; X)}{\partial x} - g(\alpha; X)\left(-\frac{m_1}{l_1} + \frac{h_1}{l_1}y(\alpha)\right)\right]$$

$$= a(\beta)\left[-\frac{m_2}{l_2}g(\beta; X) + \frac{y(\beta)}{l_2}\left(l_2\frac{\partial g(\beta; X)}{\partial x} + h_2 g(\beta; X)\right)\right]$$

$$- a(\alpha)\left[\frac{m_1}{l_1}g(\alpha; X) - \frac{y(\alpha)}{l_1}\left(-l_1\frac{\partial g(\alpha; X)}{\partial x} + h_1 g(\alpha; X)\right)\right].$$

But $g(x; X)$ must satisfy homogeneous versions of (43); that is,

$$-l_1\frac{\partial g(\alpha; X)}{\partial x} + h_1 g(\alpha; X) = 0, \qquad (44a)$$

$$l_2\frac{\partial g(\beta; X)}{\partial x} + h_2 g(\beta; X) = 0. \qquad (44b)$$

Consequently,

$$y(X) = \int_\alpha^\beta g(x; X)F(x)\,dx - \frac{m_1}{l_1}a(\alpha)g(\alpha; X) - \frac{m_2}{l_2}a(\beta)g(\beta; X).$$

Finally, when we interchange x and X and use the fact that $g(x; X)$ is symmetric,

$$y(x) = \int_\alpha^\beta g(x; X)F(X)\,dX - \frac{m_1}{l_1}a(\alpha)g(x; \alpha) - \frac{m_2}{l_2}a(\beta)g(x; \beta). \qquad \textbf{(45a)}$$

When $l_1 = l_2 = 0$ (and we set $h_1 = h_2 = 1$), (42) yields the following replacement for (45a):

$$y(x) = \int_\alpha^\beta g(x; X)F(X)\,dX + m_2 a(\beta)\frac{\partial g(x; \beta)}{\partial X} - m_1 a(\alpha)\frac{\partial g(x; \alpha)}{\partial X}. \qquad \textbf{(45b)}$$

Both (45a) and (45b) clearly indicate the dependence of $y(x)$ on all three nonhomogeneities in problem (39). The integral term accounts for the nonhomogeneity $F(x)$ in the PDE, and the remaining terms contain contributions due to nonhomogeneities in the boundary conditions. With $F(x)$ piecewise continuous, the integral term in (45) is continuous in x. Furthermore, because $g(x; X)$ is continuous and $\partial g/\partial x$ has a discontinuity only when $x = X$, it follows that the additional terms in (45) due to the nonhomogeneities in the boundary conditions are also continuous. In other words, the representation of the solution to a boundary value problem in terms of its Green's function is always a continuous function.

Example 8:   Solve the boundary value problem of Example 7.

Solution: The Green's function for this problem is

$$g(x; X) = (L\tau)^{-1}[x(L - X)H(X - x) + X(L - x)H(x - X)].$$

In Example 7 we used the direct method to find the particular solution satisfying the homogeneous differential equation and nonhomogeneous boundary conditions. Alternatively, according to equation (45b),

$$y(x) = \int_0^L g(x; X)F(X)\,dX - \tau m_2 \frac{\partial g(x; L)}{\partial X} + \tau m_1 \frac{\partial g(x; 0)}{\partial X}$$

$$= \int_0^L g(x; X)F(X)\,dX - \frac{\tau m_2}{L\tau}\left(-xH(X - x) + (L - x)H(x - X)\right)\big|_{X = L}$$

$$+ \frac{\tau m_1}{L\tau}\left(-xH(X - x) + (L - x)H(x - X)\right)\big|_{X = 0}$$

$$= \int_0^L g(x; X)F(X)\,dX + \frac{m_2}{L}x + \frac{m_1}{L}(L - x)$$

$$= \int_0^L g(x; X)F(X)\,dX + (m_2 - m_1)\frac{x}{L} + m_1. \qquad \blacksquare$$

Example 9: Solve the boundary value problem

$$\frac{d^2y}{dx^2} + 4y = F(x), \qquad \alpha < x < \beta,$$

$$y(\alpha) = m_1, \qquad y'(\beta) = m_2.$$

Solution: According to Example 2, the Green's function for this problem is

$$g(x; X) = \frac{-1}{2\cos 2(\beta - \alpha)}(\sin 2(x - \alpha)\cos 2(\beta - X)H(X - x)$$

$$+ \sin 2(X - \alpha)\cos 2(\beta - x)H(x - X)).$$

To account for the nonhomogeneities m_1 and m_2 in the boundary conditions, we use the term in (45a) containing m_2 and the term in (45b) containing m_1:

$$y(x) = \int_\alpha^\beta g(x; X)F(X)\,dX - m_1 \frac{\partial g(x; \alpha)}{\partial X} - m_2 g(x; \beta)$$

$$= \int_\alpha^\beta g(x; X)F(X)\,dX + \frac{m_1}{2\cos 2(\beta - \alpha)}$$

$$\times \left(2\sin 2(x - \alpha)\sin 2(\beta - \alpha)H(\alpha - x) + 2\cos 2(\beta - x)H(x - \alpha)\right)$$

$$+ \frac{m_2}{2\cos 2(\beta - \alpha)}(\sin 2(x - \alpha)H(\beta - x) + \sin 2(\beta - \alpha)\cos 2(\beta - x)H(x - \beta))$$

$$= \int_\alpha^\beta g(x; X)F(X)\,dX + \frac{2m_1 \cos 2(\beta - x) + m_2 \sin 2(x - \alpha)}{2\cos 2(\beta - \alpha)}. \qquad \blacksquare$$

Exercises 11.4

Do the exercises in Part D first.

Part A—Heat Conduction

1. What is the Green's function for the boundary value problem for steady-state temperature in a rod from $x = 0$ to $x = L$ with constant thermal conductivity k and zero end temperatures?

2. Solve the boundary value problem

$$-\frac{d}{dx}\left(\kappa \frac{dU}{dx}\right) = F(x), \qquad \alpha < x < \beta,$$

$$U(\alpha) = 0 = U(\beta)$$

for steady-state temperature in a rod from $x = \alpha$ to $x = \beta$ with variable thermal conductivity $\kappa(x)$ and heat generation $F(x)$. Interpret the Green's function physically.

3. Two rods of lengths L_1 and L_2 and constant thermal conductivities κ_1 and κ_2 are joined end to end (the left end of L_1 at $x = 0$ and the right end of L_2 at $x = L_1 + L_2$). If the ends at $x = 0$ and $x = L_1 + L_2$ are kept at temperature zero, what is the Green's function for steady-state temperature in the rods?

Part B—Vibrations

In Exercises 4–9, the function $F(x)$ describes the appplied force on a massless string with constant tension τ stretched between two fixed points $x = 0$ and $x = L$. Find and sketch a graph of the displacement $y(x)$ in the string.

4. $F(x) = k < 0$ a constant

5. $F(x) = \begin{cases} -kx & 0 < x \le L/2 \\ k(x - L) & L/2 \le x < L \end{cases}$, $k < 0$ a constant

6. $F(x) = \begin{cases} 0 & 0 < x < L/4 \\ k & L/4 < x < 3L/4, \\ 0 & 3L/4 < x < L \end{cases}$ $k < 0$ a constant

7. $F(x)$ is due to two concentrated loads of magnitude $\bar{k}$ placed at $x = L/4$ and $x = 3L/4$.

8. $F(x)$ is due to the combination of the constant force k in Exercise 4 and the concentrated loads $\bar{k}$ in Exercise 7.

9. $F(x) = \begin{cases} k & 0 < x < L/4 \\ 0 & L/4 < x < 3L/4, \\ k & 3L/4 < x < L \end{cases}$ $k < 0$ a constant

10. Solve Exercise 13 in Section 1.3.

11. Solve Exercise 10 if a thin ring of mass m is attached halfway along the length of the bar.

12. Solve Exercise 10 if a mass M is attached to the lower end of the bar.

13. The bar in Exercise 12 is hung from a spring with constant k, and a thin ring of mass m is attached halfway along the length of the bar. Find displacements of its cross sections in the coordinate system shown in Figure 11.9.

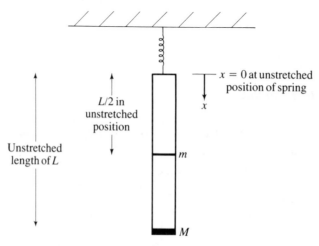

Figure 11.9

In Exercises 14–19, the function F(x) describes the applied force on a beam of length L ($0 \le x \le L$), and the conditions represent boundary conditions at the ends of the beam. Use the Green's functions from Exercises 16–19 in Section 11.3 to find the static deflection of the beam. Sketch the deflection curve in Exercises 14–17.

14. $F(x)$ is due to a concentrated load of magnitude unity at $x = L/2$, and the weight of the beam is assumed negligible:

$$y(0) = y'(0) = 0 = y''(L) = y'''(L).$$

(See also Exercise 10 in Section 11.1.)

15. $F(x)$ is due to the load of Exercise 14 placed at $x = L$. (See also Exercise 11 in Section 11.1.)

16. $F(x)$ is due only to the weight per unit x-length w of a uniform beam:

$$y(0) = y''(0) = 0 = y(L) = y''(L).$$

17. $F(x)$ is due to a uniform weight per unit x-length w of a uniform beam and a concentrated load of magnitude k at $x = L/2$:

$$y(0) = y'(0) = 0 = y(L) = y'(L).$$

18. $F(x) = \begin{cases} -w & 0 < x < L/4 \\ -(w + W) & L/4 < x < 3L/4, \\ -w & 3L/4 < x < L \end{cases} \quad \begin{matrix} w = \text{constant} \\ W = \text{constant} \end{matrix},$

$$y(0) = y'(0) = 0 = y''(L) = y'''(L)$$

19. $F(x)$ is due to a uniform weight per unit x-length W on $0 < x < L/2$ and a concentrated load of magnitude k at $x = L/4$. The weight of the beam itself is negligible:

$$y(0) = y'(0) = 0 = y(L) = y''(L).$$

Part D—General Results

In Exercises 20–27, find an integral representation for the solution of the boundary value problem.

20. $\dfrac{d^2y}{dx^2} = F(x), \quad 1 < x < 2, \quad y'(1) = m_1, y(2) = m_2.$ What is the solution when $F(x) = xe^x$?

21. $\dfrac{d^2y}{dx^2} + y = F(x), \quad 0 < x < 1, \quad y(0) = m_1, y'(1) = m_2.$ What is the solution when $F(x) = \cos x$?

22. $\dfrac{d^2y}{dx^2} + k^2y = F(x), \quad \alpha < x < \beta \, (k > 0 \text{ a constant}), y(\alpha) = 0, y'(\beta) = 1.$ Is there any restriction on the value of k? What is the solution when $F(x) = 1$?

23. $\dfrac{d^2y}{dx^2} + k^2y = F(x), \quad \alpha < x < \beta \, (k > 0 \text{ a constant}), y(\alpha) = y(\beta), \quad y'(\alpha) = y'(\beta).$ (See Exercise 13 in Section 11.3 for the Green's function.) What is the solution when $F(x) = x$?

24. $(x + 1)\dfrac{d^2y}{dx^2} + \dfrac{dy}{dx} = F(x), \quad 0 < x < 1, y(0) = 0, \quad y(1) = 0.$ What is the solution when $F(x) = x$?

25. $\dfrac{d^2y}{dx^2} - 4\dfrac{dy}{dx} + 8y = F(x), \quad 0 < x < \pi, \quad y(0) = y(\pi), \quad y'(0) = 0.$ What is the solution when $F(x) = e^{2x}$?

26. $\dfrac{d}{dx}\left(x\dfrac{dy}{dx}\right) = F(x), \quad 0 < \alpha < x < \beta, \quad y(\alpha) - y'(\alpha) = m_1, \quad y(\beta) = m_2.$

27. Show that the solution of nonhomogeneous problem (39) can be expressed in the form

$$y(x) = \int_\alpha^\beta g(x; X) F(X)\, dX + \frac{m_2}{B_2 y_1} y_1(x) + \frac{m_1}{B_1 y_2} y_2(x),$$

where $y_1(x)$ and $y_2(x)$ are nontrivial solutions of the associated homogeneous equation that satisfy $B_1(y_1) = 0$ and $B_2(y_2) = 0$, respectively.

11.5 Modified Green's Functions

When homogeneous problem (27) has nontrivial solutions, Green's function for the operator L and boundary conditions (27b, c) does not exist. Another way of saying the same thing is that Green's function does not exist when $\lambda = 0$ is an eigenvalue of the associated problem

$$\frac{d}{dx}\left(a(x)\frac{dy}{dx}\right) + [c(x) + \lambda p(x)]y = 0, \tag{46a}$$

$$B_1 y = 0, \tag{46b}$$

$$B_2 y = 0. \tag{46c}$$

A physical example to illustrate this is the boundary value problem

$$-\kappa\frac{d^2 U}{dx^2} = F(x), \qquad 0 < x < L,$$

$$U'(0) = 0,\ U'(L) = 0$$

for steady-state heat conduction in a rod with insulated sides and ends. The associated homogeneous problem has nontrivial solutions $U = \text{constant}$. Notice that if we integrate the differential equation from $x = 0$ to $x = L$,

$$\int_0^L F(x)\, dx = \int_0^L -\kappa\frac{d^2 U}{dx^2}\, dx = \left\{-\kappa\frac{dU}{dx}\right\}_0^L = 0.$$

Thus, if there is to be a solution to this problem, $F(x)$ cannot be specified arbitrarily; it must satisfy the condition

$$\int_0^L F(x)\, dx = 0. \tag{47}$$

Physically this means that with insulated sides and ends, the only way a steady-state condition can prevail is if total internal heat generation is zero.

Since the delta function $\delta(x - X)$ does not satisfy this condition (a unit point source at $x = X$), there can be no solution to

$$-\kappa\frac{d^2 g}{dx^2} = \delta(x - X),$$

$$g'(0; X) = 0, \qquad g'(L; X) = 0$$

for the associated Green's function $g(x; X)$.

The condition equivalent to (47) in more general problems with homogeneous boundary conditions is contained in the following theorem.

Theorem 7
___

When a homogeneous boundary value problem

$$Ly = \frac{d}{dx}\left(a\frac{dy}{dx}\right) + cy = 0, \qquad \alpha < x < \beta, \tag{48a}$$

$$B_1 y = 0, \tag{48b}$$

$$B_2 y = 0 \tag{48c}$$

has nontrivial solutions $w(x)$, the nonhomogeneous problem

$$Ly = \frac{d}{dx}\left(a\frac{dy}{dx}\right) + cy = F(x), \tag{49a}$$

$$B_1 y = 0, \tag{49b}$$

$$B_2 y = 0 \tag{49c}$$

has a solution if and only if

$$\int_\alpha^\beta F(x)w(x)\,dx = 0 \tag{50}$$

for every such solution $w(x)$.
___

It is easy to establish the necessity of condition (50). If $y(x)$ is a solution of (49), then

$$\int_\alpha^\beta F(x)w(x)\,dx = \int_\alpha^\beta (Ly)w(x)\,dx$$

$$= \int_\alpha^\beta y(Lw)\,dx + \{a(wy' - yw')\}_\alpha^\beta \quad \text{[using Green's formula (18)]}$$

$$= a(\beta)[w(\beta)y'(\beta) - y(\beta)w'(\beta)] - a(\alpha)[w(\alpha)y'(\alpha) - y(\alpha)w'(\alpha)],$$

since $Lw = 0$. These terms both vanish when boundary conditions (49b, c) are unmixed, and they cancel when the boundary conditions are periodic.

When (48) has nontrivial solutions and consistency condition (50) is satisfied, the solution of (49) is not unique. If $y(x)$ is a solution, so also is $y(x) + Cw(x)$ for arbitrary C and $w(x)$ a solution of (48).

To solve (49) when condition (50) is satisfied, we introduce "modified" Green's functions. We do so because there can be no "ordinary" Green's function satisfying

$$Lg = \delta(x - X),$$

$$B_1 g = 0, \qquad B_2 g = 0,$$

since $\delta(x - X)$ does not satisfy (50). Two situations arise, depending on whether (48) has one or two linearly independent solutions. We consider first the case in which (48) has only one nontrivial solution that is unique to a multiplicative constant and may therefore be taken as normalized:

$$\int_\alpha^\beta [w(x)]^2\,dx = 1. \tag{51}$$

A *modified Green's function* associated with (49) is defined as a solution $\bar g(x;X)$ of

$$L\bar g = \delta(x-X) - w(x)w(X), \tag{52a}$$
$$B_1\bar g = 0, \tag{52b}$$
$$B_2\bar g = 0. \tag{52c}$$

Because the right side of equation (52a) satisfies consistency condition (50), Theorem 7 guarantees a solution $\bar g(x;X)$. But because the solution is not unique, $\bar g(x;X)$ may or may not be symmetric, depending on the method used in its construction. It is important to note, however, that because the differential equation for the ordinary Green's function is modified only by the term $w(x)w(X)$, the modified Green's function satisfies the same continuity properties as the ordinary Green's function. Indeed, we shall use these properties to find $\bar g(x;X)$.

Modified Green's functions can be used to solve problem (49), which has a solution provided $F(x)$ satisfies (50). Green's identity (33) with $u = y(x)$ and $v = \bar g(x;X)$ gives

$$\int_\alpha^\beta [yL\bar g - \bar gLy]\,dx = \left\{a(x)\left(y(x)\frac{\partial\bar g(x;X)}{\partial x} - \bar g(x;X)y'(x)\right)\right\}\Big|_\alpha^\beta.$$

It is quickly shown that with either unmixed or periodic boundary conditions, the right side of this equation vanishes. Differential equations (49a) and (52a) then give

$$0 = \int_\alpha^\beta \big(y(x)[\delta(x-X) - w(x)w(X)] - \bar g(x;X)F(x)\big)\,dx$$
$$= y(X) - C_1w(X) - \int_\alpha^\beta \bar g(x;X)F(x)\,dx,$$

where $C_1 = \int_\alpha^\beta y(x)w(x)\,dx$. Thus,

$$y(X) = \int_\alpha^\beta \bar g(x;X)F(x)\,dx + C_1w(X) \tag{53}$$

or, interchanging x and X,

$$y(x) = \int_\alpha^\beta \bar g(X;x)F(X)\,dX + C_1w(x). \tag{54}$$

Because $y(x)$ is unique only to the addition of a term $Cw(x)$, we may drop the subscript in (54) and write

$$y(x) = \int_\alpha^\beta \bar g(X;x)F(X)\,dX + Cw(x), \tag{55}$$

where C is arbitrary.

Finally, when the construction of $\bar g(x;X)$ gives a symmetric function, we may write

$$y(x) = \int_\alpha^\beta \bar g(x;X)F(X)\,dX + Cw(x), \tag{56}$$

and the form of the solution, except for the $Cw(x)$ term, is identical to that for ordinary Green's functions. Exercise 11 describes a technique for calculating symmetric modified Green's functions from nonsymmetric ones.

Example 10: Solve the boundary value problem

$$\frac{d^2y}{dx^2} + 4y = F(x), \qquad 0 < x < \pi,$$

$$y(0) = 0 = y(\pi).$$

Solution: Solutions of the homogeneous differential equation $y'' + 4y = 0$ are of the form $y = A\cos 2x + B\sin 2x$. Since the function $\sin 2x$ satisfies both boundary conditions, the Green's function for this problem does not exist. We define a modified Green's function $\bar{g}(x; X)$ as the solution of

$$\frac{d^2\bar{g}}{dx^2} + 4\bar{g} = \delta(x - X) - \frac{2}{\pi}\sin 2x \sin 2X,$$

$$\bar{g}(0; X) = 0 = \bar{g}(\pi; X).$$

($2/\pi$ is the normalizing factor.) Because $\bar{g}(x; X)$ must satisfy property (21c), and a particular solution of $\bar{g}'' + 4\bar{g} = -(2/\pi)\sin 2x \sin 2X$ is $(2\pi)^{-1}x\sin 2X\cos 2x$, we take

$$\bar{g}(x; X) = \frac{x}{2\pi}\sin 2X \cos 2x + \begin{cases} A\sin 2x + B\cos 2x & 0 \le x < X \\ C\sin 2x + D\cos 2x & X < x \le \pi \end{cases}.$$

To determine A, B, C, and D, we apply boundary conditions $\bar{g}(0; X) = 0 = \bar{g}(\pi; X)$,

$$B = 0,$$

$$\frac{1}{2}\sin 2X + D = 0,$$

and continuity conditions (21a, b) at $x = X$,

$$A\sin 2X + B\cos 2X = C\sin 2X + D\cos 2X,$$

$$(2C\cos 2X - 2D\sin 2X) - (2A\cos 2X - 2B\sin 2X) = 1.$$

These four equations require that

$$B = 0, \qquad D = -\frac{1}{2}\sin 2X, \quad \text{and} \quad C = A + \frac{1}{2}\cos 2X,$$

where $A = A(X)$ is an arbitrary function of X. A modified Green's function is therefore

$$\bar{g}(x; X) = \frac{x}{2\pi}\sin 2X \cos 2x + \begin{cases} A\sin 2x & 0 \le x \le X \\ \left(A + \frac{1}{2}\cos 2X\right)\sin 2x - \frac{1}{2}\sin 2X \cos 2x & X \le x \le \pi \end{cases}$$

$$= \frac{x}{2\pi}\sin 2X \cos 2x + \begin{cases} A\sin 2x & 0 \le x \le X \\ A\sin 2x + \frac{1}{2}\sin 2(x - X) & X \le x \le \pi \end{cases}$$

$$= \frac{x}{2\pi}\sin 2X \cos 2x + A\sin 2x + \frac{1}{2}\sin 2(x - X)H(x - X).$$

Notice that the arbitrariness in $\bar{g}(x; X)$ is a constant $A(X)$ times $w(x)$, the solution of the homogeneous problem. Because $\bar{g}(x; X)$ is not symmetric, we use equation (55) to express the solution of the original boundary value problem in the form

$$
\begin{aligned}
y(x) &= \int_0^\pi \bar{g}(X; x)F(X)\,dX + C\sin 2x \\
&= \int_0^\pi \left(\frac{X}{2\pi}\sin 2x \cos 2X + A(x)\sin 2X + \frac{1}{2}\sin 2(X - x)H(X - x)\right)F(X)\,dX \\
&\quad + C\sin 2x \qquad (C \text{ a constant}) \\
&= C\sin 2x + \frac{\sin 2x}{2\pi}\int_0^\pi X\cos 2X\,F(X)\,dX + A(x)\int_0^\pi F(X)\sin 2X\,dX \\
&\quad + \frac{1}{2}\int_x^\pi \sin 2(X - x)\,F(X)\,dX.
\end{aligned}
$$

Since the first integral is a constant, the second term may be grouped with $C\sin 2x$. Furthermore, the second integral vanishes because of consistency condition (50). Thus, the final solution is

$$
y(x) = C\sin 2x + \frac{1}{2}\int_x^\pi \sin 2(X - x)F(X)\,dX. \qquad \blacksquare
$$

We have considered the situation in which the homogeneous problem (48) corresponding to (49) has a single nontrivial solution (unique to a multiplicative constant). The remaining possibility is that all solutions of (48a) satisfy boundary conditions (48b, c). In such a case, we can always find two orthonormal solutions $v(x)$ and $w(x)$ of $Ly = 0$. If $\psi(x)$ and $\phi(x)$ are linearly independent solutions, two orthonormal solutions are

$$
v(x) = \psi(x)\left(\int_\alpha^\beta [\psi(x)]^2\,dx\right)^{-1/2}
$$

and

$$
w(x) = \left(\phi(x) - v(x)\int_\alpha^\beta \phi(x)v(x)\,dx\right)\left(\int_\alpha^\beta \left(\phi(x) - v(x)\int_\alpha^\beta \phi(x)v(x)\,dx\right)^2 dx\right)^{-1/2}.
$$

[$\psi(x)$ is normalized to form $v(x)$. For $w(x)$, the component of $\phi(x)$ in the "direction" of $v(x)$ is removed, and the result is then normalized.] We define a modified Green's function $\bar{g}(x; X)$ associated with (49) as a solution of

$$
L\bar{g} = \delta(x - X) - w(x)w(X) - v(x)v(X), \tag{57a}
$$

$$
B_1\bar{g} = 0, \tag{57b}
$$

$$
B_2\bar{g} = 0. \tag{57c}
$$

Because the right side of (57a) satisfies consistency condition (50), $\bar{g}(x; X)$ must indeed exist. Green's identity once again gives the solution of (49) as

$$y(x) = \int_\alpha^\beta \bar{g}(X;x)F(X)\,dX + Cw(x) + Dv(x), \tag{58}$$

where C and D are arbitrary constants.

Example 11:   Solve the boundary value problem

$$\frac{d^2y}{dx^2} + y = F(x), \qquad 0 < x < 2\pi,$$

$$y(0) = y(2\pi), \qquad y'(0) = y'(2\pi).$$

Solution: The homogeneous problem has nontrivial solutions $\sin x$ and $\cos x$. Because these functions are orthogonal, a modified Green's function for this problem is defined by

$$\frac{d^2\bar{g}}{dx^2} + \bar{g} = \delta(x - X) - \pi^{-1}(\sin x \sin X + \cos x \cos X),$$

$$\bar{g}(0;X) = \bar{g}(2\pi;X), \qquad \frac{\partial\bar{g}(0;X)}{\partial x} = \frac{\partial\bar{g}(2\pi;X)}{\partial x}.$$

A solution of the differential equation is

$$\bar{g}(x;X) = \frac{x}{2\pi}\sin(X - x) + \begin{cases} A\sin x + B\cos x & 0 \le x < X \\ C\sin x + D\cos x & X < x \le 2\pi \end{cases}.$$

To determine A, B, C, and D, we first apply the boundary conditions

$$B = \sin X + D,$$

$$\frac{\sin X}{2\pi} + A = \frac{\sin X}{2\pi} - \cos X + C,$$

and then continuity conditions (21a, b) at $x = X$,

$$A\sin X + B\cos X = C\sin X + D\cos X,$$

$$C\cos X - D\sin X - A\cos X + B\sin X = 1.$$

These four conditions require that $A = C - \cos X$ and $B = D + \sin X$, where $C = C(X)$ and $D = D(X)$ are arbitrary functions of X. A modified Green's function is therefore

$$\bar{g}(x;X) = \frac{x}{2\pi}\sin(X - x) + C\sin x + D\cos x + \begin{cases} \sin X \cos x - \cos X \sin x & 0 \le x \le X \\ 0 & X \le x \le 2\pi \end{cases}$$

$$= C\sin x + D\cos x + \sin(X - x)\begin{cases} \dfrac{x}{2\pi} + 1 & 0 \le x \le X \\[2mm] \dfrac{x}{2\pi} & X \le x \le 2\pi \end{cases}$$

$$= C\sin x + D\cos x + \sin(X - x)\left(\frac{x}{2\pi} + H(X - x)\right).$$

According to (58), the solution of the boundary value problem is

$$
\begin{aligned}
y(x) &= \int_0^{2\pi} \bar{g}(X;x)F(X)\,dX + E\sin x + G\cos x \\
&= \int_0^{2\pi} \left[C\sin X + D\cos X + \sin(x - X)\left(\frac{X}{2\pi} + H(x - X)\right)\right] F(X)\,dX \\
&\quad + E\sin x + G\cos x \\
&= E\sin x + G\cos x + \int_0^{2\pi} \sin(x - X)\left(\frac{X}{2\pi} + H(x - X)\right) F(X)\,dX,
\end{aligned}
$$

since $F(x)$ must satisfy the consistency conditions

$$
\int_0^{2\pi} F(x)\sin x\,dx = 0 = \int_0^{2\pi} F(x)\cos x\,dx. \qquad\blacksquare
$$

When boundary conditions in (49b, c) are nonhomogeneous (and therefore unmixed), it is also necessary to introduce modified Green's functions into the results of Section 11.4. The following results are proved in Exercises 4 and 9.

When (48) has only one solution $w(x)$ (unique to a multiplicative constant), the solution of

$$
Ly = \frac{d}{dx}\left(a\frac{dy}{dx}\right) + cy = F(x), \qquad \alpha < x < \beta, \tag{59a}
$$

$$
B_1 y = m_1, \tag{59b}
$$

$$
B_2 y = m_2 \tag{59c}
$$

is

$$
y(x) = \int_\alpha^\beta \bar{g}(X;x)F(X)\,dX + Cw(x) - \frac{m_1}{l_1}a(\alpha)\bar{g}(\alpha;x)
$$

$$
-\frac{m_2}{l_2}a(\beta)\bar{g}(\beta;x) \tag{60a}
$$

or, when $l_1 = l_2 = 0$,

$$
y(x) = \int_\alpha^\beta \bar{g}(X;x)F(X)\,dX + Cw(x) + m_2 a(\beta)\frac{\partial\bar{g}(\beta;x)}{\partial X} - m_1 a(\alpha)\frac{\partial\bar{g}(\alpha;x)}{\partial X}. \tag{60b}
$$

If (48) has two linearly independent solutions $v(x)$ and $w(x)$, the quantity $Cw(x)$ in equations (60) is replaced by $Cw(x) + Dv(x)$, and the solutions are otherwise the same.

In all cases, a solution of (59) exists if and only if $F(x)$, m_1, and m_2 satisfy the consistency condition

$$
\int_\alpha^\beta F(x)w(x)\,dx = \frac{m_2}{l_2}a(\beta)w(\beta) + \frac{m_1}{l_1}a(\alpha)w(\alpha) \tag{61a}
$$

or, when $l_1 = l_2 = 0$,

$$
\int_\alpha^\beta F(x)w(x)\,dx = m_1 a(\alpha)w'(\alpha) - m_2 a(\beta)w'(\beta) \tag{61b}
$$

for every solution $w(x)$ of the corresponding homogeneous problem.

Exercises 11.5

1. Solve the boundary value problem

$$-\kappa \frac{d^2U}{dx^2} = F(x), \qquad 0 < x < L,$$

$$U'(0) = 0 = U'(L)$$

when $F(x)$ satisfies consistency condition (47). Calculate the solution in closed form when $F(x) = \cos(\pi x/L)$.

2. Verify that the result in Example 11 gives the correct solution when $F(x) = \sin 2x$.

3. (a) Simplify the solution to Example 10 when $F(x) = \cos 2x$.

   (b) Use equation (60b) to find the solution when the boundary conditions are nonhomogeneous:

   $$y(0) = m_1, \qquad y(\pi) = m_2.$$

   What condition must be imposed on m_1 and m_2?

4. Verify consistency conditions (61) for the nonhomogeneous problem (59).

5. Solve the boundary value problem

$$\frac{d^2y}{dx^2} + k^2y = F(x), \qquad 0 < x < L \qquad (k > 0 \text{ a constant}),$$

$$y(0) = 0 = y(L).$$

6. (a) Use the result of Exercise 5 to solve

$$\frac{d^2y}{dx^2} + \frac{9\pi^2}{L^2}y = F(x), \qquad 0 < x < L,$$

$$y(0) = m_1, \qquad y(L) = m_2.$$

   (b) Simplify the solution when $F(x) = x$. What is the consistency condition?

7. Solve the boundary value problem

$$\frac{d^2y}{dx^2} + k^2y = F(x), \qquad 0 < x < L \qquad (k > 0 \text{ a constant}),$$

$$y(0) = 0 = y'(L).$$

8. (a) Use the result of Exercise 7 to solve

$$\frac{d^2y}{dx^2} + \frac{25\pi^2}{4L^2}y = F(x), \qquad 0 < x < L,$$

$$y(0) = m_1, \qquad y'(L) = m_2.$$

   (b) Simplify the solution when $F(x) = x^2$. What is the consistency condition?

9. Verify the results in equations (60).

10. A modified Green's function for boundary value problem (59), when the corresponding homogeneous problem has only one solution $w(x)$ (unique to a multiplicative constant), is defined by boundary value problem (52). In this exercise we show that modified Green's functions can be defined in other ways. The homogeneous boundary value problem associated with the

heat conduction problem

$$-\kappa \frac{d^2 U}{dx^2} = F(x), \qquad 0 < x < L,$$

$$U'(0) = m_1, \qquad U'(L) = m_2$$

has nontrivial solutions $y = $ constant.

(a) Show that when a function $\bar{\bar{g}}(x; X)$ satisfies

$$-\kappa \frac{d^2 \bar{\bar{g}}}{dx^2} = \delta(x - X),$$

$$\bar{\bar{g}}'(0; X) = \frac{1}{2\kappa}, \qquad \bar{\bar{g}}'(L; X) = \frac{-1}{2\kappa},$$

consistency condition (61a) for nonhomogeneous problems is satisfied.

(b) Use Green's formula (33) to show that $U(x)$ can be expressed in the form

$$U(x) = \int_0^L \bar{\bar{g}}(X; x) F(X) \, dX + \kappa [m_2 \bar{\bar{g}}(L; x) - m_1 \bar{\bar{g}}(0; x)] + C,$$

where C is an arbitrary constant. Find $\bar{\bar{g}}(x; X)$ and simplify this solution.

(c) Use the result in (b) to find the solution to the boundary value problem of Exercise 1 when $F(x) = \cos(\pi x / L)$.

11. (a) Show that there is only one modified Green's function $\bar{g}_s(x; X)$ satisfying (52) that is orthogonal to $w(x)$ and that this function is given by

$$\bar{g}_s(x; X) = \bar{g}(x; X) - w(x) \left(\int_\alpha^\beta \bar{g}(\xi; X) w(\xi) \, d\xi \right),$$

where $\bar{g}(x; X)$ is any modified Green's function whatsoever.

(b) Use Green's identity (34) with $u = \bar{g}_s(x; X)$ and $v = \bar{g}_s(x; Y)$ to show that $\bar{g}_s(x; X)$ is symmetric. Are there any other symmetric modified Green's functions?

12. Use Exercise 11 to find symmetric modified Green's functions for the problem in Exercise 1.

13. Use Exercise 11 to find symmetric modified Green's functions for the problem in Example 10.

14. (a) Show that there is only one modified Green's function $\bar{g}_s(x; X)$ satisfying (57) that is orthogonal to $w(x)$ and $v(x)$ and that this function is given by

$$\bar{g}_s(x; X) = \bar{g}(x; X) - w(x) \left(\int_\alpha^\beta \bar{g}(\xi; X) w(\xi) \, d\xi \right) - v(x) \left(\int_\alpha^\beta \bar{g}(\xi; X) v(\xi) \, d\xi \right),$$

where $\bar{g}(x; X)$ is any modified Green's function whatsoever.

(b) Use Green's identity (34) with $u = \bar{g}_s(x; X)$ and $v = \bar{g}_s(x; Y)$ to show that $\bar{g}_s(x; X)$ is symmetric. Are there any other symmetric modified Green's functions?

15. Use Exercise 14 to find symmetric modified Green's functions for the problem in Example 11.

11.6 Green's Functions for Initial Value Problems

When the conditions that accompany differential equation (19a) are of the form

$$y(\alpha) = 0, \qquad y'(\alpha) = 0, \tag{62}$$

they are called *initial conditions,* and the problem is known as an *initial value problem* rather than a boundary value problem. Because this situation arises most frequently when the independent variable is time t, we rewrite the initial value problem in the form

$$Ly = \frac{d}{dt}\left(a(t)\frac{dy}{dt}\right) + c(t)y = F(t), \qquad t > t_0, \tag{63a}$$

$$y(t_0) = m_1, \tag{63b}$$

$$y'(t_0) = m_2. \tag{63c}$$

Initial time t_0 is often chosen as $t_0 = 0$, but for the sake of generality we maintain arbitrary t_0.

It might seem natural to define the Green's function $g(t; T)$ for this problem as the function $g(t; T)$ satisfying

$$\frac{d}{dt}\left(a(t)\frac{dg}{dt}\right) + c(t)g = \delta(t - T), \tag{64a}$$

$$g(t_0; T) = 0 \qquad \frac{dg(t_0; T)}{dt} = 0. \tag{64b}$$

Unfortunately, this would lead to improper integral representations of solutions of (63), together with associated convergence problems. Instead, we define the Green's function $g(t; T)$ as what is called a *causal fundamental solution* of (63); it is the solution of

$$g(t; T) = 0, \qquad t_0 < t < T, \tag{65a}$$

$$Lg = \delta(t - T). \tag{65b}$$

Physically $g(t; T)$ is the reaction of the system described by (63) to a unit impulse at time T. Naturally, for time $t < T$, the system must be identically equal to zero [hence the requirement (65a)].

Provided $a(t)$ does not vanish for $t \geq t_0$, the solution of (65) exists and is unique. Furthermore, corresponding to properties (21), which characterize the Green's function for boundary value problem (19), the following conditions characterize the Green's function for initial value problem (63):

$$g(t; T) = 0, \qquad t_0 < t < T, \tag{66a}$$

$$Lg = \frac{d}{dt}\left(a(t)\frac{dg}{dt}\right) + c(t)g = 0, \qquad t > T, \tag{66b}$$

$$g(T+; T) = 0, \tag{66c}$$

$$\frac{dg(T+; T)}{dt} = \frac{1}{a(T)}. \tag{66d}$$

When $u(t)$ and $v(t)$ are linearly independent solutions of (66b), the function

$$g(t; T) = \frac{1}{J(u, v)}[u(T)v(t) - v(T)u(t)]H(t - T) \tag{67}$$

clearly satisfies (66) and must therefore be the Green's function for (63). This formula replaces (29) for boundary value problems, but notice that the condition that the associated homogeneous system have only the trivial solution is absent for initial value problems (it is always satisfied).

Example 12:   What is the Green's function for the initial value problem

$$M\frac{d^2y}{dt^2} + ky = F(t), \qquad t > 0,$$

$$y(0) = m_1, \qquad y'(0) = m_2$$

for displacements of a mass M on the end of a spring with constant k?

Solution: Since $\sin\sqrt{k/M}\,t$ and $\cos\sqrt{k/M}\,t$ are solutions of $My'' + ky = 0$, the Green's function, according to (67), is

$$g(t;T) = \frac{1}{J(\sin\sqrt{k/M}\,t,\cos\sqrt{k/M}\,t)}\left(\sin\sqrt{\frac{k}{M}}\,T\cos\sqrt{\frac{k}{M}}\,t\right.$$

$$\left. - \cos\sqrt{\frac{k}{M}}\,T\sin\sqrt{\frac{k}{M}}\,t\right)H(t-T)$$

$$= \frac{1}{-\sqrt{kM}}\sin\sqrt{\frac{k}{M}}\,(T-t)\,H(t-T)$$

$$= \frac{1}{\sqrt{kM}}\sin\sqrt{\frac{k}{M}}\,(t-T)\,H(t-T). \qquad\blacksquare$$

The solution of an initial value problem can be expressed in terms of its Green's function. In particular, the solution of problem (63) is

$$y(t) = \int_{t_0}^{t} g(t;T)F(T)\,dT + a(t_0)\left(m_2 g(t;t_0) - m_1\frac{\partial g(t;t_0)}{\partial T}\right). \tag{68}$$

The integral term, which accounts for the nonhomogeneity in the differential equation, is interpreted as the superposition of incremental results. Because the Green's function $g(t;T)$ is the result at time t due to a unit impulse $\delta(t-T)$ at time T, $g(t;T)F(T)\,dT$ is the result at time t due to an incremental "force" $F(T)\,dT$ over dT. The integral then adds over all contributions, beginning at time t_0, to give the final result at time t. The last two terms in (68) account for nonhomogeneities in initial conditions (63b, c).

Example 13:   What is the solution of the problem in Example 12?

Solution: According to (68), the solution is

$$y(t) = \int_0^t \frac{1}{\sqrt{kM}}\sin\sqrt{\frac{k}{M}}(t-T)H(t-T)F(T)\,dT$$

$$+ M\left(\frac{m_2}{\sqrt{kM}}\sin\sqrt{\frac{k}{M}}\,t + \frac{m_1}{\sqrt{kM}}\sqrt{\frac{k}{M}}\cos\sqrt{\frac{k}{M}}\,t\right)$$

$$= \frac{1}{\sqrt{kM}}\int_0^t \sin\sqrt{\frac{k}{M}}(t-T)\,F(T)\,dT + \sqrt{\frac{M}{k}}\,m_2\sin\sqrt{\frac{k}{M}}\,t + m_1\cos\sqrt{\frac{k}{M}}\,t. \qquad\blacksquare$$

Exercises 11.6

1. A particle of mass M moves along the x-axis under the action of a force that is an explicit function $F(t)$ $(t \geq 0)$ of time t only. Find an integral representation for its position as a function of time t if at time $t = 0$ it is moving with velocity v_0 at position x_0.

2. A mass M is suspended from a spring (with constant k). Vertical oscillations are initiated at time $t = 0$ by displacing M from its equilibrium position and giving it an initial speed. If motion takes place in a medium that causes a damping force proportional to velocity, and an external force $F(t)$ $(t \geq 0)$ acts on M, find an integral representation for the position of M as a function of time t.

3. (a) Show that the solution of problem (63) can be expressed in the form

$$y(t) = \frac{1}{J(u, v)} \left(\int_{t_0}^{t} [u(T)v(t) - v(T)u(t)]F(T)\,dT + a(t_0)[m_1 v'(t_0) - m_2 v(t_0)]u(t) \right.$$
$$\left. + a(t_0)[m_2 u(t_0) - m_1 u'(t_0)]v(t) \right),$$

where $u(t)$ and $v(t)$ are any two linearly independent solutions of $Ly = 0$.

(b) Use the result in (a) to show that $y(t)$ can also be written in the form

$$y(t) = \frac{1}{a(t_0)} \int_{t_0}^{t} [u(T)v(t) - v(T)u(t)]F(T)\,dT + m_1 u(t) + m_2 v(t),$$

where $u(t)$ and $v(t)$ are solutions of $Ly = 0$ satisfying

$$u(t_0) = 1, \qquad u'(t_0) = 0; \qquad v(t_0) = 0, \qquad v'(t_0) = 1.$$

4. Use Exercise 3(b) to obtain the solution for Example 13.

5. Use Exercise 3(b) to solve Exercise 2.

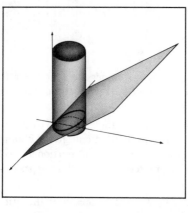

CHAPTER
TWELVE

Green's Functions
for Partial Differential Equations

12.1 Generalized Functions and Green's Identities

In this chapter we develop Green's functions for boundary value problems (and initial boundary value problems) associated with partial differential equations. Solutions to such problems can then be represented in terms of integrals of source functions and Green's functions. We begin by discussing multidimensional delta functions and Green's identities.

Two- and three-dimensional delta functions, like $\delta(x - c)$, are defined from a functional point of view. We discuss two-dimensional functions, but three-dimensional results are analogous. The generalized function $\delta(x - a, y - b)$ maps a function $f(x, y)$ continuous at (a, b) onto its value at (a, b); that is,

$$f(x, y) \xrightarrow{\delta(x - a,\, y - b)} f(a, b) = \int_{-\infty}^{\infty} \int_{-\infty}^{\infty} \delta(x - a,\, y - b) f(x, y)\, dA. \tag{1}$$

Because successive applications of delta functions lead to

$$\int_{-\infty}^{\infty} \int_{-\infty}^{\infty} \delta(x - a)\delta(y - b) f(x, y)\, dy\, dx = \int_{-\infty}^{\infty} \delta(x - a) f(x, b)\, dx = f(a, b), \tag{2}$$

it follows that

$$\delta(x - a, y - b) = \delta(x - a)\delta(y - b). \tag{3}$$

In other words, the two-dimensional delta function in Cartesian coordinates is the product of two one-dimensional delta functions. Corresponding to property (8) in Chapter 11, we take

$$\iint_R \delta(x - a, y - b) f(x, y) \, dA = \begin{cases} f(a, b) & (a, b) \text{ in } R \\ 0 & (a, b) \text{ not in } R \end{cases}. \tag{4}$$

Delta functions in curvilinear coordinates are defined analogously to those in Cartesian coordinates, but their expressions in terms of products of one-dimensional delta functions are complicated by formulas for area and volume elements in curvilinear coordinates. To illustrate, suppose that a point with Cartesian coordinates (x_0, y_0) has polar coordinates (r_0, θ_0). The delta function $\delta(r - r_0, \theta - \theta_0)$ in polar coordinates is that generalized function that assigns to a function $f(r, \theta)$, continuous at (r_0, θ_0), its value at (r_0, θ_0),

$$\iint_{R^2} \delta(r - r_0, \theta - \theta_0) f(r, \theta) \, dA = f(r_0, \theta_0), \tag{5a}$$

where R^2 refers to the xy-plane. But because $dA = r \, dr \, d\theta$, (5a) is expressible in the form

$$\int_{-\pi}^{\pi} \int_0^{\infty} \delta(r - r_0, \theta - \theta_0) f(r, \theta) r \, dr \, d\theta = f(r_0, \theta_0). \tag{5b}$$

Since
$$\int_{-\pi}^{\pi} \int_0^{\infty} \delta(r - r_0)\delta(\theta - \theta_0) f(r, \theta) \, dr \, d\theta = f(r_0, \theta_0), \tag{6}$$

it follows that $r\delta(r - r_0, \theta - \theta_0) = \delta(r - r_0)\delta(\theta - \theta_0)$, or

$$\delta(r - r_0, \theta - \theta_0) = \frac{1}{r}\delta(r - r_0)\delta(\theta - \theta_0). \tag{7}$$

Since the delta function $\delta(x - x_0)\delta(y - y_0)$ and that in (7) pick out the value of a function at the same point, we may write

$$\delta(x - x_0)\delta(y - y_0) = \frac{1}{r}\delta(r - r_0)\delta(\theta - \theta_0). \tag{8a}$$

Similarly, transformation laws from delta functions in Cartesian coordinates to those in cylindrical and spherical coordinates are

$$\delta(x - x_0)\delta(y - y_0)\delta(z - z_0) = \frac{1}{r}\delta(r - r_0)\delta(\theta - \theta_0)\delta(z - z_0) \tag{8b}$$

and
$$\delta(x - x_0)\delta(y - y_0)\delta(z - z_0) = \frac{1}{r^2 \sin\phi}\delta(r - r_0)\delta(\theta - \theta_0)\delta(\phi - \phi_0). \tag{8c}$$

Many curvilinear coordinate systems, and in particular the above three, have *singular points*—points at which transformations between them and Cartesian coordinates fail to be one to one. In polar coordinates, the origin is singular, and in cylindrical and spherical coordinates, the z-axis is singular. Transformation laws (8) are not valid at singular points. To understand this, we first note that when the functional on the right side of (8a) operates on a function $f(r, \theta)$, it produces $f(r_0, \theta_0)$, the value of the function at (r_0, θ_0). But if $r_0 = 0$, the value of the function $f(r, \theta)$ does not depend on the value of θ; its value is completely dictated by setting $r = 0$. This means that when $r_0 = 0$, $\delta(\theta - \theta_0)$ on the right side of (8a) is redundant. To see how to remove this delta function, notice that if we write $F(0)$ for the value of $f(0, \theta)$, then

$$\int_0^\infty \delta(r) f(r, \theta)\, dr = F(0).$$

Integration of this result with respect to θ gives

$$\int_{-\pi}^{\pi} \int_0^\infty \delta(r) f(r, \theta)\, dr\, d\theta = \int_{-\pi}^{\pi} F(0)\, d\theta$$

or

$$\int_{-\pi}^{\pi} \int_0^\infty \frac{\delta(r)}{r} f(r, \theta) r\, dr\, d\theta = 2\pi F(0).$$

Thus,

$$\int_{-\pi}^{\pi} \int_0^\infty \frac{\delta(r)}{2\pi r} f(r, \theta) r\, dr\, d\theta = F(0).$$

But this equation implies that $\delta(r)/(2\pi r)$ must be the delta function at the origin, that is,

$$\delta(x)\delta(y) = \frac{\delta(r)}{2\pi r}. \tag{9}$$

A similar discussion in cylindrical coordinates shows that

$$\delta(x)\delta(y)\delta(z - z_0) = \frac{\delta(r)\delta(z - z_0)}{2\pi r}. \tag{10}$$

In spherical coordinates, we obtain

$$\delta(x)\delta(y)\delta(z - z_0) = \begin{cases} \dfrac{\delta(r - r_0)\delta(\phi)}{2\pi r^2 \sin\phi} & z_0 > 0 \\[3mm] \dfrac{\delta(r - r_0)\delta(\phi + \pi)}{2\pi r^2 \sin\phi} & z_0 < 0 \end{cases} \tag{11a}$$

and

$$\delta(x)\delta(y)\delta(z) = \frac{\delta(r)}{4\pi r^2}. \tag{11b}$$

Boundary value problems are associated with elliptic PDEs. We consider only two types in this chapter, those associated with the Helmholtz and Poisson's equations. The two-dimensional Helmholtz equation is

$$\nabla^2 u + k^2 u = F(x, y), \qquad (x, y) \text{ in } A, \tag{12}$$

where A is some open region of the xy-plane (with a piecewise smooth boundary), and Poisson's equation is

$$\nabla^2 u = F(x, y), \qquad (x, y) \text{ in } A. \tag{13}$$

Green's (second) identity for both of these operators states that for functions $u(x, y)$ and $v(x, y)$ that have continuous first partial derivatives and piecewise continuous second partials in A,

$$\iint_A (v\nabla^2 u - u\nabla^2 v)\, dA = \oint_{\beta(A)} (v\nabla u - u\nabla v) \cdot \hat{\mathbf{n}}\, ds, \qquad (14a)$$

where $\hat{\mathbf{n}}$ is the unit outward normal vector to the boundary $\beta(A)$ of A (see Appendix C). This identity is also valid when $u(x, y)$ and/or $v(x, y)$ satisfy the PDEs $\nabla^2 u + k^2 u = \delta(x - X, y - Y)$ or $\nabla^2 u = \delta(x - X, y - Y)$. These extensions parallel those in Theorems 4 and 5 in Chapter 11 for Green's formulas.

The three-dimensional version of Green's identity is

$$\iiint_V (v\nabla^2 u - u\nabla^2 v)\, dV = \iint_{\beta(V)} (v\nabla u - u\nabla v) \cdot \hat{\mathbf{n}}\, dS, \qquad (14b)$$

where V is a volume in space with piecewise smooth boundary $\beta(V)$. It is also valid when either $u(x, y, z)$ or $v(x, y, z)$ satisfies PDE $\nabla^2 u + k^2 u = \delta(x - X, y - Y, z - Z)$ or PDE $\nabla^2 u = \delta(x - X, y - Y, z - Z)$.

12.2 Green's Functions for Dirichlet Boundary Value Problems

Dirichlet problems for the two-dimensional Helmholtz equation take the form

$$Lu = \nabla^2 u + k^2 u = F(x, y), \qquad (x, y) \text{ in } A, \qquad (15a)$$

$$u(x, y) = K(x, y), \qquad (x, y) \text{ on } \beta(A). \qquad (15b)$$

For $k = 0$, we have the special case of Poisson's equation. When $F(x, y)$ has continuous first derivatives and piecewise continuous second derivatives in A, as does $K(x, y)$ on $\beta(A)$, problem (15) has a unique solution. A simplified example was discussed in Section 5.6 [see problem (74)]. In practical situations when $F(x, y)$ and $K(x, y)$ may not satisfy these conditions, verification of uniqueness is much more difficult, as is finding the solution by previous methods. Green's functions are an excellent alternative.

We define the Green's function $G(x, y; X, Y)$ for problem (15) as the solution of

$$LG = \nabla^2 G + k^2 G = \delta(x - X, y - Y), \qquad (x, y) \text{ in } A, \qquad (16a)$$

$$G(x, y; X, Y) = 0, \qquad (x, y) \text{ on } \beta(A). \qquad (16b)$$

It is the solution of (15) due to a unit point source at (X, Y) when boundary conditions are homogeneous. It is straightforward, then, to prove that the function

$$u(x, y) = \iint_A G(x, y; X, Y) F(X, Y)\, dA \qquad (17)$$

satisfies (15a) (since integrations with respect to X and Y may be interchanged with differentiations with respect to x and y). Additional terms must be added to (17) in order to account for the nonhomogeneity $K(x, y)$ in boundary condition (15b). But clearly, $u(x, y) = 0$ on $\beta(A)$. In other words, when $G(x, y; X, Y)$ is the Green's function for (15), the function $u(x, y)$ in (17) satisfies

$$Lu = \nabla^2 u + k^2 u = F(x, y), \qquad (x, y) \text{ in } A, \tag{18a}$$

$$u(x, y) = 0, \qquad (x, y) \text{ on } \beta(A). \tag{18b}$$

For boundary value problems associated with ODEs, we derived general formulas [equations (28) and (29) in Chapter 11] for Green's functions. This was possible because boundaries for ODEs consist of two points. For PDEs, boundaries consist of curves for two-dimensional problems and surfaces for three-dimensional problems. As a result, it is impossible to find formulas for Green's functions associated with multivariable boundary value problems. At best, we can hope to develop general techniques useful in large classes of problems. We illustrate some of these methods in this section. Before doing so, however, notice that if we substitute $u = G(x, y; X, Y)$ and $v = G(x, y; R, S)$ into Green's identity (14a),

$$\iint_A [G(x, y; R, S)\nabla^2 G(x, y; X, Y) - G(x, y; X, Y)\nabla^2 G(x, y; R, S)] \, dA = 0$$

[since $G(x, y; R, S)$ and $G(x, y; X, Y)$ satisfy boundary condition (16b)]. But because G is a solution of PDE (16a), we may write

$$\begin{aligned}
0 &= \iint_A \{G(x, y; R, S)[\delta(x - X, y - Y) - k^2 G(x, y; X, Y)] \\
&\quad - G(x, y; X, Y)[\delta(x - R, y - S) - k^2 G(x, y; R, S)]\} \, dA \\
&= G(X, Y; R, S) - G(R, S; X, Y).
\end{aligned}$$

In other words, the Green's function is symmetric under an interchange of first and second variables with third and fourth:

$$G(x, y; X, Y) = G(X, Y; x, y). \tag{19}$$

This result is also valid when boundary condition (15b) is replaced by either a Neumann or a Robin condition.

We now illustrate four techniques for finding Green's functions.

Full Eigenfunction Expansion

In this method, the Green's function is expanded in terms of orthonormal eigenfunctions of the associated eigenvalue problem

$$Lu + \lambda^2 u = 0, \qquad (x, y) \text{ in } A, \tag{20a}$$

$$u = 0, \qquad (x, y) \text{ on } \beta(A). \tag{20b}$$

We illustrate with the following example.

Example 1:   Find the Green's function associated with the Dirichlet problem for the two-dimensional Laplacian on a rectangle $A: 0 \le x \le L, 0 \le y \le L'$.

Solution: Separation of variables on

$$\nabla^2 u + \lambda^2 u = 0, \qquad (x, y) \text{ in } A, \qquad \text{(21a)}$$

$$u = 0, \qquad (x, y) \text{ on } \beta(A), \qquad \text{(21b)}$$

leads to normalized eigenfunctions

$$u_{mn}(x, y) = \frac{2}{\sqrt{LL'}} \sin \frac{n\pi x}{L} \sin \frac{m\pi y}{L'},$$

corresponding to eigenvalues $\lambda_{mn}^2 = (n\pi/L)^2 + (m\pi/L')^2$ (see Section 5.5). The eigenfunction expansion of $G(x, y; X, Y)$ in terms of these eigenfunctions is

$$G(x, y; X, Y) = \sum_{m=1}^{\infty} \sum_{n=1}^{\infty} c_{mn} u_{mn}(x, y), \qquad \text{(22)}$$

and this representation satisfies the boundary condition that G vanish on the edges of the rectangle. To calculate the coefficients c_{mn}, we substitute (22) into the PDE $\nabla^2 G = \delta(x - X, y - Y)$ for G and expand $\delta(x - X, y - Y)$ in terms of the $u_{mn}(x, y)$:

$$\sum_{m=1}^{\infty} \sum_{n=1}^{\infty} c_{mn} \left(-\frac{n^2 \pi^2}{L^2} - \frac{m^2 \pi^2}{L'^2} \right) u_{mn}(x, y)$$

$$= \delta(x - X, y - Y)$$

$$= \sum_{m=1}^{\infty} \sum_{n=1}^{\infty} \left(\int_0^L \int_0^{L'} \delta(x - X) \delta(y - Y) u_{mn}(x, y) \, dy \, dx \right) u_{mn}(x, y)$$

$$= \sum_{m=1}^{\infty} \sum_{n=1}^{\infty} u_{mn}(X, Y) u_{mn}(x, y).$$

Consequently, $c_{mn} = u_{mn}(X, Y)/(-\lambda_{mn}^2)$, and

$$G(x, y; X, Y) = \sum_{m=1}^{\infty} \sum_{n=1}^{\infty} \frac{u_{mn}(X, Y)}{-\lambda_{mn}^2} u_{mn}(x, y)$$

$$= \frac{-4}{LL'} \sum_{m=1}^{\infty} \sum_{n=1}^{\infty} \frac{1}{\left(\dfrac{n\pi}{L} \right)^2 + \left(\dfrac{m\pi}{L'} \right)^2} \sin \frac{n\pi X}{L} \sin \frac{m\pi Y}{L'} \sin \frac{n\pi x}{L} \sin \frac{m\pi y}{L'}. \qquad \text{(23)}$$

In Exercise 1 it is shown that (23) can also be obtained using Green's identity (14a). This avoids the interchange of the Laplacian and summation operations and the eigenfunction expansion of $\delta(x - X, y - Y)$. ∎

A general formula for full eigenfunction expansions can be found in Exercise 2, but such expansions are of limited calculational utility. First, they are possible only when the eigenvalue problem can be separated, and this requires that the boundary of A consist of coordinate curves (or coordinate surfaces, in three-dimensional problems). Second, in the case in which the full eigenfunction expansion is available, a partial eigenfunction expansion that converges more rapidly is also available.

Partial Eigenfunction Expansion

Like the full eigenfunction expansion, this method requires that region A be bounded by coordinate curves (or coordinate surfaces, in three-dimensional problems). It differs in that separation is considered on the homogeneous problem

$$Lu = 0, \qquad (x, y) \text{ in } A, \tag{24a}$$

$$u = 0, \qquad (x, y) \text{ on } \beta(A), \tag{24b}$$

and is carried out until one variable remains. An eigenfunction expansion for the Green's function is then found in terms of normalized eigenfunctions already determined, with coefficients that are functions of the remaining variable. We illustrate once again with the problem in Example 1.

Example 2:   Find a partial eigenfunction representation for the Green's function of Example 1.

Solution: Separation of variables on

$$\nabla^2 u = 0, \qquad (x, y) \text{ in } A, \tag{25a}$$

$$u = 0, \qquad (x, y) \text{ on } \beta(A), \tag{25b}$$

leads to normalized eigenfunctions $f_n(x) = \sqrt{2/L}\, \sin(n\pi x/L)$. We expand $G(x, y; X, Y)$ in terms of these:

$$G(x, y; X, Y) = \sum_{n=1}^{\infty} a_n(y) f_n(x). \tag{26}$$

In actual fact, coefficients $a_n(y)$ must also be functions of X and Y, but we shall understand this dependence implicitly rather than express it explicitly. To determine the $a_n(y)$, we substitute (26) into the PDE $\nabla^2 G = \delta(x - X, y - Y)$ for G and expand $\delta(x - X, y - Y)$ in terms of the $f_n(x)$:

$$\sum_{n=1}^{\infty} \frac{-n^2\pi^2}{L^2} a_n f_n(x) + \sum_{n=1}^{\infty} \frac{d^2 a_n}{dy^2} f_n(x) = \delta(x - X, y - Y)$$

$$= \sum_{n=1}^{\infty} \left(\int_0^L \delta(x - X, y - Y) f_n(x)\, dx \right) f_n(x)$$

$$= \sum_{n=1}^{\infty} f_n(X) \delta(y - Y) f_n(x).$$

This equation and the boundary conditions $G(x, 0; X, Y) = 0 = G(x, L'; X, Y)$ require the $a_n(y)$ to satisfy

$$\frac{d^2 a_n}{dy^2} - \frac{n^2\pi^2}{L^2} a_n = \delta(y - Y) f_n(X), \qquad 0 < y < L',$$

$$a_n(0) = 0, \qquad a_n(L') = 0.$$

We can solve this boundary value problem most easily by using our theory of Green's functions for ODEs. Since a solution of the homogeneous equation that satisfies the first boundary condition is $\sinh(n\pi y/L)$, and one that satisfies the second is $\sinh[n\pi(L'-y)/L]$, equation (29) in Chapter 11 gives

$$a_n(y) = \frac{1}{J}\left(\sinh\frac{n\pi y}{L}\sinh\frac{n\pi}{L}(L'-Y)H(Y-y) + \sinh\frac{n\pi Y}{L}\sinh\frac{n\pi}{L}(L'-y)H(y-Y)\right),$$

where J is the conjunct of $\sinh(n\pi y/L)$ and $\sinh[n\pi(L'-y)/L]$,

$$J = \frac{1}{f_n(X)}\left[\sinh\frac{n\pi y}{L}\left(\frac{-n\pi}{L}\right)\cosh\frac{n\pi}{L}(L'-y) - \left(\frac{n\pi}{L}\right)\cosh\frac{n\pi y}{L}\sinh\frac{n\pi}{L}(L'-y)\right]$$

$$= -\frac{n\pi\sinh(n\pi L'/L)}{\sqrt{2L}\,\sin(n\pi X/L)}.$$

Thus, an alternative expression to the double-series, full eigenfunction expansion for $G(x, y; X, Y)$ is the single-series, partial eigenfunction expansion

$$G(x, y; X, Y) = \sum_{n=1}^{\infty} \frac{-2\sin\dfrac{n\pi X}{L}\sin\dfrac{n\pi x}{L}}{n\pi\sinh\dfrac{n\pi L'}{L}}\left(\sinh\frac{n\pi y}{L}\sinh\frac{n\pi}{L}(L'-Y)H(Y-y)\right.$$

$$\left. + \sinh\frac{n\pi Y}{L}\sinh\frac{n\pi}{L}(L'-y)H(y-Y)\right)$$

$$= \begin{cases} \displaystyle\sum_{n=1}^{\infty} \frac{-2\sin\dfrac{n\pi X}{L}\sin\dfrac{n\pi x}{L}\sinh\dfrac{n\pi y}{L}\sinh\dfrac{n\pi}{L}(L'-Y)}{n\pi\sinh\dfrac{n\pi L'}{L}} & 0 \le y \le Y \\[3em] \displaystyle\sum_{n=1}^{\infty} \frac{-2\sin\dfrac{n\pi X}{L}\sin\dfrac{n\pi x}{L}\sinh\dfrac{n\pi Y}{L}\sinh\dfrac{n\pi}{L}(L'-y)}{n\pi\sinh\dfrac{n\pi L'}{L}} & Y \le y \le L' \end{cases} \qquad (27)$$

It is clear that we could find an equivalent solution by expanding G in a Fourier sine series in y. The result would be

$$G = \begin{cases} \displaystyle\sum_{n=1}^{\infty} \frac{-2\sin\dfrac{n\pi Y}{L'}\sin\dfrac{n\pi y}{L'}\sinh\dfrac{n\pi x}{L'}\sinh\dfrac{n\pi}{L'}(L-X)}{n\pi\sinh\dfrac{n\pi L}{L'}} & 0 \le x \le X \\[3em] \displaystyle\sum_{n=1}^{\infty} \frac{-2\sin\dfrac{n\pi Y}{L'}\sin\dfrac{n\pi y}{L'}\sinh\dfrac{n\pi X}{L'}\sinh\dfrac{n\pi}{L'}(L-x)}{n\pi\sinh\dfrac{n\pi L}{L'}} & X \le x \le L \end{cases} \qquad (28)$$

A natural question to ask is, when should each of these expressions for $G(x, y; X, Y)$ be used? Since each is a Fourier series [(27) in x and (28) in y], rates of convergence of the series will depend on the relative magnitudes of coefficients. The coefficient of $\sin(n\pi x/L)$ in (27) for $y > Y$ is

$$\frac{-2\sin\dfrac{n\pi X}{L}\sinh\dfrac{n\pi Y}{L}\sinh\dfrac{n\pi}{L}(L'-y)}{n\pi\sinh\dfrac{n\pi L'}{L}},$$

and for large n we may drop the negative exponentials in the hyperbolic functions and approximate this quantity with

$$-\frac{e^{n\pi Y/L}\,e^{n\pi(L'-y)/L}}{n\pi e^{n\pi L'/L}}\sin\frac{n\pi X}{L}=\frac{-1}{n\pi}e^{n\pi(Y-y)/L}\sin\frac{n\pi X}{L}.$$

Similarly, when $y < Y$, the coefficient can, for large n, be approximated by

$$\frac{-1}{n\pi}e^{n\pi(y-Y)/L}\sin\frac{n\pi X}{L}.$$

Corresponding coefficients in (28) are approximated for large n by

$$\frac{-1}{n\pi}e^{-n\pi|X-x|/L'}\sin\frac{n\pi Y}{L'}.$$

It follows that to calculate $G(x, y; X, Y)$ at a value of x that is substantially different from X, it would be wise to use (28), and, conversely, when y is markedly different from Y, (27) would provide faster convergence.

   In addition, when boundary integrals arise for the solution of Dirichlet's problem (15) [and this occurs for nonhomogeneous boundary conditions (15b)], it is advantageous to use (27) for integrations along $y = 0$ and $y = L'$ but use (28) along $x = 0$ and $x = L$.   ∎

Splitting Technique

Sometimes it is convenient to separate G into two parts, $G = U + g$, where U contains the singular part of G due to the delta function in (16a) and g guarantees that G satisfies the boundary conditions associated with L. This splitting technique permits consideration of the singular nature of the Green's function without the annoyance of boundary conditions. [The technique could have been used for ODEs, but it was unnecessary because formulas (28) and (29) in Chapter 11 were presented for Green's functions.] To be more specific, for the Green's function satisfying (16), we set $G = U + g$, where $U(x, y; X, Y)$ satisfies the PDE

$$LU = \delta(x - X, y - Y) \tag{29}$$

and g satisfies the boundary value problem

$$Lg = 0, \qquad (x, y) \text{ in } A, \tag{30a}$$

$$g = -U, \qquad (x, y) \text{ on } \beta(A). \tag{30b}$$

Because $U(x, y; X, Y)$ is not required to satisfy boundary conditions, it is often called the *free-space Green's function for the operator L*. Free-space Green's functions for the

Helmholtz, modified Helmholtz, and Laplace operators in two and three dimensions are listed in Table 12.1. Each is singular at the source point (X, Y).

Table 12.1   *Free-Space Green's Functions*

	∇^2 Laplacian	$\nabla^2 + k^2$ Helmholtz	$\nabla^2 - k^2$ Modified Helmholtz
xy-plane	$\dfrac{1}{2\pi}\ln\sqrt{(x-X)^2 + (y-Y)^2}$	$\dfrac{1}{4}Y_0[k\sqrt{(x-X)^2 + (y-Y)^2}]$	$-\dfrac{1}{2\pi}K_0[k\sqrt{(x-X)^2 + (y-Y)^2}]$
xyz-space	$\dfrac{-1}{4\pi\sqrt{(x-X)^2 + (y-Y)^2 + (z-Z)^2}}$	$-\dfrac{e^{ikr}}{4\pi},\ -\dfrac{e^{-ikr}}{4\pi}$	$-\dfrac{e^{kr}}{4\pi r},\ -\dfrac{e^{-kr}}{4\pi r}$

We illustrate the splitting technique in the following example.

Example 3:   Find the Green's function for the Dirichlet problem associated with Laplace's equation on a circle $0 \le r \le r_0$.

Solution: The Green's function associated with the Dirichlet problem for the Laplacian on a circle centered at the origin with radius r_0 satisfies

$$\nabla^2 G = \frac{\delta(r - R)\delta(\theta - \Theta)}{r}, \qquad 0 < r < r_0, \qquad -\pi < \theta \le \pi, \qquad \textbf{(31a)}$$

$$G(r_0, \theta; R, \Theta) = 0, \qquad -\pi < \theta \le \pi. \qquad \textbf{(31b)}$$

The free-space Green's function for the two-dimensional Laplacian with singularity at (R, Θ) is

$$U(r, \theta; R, \Theta) = \frac{1}{2\pi}\ln\sqrt{(r\cos\theta - R\cos\Theta)^2 + (r\sin\theta - R\sin\Theta)^2}$$

$$= \frac{1}{4\pi}\ln[r^2 + R^2 - 2rR\cos(\theta - \Theta)]$$

(see Table 12.1). When we split G into $G = U + g$, g must satisfy

$$\nabla^2 g = 0, \qquad 0 < r < r_0, \qquad -\pi < \theta \le \pi, \qquad \textbf{(32a)}$$

$$g(r_0, \theta; R, \Theta) = -\frac{1}{4\pi}\ln[r_0^2 + R^2 - 2r_0 R\cos(\theta - \Theta)], \qquad -\pi < \theta \le \pi. \qquad \textbf{(32b)}$$

Separation of variables on the PDE, together with boundedness at $r = 0$, leads to a solution of the form

$$g(r, \theta; R, \Theta) = \frac{a_0}{\sqrt{2\pi}} + \sum_{n=1}^{\infty}\left(a_n r^n \frac{\cos n\theta}{\sqrt{\pi}} + b_n r^n \frac{\sin n\theta}{\sqrt{\pi}}\right)$$

[see equation (33a) in Section 5.3]. Boundary condition (32b) requires that

$$\frac{a_0}{\sqrt{2\pi}} + \sum_{n=1}^{\infty}\left(a_n r_0^n \frac{\cos n\theta}{\sqrt{\pi}} + b_n r_0^n \frac{\sin n\theta}{\sqrt{\pi}}\right) = \frac{-1}{4\pi}\ln[r_0^2 + R^2 - 2r_0 R\cos(\theta - \Theta)]$$

$$= \frac{-1}{4\pi}\ln r_0^2 - \frac{1}{4\pi}\ln\left[1 + \left(\frac{R}{r_0}\right)^2 - 2\left(\frac{R}{r_0}\right)\cos(\theta - \Theta)\right].$$

With the result

$$\sum_{n=1}^{\infty} \frac{\alpha^n \cos n\phi}{n} = -\frac{1}{2}\ln(1 + \alpha^2 - 2\alpha \cos \phi) \qquad (|\alpha| < 1), \tag{33}$$

we may write

$$\frac{a_0}{\sqrt{2\pi}} + \sum_{n=1}^{\infty} \left(a_n r_0^n \frac{\cos n\theta}{\sqrt{\pi}} + b_n r_0^n \frac{\sin n\theta}{\sqrt{\pi}} \right)$$

$$= \frac{-1}{4\pi}\ln r_0^2 + \frac{1}{2\pi}\sum_{n=1}^{\infty} \frac{(R/r_0)^n}{n}\cos n(\theta - \Theta)$$

$$= \frac{-1}{4\pi}\ln r_0^2 + \frac{1}{2\pi}\sum_{n=1}^{\infty} \frac{(R/r_0)^n}{n}(\cos n\theta \cos n\Theta + \sin n\theta \sin n\Theta).$$

Comparison of coefficients requires that

$$\frac{a_0}{\sqrt{2\pi}} = \frac{-1}{4\pi}\ln r_0^2, \qquad \frac{a_n r_0^n}{\sqrt{\pi}} = \frac{(R/r_0)^n}{2\pi n}\cos n\Theta, \qquad \frac{b_n r_0^n}{\sqrt{\pi}} = \frac{(R/r_0)^n}{2\pi n}\sin n\Theta,$$

and therefore

$$g(r, \theta; R, \Theta) = \frac{-1}{2\pi}\ln r_0 + \sum_{n=1}^{\infty} r^n \left(\frac{(R/r_0)^n}{2\pi n r_0^n}\cos n\theta \cos n\Theta + \frac{(R/r_0)^n}{2\pi n r_0^n}\sin n\theta \sin n\Theta \right)$$

$$= \frac{-1}{2\pi}\ln r_0 + \frac{1}{2\pi}\sum_{n=1}^{\infty} \frac{(rR/r_0^2)^n}{n}\cos n(\theta - \Theta).$$

But identity (33) permits evaluation of this series in closed form:

$$g(r, \theta; R, \Theta) = \frac{-1}{2\pi}\ln r_0 - \frac{1}{4\pi}\ln\left[1 + \left(\frac{rR}{r_0^2}\right)^2 - 2\left(\frac{rR}{r_0^2}\right)\cos(\theta - \Theta) \right]$$

$$= \frac{1}{2\pi}\ln r_0 - \frac{1}{4\pi}\ln\left[r_0^4 + R^2 r^2 - 2r_0^2 Rr \cos(\theta - \Theta) \right].$$

Finally,

$$G(r, \theta; R, \Theta) = U + g = \frac{1}{4\pi}\ln\left[r^2 + R^2 - 2Rr\cos(\theta - \Theta) \right] + \frac{1}{2\pi}\ln r_0$$

$$- \frac{1}{4\pi}\ln[r_0^4 + R^2 r^2 - 2r_0^2 Rr \cos(\theta - \Theta)]. \tag{34}$$

This result is also obtained with a partial eigenfunction expansion in Exercise 13. ∎

The splitting technique points out a distinct difference between Green's functions for one-dimensional problems and those for multidimensional problems. Green's function $g(x; X)$ for a one-dimensional boundary value problem (associated with a second-order ODE) is a continuous function of x (or can be made so) with a jump discontinuity in its first derivative. Green's functions for multidimensional boundary value problems can always be represented as the sum of a free-space Green's function U

and a regular part g, and, according to Table 12.1, free-space Green's functions are always singular at the source point. Thus, multivariable Green's functions always have discontinuities at source points.

Method of Images

The method of images is simply physical reasoning and intelligent guesswork in arriving at the function g in the splitting technique, and as such it works only on Laplace's equation with very simple geometries. When the Green's function G for a domain A is split into $U + g$, the free-space Green's function U can be regarded as the potential due to a unit point source interior to A. This source, by itself, induces an undesirable potential on $\beta(A)$. What is needed is a source distribution exterior to A whose potential g will cancel the effect of U on $\beta(A)$. (The fact that this distribution is exterior to A guarantees that $G = U + g$ satisfies $\nabla^2 G = \delta$ interior to A.)

We illustrate with the following three-dimensional problem.

Example 4:   Find the Green's function associated with the three-dimensional Dirichlet problem in a sphere of radius r_0.

Solution: The Green's function satisfies

$$\nabla^2 G = \frac{\delta(r - R)\delta(\theta - \Theta)\delta(\phi - \Phi)}{r^2 \sin \phi}, \qquad 0 < r < r_0,$$

$$-\pi < \theta \le \pi, \qquad 0 < \phi < \pi, \tag{35a}$$

$$G(r_0, \theta, \phi; R, \Theta, \Phi) = 0, \qquad -\pi < \theta \le \pi, \qquad 0 < \phi < \pi. \tag{35b}$$

According to Table 12.1, the free-space Green's function with source point (X, Y, Z) is $-1/[4\pi\sqrt{(x - X)^2 + (y - Y)^2 + (z - Z)^2}]$. When (R, Θ, Φ) are the spherical coordinates of (X, Y, Z), this function becomes

$$U(r, \theta, \phi; R, \Theta, \Phi) = \frac{-1}{4\pi\sqrt{r^2 + R^2 - 2Rr[\cos \phi \cos \Phi + \sin \phi \sin \Phi \cos(\theta - \Theta)]}}.$$

What the method of images suggests is finding a source distribution exterior to the sphere, the potential g for which is such that $G = U + g$ vanishes on $r = r_0$. We might first consider whether a single source of magnitude q at a point $(R^*, \Theta^*, \Phi^*)(R^* > r_0)$ might suffice. Symmetry would suggest that such a source could eliminate U on $r = r_0$, which is symmetric around the line through the origin, and (R, Θ, Φ) (Figure 12.1) only if (R^*, Θ^*, Φ^*) were to lie on the line also. We assume, therefore, that $\Theta^* = \Theta$ and $\Phi^* = \Phi$, in which case the condition that $G = U + g$ vanish on $r = r_0$ is

$$0 = \frac{-1}{4\pi\sqrt{r_0^2 + R^2 - 2r_0 R[\cos \phi \cos \Phi + \sin \phi \sin \Phi \cos(\theta - \Theta)]}}$$

$$+ \frac{-q}{4\pi\sqrt{r_0^2 + R^{*2} - 2r_0 R^*[\cos \phi \cos \Phi + \sin \phi \sin \Phi \cos(\theta - \Theta)]}}$$

or $\quad -q\sqrt{r_0^2 + R^2 - 2r_0R[\cos\phi\cos\Phi + \sin\phi\sin\Phi\cos(\theta - \Theta)]}$
$$= \sqrt{r_0^2 + R^{*2} - 2r_0R^*[\cos\phi\cos\Phi + \sin\phi\sin\Phi\cos(\theta - \Theta)]}.$$

Since this condition must be valid for all ϕ and θ, we set $\phi = 0$ and $\phi = \pi$:

$$-q\sqrt{r_0^2 + R^2 - 2r_0R\cos\Phi} = \sqrt{r_0^2 + R^{*2} - 2r_0R^*\cos\Phi},$$
$$-q\sqrt{r_0^2 + R^2 + 2r_0R\cos\Phi} = \sqrt{r_0^2 + R^{*2} + 2r_0R^*\cos\Phi}.$$

These two equations imply that $R^* = r_0^2/R$ and $q = -r_0/R$, and with these, $U + g$ vanishes identically on $r = r_0$. Thus, the Green's function for the Laplacian inside a sphere of radius r_0 is

$$G(r, \theta, \phi; R, \Theta, \Phi) = \frac{-1}{4\pi\sqrt{r^2 + R^2 - 2Rr[\cos\phi\cos\Phi + \sin\phi\sin\Phi\cos(\theta - \Theta)]}}$$

$$+ \frac{r_0}{4\pi R\sqrt{r^2 + \left(\dfrac{r_0^2}{R}\right)^2 - 2r\left(\dfrac{r_0^2}{R}\right)[\cos\phi\cos\Phi + \sin\phi\sin\Phi\cos(\theta - \Theta)]}}$$

$$= \frac{-1}{4\pi\sqrt{r^2 + R^2 - 2Rr[\cos\phi\cos\Phi + \sin\phi\sin\Phi\cos(\theta - \Theta)]}}$$

$$+ \frac{r_0}{4\pi\sqrt{R^2r^2 + r_0^4 - 2r_0^2Rr[\cos\phi\cos\Phi + \sin\phi\sin\Phi\cos(\theta - \Theta)]}}.$$

$$\blacksquare \quad (36)$$

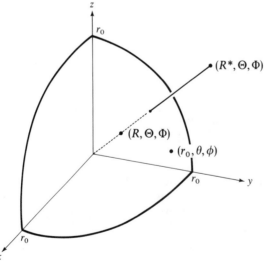

Figure 12.1

Exercises 12.2

1. Show that coefficients c_{mn} in (22) can be obtained by substituting $u = G(x, y; X, Y)$ and $v = u_{mn}(x, y)$ in Green's identity (14a).

2. Show that when $u_n(x, y)$ are orthonormal eigenfunctions of the eigenvalue problem

$$\nabla^2 u + \lambda^2 u = 0, \qquad (x, y) \text{ in } A, \qquad\qquad (37a)$$

$$u = 0, \qquad (x, y) \text{ on } \beta(A), \qquad\qquad (37b)$$

associated with the Dirichlet problem

$$\nabla^2 u = F(x, y), \qquad (x, y) \text{ in } A, \qquad\qquad (38a)$$

$$u = K(x, y), \qquad (x, y) \text{ on } \beta(A), \qquad\qquad (38b)$$

the full eigenfunction expansion for the Green's function is

$$G(x, y; X, Y) = \sum_{n=1}^{\infty} \frac{u_n(X, Y)u_n(x, y)}{-\lambda_n^2}. \qquad\qquad (39)$$

(This expansion should be compared with that in Exercise 21 of Section 11.3 for the Green's function of an ODE.)

In Exercises 3–8, use Exercise 2 (and its extension to three dimensions) to find full eigenfunction expansions for the Green's function associated with the Dirichlet problem for Poisson's equation on the given domain.

3. $0 \le r < r_0, \quad -\pi < \theta \le \pi$
4. $0 \le r < r_0, \quad 0 < \theta < \pi$

5. $0 \le r < r_0, \quad 0 < \theta < L$
6. $0 < x < L, \quad 0 < y < L', \quad 0 < z < L''$

7. $0 \le r < r_0, \quad -\pi < \theta \le \pi, \quad 0 < z < L$
8. $0 \le r < r_0, \quad -\pi < \theta \le \pi, \quad 0 \le \phi \le \pi$

9. Use the method of images and the result of Example 4 to find the Green's function for the Dirichlet problem associated with Poisson's equation in a hemisphere of radius r_0.

10. Use a "modified" method of images to find the Green's function for the Dirichlet problem associated with the two-dimensional Laplacian on a circle of radius r_0. Assume that g consists of a potential due to an exterior, negative unit point source plus a constant potential.

11. Use the result of Exercise 10 and the method of images to find the Green's function for the Dirichlet problem associated with Poisson's equation on a semicircle $0 < r < r_0, 0 < \theta < \pi$. How does it compare with the representation in Exercise 4?

12. Use the method of images to find an expression for the Green's function of the Dirichlet problem for the Laplacian on the rectangle $0 < x < L, 0 < y < L'$.

13. In this exercise we use a partial eigenfunction expansion to find Green's function (34) for problem (31).

(a) Show that the partial eigenfunction expansion for $G(r, \theta; R, \Theta)$ is

$$G(r, \theta; R, \Theta) = \frac{a_0(r)}{\sqrt{2\pi}} + \sum_{n=1}^{\infty} \left(a_n(r) \frac{\cos n\theta}{\sqrt{\pi}} + b_n(r) \frac{\sin n\theta}{\sqrt{\pi}} \right).$$

(b) Substitute the expansion in (a) into PDE (31a), and expand $\delta(r - R)\delta(\theta - \Theta)/r$ in a Fourier series to obtain the following boundary value problems for the coefficients:

$$\frac{d}{dr}\left(r \frac{da_0}{dr} \right) = \frac{\delta(r - R)}{\sqrt{2\pi}}, \qquad a_0(r_0) = 0;$$

$$\frac{d}{dr}\left(r \frac{da_n}{dr} \right) - \frac{n^2}{r} a_n = \delta(r - R) \frac{\cos n\theta}{\sqrt{\pi}}, \qquad a_n(r_0) = 0;$$

$$\frac{d}{dr}\left(r \frac{db_n}{dr} \right) - \frac{n^2}{r} b_n = \delta(r - R) \frac{\sin n\theta}{\sqrt{\pi}}, \qquad b_n(r_0) = 0.$$

(c) The systems in (b) are "singular" in the sense that there is only one boundary condition and the coefficient r in the derivative term vanishes at $r = 0$. As a result, equations (28) and (29) in Chapter 11 cannot be used to find a_n and b_n. Instead, use properties (21a–c) from Chapter 11 and the one boundary condition to show that

$$
a_0(r) = \begin{cases} \dfrac{\ln(R/r_0)}{\sqrt{2\pi}} & 0 \le r \le R \\[3mm] \dfrac{\ln(r/r_0)}{\sqrt{2\pi}} & R \le r \le r_0 \end{cases},
$$

$$
a_n(r) = \begin{cases} \dfrac{\cos n\Theta}{2\sqrt{\pi n}}\left[\left(\dfrac{rR}{r_0^2}\right)^n - \left(\dfrac{r}{R}\right)^n\right] & 0 \le r \le R \\[4mm] \dfrac{\cos n\Theta}{2\sqrt{\pi n}}\left[\left(\dfrac{rR}{r_0^2}\right)^n - \left(\dfrac{R}{r}\right)^n\right] & R \le r \le r_0 \end{cases},
$$

$$
b_n(r) = \begin{cases} \dfrac{\sin n\Theta}{2\sqrt{\pi n}}\left[\left(\dfrac{rR}{r_0^2}\right)^n - \left(\dfrac{r}{R}\right)^n\right] & 0 \le r \le R \\[4mm] \dfrac{\sin n\Theta}{2\sqrt{\pi n}}\left[\left(\dfrac{rR}{r_0^2}\right)^n - \left(\dfrac{R}{r}\right)^n\right] & R \le r \le r_0 \end{cases}.
$$

(d) Find $G(r, \theta; R, \Theta)$ and use (33) to reduce the function to the form in (34).

14. Use the technique of Exercise 13 to find a partial eigenfunction expansion for the Green's function of the Dirichlet problem for the Laplacian on the semicircle $0 < r < r_0$, $0 < \theta < \pi$. Show that it can be expressed in the form of Exercise 11.

15. Use the technique of Exercise 13 to find the partial eigenfunction expansion for the Green's function of Exercise 5.

16. Find a partial eigenfunction expansion for the Green's function of Exercise 6 using eigenfunctions in x and y.

17. Show that when $u_n(x, y)$ are orthonormal eigenfunctions of eigenvalue problem (20), the full eigenfunction expansion for the Green's function of the boundary value problem

$$
\nabla^2 u + k^2 u = F(x, y), \qquad (x, y) \text{ in } A, \tag{40a}
$$

$$
u = K(x, y), \qquad (x, y) \text{ on } \beta(A), \tag{40b}
$$

is

$$
G(x, y; X, Y) = \sum_{n=1}^{\infty} \frac{u_n(X, Y)u_n(x, y)}{k^2 - \lambda_n^2}, \tag{41}
$$

provided $k \ne \lambda_n$ for any n. (The exceptional case is discussed in Exercise 8 of Section 12.3.)

In Exercises 18–24, use Exercise 17 to state Green's functions for problem (40) on the given domain. (See Example 1 and Exercises 3–8 for eigenpairs.)

18. $0 < x < L$, $\quad 0 < y < L'$

19. $0 \le r < r_0$, $\quad -\pi < \theta \le \pi$

20. $0 \le r < r_0$, $\quad 0 < \theta < \pi$

21. $0 < r < r_0$, $\quad 0 < \theta < L$

22. $0 < x < L$, $\quad 0 < y < L'$, $\quad 0 < z < L''$

23. $0 \le r < r_0$, $\quad -\pi < \theta \le \pi$, $\quad 0 < z < L$

24. $0 \le r < r_0$, $\quad -\pi < \theta \le \pi$, $\quad 0 \le \phi \le \pi$

12.3 Solutions of Dirichlet Boundary Value Problems on Finite Regions

In this section we use Green's functions to solve Dirichlet boundary value problems associated with Poisson's equation on finite regions. Identical results for the Helmholtz equation are discussed in the exercises.

The Dirichlet boundary value problem for Poisson's equation in two dimensions is

$$\nabla^2 u = F(x, y), \qquad (x, y) \text{ in } A, \qquad\qquad \textbf{(42a)}$$

$$u = K(x, y), \qquad (x, y) \text{ on } \beta(A), \qquad\qquad \textbf{(42b)}$$

where A is a region with finite area. When $K(x, y) \equiv 0$, the solution is given by integral (17). The following theorem indicates that a line integral involving the normal derivative of $G(x, y; X, Y)$ incorporates nonzero $K(x, y)$.

Theorem 1

When $G(x, y; X, Y)$ is the Green's function for Dirichlet problem (42), the solution to (42) is

$$u(x, y) = \iint_A G(x, y; X, Y) F(X, Y) \, dA + \oint_{\beta(A)} K(X, Y) \frac{\partial G(x, y; X, Y)}{\partial N} \, ds, \qquad \textbf{(43)}$$

where $\partial G / \partial N$ is the outward normal derivative of G with respect to the (X, Y) variables.

Proof: If in Green's identity (14a) we let $u = G(x, y; X, Y)$ and $v = u(x, y)$ be the solution of (42),

$$\iint_A (u \nabla^2 G - G \nabla^2 u) \, dA = \oint_{\beta(A)} (u \nabla G - G \nabla u) \cdot \hat{\mathbf{n}} \, ds.$$

Because $\nabla^2 u = F$ and $\nabla^2 G = \delta(x - X, y - Y)$ in A, and $u = K$ and $G = 0$ on $\beta(A)$,

$$\iint_A [u(x, y)\delta(x - X, y - Y) - G(x, y; X, Y) F(x, y)] \, dA$$

$$= \oint_{\beta(A)} K(x, y) \nabla G(x, y; X, Y) \cdot \hat{\mathbf{n}} \, ds$$

or $$u(X, Y) = \iint_A G(x, y; X, Y) F(x, y) \, dy \, dx + \oint_{\beta(A)} K(x, y) \frac{\partial G(x, y; X, Y)}{\partial n} \, ds.$$

When we interchange (x, y) and (X, Y),

$$u(x, y) = \iint_A G(X, Y; x, y) F(X, Y) \, dY \, dX + \oint_{\beta(A)} K(X, Y) \frac{\partial G(X, Y; x, y)}{\partial N} \, ds$$

$$= \iint_A G(x, y; X, Y) F(X, Y) \, dY \, dX + \oint_{\beta(A)} K(X, Y) \frac{\partial G(x, y; X, Y)}{\partial N} \, ds$$

[because $G(x, y; X, Y)$ is symmetric.]   ∎

It is often helpful to interpret the integral terms in (43) physically. From an electrostatic point of view, problem (42) defines potential in a region A due to an area charge density determined by $F(x, y)$ and a boundary potential $K(x, y)$. (In actual fact, we are considering any cross section of a z-symmetric three-dimensional problem.) The area integral in (43) represents that part of the potential due to the interior charge, and the line integral is the boundary potential contribution. The Green's function $G(x, y; X, Y)$ is the potential at (x, y) due to a unit charge at (X, Y) when the boundary potential on $\beta(A)$ vanishes (which would be the case, say, for a grounded metallic surface). The double integral superposes over all elemental contributions $G(x, y; X, Y)F(X, Y)\,dY\,dX$ of internal charge.

From a heat conduction point of view, problem (42) describes steady-state temperature in a region A due to internal heat generation determined by $F(x, y)$ and boundary temperature $K(x, y)$. The area integral in (43) represents that part of the temperature due to internal sources. The Green's function is the temperature at (x, y) due to a unit source at (X, Y) when the boundary temperature is made to vanish. The line integral represents the effect of imposed boundary temperatures.

Finally, problem (42) also describes static deflections of a membrane stretched tautly over A. The double integral represents the effect due to applied forces [contained in $F(x, y)$], and the line integral determines the effect of boundary displacements.

We noted in Section 12.2 that $G(x, y; X, Y)$ is not continuous; it has a singularity when $(x, y) = (X, Y)$. The discontinuity cannot be too severe, however, since existence of the area integral in (43) (which integrates over the singularity) is guaranteed by Theorem 2. To illustrate this point, suppose A is the circle $r < r_0$ and $K = 0$ on $\beta(A)$. According to (43), the solution to problem (42) at any point (r, θ) in this case is

$$u(r, \theta) = \iint_A G(r, \theta; R, \Theta)F(R, \Theta)\,dA.$$

For simplicity, we consider the origin, in which case

$$u(0, \theta) = \iint_A G(0, \theta; R, \Theta)F(R, \Theta)\,dA.$$

Using equation (34) for $G(r, \theta; R, \Theta)$,

$$u(0, \theta) = \iint_A \frac{1}{2\pi}\ln\left(\frac{R}{r_0}\right)F(R, \Theta)\,dA,$$

and indeed we can see that $\ln(R/r_0)$ is singular at $R = 0$. However, the area element $dA = R\,dR\,d\Theta$ effectively removes this singularity, and

$$u(0, \theta) = \int_{-\pi}^{\pi}\int_0^{r_0} \frac{1}{2\pi}\ln\left(\frac{R}{r_0}\right)F(R, \Theta)R\,dR\,d\Theta$$

must converge. In particular, if $F(R, \Theta) \equiv 1$, integration by parts gives

$$u(0, \theta) = \frac{1}{2\pi}\int_{-\pi}^{\pi}\int_0^{r_0} R\ln\left(\frac{R}{r_0}\right)dR\,d\Theta = -\frac{r_0^2}{4}.$$

For three-dimensional problems

$$\nabla^2 u = F(x, y, z), \qquad (x, y, z) \text{ in } V, \tag{44a}$$

$$u = K(x, y, z), \qquad (x, y, z) \text{ on } \beta(V), \tag{44b}$$

the solution is

$$u(x, y, z) = \iiint_V G(x, y, z; X, Y, Z) F(X, Y, Z) \, dV$$

$$+ \iint_{\beta(V)} K(X, Y, Z) \frac{\partial G(x, y, z; X, Y, Z)}{\partial N} \, dS. \tag{45}$$

We now consider some examples.

Example 5:   Solve the boundary value problem

$$\nabla^2 u = F(r, \theta), \qquad 0 < r < r_0, \qquad -\pi < \theta \le \pi, \tag{46a}$$

$$u(r_0, \theta) = K(\theta), \qquad -\pi < \theta \le \pi. \tag{46b}$$

Solution: According to (43), the solution can be represented in the form

$$u(r, \theta) = \iint_A G(r, \theta; R, \Theta) F(R, \Theta) \, dA + \oint_{\beta(A)} K(\Theta) \frac{\partial G(r, \theta; r_0, \Theta)}{\partial R} \, ds,$$

where $G(r, \theta; R, \Theta)$ is the Green's function

$$G(r, \theta; R, \Theta) = \frac{1}{4\pi} \ln \left(r_0^2 \frac{r^2 + R^2 - 2rR \cos(\theta - \Theta)}{r_0^4 + r^2 R^2 - 2r_0^2 rR \cos(\theta - \Theta)} \right)$$

[see equation (34)]. Now,

$$\frac{\partial G(r, \theta; r_0, \Theta)}{\partial R} = \frac{1}{4\pi} \left(\frac{2R - 2r \cos(\theta - \Theta)}{r^2 + R^2 - 2rR \cos(\theta - \Theta)} - \frac{2r^2 R - 2r_0^2 r \cos(\theta - \Theta)}{r_0^4 + r^2 R^2 - 2r_0^2 Rr \cos(\theta - \Theta)} \right)_{|R = r_0}$$

$$= \frac{1}{4\pi} \left(\frac{2r_0 - 2r \cos(\theta - \Theta)}{r^2 + r_0^2 - 2rr_0 \cos(\theta - \Theta)} - \frac{2r^2 r_0 - 2r_0^2 r \cos(\theta - \Theta)}{r_0^4 + r^2 r_0^2 - 2r_0^3 r \cos(\theta - \Theta)} \right)$$

$$= \frac{1}{2\pi r_0} \frac{r_0^2 - r^2}{r^2 + r_0^2 - 2r_0 r \cos(\theta - \Theta)}.$$

Thus,

$$u(r, \theta) = \iint_A G(r, \theta; R, \Theta) F(R, \Theta) \, dA + \int_{-\pi}^{\pi} K(\Theta) \frac{r_0^2 - r^2}{2\pi r_0 [r^2 + r_0^2 - 2r_0 r \cos(\theta - \Theta)]} r_0 \, d\Theta$$

$$= \iint_A G(r, \theta; R, \Theta) F(R, \Theta) \, dA + \frac{r_0^2 - r^2}{2\pi} \int_{-\pi}^{\pi} \frac{K(\Theta)}{r^2 + r_0^2 - 2r_0 r \cos(\theta - \Theta)} \, d\Theta. \tag{47}$$

When $F(r, \theta) \equiv 0$, the solution of Laplace's equation is

$$u(r, \theta) = \frac{r_0^2 - r^2}{2\pi} \int_{-\pi}^{\pi} \frac{K(\Theta)}{r^2 + r_0^2 - 2r_0 r \cos(\theta - \Theta)} d\Theta,$$

Poisson's integral formula for a circle [see equation (36) in Section 5.3].   ∎

Example 6:   Solve the following Dirichlet problem:

$$\nabla^2 u = F(x, y), \qquad 0 < x < L, \qquad 0 < y < L', \tag{48a}$$

$$u(x, 0) = f(x), \qquad 0 < x < L, \tag{48b}$$

$$u(L, y) = 0, \qquad 0 < y < L', \tag{48c}$$

$$u(x, L') = 0, \qquad 0 < x < L, \tag{48d}$$

$$u(0, y) = g(y), \qquad 0 < y < L'. \tag{48e}$$

Solution: The solution can be represented in the form

$$u(x, y) = \iint_A G(x, y; X, Y) F(X, Y) \, dA + \int_0^L -f(X) \frac{\partial G(x, y; X, 0)}{\partial Y} dX$$

$$+ \int_{L'}^0 -g(Y) \frac{\partial G(x, y; 0, Y)}{\partial X} (-dY),$$

where G is given by either (27) or (28). For the first line integral, we use (27) in the form

$$G(x, y; X, Y) = \begin{cases} \displaystyle\sum_{n=1}^{\infty} \frac{-2 \sin \dfrac{n\pi X}{L} \sin \dfrac{n\pi x}{L} \sinh \dfrac{n\pi Y}{L} \sinh \dfrac{n\pi(L' - y)}{L}}{n\pi \sinh \dfrac{n\pi L'}{L}} & 0 \le Y \le y \\[4em] \displaystyle\sum_{n=1}^{\infty} \frac{-2 \sin \dfrac{n\pi X}{L} \sin \dfrac{n\pi x}{L} \sinh \dfrac{n\pi y}{L} \sinh \dfrac{n\pi(L' - y)}{L}}{n\pi \sinh \dfrac{n\pi L'}{L}} & y \le Y \le L' \end{cases}$$

to calculate

$$\frac{\partial G(x, y; X, 0)}{\partial Y} = \sum_{n=1}^{\infty} \frac{-2 \sin \dfrac{n\pi X}{L} \sin \dfrac{n\pi x}{L} \left(\dfrac{n\pi}{L}\right) \sinh \dfrac{n\pi(L' - y)}{L}}{n\pi \sinh \dfrac{n\pi L'}{L}}.$$

A similar calculation using (28) gives

$$\frac{\partial G(x, y; 0, Y)}{\partial X} = \sum_{n=1}^{\infty} \frac{-2 \sin \dfrac{n\pi Y}{L'} \sin \dfrac{n\pi y}{L'} \left(\dfrac{n\pi}{L'}\right) \sinh \dfrac{n\pi(L - x)}{L'}}{n\pi \sinh \dfrac{n\pi L}{L'}},$$

and therefore

$$u(x, y) = \iint_A G(x, y; X, Y) F(X, Y) \, dA$$

$$- \int_0^L f(X) \left(\sum_{n=1}^\infty \frac{-2 \sin \dfrac{n\pi X}{L} \sin \dfrac{n\pi x}{L} \left(\dfrac{n\pi}{L} \right) \sinh \dfrac{n\pi}{L}(L' - y)}{n\pi \sinh \dfrac{n\pi L'}{L}} \right) dX$$

$$- \int_0^{L'} g(Y) \left(\sum_{n=1}^\infty \frac{-2 \sin \dfrac{n\pi Y}{L'} \sin \dfrac{n\pi y}{L'} \left(\dfrac{n\pi}{L'} \right) \sinh \dfrac{n\pi}{L'}(L - x)}{n\pi \sinh \dfrac{n\pi L}{L'}} \right) dY$$

$$= \int_0^{L'} \int_0^L G(x, y; X, Y) F(X, Y) \, dX \, dY$$

$$+ \frac{2}{L} \sum_{n=1}^\infty \frac{\sin \dfrac{n\pi x}{L} \sinh \dfrac{n\pi(L' - y)}{L}}{\sinh \dfrac{n\pi L'}{L}} \int_0^L f(X) \sin \frac{n\pi X}{L} \, dX$$

$$+ \frac{2}{L'} \sum_{n=1}^\infty \frac{\sin \dfrac{n\pi y}{L'} \sinh \dfrac{n\pi(L - x)}{L'}}{\sinh \dfrac{n\pi L}{L'}} \int_0^{L'} g(Y) \sin \frac{n\pi Y}{L'} \, dY. \qquad \blacksquare \quad (49)$$

Special cases of this problem that lead to solutions found in previous chapters are contained in Exercises 1 and 2.

Example 7:   Solve the following Dirichlet problem on a sphere:

$$\nabla^2 u = F(r, \theta, \phi), \qquad 0 < r < r_0, \qquad -\pi < \theta \leq \pi, \qquad 0 < \phi < \pi, \quad (50a)$$
$$u(r_0, \theta, \phi) = K(\theta, \phi), \qquad -\pi < \theta \leq \pi, \qquad 0 \leq \phi \leq \pi. \quad (50b)$$

Solution: The solution can be represented in the form

$$u(r, \theta, \phi) = \iiint_V G(r, \theta, \phi; R, \Theta, \Phi) F(R, \Theta, \Phi) \, dV + \iint_{\beta(V)} K(\Theta, \Phi) \frac{\partial G(r, \theta, \phi; r_0, \Theta, \Phi)}{\partial R} \, dS,$$

where the Green's function is contained in equation (36). Since $\partial G(r, \theta, \phi; r_0, \Theta, \Phi)/\partial R$ is equal to

$$\frac{1}{4\pi} \left(\frac{r_0 - r[\cos\phi \cos\Phi + \sin\phi \sin\Phi \cos(\theta - \Theta)]}{[r^2 + r_0^2 - 2rr_0(\cos\phi \cos\Phi + \sin\phi \sin\Phi \cos(\theta - \Theta))]^{3/2}} \right)$$
$$- \frac{r_0}{4\pi} \left(\frac{r_0 r^2 - r_0^2 r[\cos\phi \cos\Phi + \sin\phi \sin\Phi \cos(\theta - \Theta)]}{[r_0^2 r^2 + r_0^4 - 2r_0^3 r(\cos\phi \cos\Phi + \sin\phi \sin\Phi\cos(\theta - \Theta))]^{3/2}} \right)$$

$$= \frac{1}{4\pi} \left(\frac{r_0 - r[\cos\phi\cos\Phi + \sin\phi\sin\Phi\cos(\theta - \Theta)]}{(r^2 + r_0^2 - 2rr_0[\cos\phi\cos\Phi + \sin\phi\sin\Phi\cos(\theta - \Theta)])^{3/2}} \right)$$

$$- \frac{r}{4\pi r_0} \left(\frac{r - r_0[\cos\phi\cos\Phi + \sin\phi\sin\Phi\cos(\theta - \Theta)]}{(r^2 + r_0^2 - 2rr_0[\cos\phi\cos\Phi + \sin\phi\sin\Phi\cos(\theta - \Theta)])^{3/2}} \right)$$

$$= \frac{r_0^2 - r^2}{4\pi r_0(r^2 + r_0^2 - 2rr_0[\cos\phi\cos\Phi + \sin\phi\sin\Phi\cos(\theta - \Theta)])^{3/2}},$$

we find that

$$u(r, \theta, \phi) = \iiint_V G(r, \theta, \phi; R, \Theta, \Phi) F(R, \Theta, \Phi) \, dV$$

$$+ \int_{-\pi}^{\pi} \int_0^{\pi} \frac{(r_0^2 - r^2)K(\Theta, \Phi)r_0^2 \sin\Phi}{4\pi r_0(r^2 + r_0^2 - 2rr_0[\cos\phi\cos\Phi + \sin\phi\sin\Phi\cos(\theta - \Theta)])^{3/2}} \, d\Phi \, d\Theta$$

$$= \iiint_V G(r, \theta, \phi; R, \Theta, \Phi) F(R, \Theta, \Phi) \, dV + \frac{r_0^3 - r^2 r_0}{4\pi}$$

$$\times \int_{-\pi}^{\pi} \int_0^{\pi} \frac{K(\Theta, \Phi)\sin\Phi}{(r^2 + r_0^2 - 2rr_0[\cos\phi\cos\Phi + \sin\phi\sin\Phi\cos(\theta - \Theta)])^{3/2}} \, d\Phi \, d\Theta. \quad (51)$$

■

Exercises 12.3

1. Use the result of Example 6 to solve Exercise 18 in Section 3.2.
2. Use the result of Example 6 to solve Exercise 42 in Section 6.2.
3. Find an integral representation for the solution of the boundary value problem

$$\nabla^2 u = F(x, y), \qquad 0 < x < L, \qquad 0 < y < L',$$
$$u(x, 0) = 0, \qquad 0 < x < L,$$
$$u(L, y) = g(y), \qquad 0 < y < L',$$
$$u(x, L') = f(x), \qquad 0 < x < L,$$
$$u(0, y) = 0, \qquad 0 < y < L'.$$

4. Find an integral representation for the solution of the following Dirichlet problem on a semicircle:

$$\nabla^2 u = F(r, \theta), \qquad 0 < r < r_0, \qquad 0 < \theta < \pi,$$
$$u(r_0, \theta) = f(\theta), \qquad 0 < \theta < \pi,$$
$$u(r, 0) = g_1(r), \qquad 0 < r < r_0,$$
$$u(r, \pi) = g_2(r), \qquad 0 < r < r_0.$$

(See Exercise 11 in Section 12.2 for the Green's function.)

In the remaining exercises we discuss results for the Dirichlet problem associated with the Helmholtz equation

$$(\nabla^2 + k^2)u = F(x, y), \qquad (x, y) \text{ in } A, \tag{52a}$$

$$u(x, y) = K(x, y), \qquad (x, y) \text{ on } \beta(A), \tag{52b}$$

where $k > 0$ is a constant.

5. Verify that (43) is the solution of problem (52) when $G(x, y; X, Y)$ is the Green's function satisfying

$$[\nabla^2 + k^2]G = \delta(x - X, y - Y), \qquad (x, y) \text{ in } A, \tag{53a}$$

$$G = 0, \qquad (x, y) \text{ on } \beta(A). \tag{53b}$$

6. What is the result corresponding to that in Exercise 5 for three-dimensional problems?

The homogeneous Dirichlet problem for the Laplacian

$$\nabla^2 u = 0, \qquad (x, y) \text{ in } A,$$

$$u = 0, \qquad (x, y) \text{ on } \beta(A),$$

has only the trivial solution. The homogeneous Dirichlet problem

$$[\nabla^2 + k^2]u = 0, \qquad (x, y) \text{ in } A,$$

$$u = 0, \qquad (x, y) \text{ on } \beta(A),$$

on the other hand, may have nontrivial solutions. In this case, it is necessary to introduce modified Green's functions. We illustrate this in Exercise 7 and discuss it in general in Exercise 8.

7. (a) Show that when A is the square $0 < x, \ y < L$, $w(x, y) = (2/L)\sin(\pi x/L)\sin(\pi y/L)$ is a (nontrivial) solution of

$$\nabla^2 u + \frac{2\pi^2}{L^2}u = 0, \qquad (x, y) \text{ in } A,$$

$$u = 0, \qquad (x, y) \text{ on } \beta(A).$$

(b) Prove that when the problem

$$\nabla^2 u + \frac{2\pi^2}{L^2}u = F(x, y), \qquad (x, y) \text{ in } A,$$

$$u = 0, \qquad (x, y) \text{ on } \beta(A),$$

has a solution $u(x, y)$, $F(x, y)$ satisfies

$$\int_0^L \int_0^L F(x, y)w(x, y)\,dy\,dx = 0.$$

[The converse is also valid; that is, when $F(x, y)$ satisfies this condition, the nonhomogeneous problem has a solution $u(x, y)$. It is not unique; $u(x, y) + Cw(x, y)$ is also a solution for any constant C.]

(c) Because the delta function does not satisfy the condition in (b), there can be no Green's function satisfying

$$\nabla^2 G + \frac{2\pi^2}{L^2} G = \delta(x - X, y - Y), \qquad (x, y) \text{ in } A,$$

$$G = 0, \qquad (x, y) \text{ on } \beta(A).$$

We therefore introduce a modified Green's function $\bar{G}(x, y; X, Y)$, satisfying

$$\left(\nabla^2 + \frac{2\pi^2}{L^2}\right)\bar{G} = \delta(x - X, y - Y) - w(x, y)w(X, Y), \qquad (x, y) \text{ in } A,$$

$$\bar{G} = 0, \qquad (x, y) \text{ on } \beta(A).$$

Show that the right side of the PDE for $\bar{G}$ satisfies the condition in (b).

(d) Find a partial eigenfunction expansion for $\bar{G}$ in terms of the normalized eigenfunctions $\sqrt{2/L} \sin(n\pi x/L)$.

(e) Find an integral representation for the solution of the boundary value problem in (b) in terms of $F(x, y)$ and $\bar{G}(x, y; X, Y)$.

8. (a) Show that when the homogeneous problem

$$[\nabla^2 + k^2]u = 0, \qquad (x, y) \text{ in } A, \qquad (54a)$$

$$u = 0, \qquad (x, y) \text{ on } \beta(A), \qquad (54b)$$

has nontrivial solutions $w(x, y)$, nonhomogeneous problem (52) has a solution only if $F(x, y)$ and $K(x, y)$ satisfy the condition that for every such solution $w(x, y)$,

$$\iint_A F(x, y)w(x, y)\, dA = -\oint_{\beta(A)} K(x, y)\frac{\partial w(x, y)}{\partial n}\, ds, \qquad (55)$$

where $\partial w/\partial n$ is the derivative of w in the outwardly normal direction to $\beta(A)$. [The converse result is also valid; that is, when (55) is satisfied, (52) has a solution that is unique to an additive term $Cw(x, y)$, C an arbitrary constant.]

(b) Show that the solution of (52) can be expressed in the form

$$u(x, y) = \iint_A \bar{G}(X, Y; x, y)F(X, Y)\, dA$$

$$+ \oint_{\beta(A)} K(X, Y)\frac{\partial \bar{G}(X, Y; x, y)}{\partial N}\, ds + Cw(x, y), \qquad (56)$$

where $\bar{G}(x, y; X, Y)$ is a modified Green's function satisfying

$$[\nabla^2 + k^2]\bar{G} = \delta(x - X, y - Y) - w(x, y)w(X, Y), \qquad (x, y) \text{ in } A, \qquad (57a)$$

$$\bar{G} = 0, \qquad (x, y) \text{ on } \beta(A), \qquad (57b)$$

and $w(x, y)$ is a normalized solution of (54).

12.4 Solutions of Neumann Boundary Value Problems on Finite Regions

The Neumann problem for Poisson's equation

$$\nabla^2 u = F(x, y), \qquad (x, y) \text{ in } A, \tag{58a}$$

$$\frac{\partial u}{\partial n} = K(x, y), \qquad (x, y) \text{ on } \beta(A), \tag{58b}$$

is more difficult to handle than the Dirichlet problem because the corresponding homogeneous problem,

$$\nabla^2 u = 0, \qquad (x, y) \text{ in } A, \tag{59a}$$

$$\frac{\partial u}{\partial n} = 0, \qquad (x, y) \text{ on } \beta(A), \tag{59b}$$

always has nontrivial solutions $u = $ constant. As a result, (58) does not have a unique solution; if $u(x, y)$ is a solution, so also is $u(x, y) + $ constant. The following theorem shows that for there to be a solution of (58) at all, $F(x, y)$ and $K(x, y)$ must satisfy a consistency condition.

Theorem 2
___

Neumann problem (58) has a solution if and only if

$$\iint_A F(x, y) \, dA = \oint_{\beta(A)} K(x, y) \, ds. \tag{60}$$

___

When (58) is a steady-state heat conduction problem, condition (60) implies that heat generated within A must be compensated by heat crossing its boundary. This condition is the two-dimensional analog of condition (61a) in Chapter 11; its necessity is easily established with Green's theorem:

$$\oint_{\beta(A)} K(x, y) \, ds = \oint_{\beta(A)} \frac{\partial u}{\partial n} \, ds = \oint_{\beta(A)} \nabla u \cdot \bar{n} \, ds$$

$$= \iint_A \nabla^2 u \, dA = \iint_A F(x, y) \, dA.$$

According to the following theorem, solutions of Neumann problems can be expressed in terms of modified Green's functions.

Theorem 3
___

When consistency condition (60) is satisfied, the solution of Neumann problem (58) is

$$u(x, y) = \iint_A N(x, y; X, Y) F(X, Y) \, dA - \oint_{\beta(A)} N(x, y; X, Y) K(X, Y) \, ds + C, \tag{61}$$

where C is an arbitrary constant and $N(x, y; X, Y)$ is the symmetric modified Green's function satisfying

$$\nabla^2 N = \delta(x - X, y - Y) - \frac{1}{\text{area }(A)}, \qquad (x, y) \text{ in } A, \tag{62a}$$

$$\frac{\partial N}{\partial n} = 0, \qquad (x, y) \text{ on } \beta(A). \tag{62b}$$

Proof:　In Green's identity (14a) on A, we let $u = N(x, y; X, Y)$ and $v = u(x, y)$, the solution of (58):

$$\iint_A (u\nabla^2 N - N\nabla^2 u)\, dA = \oint_{\beta(A)} (u\nabla N - N\nabla u) \cdot \hat{\mathbf{n}}\, ds.$$

Because $\nabla^2 u = F$ in A, $\nabla^2 N = \delta(x - X, y - Y) - 1/\text{area }(A)$, and $\partial u/\partial n = K$ and $\partial N/\partial n = 0$ on $\beta(A)$,

$$\iint_A \left(u(x, y)\left[\delta(x - X, y - Y) - \frac{1}{\text{area }(A)} \right] - N(x, y; X, Y)F(x, y) \right) dA$$

$$= \oint_{\beta(A)} -N(x, y; X, Y)K(x, y)\, ds$$

or

$$u(X, Y) = \iint_A N(x, y; X, Y)F(x, y)\, dA - \oint_{\beta(A)} N(x, y; X, Y)K(x, y)\, ds + \frac{C_1}{\text{area }(A)},$$

where $C_1 = \iint_A u(x, y)\, dA$. When we interchange (x, y) and (X, Y),

$$u(x, y) = \iint_A N(X, Y; x, y)F(X, Y)\, dA - \oint_{\beta(A)} N(X, Y; x, y)K(X, Y)\, ds + C \tag{63}$$

$$= \iint_A N(x, y; X, Y)F(X, Y)\, dA - \oint_{\beta(A)} N(x, y; X, Y)K(X, Y)\, ds + C,$$

where we have replaced $C_1/\text{area }(A)$ by C, since $u(x, y)$ is unique only to an additive constant.　∎

If the modified Green's function $N(x, y; X, Y)$ is not symmetric, equation (63) must be used for the solution in place of (61).

Solutions to three-dimensional Neumann problems

$$\nabla^2 u = F(x, y, z), \qquad (x, y, z) \text{ in } V, \tag{64a}$$

$$\frac{\partial u}{\partial n} = K(x, y, z), \qquad (x, y, z) \text{ on } \beta(V), \tag{64b}$$

exist if and only if $F(x, y, z)$ and $K(x, y, z)$ satisfy

$$\iiint_V F(x, y, z)\, dV = \iint_{\beta(V)} K(x, y, z)\, dS. \tag{65}$$

When this condition is satisfied, the solution of (64) is

$$u(x, y, z) = \iiint_V N(x, y, z; X, Y, Z) F(X, Y, Z) \, dV$$

$$- \iint_{\beta(V)} N(x, y, z; X, Y, Z) K(X, Y, Z) \, dS + C, \qquad \text{(66)}$$

where C is an arbitrary constant and $N(x, y, z; X, Y, Z)$ is the symmetric modified Green's function satisfying

$$\nabla^2 N = \delta(x - X, y - Y, z - Z) - \frac{1}{\text{volume } (V)}, \qquad (x, y, z) \text{ in } V, \qquad \text{(67a)}$$

$$\frac{\partial N}{\partial n} = 0, \qquad (x, y, z) \text{ on } \beta(V). \qquad \text{(67b)}$$

When $N(x, y, z; X, Y, Z)$ is not symmetric in (x, y, z) and (X, Y, Z), (66) must be replaced by

$$u(x, y, z) = \iiint_V N(X, Y, Z; x, y, z) F(X, Y, Z) \, dV$$

$$- \iint_{\beta(V)} N(X, Y, Z; x, y, z) K(X, Y, Z) \, dS + C. \qquad \text{(68)}$$

As an example, we consider the following Neumann problem on a rectangle.

Example 8:   Use a modified Green's function to solve the boundary value problem

$$\frac{\partial^2 V}{\partial x^2} + \frac{\partial^2 V}{\partial y^2} = 0, \qquad 0 < x < L, \qquad 0 < y < L',$$

$$\frac{\partial V(0, y)}{\partial x} = 0, \qquad 0 < y < L',$$

$$\frac{\partial V(L, y)}{\partial x} = 0, \qquad 0 < y < L',$$

$$\frac{\partial V(x, 0)}{\partial y} = 0, \qquad 0 < x < L,$$

$$\frac{\partial V(x, L')}{\partial y} = f(x), \qquad 0 < x < L.$$

Solution: Modified Green's functions $N(x, y; X, Y)$ for this problem must satisfy

$$\frac{\partial^2 N}{\partial x^2} + \frac{\partial^2 N}{\partial y^2} = \delta(x - X, y - Y) - \frac{1}{LL'}, \qquad 0 < x < L, \qquad 0 < y < L',$$

$$N_x(0, y) = 0, \qquad 0 < y < L',$$
$$N_x(L, y) = 0, \qquad 0 < y < L',$$
$$N_y(x, 0) = 0, \qquad 0 < x < L,$$
$$N_y(x, L') = 0, \qquad 0 < x < L.$$

Substitution of a partial eigenfunction expansion,

$$N(x, y; X, Y) = \sum_{n=0}^{\infty} a_n(y) f_n(x) = \frac{a_0(y)}{\sqrt{L}} + \sum_{n=1}^{\infty} a_n(y) \sqrt{\frac{2}{L}} \cos \frac{n\pi x}{L},$$

into the PDE for $N(x, y; X, Y)$ gives

$$\sum_{n=0}^{\infty} -\frac{n^2\pi^2}{L^2} a_n f_n(x) + \sum_{n=0}^{\infty} \frac{d^2 a_n}{dy^2} f_n(x) = \delta(x - X, y - Y) - \frac{1}{LL'}$$

$$= \sum_{n=0}^{\infty} \left(\int_0^L \left[\delta(x - X)\delta(y - Y) - \frac{1}{LL'} \right] f_n(x)\, dx \right) f_n(x)$$

$$= \frac{1}{\sqrt{L}} \left(\delta(y - Y) - \frac{1}{L'} \right) f_0(x) + \sum_{n=1}^{\infty} f_n(X)\delta(y - Y) f_n(x).$$

This equation, along with the boundary conditions $N_y(x, 0) = 0 = N_y(x, L')$, requires coefficients $a_n(y)$ to satisfy

$$\frac{d^2 a_0}{dy^2} = \frac{1}{\sqrt{L}} \left(\delta(y - Y) - \frac{1}{L'} \right), \qquad 0 < y < L',$$

$$a_0'(0) = a_0'(L') = 0,$$

and, for $n > 0$,

$$\frac{d^2 a_n}{dy^2} - \frac{n^2\pi^2}{L^2} a_n = f_n(X)\delta(y - Y), \qquad 0 < y < L',$$

$$a_n'(0) = a_n'(L') = 0.$$

Since the general solution of the differential equation $d^2 a_n/dy^2 - (n^2\pi^2/L^2)a_n = 0$ is $A \cosh(n\pi y/L) + B \sinh(n\pi y/L)$, we take

$$a_n(y) = \begin{cases} A \cosh\dfrac{n\pi y}{L} + B \sinh\dfrac{n\pi y}{L} & 0 \le y < Y \\[2mm] C \cosh\dfrac{n\pi y}{L} + D \sinh\dfrac{n\pi y}{L} & Y < y \le L' \end{cases}$$

The boundary conditions require that

$$\frac{n\pi}{L} B = 0, \qquad C \sinh\frac{n\pi L'}{L} + D \cosh\frac{n\pi L'}{L} = 0,$$

and continuity conditions (21a, b) from Chapter 11 necessitate that

$$A \cosh\frac{n\pi Y}{L} + B \sinh\frac{n\pi Y}{L} = C \cosh\frac{n\pi Y}{L} + D \sinh\frac{n\pi Y}{L},$$

$$\left(C \sinh\frac{n\pi Y}{L} + D \cosh\frac{n\pi Y}{L} \right) - \left(A \sinh\frac{n\pi Y}{L} + B \cosh\frac{n\pi Y}{L} \right) = \frac{L}{n\pi} f_n(X).$$

These four equations can be solved for

$$A = \frac{-L\cosh\dfrac{n\pi}{L}(L'-Y)f_n(X)}{n\pi\sinh(n\pi L'/L)}, \qquad B = 0, \qquad C = \frac{-L\cosh\dfrac{n\pi L'}{L}\cosh\dfrac{n\pi Y}{L}f_n(X),}{n\pi\sinh(n\pi L'/L)},$$

$$D = \frac{L}{n\pi}\cosh\frac{n\pi Y}{L}f_n(X),$$

and hence

$$a_n(y) = \begin{cases} \dfrac{-L\cosh\dfrac{n\pi}{L}(L'-Y)\cosh\dfrac{n\pi y}{L}f_n(X)}{n\pi\sinh(n\pi L'/L)} & 0 \le y \le Y \\[3ex] \dfrac{-L\cosh\dfrac{n\pi L'}{L}\cosh\dfrac{n\pi Y}{L}\cosh\dfrac{n\pi y}{L}f_n(X)}{n\pi\sinh(n\pi L'/L)} + \dfrac{L\cosh\dfrac{n\pi Y}{L}\sinh\dfrac{n\pi y}{L}f_n(X)}{n\pi} & Y \le y \le L' \end{cases}$$

$$= \begin{cases} \dfrac{-L\cosh\dfrac{n\pi}{L}(L'-Y)\cosh\dfrac{n\pi y}{L}f_n(X)}{n\pi\sinh(n\pi L'/L)} & 0 \le y \le Y \\[3ex] \dfrac{-L\cosh\dfrac{n\pi Y}{L}\cosh\dfrac{n\pi}{L}(L'-y)f_n(X)}{n\pi\sinh(n\pi L'/L)} & Y \le y \le L' \end{cases}$$

Because $-y^2/(2\sqrt{L}L')$ is a solution of $d^2a_0/dy^2 = -1/(\sqrt{L}L')$, we take

$$a_0(y) = \begin{cases} Ay + B - \dfrac{y^2}{2\sqrt{L}\,L'} & 0 \le y < Y \\[3ex] Dy + C - \dfrac{y^2}{2\sqrt{L}\,L'} & Y < y \le L' \end{cases}.$$

Boundary conditions $a_0'(0) = 0 = a_0'(L')$, and continuity conditions (21a, b) from Chapter 11, require that

$$A = 0, \qquad\qquad D - \frac{1}{\sqrt{L}} = 0,$$

$$AY + B = DY + C, \qquad D - A = \frac{1}{\sqrt{L}}.$$

These equations yield $A = 0$, $D = 1/\sqrt{L}$, and $B = Y/\sqrt{L} + C$, where C is arbitrary, and hence

$$a_0(y) = \begin{cases} \dfrac{Y}{\sqrt{L}} + C - \dfrac{y^2}{2\sqrt{L}\,L'} & 0 \le y \le Y \\[3ex] \dfrac{y}{\sqrt{L}} + C - \dfrac{y^2}{2\sqrt{L}\,L'} & Y \le y \le L' \end{cases}.$$

A modified Green's function is therefore

$$N(x, y; X, Y) = \begin{cases} \dfrac{Y}{L} + \dfrac{C}{\sqrt{L}} - \dfrac{y^2}{2LL'} - \displaystyle\sum_{n=1}^{\infty} \dfrac{2\cos\dfrac{n\pi X}{L}\cosh\dfrac{n\pi y}{L}\cosh\dfrac{n\pi(L'-Y)}{L}}{n\pi\sinh(n\pi L'/L)}\cos\dfrac{n\pi x}{L} & 0 \le y \le Y \\[4mm] \dfrac{y}{L} + \dfrac{C}{\sqrt{L}} - \dfrac{y^2}{2LL'} - \displaystyle\sum_{n=1}^{\infty} \dfrac{2\cos\dfrac{n\pi X}{L}\cosh\dfrac{n\pi Y}{L}\cosh\dfrac{n\pi(L'-y)}{L}}{n\pi\sinh(n\pi L'/L)}\cos\dfrac{n\pi x}{L} & Y \le y \le L' \end{cases}.$$

Because $N(x, y; X, Y)$ is not symmetric, we use (63) to express the solution of the original boundary value problem as a line integral along the edge $C': y = L'$,

$$V(x, y) = -\int_{C'} N(X, Y; x, y)f(X)\,ds + D$$
$$= -\int_0^L N(X, L'; x, y)f(X)\,dX + D,$$

where D is an arbitrary constant, and

$$N(X, Y; x, y) = \begin{cases} \dfrac{y}{L} + \dfrac{C}{\sqrt{L}} - \dfrac{Y^2}{2LL'} - \displaystyle\sum_{n=1}^{\infty} \dfrac{2\cos\dfrac{n\pi X}{L}\cosh\dfrac{n\pi Y}{L}\cosh\dfrac{n\pi(L'-y)}{L}}{n\pi\sinh(n\pi L'/L)}\cos\dfrac{n\pi x}{L} & 0 \le Y \le y \\[4mm] \dfrac{Y}{L} + \dfrac{C}{\sqrt{L}} - \dfrac{Y^2}{2LL'} - \displaystyle\sum_{n=1}^{\infty} \dfrac{2\cos\dfrac{n\pi X}{L}\cosh\dfrac{n\pi y}{L}\cosh\dfrac{n\pi(L'-Y)}{L}}{n\pi\sinh(n\pi L'/L)}\cos\dfrac{n\pi x}{L} & y \le Y \le L' \end{cases}.$$

When we use the latter of these expressions to evaluate $N(X, L'; x, y)$ along C',

$$V(x, y) = -\int_0^L \left(\dfrac{L'}{L} + \dfrac{C}{\sqrt{L}} - \dfrac{L'}{2L} - \sum_{n=1}^{\infty} \dfrac{2\cos\dfrac{n\pi X}{L}\cosh\dfrac{n\pi y}{L}}{n\pi\sinh(n\pi L'/L)}\cos\dfrac{n\pi x}{L} \right)f(X)\,dX + D.$$

Since $f(x)$ must satisfy the consistency condition

$$\int_0^L f(x)\,dx = 0,$$

this solution reduces to

$$V(x, y) = D + \sum_{n=1}^{\infty} a_n \cosh\dfrac{n\pi y}{L}\cos\dfrac{n\pi x}{L},$$

where

$$a_n = \dfrac{2}{n\pi\sinh(n\pi L'/L)}\int_0^L f(X)\cos\dfrac{n\pi X}{L}\,dX.$$

Had the nonhomogeneity been along either of the boundaries $x = 0$ or $x = L$, or both, an eigenfunction expansion for $N(x, y; X, Y)$ in terms of functions $g_0(y) = 1/\sqrt{L'}$ and $g_n(y) = \sqrt{2/L'}\cos(n\pi y/L')$ would have been used (see Exercise 1). ∎

Exercises 12.4

1. **(a)** Solve Example 8 when boundary conditions along $x = L$, $y = 0$, and $y = L'$ are homogeneous and that along $x = 0$ is $V_x(0, y) = f(y)$, $0 < y < L'$.
   (b) Find $V(x, y)$ when $f(y) = \delta(y - L'/4) - \delta(y - 3L'/4)$ and $V(0, L'/2) = 0$. What is the value of $V(x, y)$ at all points on the line $y = L'/2$?

2. What is the solution to Example 8 if the boundary condition along $y = 0$ is also nonhomogeneous, $V_y(x, 0) = g(x)$?

3. Verify that the steady-state heat conduction problem

$$\frac{\partial^2 U}{\partial x^2} + \frac{\partial^2 U}{\partial y^2} = -\frac{1}{\kappa}, \qquad 0 < x < L, \qquad 0 < y < L,$$

$$U_x(0, y) = \frac{L}{4\kappa}, \qquad 0 < y < L,$$

$$U_x(L, y) = \frac{-L}{4\kappa}, \qquad 0 < y < L,$$

$$U_y(x, 0) = \frac{L}{4\kappa}, \qquad 0 < x < L,$$

$$U_y(x, L) = \frac{-L}{4\kappa}, \qquad 0 < x < L,$$

satisfies consistency condition (60), and find its solution.

4. In this problem we develop a modified Green's function for the Neumann problem on a circle and solve the corresponding boundary value problem:

$$\nabla^2 u = F(r, \theta), \qquad 0 < r < r_0, \qquad -\pi < \theta \leq \pi,$$

$$\frac{\partial u(r_0, \theta)}{\partial r} = K(\theta), \qquad -\pi < \theta < \pi.$$

   (a) What is the boundary value problem characterizing $N(r, \theta; R, \Theta)$ for this problem?
   (b) Using a partial eigenfunction expansion identical to that in Exercise 13(a) of Section 12.2, show that coefficient functions $a_0(r)$, $a_n(r)$, and $b_n(r)$ must satisfy

$$\frac{d^2 a_0}{dr^2} + \frac{1}{r}\frac{da_0}{dr} = \frac{\delta(r - R)}{\sqrt{2\pi}\, r} - \frac{\sqrt{2}}{\sqrt{\pi}\, r_0^2}, \qquad 0 < r < r_0,$$

$$a_0'(r_0) = 0;$$

$$\frac{d^2 a_n}{dr^2} + \frac{1}{r}\frac{da_n}{dr} - \frac{n^2}{r^2} a_n = \frac{\delta(r - R)\cos n\theta}{\sqrt{\pi}\, r}, \qquad 0 < r < r_0,$$

$$a_n'(r_0) = 0;$$

$$\frac{d^2 b_n}{dr^2} + \frac{1}{r}\frac{db_n}{dr} - \frac{n^2}{r^2} b_n = \frac{\delta(r - R)\sin n\theta}{\sqrt{\pi}\, r}, \qquad 0 < r < r_0,$$

$$b_n'(r_0) = 0.$$

(c) Solve the equations in (b) and hence show that

$$
N(r, \theta; R, \Theta) = \begin{cases} \dfrac{A}{\sqrt{2\pi}} - \dfrac{r^2}{4\pi r_0^2} - \displaystyle\sum_{n=1}^{\infty} \dfrac{1}{2\pi n}\left[\left(\dfrac{rR}{r_0^2}\right)^n + \left(\dfrac{r}{R}\right)^n\right]\cos n(\theta - \Theta), & 0 \le r \le R \\[3mm] \dfrac{A}{\sqrt{2\pi}} + \dfrac{\ln(r/R)}{2\pi} - \dfrac{r^2}{4\pi r_0^2} - \displaystyle\sum_{n=1}^{\infty} \dfrac{1}{2\pi n}\left[\left(\dfrac{rR}{r_0^2}\right)^n + \left(\dfrac{R}{r}\right)^n\right]\cos n(\theta - \Theta), & R \le r \le r_0, \end{cases}
$$

where A is independent of r and θ.

(d) Use (33) to simplify the modified Green's function to

$$
N(r, \theta; R, \Theta) = \frac{A}{\sqrt{2\pi}} - \frac{r^2}{4\pi r_0^2}
$$
$$
+ \frac{1}{4\pi}\ln\left(\frac{[r^2 + R^2 - 2rR\cos(\theta - \Theta)][r_0^4 + r^2 R^2 - 2rr_0^2 R\cos(\theta - \Theta)]}{r_0^4 R^2}\right).
$$

(e) Find an integral representation for the solution of the boundary value problem in (a).

5. (a) To satisfy consistency condition (60), it is possible to change the boundary condition defining the modified Green's function instead of the PDE. Show that the function $\bar{N}(x, y; X, Y)$ defined by

$$
\nabla^2 \bar{N} = \delta(x - X, y - Y), \qquad (x, y) \text{ in } A,
$$
$$
\frac{\partial \bar{N}}{\partial n} = \frac{1}{L}, \qquad (x, y) \text{ on } \beta(A),
$$

where L is the length of $\beta(A)$, satisfies (60).

(b) Find the solution of problem (58) in terms of $\bar{N}(x, y; X, Y)$.

6. Use the modified Green's function of Exercise 5 to find the solution of the problem in Exercise 4.

7. What is the three-dimensional analog of Exercise 5?

8. (a) The Neumann problem for the Helmholtz equation is

$$
(\nabla^2 + k^2)u = F(x, y), \qquad (x, y) \text{ in } A, \tag{69a}
$$
$$
\frac{\partial u}{\partial n} = K(x, y), \qquad (x, y) \text{ on } \beta(A). \tag{69b}
$$

The homogeneous system

$$
(\nabla^2 + k^2)u = 0, \qquad (x, y) \text{ in } A, \tag{70a}
$$
$$
\frac{\partial u}{\partial n} = 0, \qquad (x, y) \text{ on } \beta(A), \tag{70b}
$$

has nontrivial solutions. (This is clear when $k = 0$, since $u = $ constant is a solution, and it is also true when $k \ne 0$.) As a result, (69) does not have a unique solution; if $u(x, y)$ is a solution, then so also is $u(x, y) + Cw(x, y)$, where $w(x, y)$ is any solution of (70). In addition, $F(x, y)$ and $K(x, y)$ must satisfy a consistency condition for there to be a solution of (69) at all: problem

(69) has solutions if and only if

$$\iint_A w(x, y)F(x, y)\, dA = \oint_{\beta(A)} w(x, y)K(x, y)\, ds \qquad (71)$$

for every solution $w(x, y)$ of (70). Prove the necessity of this condition.

(b) Show that when consistency condition (71) is satisfied, the solution of (69) is

$$u(x, y) = \iint_A N(x, y; X, Y)F(X, Y)\, dA - \oint_{\beta(A)} N(x, y; X, Y)K(X, Y)\, ds + Cw(x, y) \quad (72)$$

where $w(x, y)$ is the normalized solution of (70), C is an arbitrary constant, and $N(x, y; X, Y)$ is the symmetric modified Green's function satisfying

$$(\nabla^2 + k^2)N = \delta(x - X, y - Y) - w(x, y)w(X, Y), \qquad (x, y)\text{ in } A, \qquad (73a)$$

$$\frac{\partial N}{\partial n} = 0, \qquad (x, y)\text{ on } \beta(A). \qquad (73b)$$

9. State and prove the three-dimensional analog of Exercise 8.

12.5 Robin and Mixed Boundary Value Problems on Finite Regions

The Robin problem for Poisson's equation is

$$\nabla^2 u = F(x, y), \qquad (x, y)\text{ in } A, \qquad (74a)$$

$$l\frac{\partial u}{\partial n} + hu = K(x, y), \qquad (x, y)\text{ on } \beta(A). \qquad (74b)$$

Its solution can be represented in integral form in terms of the nonhomogeneities and the Green's function for the problem.

Theorem 4

The solution of problem (74) is

$$u(x, y) = \iint_A G(x, y; X, Y)F(X, Y)\, dA - \frac{1}{l}\oint_{\beta(A)} G(x, y; X, Y)K(X, Y)\, ds, \qquad (75)$$

where $G(x, y; X, Y)$ satisfies

$$\nabla^2 G = \delta(x - X, y - Y), \qquad (x, y)\text{ in } A, \qquad (76a)$$

$$l\frac{\partial G}{\partial n} + hG = 0, \qquad (x, y)\text{ on } \beta(A). \qquad (76b)$$

Proof: If in Green's identity (14a) on A we let $u = G(x, y; X, Y)$ and $v = u(x, y)$, the solution of (74),

$$\iint_A (u\nabla^2 G - G\nabla^2 u)\, dA = \oint_{\beta(A)} (u\nabla G - G\nabla u)\cdot \hat{\mathbf{n}}\, ds.$$

Because $\nabla^2 G = \delta(x - X, y - Y)$, $\nabla^2 u = F$, and $l\partial u/\partial n + hu = K$ and $l\partial G/\partial n + hG = 0$ on $\beta(A)$,

$$\iint_A [u(x, y)\delta(x - X, y - Y) - G(x, y; X, Y)F(x, y)]\, dA$$

$$= \oint_{\beta(A)} \left(\frac{u(x, y)}{l}[-hG(x, y; X, Y)] - \frac{G(x, y; X, Y)}{l}[K(x, y) - hu(x, y)] \right) ds$$

or $\quad u(X, Y) = \iint_A G(x, y; X, Y)F(x, y)\, dA - \frac{1}{l}\oint_{\beta(A)} G(x, y; X, Y)K(x, y)\, ds.$

When we interchange (x, y) and (X, Y),

$$u(x, y) = \iint_A G(X, Y; x, y)F(X, Y)\, dA - \frac{1}{l}\oint_{\beta(A)} G(X, Y; x, y)K(X, Y)\, ds$$

$$= \iint_A G(x, y; X, Y)F(X, Y)\, dA - \frac{1}{l}\oint_{\beta(A)} G(x, y; X, Y)K(X, Y)\, ds,$$

since $G(x, y; X, Y)$ must be symmetric (see Exercise 1). ∎

Because $G = -(l/h)\partial G/\partial n$ on $\beta(A)$, we may also express the solution in the form

$$u(x, y) = \iint_A G(x, y; X, Y)F(X, Y)\, dA + \frac{1}{h}\oint_{\beta(A)} \frac{\partial G(x, y; X, Y)}{\partial N}K(X, Y)\, ds, \qquad (77)$$

where once again $\partial G/\partial N$ indicates the outward normal derivative of G with respect to the (X, Y) variables.

For three-dimensional problems

$$\nabla^2 u = F(x, y, z), \qquad (x, y, z) \text{ in } V, \qquad (78a)$$

$$l\frac{\partial u}{\partial n} + hu = K(x, y, z), \qquad (x, y, z) \text{ on } \beta(V), \qquad (78b)$$

the solution may be represented in either of the forms

$$u(x, y, z) = \iiint_V G(x, y, z; X, Y, Z)F(X, Y, Z)\, dV$$

$$- \frac{1}{l}\iint_{\beta(V)} G(x, y, z; X, Y, Z)K(X, Y, Z)\, dS \qquad (79a)$$

or $\quad u(x, y, z) = \iiint_V G(x, y, z; X, Y, Z)F(X, Y, Z)\, dV$

$$+ \frac{1}{h}\iint_{\beta(V)} \frac{\partial G(x, y, z; X, Y, Z)}{\partial N}K(X, Y, Z)\, dS. \qquad (79b)$$

A boundary value problem is said to be *mixed* if all parts of the boundary are not subjected to the same type of condition. For instance, the unknown function may have to satisfy a Dirichlet condition on part of the boundary and a Neumann condition on the remainder.

Example 9:   Solve the boundary value problem

$$\nabla^2 u = F(r, \theta), \qquad 0 < r < r_0, \qquad 0 < \theta < \pi,$$

$$u(r_0, \theta) = K_1(\theta), \qquad 0 < \theta < \pi,$$

$$\frac{\partial u(r, 0)}{\partial \theta} = 0, \qquad 0 < r < r_0,$$

$$\frac{\partial u(r, \pi)}{\partial \theta} = 0, \qquad 0 < r < r_0.$$

Solution: The Green's function for this problem is

$$G(r, \theta; R, \Theta) = \frac{1}{4\pi} \ln\left(r_0^4 \frac{[r^2 + R^2 - 2Rr\cos(\theta + \Theta)][r^2 + R^2 - 2Rr\cos(\theta - \Theta)]}{[R^2 r^2 + r_0^4 - 2r_0^2 rR \cos(\theta + \Theta)][R^2 r^2 + r_0^4 - 2r_0^2 rR \cos(\theta - \Theta)]} \right)$$

(see Exercise 2). To solve the boundary value problem, we apply identity (14a) to the semicircle with $u = G$ and $v = u(r, \theta)$, the solution of the problem:

$$\iint_A (u\nabla^2 G - G\nabla^2 u)\, dA = \oint_{\beta(A)} (u\nabla G - G\nabla u) \cdot \hat{n}\, ds.$$

With $\nabla^2 G = \delta(r - R, \theta - \Theta)/r$, $\nabla^2 u = F$, and the boundary conditions for G and u,

$$\iint_A \left(u(r, \theta) \frac{\delta(r - R, \theta - \Theta)}{r} - G(r, \theta; R, \Theta)F(r, \theta) \right) r\, dr\, d\theta$$

$$= \int_0^\pi K_1(\theta) \frac{\partial G(r_0, \theta; R, \Theta)}{\partial r} r_0\, d\theta$$

or

$$u(R, \Theta) = \int_0^\pi \int_0^{r_0} G(r, \theta; R, \Theta)F(r, \theta) r\, dr\, d\theta$$

$$+ \int_0^\pi r_0 K_1(\theta) \frac{\partial G(r_0, \theta; R, \Theta)}{\partial r}\, d\theta.$$

When we interchange (r, θ) and (R, Θ) and note the symmetry in G,

$$u(r, \theta) = \int_0^\pi \int_0^{r_0} G(r, \theta; R, \Theta)F(R, \Theta) R\, dR\, d\Theta$$

$$+ \int_0^\pi r_0 K_1(\Theta) \frac{\partial G(r, \theta; r_0, \Theta)}{\partial R}\, d\Theta. \qquad \blacksquare$$

Exercises 12.5

1. Verify that the Green's function for the Robin problem is symmetric.

2. Show that the Green's function for the boundary value problem of Example 9 is

$$\frac{1}{4\pi} \ln \left(r_0^4 \frac{[r^2 + R^2 - 2rR\cos(\theta + \Theta)][r^2 + R^2 - 2rR\cos(\theta - \Theta)]}{[r^2R^2 + r_0^4 - 2r_0^2 rR\cos(\theta + \Theta)][r^2R^2 + r_0^4 - 2r_0^2 rR\cos(\theta - \Theta)]} \right).$$

3. Use a Green's function to find an integral representation for the solution of the boundary value problem

$$\frac{\partial^2 u}{\partial x^2} + \frac{\partial^2 u}{\partial y^2} = F(x, y), \qquad 0 < x < L, \qquad 0 < y < L,$$

$$u(0, y) = f(y), \qquad 0 < y < L,$$

$$u(L, y) = 0, \qquad 0 < y < L,$$

$$u_y(x, 0) = 0, \qquad 0 < x < L,$$

$$u(x, L) = 0, \qquad 0 < x < L.$$

4. Show that the solution of the Robin problem

$$(\nabla^2 + k^2)u = F(x, y), \qquad (x, y) \text{ in } A,$$

$$l\frac{\partial u}{\partial n} + hu = K(x, y), \qquad (x, y) \text{ on } \beta(A)$$

is (75) when $G(x, y; X, Y)$ is the associated Green's function.

12.6 Green's Functions for Heat Conduction Problems

Green's functions can also be defined for initial boundary value problems; they encompass the character of Green's functions for boundary value problems and also the "causal" features of the initial value problems of Section 11.6.

The causal Green's function for the one-dimensional heat conduction problem

$$\frac{\partial^2 U}{\partial x^2} = \frac{1}{k}\frac{\partial U}{\partial t} - \frac{g(x, t)}{\kappa}, \qquad 0 < x < L, \qquad t > 0, \tag{80a}$$

$$-l_1\frac{\partial U}{\partial x} + h_1 U = f_1(t), \qquad x = 0, \qquad t > 0, \tag{80b}$$

$$l_2\frac{\partial U}{\partial x} + h_2 U = f_2(t), \qquad x = L, \qquad t > 0, \tag{80c}$$

$$U(x, 0) = f(x), \qquad 0 < x < L, \tag{80d}$$

is defined as the solution of the corresponding problem with homogeneous initial and boundary conditions when a unit of heat is inserted at position X and time T:

$$\frac{\partial^2 U}{\partial x^2} = \frac{1}{k}\frac{\partial U}{\partial t} - \frac{\delta(x - X)\delta(t - T)}{\kappa}, \qquad 0 < x < L, \qquad t > T, \tag{81a}$$

$$-l_1 \frac{\partial U}{\partial x} + h_1 U = 0, \qquad x = 0, \qquad t > T, \tag{81b}$$

$$l_2 \frac{\partial U}{\partial x} + h_2 U = 0, \qquad x = L, \qquad t > T, \tag{81c}$$

$$U(x, t; X, T) = 0, \qquad 0 < x < L, \qquad t < T. \tag{81d}$$

For $t > T$, it can also be characterized as the solution of

$$\frac{\partial^2 G}{\partial x^2} = \frac{1}{k} \frac{\partial G}{\partial t}, \qquad 0 < x < L, \qquad t > T, \tag{82a}$$

$$-l_1 \frac{\partial G}{\partial x} + h_1 G = 0, \qquad x = 0, \qquad t > T, \tag{82b}$$

$$l_2 \frac{\partial G}{\partial x} + h_2 G = 0, \qquad x = L, \qquad t > T, \tag{82c}$$

$$G(x, T+; X, T) = \frac{k}{\kappa} \delta(x - X), \qquad 0 < x < L; \tag{82d}$$

that is, the solution of (81) is $H(t - T)G(x, t; X, T)$ when $G(x, t; X, T)$ satisfies (82). What this means is that the effect of a unit heat source at position X and time T on a rod with zero temperature is equivalent to the effect of suddenly raising the temperature of the rod at point X to k/κ at time T. The causal Green's function for (80) is $H(t - T)G(x, t; X, T)$, where $G(x, t; X, T)$ satisfies (82). In essence, then, $G(x, t; X, T)$ is the causal Green's function for problem (80); we must simply remember to set it equal to zero for $t < T$. Because of this, we shall customarily call $G(x, t; X, T)$ the *causal Green's function*.

Example 10:   Find the causal Green's function for problem (80) in the case that $l_1 = 0 = h_2$.

Solution: Separation of variables on problem (82) with $l_1 = h_2 = 0$ leads, for $t > T$, to a solution in the form

$$G(x, t; X, T) = \sum_{n=1}^{\infty} C_n e^{-(2n-1)^2 \pi^2 kt/(4L^2)} f_n(x),$$

where $f_n(x) = \sqrt{2/L} \sin[(2n - 1)\pi x/(2L)]$. If $\delta(x - X)$ is given an eigenfunction expansion in terms of the $\{f_n(x)\}$, the initial condition requires that

$$\sum_{n=1}^{\infty} C_n e^{-(2n-1)^2 \pi^2 kT/(4L^2)} f_n(x) = \frac{k}{\kappa} \sum_{n=1}^{\infty} \left(\int_0^L \delta(x - X) f_n(x)\, dx \right) f_n(x)$$

$$= \frac{k}{\kappa} \sum_{n=1}^{\infty} f_n(X) f_n(x).$$

It follows, then, that

$$C_n e^{-(2n-1)^2 \pi^2 kT/(4L^2)} = \frac{k}{\kappa} f_n(X)$$

and

$$G(x, t; X, T) = \sum_{n=1}^{\infty} \frac{k}{\kappa} e^{-(2n-1)^2 \pi^2 k(t-T)/(4L^2)} f_n(X) f_n(x)$$

$$= \frac{2k}{\kappa L} \sum_{n=1}^{\infty} e^{-(2n-1)^2 \pi^2 k(t-T)/(4L^2)} \sin \frac{(2n-1)\pi X}{2L} \sin \frac{(2n-1)\pi x}{2L}. \qquad \blacksquare$$

The solution of problem (80) can be expressed in terms of the causal Green's function for the problem:

$$U(x, t) = \int_0^t \int_0^L G(x, t; X, T) g(X, T) \, dX \, dT + \frac{\kappa}{k} \int_0^L G(x, t; X, 0) f(X) \, dX$$

$$+ \kappa \int_0^t \left(G(x, t; L, T) \frac{f_2(T)}{l_2} + G(x, t; 0, T) \frac{f_1(T)}{l_1} \right) dT. \qquad \text{(83a)}$$

The first term is the contribution of the internal heat source from $t = 0$ to present time, the second term is due to the initial temperature distribution in the rod, and the last integral represents the effects of heat transfer at the ends of the rod. Boundary conditions (82b, c) can be used to rewrite the last integral in the form

$$U(x, t) = \int_0^t \int_0^L G(x, t; X, T) g(X, T) \, dX \, dT + \frac{\kappa}{k} \int_0^L G(x, t; X, 0) f(X) \, dX$$

$$+ \kappa \int_0^t \left(-\frac{\partial G(x, t; L, T)}{\partial X} \frac{f_2(T)}{h_2} + \frac{\partial G(x, t; 0, T)}{\partial X} \frac{f_1(T)}{h_1} \right) dT \qquad \text{(83b)}$$

(see Exercise 11). This form must be used when $l_1 = l_2 = 0$.

Example 11:   Solve the heat conduction problem in Example 2 of Section 6.2.

Solution: The Green's function for this problem was obtained in the previous example. With $g(x, t) \equiv 0$, and $f_2(t)$ replaced by $-\kappa^{-1} f_2(t)$, we use (83a, b) to write

$$U(x, t) = \frac{\kappa}{k} \int_0^L G(x, t; X, 0) f(X) \, dX$$

$$+ \kappa \int_0^t \left(-G(x, t; L, T) \frac{f_2(T)}{\kappa l_2} + \frac{\partial G(x, t; 0, T)}{\partial X} \frac{f_1(T)}{h_1} \right) dT$$

$$= \frac{\kappa}{k} \int_0^L \left(\frac{2k}{\kappa L} \sum_{n=1}^{\infty} e^{-(2n-1)^2 \pi^2 kt/(4L^2)} \sin \frac{(2n-1)\pi X}{2L} \sin \frac{(2n-1)\pi x}{2L} \right) f(X) \, dX$$

$$- \int_0^t \left(\frac{2k}{\kappa L} \sum_{n=1}^{\infty} e^{-(2n-1)^2 \pi^2 k(t-T)/(4L^2)} \sin \frac{(2n-1)\pi}{2} \sin \frac{(2n-1)\pi x}{2L} \right) f_2(T) \, dT$$

$$+ \kappa \int_0^t \left(\frac{2k}{\kappa L} \sum_{n=1}^{\infty} e^{-(2n-1)^2 \pi^2 k(t-T)/(4L^2)} \left(\frac{(2n-1)\pi}{2L} \right) \sin \frac{(2n-1)\pi x}{2L} \right) f_1(T) \, dT.$$

When we interchange orders of summation and integration,

$$U(x,t) = \frac{2}{L}\sum_{n=1}^{\infty}\left(\int_0^L f(X)\sin\frac{(2n-1)\pi X}{2L}\,dX\right)e^{-(2n-1)^2\pi^2kt/(4L^2)}\sin\frac{(2n-1)\pi x}{2L}$$

$$+\frac{2k}{L}\sum_{n=1}^{\infty}\left(\int_0^t\left[\left(\frac{(2n-1)\pi}{2L}\right)f_1(T)+\frac{(-1)^n}{\kappa}f_2(T)\right]\right.$$

$$\left.\times\, e^{-(2n-1)^2\pi^2k(t-T)/(4L^2)}\,dT\right)\sin\frac{(2n-1)\pi x}{2L},$$

and this is solution (46) in Section 6.2.   ■

The causal Green's function for the two-dimensional heat conduction problem

$$\nabla^2 U = \frac{1}{k}\frac{\partial U}{\partial t} - \frac{g(x,y,t)}{\kappa}, \qquad (x,y)\text{ in }A, \qquad t>0, \tag{84a}$$

$$l\frac{\partial U}{\partial n} + hU = F(x,y,t), \qquad (x,y)\text{ on }\beta(A), \qquad t>0, \tag{84b}$$

$$U(x,y,0) = f(x,y), \qquad (x,y)\text{ in }A, \tag{84c}$$

is defined as the solution of

$$\nabla^2 U = \frac{1}{k}\frac{\partial U}{\partial t} - \frac{\delta(x-X,\,y-Y)\delta(t-T)}{\kappa}, \qquad (x,y)\text{ in }A, \qquad t>T, \tag{85a}$$

$$l\frac{\partial U}{\partial n} + hU = 0, \qquad (x,y)\text{ on }\beta(A), \qquad t>T, \tag{85b}$$

$$U(x,y,t;X,Y,T) = 0, \qquad (x,y)\text{ in }A, \qquad t<T. \tag{85c}$$

It is also given by $H(t-T)G(x,y,t;X,Y,T)$, where $G(x,y,t;X,Y,T)$ satisfies

$$\nabla^2 G = \frac{1}{k}\frac{\partial G}{\partial t}, \qquad (x,y)\text{ in }A, \qquad t>T, \tag{86a}$$

$$l\frac{\partial G}{\partial n} + hG = 0, \qquad (x,y)\text{ on }\beta(A), \qquad t>T, \tag{86b}$$

$$G(x,y,T+;X,Y,T) = \frac{k}{\kappa}\delta(x-X,\,y-Y), \qquad (x,y)\text{ in }A. \tag{86c}$$

The solution of problem (84) can then be expressed in the form

$$U(x,y,t) = \int_0^t\iint_A G(x,y,t;X,Y,T)g(X,Y,T)\,dA\,dT$$

$$+\frac{\kappa}{k}\iint_A G(x,y,t;X,Y,0)f(X,Y)\,dA$$

$$+\frac{\kappa}{l}\int_0^t\oint_{\beta(A)} G(x,y,t;X,Y,T)F(X,Y,T)\,ds\,dT \tag{87a}$$

or $$U(x, y, t) = \int_0^t \iint_A G(x, y, t; X, Y, T)g(X, Y, T)\,dA\,dT$$

$$+ \frac{\kappa}{k} \iint_A G(x, y, t; X, Y, 0)f(X, Y)\,dA$$

$$- \frac{\kappa}{h} \int_0^t \oint_{\beta(A)} F(X, Y, T)\frac{\partial G(x, y, t; X, Y, T)}{\partial N}\,ds\,dT. \qquad \text{(87b)}$$

Exercises 12.6

In Exercises 1–4, find the causal Green's function for problem (80) when the values for l_1, l_2, h_1, and h_2 are as specified.

1. $l_1 = l_2 = 0, \quad h_1 = h_2 = 1$
2. $h_1 = h_2 = 0, \quad l_1 = l_2 = 1$
3. $l_2 = h_1 = 0, \quad l_1 = h_2 = 1$
4. $l_1 = 0, \quad h_1 = 1, \quad l_2 h_2 \neq 0$

In Exercises 5–9, use formulas (83a, b) to solve the initial boundary value problem.

5. Exercise 8 in Section 3.3.
6. Exercise 9 in Section 3.3.
7. Exercise 1 in Section 6.2.
8. Exercise 7 in Section 6.2.
9. Exercise 15 in Section 6.2.

10. (a) What is the causal Green's function for problem (80)?

    (b) Use the representation in (a) to show that $G(x, t; X, T)$ satisfies the "reciprocity principle"

    $$G(x, t; X, T) = G(X, t; x, T).$$

    What does this mean physically?

    (c) Use the representation in (a) to show that $G(x, t; X, T)$ satisfies the "time-translation" property

    $$G(x, t - \bar{T}; X, T) = G(x, t; X, T + \bar{T})$$

    (provided $t - T - \bar{T} > 0$). What does this mean physically?

11. Use the result in Exercise 10(b) to show that solution (83a) can be expressed in form (83b).

In Exercises 12–15, use formulas (87a, b) to solve the two-dimensional heat conduction problem.

12. Exercise 1 in Section 6.3.
13. Exercise 2(a) in Section 6.3.
14. Exercise 2(a) in Section 9.2.
15. Parts (a) and (b) of Exercise 3 in Section 9.2.
16. What are the three-dimensional analogs of equations (84)–(87)?

12.7 Green's Functions for the Wave Equation

The causal Green's function $G(x, t; X, T)$ for the one-dimensional vibration problem

$$\frac{\partial^2 y}{\partial x^2} = \frac{1}{c^2}\frac{\partial^2 y}{\partial t^2} - \frac{F(x, t)}{\rho c^2}, \qquad 0 < x < L, \qquad t > 0, \qquad \text{(88a)}$$

$$-l_1 \frac{\partial y}{\partial x} + h_1 y = f_1(t), \qquad x = 0, \qquad t > 0, \tag{88b}$$

$$l_2 \frac{\partial y}{\partial x} + h_2 y = f_2(t), \qquad x = L, \qquad t > 0, \tag{88c}$$

$$y(x, 0) = f(x), \qquad 0 < x < L, \tag{88d}$$

$$y_t(x, 0) = g(x), \qquad 0 < x < L, \tag{88e}$$

is defined as the solution of

$$\frac{\partial^2 y}{\partial x^2} = \frac{1}{c^2} \frac{\partial^2 y}{\partial t^2} - \frac{\delta(x - X)\delta(t - T)}{\rho c^2}, \qquad 0 < x < L, \qquad t > T, \tag{89a}$$

$$-l_1 \frac{\partial y}{\partial x} + h_1 y = 0, \qquad x = 0, \qquad t > T, \tag{89b}$$

$$l_2 \frac{\partial y}{\partial x} + h_2 y = 0, \qquad x = L, \qquad t > T, \tag{89c}$$

$$y(x, t; X, T) = 0, \qquad 0 < x < L, \qquad t < T. \tag{89d}$$

It is also given by $H(t - T)G(x, t; X, T)$, where $G(x, t; X, T)$ satisfies

$$\frac{\partial^2 G}{\partial x^2} = \frac{1}{c^2} \frac{\partial^2 G}{\partial t^2}, \qquad 0 < x < L, \qquad t > T, \tag{90a}$$

$$-l_1 \frac{\partial G}{\partial x} + h_1 G = 0, \qquad x = 0, \qquad t > T, \tag{90b}$$

$$l_2 \frac{\partial G}{\partial x} + h_2 G = 0, \qquad x = L, \qquad t > T, \tag{90c}$$

$$G(x, T+; X, T) = 0, \qquad 0 < x < L, \tag{90d}$$

$$G_t(x, T+; X, T) = \frac{\delta(x - X)}{\rho}, \qquad 0 < x < L. \tag{90e}$$

In other words, the effect of an instantaneous unit force at position X and time T is equivalent to the effect of giving the point at X an instantaneous initial velocity $1/\rho$. Although the causal Green's function for (88) is $H(t - T)G(x, t; X, T)$, where $G(x, t; X, T)$ satisfies (90), we shall customarily call $G(x, t; X, T)$ itself the Green's function.

Problem (90) is easily solved by separation of variables.

Example 12:   Find the causal Green's function for problem (88) when $l_1 = l_2 = 0$.

Solution: Separation of variables on (90a–d) leads, for $t > T$, to

$$G(x, t; X, T) = \sum_{n=1}^{\infty} A_n \sin \frac{n\pi c(t - T)}{L} f_n(x),$$

where $f_n(x) = \sqrt{2/L}\,\sin(n\pi x/L)$. If $\delta(x - X)$ is expanded in terms of the $\{f_n(x)\}$, initial condition (90e) requires that

$$\sum_{n=1}^{\infty}\frac{n\pi c}{L}A_n f_n(x) = \frac{1}{\rho}\sum_{n=1}^{\infty}\left(\int_0^L \delta(x - X)f_n(x)\,dx\right)f_n(x)$$

$$= \frac{1}{\rho}\sum_{n=1}^{\infty} f_n(X)f_n(x).$$

It follows, then, that

$$\frac{n\pi c}{L}A_n = \frac{1}{\rho}f_n(X)$$

and

$$G(x,t;X,T) = \sum_{n=1}^{\infty}\frac{L}{n\pi c\rho}f_n(X)\sin\frac{n\pi c(t-T)}{L}f_n(x)$$

$$= \frac{L}{\rho\pi c}\sum_{n=1}^{\infty}\frac{1}{n}\sin\frac{n\pi c(t-T)}{L}f_n(X)f_n(x).\qquad\blacksquare$$

The solution of problem (88) can be expressed in terms of its Green's function:

$$y(x,t) = \int_0^t \int_0^L G(x,t;X,T)F(X,T)\,dX\,dT$$

$$+ \rho\int_0^L\left(g(X)G(x,t;X,0) - f(X)\frac{\partial G(x,t;X,0)}{\partial T}\right)dX$$

$$+ \rho c^2\int_0^t\left(G(x,t;L,T)\frac{f_2(T)}{l_2} + G(x,t;0,T)\frac{f_1(T)}{l_1}\right)dT.\qquad\text{(91a)}$$

The first integral contains the effect of past external forces, and the second integral contains that of the initial displacement and velocity. The last integral is due to boundary disturbances. Boundary conditions (90b, c) can be used to rewrite the last integral in the form

$$y(x,t) = \int_0^t \int_0^L G(x,t;X,T)F(X,T)\,dX\,dT$$

$$+ \rho\int_0^L\left(g(X)G(x,t;X,0) - f(X)\frac{\partial G(x,t;X,0)}{\partial T}\right)dX$$

$$+ \rho c^2\int_0^t\left(-\frac{f_2(T)}{h_2}\frac{\partial G(x,t;L,T)}{\partial X} + \frac{f_1(T)}{h_1}\frac{\partial G(x,t;0,T)}{\partial X}\right)dT.\qquad\text{(91b)}$$

This form must be used when $l_1 = l_2 = 0$.

Example 13:   Solve the vibration problem of Example 3 in Section 6.2.

Solution: The Green's function for this problem was derived in Example 12. According to (91b), then,

$$y(x,t) = \rho c^2\int_0^t -\frac{\partial G(x,t;L,T)}{\partial X}g(T)\,dT$$

$$= \rho c^2 \int_0^t \left(\frac{-L}{\rho \pi c} \sum_{n=1}^{\infty} \frac{1}{n} \sin \frac{n\pi c(t-T)}{L} f'_n(L) f_n(x) \right) g(T) \, dT$$

$$= -\frac{Lc}{\pi} \sum_{n=1}^{\infty} \frac{1}{n} \left(\int_0^t \sin \frac{n\pi c(t-T)}{L} g(T) \, dT \right) f'_n(L) f_n(x).$$

When $g(t) = A \sin \omega t$ and $\omega \neq n\pi c/L$ for any integer n,

$$\int_0^t \sin \frac{n\pi c(t-T)}{L} A \sin \omega T \, dT = \frac{AL^2}{n^2\pi^2 c^2 - \omega^2 L^2} \left(\frac{n\pi c}{L} \sin \omega t - \omega \sin \frac{n\pi ct}{L} \right),$$

and therefore

$$y(x,t) = -\frac{Lc}{\pi} \sum_{n=1}^{\infty} \frac{AL^2}{n(n^2\pi^2 c^2 - \omega^2 L^2)} \left(\frac{n\pi c}{L} \sin \omega t \right.$$

$$\left. - \omega \sin \frac{n\pi ct}{L} \right) \sqrt{\frac{2}{L}} \left(\frac{n\pi}{L} \right) (-1)^n \sqrt{\frac{2}{L}} \sin \frac{n\pi x}{L}$$

$$= 2cA \sum_{n=1}^{\infty} \frac{(-1)^n}{n^2\pi^2 c^2 - \omega^2 L^2} \left(\omega L \sin \frac{n\pi ct}{L} - n\pi c \sin \omega t \right) \sin \frac{n\pi x}{L}.$$

When $g(t) = A \sin(m\pi ct/L)$,

$$\int_0^t \sin \frac{n\pi c(t-T)}{L} g(T) \, dT = \begin{cases} \dfrac{AL}{\pi c(n^2 - m^2)} \left(n \sin \dfrac{m\pi ct}{L} - m \sin \dfrac{n\pi ct}{L} \right) & n \neq m \\[2ex] \dfrac{A}{2m\pi c} \left(L \sin \dfrac{m\pi ct}{L} - m\pi ct \cos \dfrac{m\pi ct}{L} \right) & n = m \end{cases}$$

and $$y(x,t) = \frac{Lc}{-\pi} \sum_{\substack{n=1 \\ n \neq m}}^{\infty} \frac{AL}{n\pi c(n^2 - m^2)} \left(n \sin \frac{m\pi ct}{L} - m \sin \frac{n\pi ct}{L} \right) f'_n(L) f_n(x)$$

$$- \frac{Lc}{\pi} \left[\frac{A}{2m^2\pi c} \left(L \sin \frac{m\pi ct}{L} - m\pi ct \cos \frac{m\pi ct}{L} \right) \right] f'_m(L) f_m(x)$$

$$= \frac{2A}{\pi} \sum_{\substack{n=1 \\ n \neq m}}^{\infty} \frac{(-1)^n}{n^2 - m^2} \left(m \sin \frac{n\pi ct}{L} - n \sin \frac{m\pi ct}{L} \right) \sin \frac{n\pi x}{L}$$

$$+ \frac{(-1)^m A}{m\pi L} \left(m\pi ct \cos \frac{m\pi ct}{L} - L \sin \frac{m\pi ct}{L} \right) \sin \frac{m\pi x}{L}. \qquad \blacksquare$$

The causal Green's function for the two-dimensional vibration problem

$$\nabla^2 z = \frac{1}{c^2} \frac{\partial^2 z}{\partial t^2} - \frac{F(x,y,t)}{\rho c^2}, \qquad (x,y) \text{ in } A, \qquad t > 0, \qquad \text{(92a)}$$

$$l \frac{\partial z}{\partial n} + hz = K(x,y,t), \qquad (x,y) \text{ on } \beta(A), \qquad t > 0, \qquad \text{(92b)}$$

$$z(x,y,0) = f(x,y), \qquad (x,y) \text{ in } A, \qquad \text{(92c)}$$

$$z_t(x,y,0) = g(x,y), \qquad (x,y) \text{ in } A, \qquad \text{(92d)}$$

is defined as the solution of

$$\nabla^2 z = \frac{1}{c^2} \frac{\partial^2 z}{\partial t^2} - \frac{\delta(x - X, y - Y)\delta(t - T)}{\rho c^2}, \qquad (x, y) \text{ in } A, \qquad t > T, \quad \text{(93a)}$$

$$l\frac{\partial z}{\partial n} + hz = 0, \qquad (x, y) \text{ on } \beta(A), \qquad t > T, \tag{93b}$$

$$z(x, y, t; X, Y, T) = 0, \qquad (x, y) \text{ in } A, \qquad t < T. \tag{93c}$$

It is also given by $H(t - T)G(x, y, t; X, Y, T)$, where $G(x, y, t; X, Y, T)$ satisfies

$$\nabla^2 G = \frac{1}{c^2} \frac{\partial^2 G}{\partial t^2}, \qquad (x, y) \text{ in } A, \qquad t > T, \tag{94a}$$

$$l\frac{\partial G}{\partial n} + hG = 0, \qquad (x, y) \text{ on } \beta(A), \qquad t > T, \tag{94b}$$

$$G(x, y, T+; X, Y, T) = 0, \qquad (x, y) \text{ in } A, \tag{94c}$$

$$G_t(x, y, T+; X, Y, T) = \frac{\delta(x - X, y - Y)}{\rho}, \qquad (x, y) \text{ in } A. \tag{94d}$$

The solution of (92) can then be expressed in the form

$$z(x, y, t) = \int_0^t \iint_A G(x, y, t; X, Y, T)F(X, Y, T)\,dA\,dT$$

$$+ \rho \iint_A \left(g(X, Y)G(x, y, t; X, Y, 0) - f(X, Y)\frac{\partial G(x, y, t; X, Y, 0)}{\partial T} \right) dA$$

$$+ \frac{\rho c^2}{l} \int_0^t \oint_{\beta(A)} G(x, y, t; X, Y, T)K(X, Y, T)\,ds\,dT \tag{95a}$$

or

$$z(x, y, t) = \int_0^t \iint_A G(x, y, t; X, Y, T)F(X, Y, T)\,dA\,dT$$

$$+ \rho \iint_A \left(g(X, Y)G(x, y, t; X, Y, 0) - f(X, Y)\frac{\partial G(x, y, t; X, Y, 0)}{\partial T} \right) dA$$

$$- \frac{\rho c^2}{h} \int_0^t \oint_{\beta(A)} K(X, Y, T)\frac{\partial G(x, y, t; X, Y, T)}{\partial N}\,ds\,dT. \tag{95b}$$

Exercises 12.7

In Exercises 1–3, find the causal Green's function for problem (88) when values for l_1, l_2, h_1, and h_2 are as specified.

1. $h_1 = h_2 = 0, l_1 = l_2 = 1$

2. $l_2 = h_1 = 0, l_1 = h_2 = 1$

3. $l_2 = h_1 = 1, l_1 = h_2 = 0$

In Exercises 4–6, use formulas (91a, b) to solve the initial boundary value problem.

4. Exercise 13 in Section 3.3 (see also Exercise 19 in Section 6.2).

5. Exercise 21(a) in Section 6.2.

6. Exercise 22 in Section 6.2.

7. A taut string initially at rest along the x-axis has its ends fixed at $x = 0$ and $x = L$.

   (a) Find displacements in the string for an arbitrary forcing function $F(x, t)$.

   (b) Simplify the solution in (a) when $F(x, t)$ is a time-independent, constant force F_0 concentrated at $x = x_0$.

   (c) Simplify the solution in (b) further if $x_0 = L/2$.

   (d) What is the solution in (b) if x_0 is a node of the mth normal mode of vibration of the string?

8. (a) What is the causal Green's function for problem (88)?

   (b) Use the representation in (a) to show that $G(x, t; X, T)$ satisfies the "reciprocity principle"

   $$G(x, t; X, T) = G(X, t; x, T).$$

   What does this mean physically?

   (c) Use the representation in (a) to show that $G(x, t; X, T)$ satisfies the "time-translation" property

   $$G(x, t; X, T) = G(x, t + \bar{T}; X, T + \bar{T})$$

   (provided $\bar{T} > 0$). What does this mean physically?

In Exercises 9 and 10, use formulas (95a, b) to solve the two-dimensional vibration problem.

9. Exercise 6 in Section 6.3.   10. Exercise 16 in Section 9.2.

Bibliography

1. Abramowitz, M., and I. Stegun. *Handbook of Mathematical Functions.* New York: Dover, 1965.

2. Berg, P., and J. McGregor. *Elementary Partial Differential Equations.* New York: Holden-Day, 1966.

3. Carslaw, H. S. *Introduction to the Theory of Fourier Series and Integrals.* New York: Dover, 1950.

4. Carslaw, H. S., and J. C. Jaeger. *Conduction of Heat in Solids.* New York: Oxford University Press, 1959.

5. ———. *Operational Methods in Applied Mathematics.* New York: Oxford University Press, 1948.

6. Churchill, R. V. *Modern Operational Mathematics in Engineering.* New York: McGraw-Hill, 1944.

7. Churchill, R. V., and J. W. Brown. *Fourier Series and Boundary Value Problems.* New York: McGraw-Hill, 1987.

8. Coddington, E. A., and N. Levinson. *Theory of Ordinary Differential Equations.* New York: McGraw-Hill, 1955.

9. Courant, R., and D. Hilbert. *Methods of Mathematical Physics.* New York: Interscience, 1962.

10. Duff, G. F. D. *Partial Differential Equations.* Toronto: University of Toronto Press, 1956.

11. Erdelyi, A., W. Magnus, F. Oberhettinger, and F. G. Tricomi. *Higher Transcendental Functions.* New York: McGraw-Hill, 1953.

12. ———. *Tables of Integral Transforms,* Vol. 1. New York: McGraw-Hill, 1954.

13. Garabedian, P. *Partial Differential Equations.* New York: Wiley, 1964.

14. Greenberg, M. *Applications of Green's Functions in Science and Engineering.* Englewood Cliffs, NJ: Prentice-Hall, 1971.

15. Haberman, R. *Elementary Applied Partial Differential Equations.* Englewood Cliffs, NJ: Prentice-Hall, 1987.

16. Hildebrand, F. *Methods of Applied Mathematics.* Englewood Cliffs, NJ: Prentice-Hall, 1965.

17. Ince, E. L. *Ordinary Differential Equations.* New York: Dover, 1956.

18. Lighthill, M. J. *Introduction to Fourier Analysis and Generalized Functions.* Cambridge, England: Cambridge University Press, 1958.

19. Mikhlin, S. G. *Linear Equations of Mathematical Physics.* New York: Holt, Rinehart and Winston, 1967.

20. Miller, K. S. *Partial Differential Equations in Engineering Problems.* Englewood Cliffs, NJ: Prentice-Hall, 1953.

21. Morse, P. M., and H. Feshbach. *Methods of Theoretical Physics.* New York: McGraw-Hill, 1953.

22. Myint-U, T. *Partial Differential Equations of Mathematical Physics.* New York: Elsevier North-Holland, 1980.

23. Ozisik, M. N. *Heat Conduction.* New York: Wiley, 1980.

24. Sneddon, I. N. *Elements of Partial Differential Equations*. New York: McGraw-Hill, 1957.

25. ———. *Fourier Transforms*. New York: McGraw-Hill, 1951.

26. ———. *Special Functions of Mathematical Physics and Chemistry*. New York: Interscience, 1961.

27. Stakgold, I. *Boundary Value Problems of Mathematical Physics*. New York: Macmillan, 1967.

28. Titchmarsh, E. C. *Introduction to the Theory of Fourier Integrals*. Oxford: Oxford University Press, 1962.

29. Watson, G. N. *Theory of Bessel Functions*. Cambridge, England: Cambridge University Press, 1966.

30. Weinberger, H. *A First Course in Partial Differential Equations*. New York: Blaisdell, 1965.

31. Zauderer, E. *Partial Differential Equations of Applied Mathematics*. New York: Wiley, 1983.

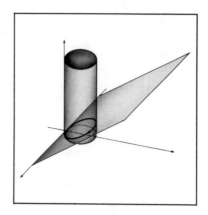

Convergence of Fourier Series

In order to establish convergence of a Fourier series to the function that it represents, we require a few preliminary results on trigonometric integrals. These results are formulated so as to make them useful for Fourier integrals in Appendix B as well.

Result 1 (Riemann's Theorem)

If $f(x)$ is piecewise continuous on $a \leq x \leq b$, then

$$\lim_{\lambda \to \infty} \int_a^b f(x) \sin \lambda x \, dx = 0 = \lim_{\lambda \to \infty} \int_a^b f(x) \cos \lambda x \, dx. \tag{1}$$

Proof: The interval $a \leq x \leq b$ can be divided into a finite number of subintervals $p \leq x \leq q$ in each of which $f(x)$ is continuous even at the end points, provided we use the limits from the interior as values of $f(x)$ at the end points. The theorem then follows if we can show that

$$\lim_{\lambda \to \infty} \int_p^q f(x) \sin \lambda x \, dx = 0 = \lim_{\lambda \to \infty} \int_p^q f(x) \cos \lambda x \, dx$$

for continuous $f(x)$ on $p \leq x \leq q$. If we divide this interval into n equal parts by points $x_j =$

$p + (q - p)j/n, j = 0, \ldots, n$, then

$$\int_p^q f(x) \sin \lambda x \, dx = \sum_{j=0}^{n-1} \int_{x_j}^{x_{j+1}} f(x) \sin \lambda x \, dx$$

$$= \sum_{j=0}^{n-1} \left(f(x_j) \int_{x_j}^{x_{j+1}} \sin \lambda x \, dx + \int_{x_j}^{x_{j+1}} [f(x) - f(x_j)] \sin \lambda x \, dx \right)$$

$$= \sum_{j=0}^{n-1} f(x_j) \left(\frac{\cos \lambda x_j - \cos \lambda x_{j+1}}{\lambda} \right)$$

$$+ \sum_{j=0}^{n-1} \int_{x_j}^{x_{j+1}} [f(x) - f(x_j)] \sin \lambda x \, dx.$$

When we use the triangle inequality, $|a + b| \le |a| + |b|$, on each of these summations, and note that $|\sin \lambda x| \le 1$, we obtain

$$\left| \int_p^q f(x) \sin \lambda x \, dx \right| \le \sum_{j=0}^{n-1} |f(x_j)| \left| \frac{\cos \lambda x_j - \cos \lambda x_{j+1}}{\lambda} \right|$$

$$+ \sum_{j=0}^{n-1} \int_{x_j}^{x_{j+1}} |f(x) - f(x_j)| \, dx.$$

Clearly, $|\cos \lambda x_j - \cos \lambda x_{j+1}| \le |\cos \lambda x_j| + |\cos \lambda x_{j+1}| \le 2$, and if we denote the maximum value of $|f(x)|$ on $p \le x \le q$ by M, then

$$\left| \int_p^q f(x) \sin \lambda x \, dx \right| \le \frac{2Mn}{\lambda} + \sum_{j=0}^{n-1} \int_{x_j}^{x_{j+1}} |f(x) - f(x_j)| \, dx.$$

Because a continuous function $[f(x)]$ on a closed interval $[p \le x \le q]$ is uniformly continuous[†] thereon, we can state that corresponding to any number $\varepsilon > 0$, no matter how small, there exists an N large enough that when $n > N$ and $x_j \le x \le x_{j+1}$,

$$|f(x) - f(x_j)| < \frac{\varepsilon}{2(q - p)}.$$

For $n > N$, then,

$$\left| \int_p^q f(x) \sin \lambda x \, dx \right| \le \frac{2Mn}{\lambda} + \sum_{j=0}^{n-1} \frac{\varepsilon}{2(q - p)} (x_{j+1} - x_j) = \frac{2Mn}{\lambda} + \frac{\varepsilon}{2}.$$

Finally, if λ is chosen so large that $2Mn/\lambda < \varepsilon/2$, then

$$\left| \int_p^q f(x) \sin \lambda x \, dx \right| < \varepsilon;$$

[†] A function $f(x)$ is *uniformly continuous on an interval I* if given any $\varepsilon > 0$, there exists a $\delta > 0$ such that whenever $|x_1 - x_2| < \delta$ and x_1 and x_2 are in I,

$$|f(x_1) - f(x_2)| < \varepsilon.$$

that is, λ can be chosen so large that the value of the integral can be made arbitrarily close to zero. This is tantamount to saying that

$$\lim_{\lambda \to \infty} \int_p^q f(x) \sin \lambda x \, dx = 0.$$

A similar proof yields the other limit.   ∎

When λ is set equal to $n\pi/L$, we obtain the following corollary to Result 1.

Corollary

If $f(x)$ is piecewise continuous on $0 \le x \le 2L$, then

$$\lim_{n \to \infty} \int_0^{2L} f(x) \cos \frac{n\pi x}{L} \, dx = 0 = \lim_{n \to \infty} \int_0^{2L} f(x) \sin \frac{n\pi x}{L} \, dx. \tag{2}$$

Result 2

If $f(x)$ is piecewise continuous on $0 \le x \le b$ and has a right derivative at $x = 0$, then

$$\lim_{\lambda \to \infty} \int_0^b f(x) \frac{\sin \lambda x}{x} \, dx = \frac{\pi}{2} f(0+). \tag{3}$$

Proof: We begin by expressing the integral in the form

$$\int_0^b f(x) \frac{\sin \lambda x}{x} \, dx = \int_0^b \left(\frac{f(x) - f(0+)}{x} \right) \sin \lambda x \, dx$$

$$+ f(0+) \int_0^b \frac{\sin \lambda x}{x} \, dx. \tag{4}$$

Now the function $[f(x) - f(0+)]/x$ is piecewise continuous on $0 \le x \le b$ [since $f(x)$ is, and provided we define the value at $x = 0$ by the limit that is the right derivative of $f(x)$ at $x = 0$]. Hence, by Riemann's theorem,

$$\lim_{\lambda \to \infty} \int_0^b \left(\frac{f(x) - f(0+)}{x} \right) \sin \lambda x \, dx = 0,$$

and the first integral on the right of (4) vanishes in the limit as $\lambda \to \infty$. Further, by the change of variable $u = \lambda x$ in the second integral, we find that

$$\lim_{\lambda \to \infty} \int_0^b \frac{\sin \lambda x}{x} \, dx = \lim_{\lambda \to \infty} \int_0^{b\lambda} \frac{\sin u}{u} \, du$$

$$= \int_0^\infty \frac{\sin u}{u} \, du = \frac{\pi}{2}. ^\dagger$$

Consequently, the limit of (4) as $\lambda \to \infty$ yields (3).   ∎

---

† This integral is quoted in many sources. See, for example, any edition of *Standard Mathematical Tables* by Chemical Rubber Publishing Company.

Result 3

If $f(x)$ is piecewise continuous on $a \le x \le b$, then at every x in $a < x < b$ at which $f(x)$ has a right and left derivative,

$$\lim_{\lambda \to \infty} \frac{1}{\pi} \int_a^b f(t) \frac{\sin \lambda(x - t)}{x - t} \, dt = \frac{f(x+) + f(x-)}{2}. \tag{5}$$

Proof:

We begin by subdividing the interval of integration,

$$\int_a^b f(t) \frac{\sin \lambda(x - t)}{x - t} \, dt = \int_a^x f(t) \frac{\sin \lambda(x - t)}{x - t} \, dt + \int_x^b f(t) \frac{\sin \lambda(x - t)}{x - t} \, dt,$$

and make the changes of variables $u = x - t$ and $u = t - x$, respectively:

$$\int_a^b f(t) \frac{\sin \lambda(x - t)}{x - t} \, dt = \int_0^{x-a} f(x - u) \frac{\sin \lambda u}{u} \, du + \int_0^{b-x} f(x + u) \frac{\sin \lambda u}{u} \, du.$$

For fixed x, $f(x - u)$ is piecewise continuous in u on $0 \le u \le x - a$ and has a right derivative at $u = 0$ [namely, the negative of the left derivative of $f(x)$ at x]. It follows, then, from Result 2 that

$$\lim_{\lambda \to \infty} \int_0^{x-a} f(x - u) \frac{\sin \lambda u}{u} \, du = \frac{\pi}{2} f(x-).$$

A similar discussion yields

$$\lim_{\lambda \to \infty} \int_0^{b-x} f(x + u) \frac{\sin \lambda u}{u} \, du = \frac{\pi}{2} f(x+),$$

and these two facts give (5).   ∎

We are now prepared to prove Theorem 2 of Section 2.1.

Result 4

If $f(x)$ is piecewise continuous and of period $2L$, then at every x at which $f(x)$ has a right and left derivative, the Fourier series of $f(x)$ converges to $[f(x+) + f(x-)]/2$.

Proof:

The nth partial sum of the Fourier series of $f(x)$ is

$$S_n(x) = \frac{a_0}{2} + \sum_{k=1}^n \left(a_k \cos \frac{k\pi x}{L} + b_k \sin \frac{k\pi x}{L} \right).$$

Substitutions from definitions (12) in Section 2.1 for a_0, a_k, and b_k yield

$$S_n(x) = \frac{1}{2L} \int_0^{2L} f(t) \, dt + \sum_{k=1}^n \left(\cos \frac{k\pi x}{L} \frac{1}{L} \int_0^{2L} f(t) \cos \frac{k\pi t}{L} \, dt \right.$$

$$\left. + \sin \frac{k\pi x}{L} \frac{1}{L} \int_0^{2L} f(t) \sin \frac{k\pi t}{L} \, dt \right)$$

$$= \frac{1}{L} \int_0^{2L} \left[\frac{1}{2} f(t) + \sum_{k=1}^n f(t) \left(\cos \frac{k\pi x}{L} \cos \frac{k\pi t}{L} + \sin \frac{k\pi x}{L} \sin \frac{k\pi t}{L} \right) \right] dt$$

$$= \frac{1}{L} \int_0^{2L} f(t) \left(\frac{1}{2} + \sum_{k=1}^n \cos \frac{k\pi(x-t)}{L} \right) dt$$

$$= \frac{1}{L} \int_0^{2L} f(t) \, \frac{\sin \dfrac{(n+1/2)\pi(x-t)}{L}}{2 \sin \dfrac{\pi(x-t)}{2L}} \; dt.^{\dagger}$$

Since the integrand is of period $2L$, we may integrate over any interval of length $2L$. We choose an interval beginning at a, where $a < x < a + 2L$, and rearrange the integrand into the following form:

$$S_n(x) = \frac{1}{L} \int_a^{a+2L} \left(f(t) \frac{x-t}{2 \sin \dfrac{\pi(x-t)}{2L}} \right) \frac{\sin \dfrac{(n+1/2)\pi(x-t)}{L}}{x-t} \; dt.$$

In order to take limits as $n \to \infty$ and apply Result 3, we require piecewise continuity of

$$F(t) = f(t) \frac{x-t}{2 \sin \dfrac{\pi(x-t)}{2L}}$$

on $a \le t \le a + 2L$ and existence of both of its one-sided derivatives at $t = x$ (x fixed). This will follow if

$$\frac{x-t}{2 \sin \dfrac{\pi(x-t)}{2L}}$$

has these properties [since $f(t)$ has, by assumption]. Since $t = x$ is the only point in the interval $a \le t \le a + 2L$ at which the denominator of this function vanishes, it follows that it is indeed piecewise continuous thereon. Furthermore, it is easily shown that this function has a right and left derivative at $t = x$. By Result 3, then,

$$\lim_{n \to \infty} S_n(x) = \lim_{n \to \infty} \frac{1}{L} \int_a^{a+2L} \left(f(t) \frac{x-t}{2 \sin \dfrac{\pi(x-t)}{2L}} \right) \frac{\sin \dfrac{(n+1/2)\pi(x-t)}{L}}{x-t} \; dt$$

$$= \frac{\pi}{L} \lim_{n \to \infty} \frac{1}{\pi} \int_a^{a+2L} F(t) \frac{\sin \dfrac{(2n+1)\pi(x-t)}{2L}}{x-t} \; dt = \frac{\pi}{2L} [F(x+) + F(x-)].$$

† We have used the identity

$$\frac{1}{2} + \sum_{k=1}^n \cos k\theta = \frac{\sin(n+1/2)\theta}{2 \sin(\theta/2)}.$$

This formula can be established by expressing $\cos k\theta$ as a complex exponential $(e^{ik\theta} + e^{-ik\theta})/2$ and summing the two resulting geometric series. The identity is regarded in the limit sense at angles for which $\sin(\theta/2) = 0$.

Since $F(x+) = \lim_{t \to x^+} F(t) = f(x+)(L/\pi)$, and similarly for $F(x-)$, it follows that

$$\lim_{n \to \infty} S_n(x) = \frac{\pi}{2L}\left(\frac{L}{\pi}f(x+) + \frac{L}{\pi}f(x-)\right)$$

$$= \frac{f(x+) + f(x-)}{2}.$$

∎

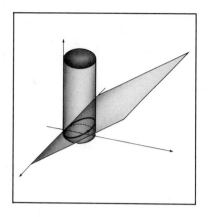

Convergence of Fourier Integrals

In order to establish convergence of a Fourier integral to the function that it represents, we require some preliminary results on trigonometric integrals. They parallel and utilize analogous properties in Appendix A.

Result 1 (Riemann's Theorem)

If $f(x)$ is piecewise continuous on every finite interval and absolutely integrable on $-\infty < x < \infty$, then

$$\lim_{\lambda \to \infty} \int_{-\infty}^{\infty} f(x) \sin \lambda x \, dx = 0 = \lim_{\lambda \to \infty} \int_{-\infty}^{\infty} f(x) \cos \lambda x \, dx. \tag{1}$$

Proof: Since

$$\lim_{\lambda \to \infty} \int_{-\infty}^{\infty} f(x) \sin \lambda x \, dx = \lim_{\lambda \to \infty} \left(\lim_{\substack{r \to \infty \\ s \to \infty}} \int_{-s}^{r} f(x) \sin \lambda x \, dx \right),$$

and the limit on r and s is absolutely and uniformly convergent with respect to λ, limits may be reversed:

$$\lim_{\lambda \to \infty} \int_{-\infty}^{\infty} f(x) \sin \lambda x \, dx = \lim_{\substack{r \to \infty \\ s \to \infty}} \left(\lim_{\lambda \to \infty} \int_{-s}^{r} f(x) \sin \lambda x \, dx \right).$$

But Riemann's theorem for finite intervals (Result 1 in Appendix A) implies that the integral on the right vanishes for all r and s.   ∎

Result 2

If $f(x)$ is piecewise continuous on every finite interval and absolutely integrable on $-\infty < x < \infty$, then at every x at which $f(x)$ has a right and left derivative,

$$\lim_{\lambda \to \infty} \frac{1}{\pi} \int_{-\infty}^{\infty} f(t) \frac{\sin \lambda(x-t)}{x-t} \, dt = \frac{f(x+) + f(x-)}{2}. \tag{2}$$

Proof:

For each fixed x, the function

$$F(t) = f(t) \frac{\sin \lambda(x-t)}{x-t}$$

is piecewise continuous in t on every finite interval [provided we define $F(x)$ by the limit as t approaches x]. Further, since

$$|F(t)| = |\lambda| |f(t)| \left| \frac{\sin \lambda(x-t)}{\lambda(x-t)} \right| \leq |\lambda| |f(t)|,$$

and $f(t)$ is absolutely integrable on $-\infty < t < \infty$, it follows that the improper integral

$$\int_{-\infty}^{\infty} F(t) \, dt = \int_{-\infty}^{\infty} f(t) \frac{\sin \lambda(x-t)}{x-t} \, dt$$

converges. If a and b are numbers such that $a < x < b$, then

$$\left| \int_{-\infty}^{\infty} F(t) \, dt - \pi \left(\frac{f(x+) + f(x-)}{2} \right) \right| \leq \int_{-\infty}^{a} |F(t)| \, dt$$

$$+ \left| \int_{a}^{b} F(t) \, dt - \pi \left(\frac{f(x+) + f(x-)}{2} \right) \right| + \int_{b}^{\infty} |F(t)| \, dt.$$

Now,

$$\int_{-\infty}^{a} |F(t)| \, dt \leq \int_{-\infty}^{a} \frac{|f(t)|}{|x-t|} \, dt \leq \frac{1}{x-a} \int_{-\infty}^{a} |f(t)| \, dt.$$

Given any $\varepsilon > 0$, there exists $a(\varepsilon) < 0$, independent of λ, such that

$$\int_{-\infty}^{a} |F(t)| \, dt \leq \frac{1}{x-a} \int_{-\infty}^{a} |f(t)| \, dt < \frac{\varepsilon}{3}.$$

Similarly, there exists $b(\varepsilon) > 0$ such that

$$\int_{b}^{\infty} |F(t)| \, dt < \frac{\varepsilon}{3}.$$

Since $f(t)$ is piecewise continuous on $a \leq t \leq b$ and has both one-sided derivatives at $t = x$, $a < x < b$, we have from Result 3 in Appendix A that

$$\lim_{\lambda \to \infty} \frac{1}{\pi} \int_{a}^{b} f(t) \frac{\sin \lambda(x-t)}{x-t} \, dt = \frac{f(x+) + f(x-)}{2};$$

that is, there exists $\lambda(\varepsilon)$ such that whenever $\lambda > \lambda(\varepsilon)$,

$$\left| \int_a^b f(t) \frac{\sin \lambda(x-t)}{x-t} dt - \pi\left(\frac{f(x+)+f(x-)}{2} \right) \right| < \frac{\varepsilon}{3}.$$

Combining these three results, we have, for $\lambda > \lambda(\varepsilon)$,

$$\left| \int_{-\infty}^{\infty} F(t)\, dt - \pi\left(\frac{f(x+)+f(x-)}{2} \right) \right| < \varepsilon.$$

Since ε can be made arbitrarily small, it follows that

$$\lim_{\lambda \to \infty} \frac{1}{\pi} \int_{-\infty}^{\infty} f(t) \frac{\sin \lambda(x-t)}{x-t} dt = \frac{f(x+)+f(x-)}{2}. \qquad \blacksquare$$

We can now establish Theorem 1 in Section 7.2.

Result 3 (Fourier Integral Theorem)

If $f(x)$ is piecewise continuous on every finite interval and absolutely integrable on $-\infty < x < \infty$, then at every x at which $f(x)$ has a right and left derivative,

$$\frac{f(x+)+f(x-)}{2} = \int_0^{\infty} [A(\lambda)\cos \lambda x + B(\lambda)\sin \lambda x]\, d\lambda \qquad \text{(3a)}$$

when $A(\lambda) = \dfrac{1}{\pi} \displaystyle\int_{-\infty}^{\infty} f(x)\cos \lambda x\, dx, \qquad B(\lambda) = \dfrac{1}{\pi} \displaystyle\int_{-\infty}^{\infty} f(x)\sin \lambda x\, dx.$ $\qquad$ **(3b)**

Proof: By Result 2, we may write

$$\frac{f(x+)+f(x-)}{2} = \lim_{\alpha \to \infty} \frac{1}{\pi} \int_{-\infty}^{\infty} f(t) \frac{\sin \alpha(x-t)}{x-t} dt.$$

Since $\displaystyle\int_0^{\alpha} \cos \lambda(x-t)\, d\lambda = \left\{ \frac{\sin \lambda(x-t)}{x-t} \right\}_0^{\alpha} = \frac{\sin \alpha(x-t)}{x-t},$

it follows that

$$\frac{f(x+)+f(x-)}{2} = \lim_{\alpha \to \infty} \frac{1}{\pi} \int_{-\infty}^{\infty} f(t) \left(\int_0^{\alpha} \cos \lambda(x-t)\, d\lambda \right) dt$$

$$= \lim_{\alpha \to \infty} \frac{1}{\pi} \int_{-\infty}^{\infty} \int_0^{\alpha} f(t)\cos \lambda(x-t)\, d\lambda\, dt.$$

Since $\displaystyle\int_{-\infty}^{\infty} f(t)\cos \lambda(x-t)\, dt$

is uniformly convergent with respect to λ, we may interchange the order of integration and write

$$\frac{f(x+) + f(x-)}{2} = \lim_{\alpha \to \infty} \frac{1}{\pi} \int_0^\alpha \int_{-\infty}^\infty f(t) \cos \lambda(x - t)\, dt\, d\lambda$$

$$= \frac{1}{\pi} \int_0^\infty \int_{-\infty}^\infty f(t) \cos \lambda(x - t)\, dt\, d\lambda$$

$$= \frac{1}{\pi} \int_0^\infty \int_{-\infty}^\infty f(t)[\cos \lambda x \cos \lambda t + \sin \lambda x \sin \lambda t]\, dt\, d\lambda.$$

This is the result in equation (3).   ∎

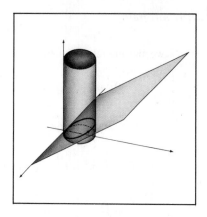

A P P E N D I X
C

Vector Analysis

In this appendix we briefly mention the theorems from vector analysis that are used throughout the book.

When $f(x, y, z)$ is a scalar function with first partial derivatives in some region V of space, its gradient is a vector-valued function defined by

$$\text{grad } f = \nabla f = \frac{\partial f}{\partial x}\hat{\mathbf{i}} + \frac{\partial f}{\partial y}\hat{\mathbf{j}} + \frac{\partial f}{\partial z}\hat{\mathbf{k}}. \tag{1}$$

This is a very important vector in applied mathematics, principally due to the properties stated in the following theorem.

Theorem 1

The directional derivative of a function $f(x, y, z)$ in any direction is the component of ∇f in that direction. Furthermore, $f(x, y, z)$ increases most rapidly in the direction ∇f, and its rate of change in this direction is $|\nabla f|$.

When $\mathbf{F}(x, y, z) = P(x, y, z)\hat{\mathbf{i}} + Q(x, y, z)\hat{\mathbf{j}} + R(x, y, z)\hat{\mathbf{k}}$ is a vector function with first partial derivatives, its divergence and curl are defined as

$$\text{div } \mathbf{F} = \nabla \cdot \mathbf{F} = \frac{\partial P}{\partial x} + \frac{\partial Q}{\partial y} + \frac{\partial R}{\partial z}, \tag{2}$$

$$\text{curl } \mathbf{F} = \nabla \times \mathbf{F} = \left(\frac{\partial R}{\partial y} - \frac{\partial Q}{\partial z} \right) \hat{\mathbf{i}} + \left(\frac{\partial P}{\partial z} - \frac{\partial R}{\partial x} \right) \hat{\mathbf{j}} + \left(\frac{\partial Q}{\partial x} - \frac{\partial P}{\partial y} \right) \hat{\mathbf{k}}. \qquad (3)$$

The gradient, divergence, and curl are linear operators that satisfy the following identities:

$$\nabla(fg) = f\nabla g + g\nabla f, \qquad\qquad\qquad (4a)$$

$$\nabla \cdot (f\mathbf{F}) = \nabla f \cdot \mathbf{F} + f\nabla \cdot \mathbf{F}, \qquad\qquad (4b)$$

$$\nabla \times (f\mathbf{F}) = \nabla f \times \mathbf{F} + f(\nabla \times \mathbf{F}), \qquad\quad (4c)$$

$$\nabla \cdot (\mathbf{F} \times \mathbf{G}) = \mathbf{G} \cdot (\nabla \times \mathbf{F}) - \mathbf{F} \cdot (\nabla \times \mathbf{G}), \quad (4d)$$

$$\nabla \times (\nabla f) = \mathbf{0}, \qquad\qquad\qquad\qquad (4e)$$

$$\nabla \cdot (\nabla \times \mathbf{F}) = 0, \qquad\qquad\qquad\quad (4f)$$

provided $f(x, y, z)$ and the components of vectors are sufficiently differentiable.

The line integral

$$\int_C \mathbf{F} \cdot d\mathbf{r} = \int_C P\,dx + Q\,dy + R\,dz$$

of a continuous vector function $\mathbf{F} = P\hat{\mathbf{i}} + Q\hat{\mathbf{j}} + R\hat{\mathbf{k}}$ along a smooth curve C can always be evaluated by substituting from parametric equations for C and evaluating the resulting definite integral. For example, the value of

$$\int_C y\,dx + x\,dy + z\,dz$$

along the curve $C: x = t^2$, $y = t + 1$, $z = 3t$, $0 \le t \le 1$, can be calculated with the definite integral

$$\int_0^1 (t + 1)(2t\,dt) + t^2\,dt + 3t(3\,dt) = \int_0^1 (3t^2 + 11t)\,dt = \frac{13}{2}.$$

In the event that a line integral is independent of path, and this occurs when $\mathbf{F}$ is the gradient of some scalar function $f(x, y, z)$, the value of the line integral is the difference in the values of $f(x, y, z)$ at terminal and initial points. The above line integral is independent of path, since $\nabla(xy + z^2/2) = y\hat{\mathbf{i}} + x\hat{\mathbf{j}} + z\hat{\mathbf{k}}$, and therefore

$$\int_C y\,dx + x\,dy + z\,dz = \left\{ xy + \frac{z^2}{2} \right\}_{(0,1,0)}^{(1,2,3)} = \frac{13}{2}.$$

The surface integral

$$\iint_S \mathbf{F} \cdot \hat{\mathbf{n}}\,dS$$

of a vector function $\mathbf{F}(x, y, z)$ over a smooth surface S with unit normal vector $\hat{\mathbf{n}}$ is usually evaluated by projecting the surface in a one-to-one fashion onto a coordinate plane, expressing $\mathbf{F} \cdot \hat{\mathbf{n}}$ and dS in terms of coordinates in this plane, and evaluating the resulting double integral. For example, when $\mathbf{F} = x^2 y\hat{\mathbf{i}} + xz\hat{\mathbf{j}}$ and when $\hat{\mathbf{n}}$ is the upper normal to the surface $S: z = 4 - x^2 - y^2, z \geq 0$, it is appropriate to project S onto the xy-plane (Figure C.1). The unit upper normal to S is

$$\hat{\mathbf{n}} = \frac{\mathbf{V}(z - 4 + x^2 + y^2)}{|\mathbf{V}(z - 4 + x^2 + y^2)|} = \frac{(2x, 2y, 1)}{\sqrt{1 + 4x^2 + 4y^2}}.$$

The relationship between a rectangular area $dy\,dx$ in the xy-plane and its projection dS on S is

$$dS = \sqrt{1 + \left(\frac{\partial z}{\partial x}\right)^2 + \left(\frac{\partial z}{\partial y}\right)^2}\, dy\,dx = \sqrt{1 + 4x^2 + 4y^2}\, dy\,dx.$$

Since S projects onto the circle $x^2 + y^2 \leq 4$, the value of the surface integral of $\mathbf{F}$ over S is

$$\iint_S \mathbf{F} \cdot \hat{\mathbf{n}}\, dS = \int_{-2}^{2} \int_{-\sqrt{4-x^2}}^{\sqrt{4-x^2}} (x^2y, xz, 0) \cdot \frac{(2x, 2y, 1)}{\sqrt{1 + 4x^2 + 4y^2}} \sqrt{1 + 4x^2 + 4y^2}\, dy\,dx$$

$$= \int_{-2}^{2} \int_{-\sqrt{4-x^2}}^{\sqrt{4-x^2}} (2x^3y + 2xyz)\, dy\,dx$$

$$= \int_{-2}^{2} \int_{-\sqrt{4-x^2}}^{\sqrt{4-x^2}} [2x^3y + 2xy(4 - x^2 - y^2)]\, dy\,dx$$

$$= 0.$$

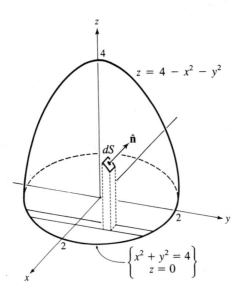

Figure C.1

When a surface does not project in a one-to-one fashion onto a coordinate plane (such would be the case, for example, if the surface were closed), it must be divided into subsurfaces that do project one-to-one. Alternatively, if the surface is indeed closed, the surface integral can be replaced by a triple integral over its interior. This is the result of the following theorem.

Theorem 2 (Divergence Theorem)

Let S be a piecewise smooth surface enclosing a volume V. Let $\mathbf{F}(x, y, z)$ be a vector function whose components have continuous first partial derivatives inside and on S. If $\hat{\mathbf{n}}$ is the unit outward-pointing normal to S, then

$$\oiint_S \mathbf{F} \cdot \hat{\mathbf{n}}\, dS = \iiint_V \nabla \cdot \mathbf{F}\, dV. \tag{5}$$

For example, consider evaluating the surface integral of $\mathbf{F} = x\hat{\mathbf{i}} + y\hat{\mathbf{j}} + z\hat{\mathbf{k}}$ over the surface S that encloses the volume described by $x^2 + y^2 \leq 4$, $0 \leq z \leq 2$ (Figure C.2). To do so by surface integrals would require that the top and bottom of the cylinder be projected onto the xy-plane and that the cylindrical side be divided into two parts, each of which projects one-to-one onto the xz-plane (or yz-plane). Alternatively, the divergence theorem yields

$$\oiint_S \mathbf{F} \cdot \hat{\mathbf{n}}\, dS = \iiint_V \nabla \cdot \mathbf{F}\, dV = \iiint_V (1+1+1)\, dV = 3 \iiint_V dV = 3(\text{volume of } V) = 24\pi.$$

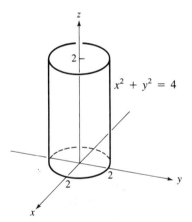

Figure C.2

If we set $\mathbf{F} = u\nabla v$ in (5), where u and v are arbitrary functions of x, y, and z, and use identity (4b), we immediately obtain

$$\oiint_S (u\nabla v) \cdot \hat{\mathbf{n}}\, dS = \iiint_V (u\nabla^2 v + \nabla u \cdot \nabla v)\, dV. \tag{6}$$

This result is called *Green's first identity*. When u and v are interchanged in (6) and the equations are subtracted, the result is called *Green's second identity*:

$$\oiint_S (u\nabla v - v\nabla u) \cdot \hat{\mathbf{n}}\, dS = \iiint_V (u\nabla^2 v - v\nabla^2 u)\, dV. \tag{7}$$

Stokes's theorem relates line integrals around closed curves to surface integrals over surfaces that have the curves as boundaries.

Theorem 3 (Stokes's Theorem)

Let C be a closed, piecewise smooth, non-self-intersecting curve, and let S be a piecewise smooth (orientable) surface with C as boundary (Figure C.3). Let $\mathbf{F}$ be a vector function whose components have continuous first partial derivatives in a region that contains S and C in its interior. Then,

$$\oint_C \mathbf{F} \cdot d\mathbf{r} = \iint_S (\mathbf{\nabla} \times \mathbf{F}) \cdot \hat{\mathbf{n}} \, dS, \tag{8}$$

where $\hat{\mathbf{n}}$ is the unit normal to S chosen in the following way. If when moving along C, the surface S is on the left side, then $\hat{\mathbf{n}}$ must be chosen as the unit normal on that side. On the other hand, if when moving along C, the surface is on the right, then $\hat{\mathbf{n}}$ must be chosen on the opposite side of S.

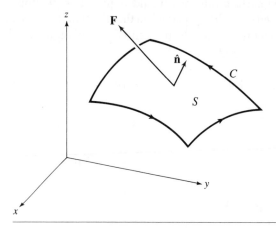

Figure C.3

For example, consider the line integral

$$\oint_C y^2 \, dx + xy \, dy + xz \, dz,$$

where C is the curve of intersection of the surfaces $x^2 + y^2 = 2y$ and $y = z$, directed so that y increases when x is positive (Figure C.4). If we choose S as that part of the plane $y = z$ interior to C, then

$$\hat{\mathbf{n}} = \frac{\mathbf{\nabla}(z - y)}{|\mathbf{\nabla}(z - y)|} = \frac{(0, -1, 1)}{\sqrt{2}}.$$

Since $\mathbf{\nabla} \times \mathbf{F} = (0, -z, -y)$, it follows by Stokes's theorem that

$$\oint_C y^2 \, dx + xy \, dy + xz \, dz = \iint_S (0, -z, -y) \cdot \frac{(0, -1, 1)}{\sqrt{2}} \, dS$$

$$= \iint_S \frac{z - y}{\sqrt{2}} \, dS$$

$$= 0,$$

since $z = y$ at every point of S.

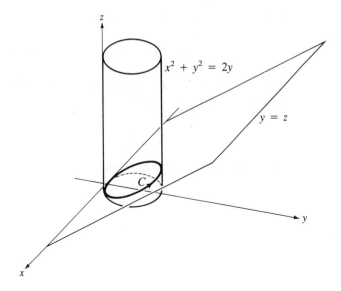

Figure C.4

When C is a curve in the xy-plane (directed counterclockwise) and S is chosen as that part A of the xy-plane interior to C, we obtain Green's theorem as a special case of Stokes's theorem (Figure C.5):

$$\oint_C \mathbf{F} \cdot d\mathbf{r} = \oint_C P(x, y)\, dx + Q(x, y)\, dy$$

$$= \iint_A \left(\frac{\partial Q}{\partial x} - \frac{\partial P}{\partial y} \right) dy\, dx. \tag{9}$$

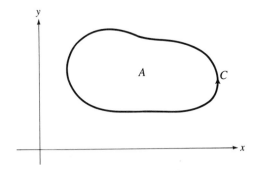

Figure C.5

The two-dimensional version of Green's first identity is obtained from (9) by setting $P = -u\,\partial v/\partial y$ and $Q = u\,\partial v/\partial x$, where u and v are functions of x and y:

$$\oint_C (u\nabla v) \cdot \hat{\mathbf{n}}\, ds = \iint_A (u\nabla^2 v + \nabla u \cdot \nabla v)\, dA. \tag{10}$$

Interchanging u and v and subtracting gives the two-dimensional second identity,

$$\oint_C (u\nabla v - v\nabla u) \cdot \hat{\mathbf{n}}\, ds = \iint_A (u\nabla^2 v - v\nabla^2 u)\, dA. \tag{11}$$

An alternative form of Green's theorem, which casts it as a two-dimensional version of the divergence theorem, is

$$\oint_C \mathbf{F} \cdot \hat{\mathbf{n}}\, ds = \iint_A \nabla \cdot \mathbf{F}\, dA, \tag{12}$$

where $\hat{\mathbf{n}}$ is the outward-pointing normal to C.

Answers to Selected Exercises

Section 1.1

2. (a) $V(0, y, z) = f_1(y, z), y > 0, z > 0;$
$V(L, y, z) = f_2(y, z), y > 0, z > 0;$
$V(x, 0, z) = f_3(x, z), 0 < x < L, z > 0;$
$V(x, y, 0) = f_4(x, y), 0 < x < L, y > 0$

(b) $\dfrac{-\partial V(0, y, z)}{\partial x} = f_1(y, z), y > 0, z > 0;$

$\dfrac{\partial V(L, y, z)}{\partial x} = f_2(y, z), y > 0, z > 0;$

$\dfrac{-\partial V(x, 0, z)}{\partial y} = f_3(x, z), 0 < x < L, z > 0;$

$\dfrac{-\partial V(x, y, 0)}{\partial z} = f_4(x, y), 0 < x < L, y > 0$

(c) $-l_1 \dfrac{\partial V(0, y, z)}{\partial x} + h_1 V(0, y, z) = f_1(y, z),$

$y > 0, z > 0;$

$l_2 \dfrac{\partial V(L, y, z)}{\partial x} + h_2 V(L, y, z) = f_2(y, z),$

$y > 0, z > 0;$

$-l_3 \dfrac{\partial V(x, 0, z)}{\partial y} + h_3 V(x, 0, z) = f_3(x, z),$

$0 < x < L, z > 0;$

$-l_4 \dfrac{\partial V(x, y, 0)}{\partial z} + h_4 V(x, y, 0) = f_4(x, y),$

$0 < x < L, y > 0$

4. (a) $V(r_0, \theta) = f_1(\theta), 0 < \theta < \pi; V(r, 0) = f_2(r),$
$0 < r < r_0; V(r, \pi) = f_3(r), 0 < r < r_0$

(b) $\dfrac{\partial V(r_0, \theta)}{\partial r} = f_1(\theta), 0 < \theta < \pi;$

$-\dfrac{1}{r} \dfrac{\partial V(r, 0)}{\partial \theta} = f_2(r), 0 < r < r_0;$

$\dfrac{1}{r} \dfrac{\partial V(r, \pi)}{\partial \theta} = f_3(r), 0 < r < r_0$

(c) $l_1 \dfrac{\partial V(r_0, \theta)}{\partial r} + h_1 V(r_0, \theta) = f_1(\theta), 0 < \theta < \pi;$

$-\dfrac{l_2}{r} \dfrac{\partial V(r, 0)}{\partial \theta} + h_2 V(r, 0) = f_2(r), 0 < r < r_0;$

$\dfrac{l_3}{r} \dfrac{\partial V(r, \pi)}{\partial \theta} + h_3 V(r, \pi) = f_3(r), 0 < r < r_0$

7. (a) $V(r_0, \theta, \phi) = f_1(\theta, \phi), -\pi < \theta \le \pi, 0 \le \phi < \dfrac{\pi}{2};$

$V\left(r, \theta, \dfrac{\pi}{2}\right) = f_2(r, \theta), 0 \le r < r_0, -\pi < \theta \le \pi$

(b) $\dfrac{\partial V(r_0, \theta, \phi)}{\partial r} = f_1(\theta, \phi), -\pi < \theta \le \pi, 0 \le \phi < \dfrac{\pi}{2};$

$\dfrac{1}{r} \dfrac{\partial V(r, \theta, \pi/2)}{\partial \phi} = f_2(r, \theta), 0 < r < r_0, -\pi < \theta \le \pi$

(c) $l_1 \dfrac{\partial V(r_0, \theta, \phi)}{\partial r} + h_1 V(r_0, \theta, \phi) = f_1(\theta, \phi),$

$-\pi < \theta \le \pi, 0 \le \phi < \dfrac{\pi}{2};$

$\dfrac{l_2}{r} \dfrac{\partial V(r, \theta, \pi/2)}{\partial \phi} + h_2 V\left(r, \theta, \dfrac{\pi}{2}\right) = f_2(r, \theta),$

$0 < r < r_0, -\pi < \theta \le \pi$

Section 1.2

3. $\dfrac{\partial U}{\partial t} = k \dfrac{\partial^2 U}{\partial x^2}, 0 < x < L, t > 0; U_x(0, t) = 0, t > 0;$

$U(L, t) = 100, t > 0; U(x, 0) = f(x), 0 < x < L$

5. $\dfrac{\partial U}{\partial t} = k \dfrac{\partial^2 U}{\partial x^2}, 0 < x < L, t > 0,$

$-\kappa \dfrac{\partial U}{\partial x} + \mu_0 U = \mu_0 U_0, x = 0, t > 0,$

$\kappa \dfrac{\partial U}{\partial x} + \mu_L U = \mu_L U_L, x = L, t > 0; U(x, 0) = f(x),$

$0 < x < L$

7. $\dfrac{\partial U}{\partial t} = k\dfrac{\partial^2 U}{\partial x^2}, 0 < x < L, t > 0; -\kappa\dfrac{\partial U}{\partial x} = Q_0,$

$x = 0, t > 0; \kappa\dfrac{\partial U}{\partial x} = -\dfrac{Q_L(t)}{A}, x = L, t > 0;$

$U(x, 0) = f(x), 0 < x < L$

10. $\dfrac{\partial U}{\partial t} = k\left(\dfrac{\partial^2 U}{\partial r^2} + \dfrac{1}{r}\dfrac{\partial U}{\partial r} + \dfrac{1}{r^2}\dfrac{\partial^2 U}{\partial \theta^2}\right) + \dfrac{kg(r)}{\kappa},$

$0 < r < r_0, -\pi < \theta \le \pi, t > 0; \kappa\dfrac{\partial U}{\partial r} + \mu U = 0,$

$r = r_0, -\pi < \theta \le \pi, t > 0; U(r, \theta, 0) = f(r, \theta),$

$0 \le r < r_0, -\pi < \theta \le \pi,$ where

$$g(r) = \begin{cases} 0 & 0 < r < r_1 \\ q & r_1 < r < r_2 \\ 0 & r_2 < r < r_0 \end{cases}$$

12. $\dfrac{\partial U}{\partial t} = k\left(\dfrac{\partial^2 U}{\partial r^2} + \dfrac{1}{r}\dfrac{\partial U}{\partial r} + \dfrac{1}{r^2}\dfrac{\partial^2 U}{\partial \theta^2} + \dfrac{\partial^2 U}{\partial z^2}\right),$

$0 < r < r_0, -\pi < \theta \le \pi, 0 < z < L, t > 0;$
$U_z(r, \theta, 0, t) = 0, 0 \le r < r_0, -\pi < \theta \le \pi, t > 0;$
$U_z(r, \theta, L, t) = 0, 0 \le r < r_0, -\pi < \theta \le \pi, t > 0;$
$U(r_0, \theta, z, t) = f_1(\theta, t), -\pi < \theta \le \pi, 0 < z < L,$
$t > 0; U(r, \theta, z, 0) = f(r, \theta, z), 0 \le r < r_0,$
$-\pi < \theta \le \pi, 0 < z < L$

16. $\dfrac{\partial U}{\partial t} = k\left(\dfrac{\partial^2 U}{\partial r^2} + \dfrac{1}{r}\dfrac{\partial U}{\partial r} + \dfrac{1}{r^2}\dfrac{\partial^2 U}{\partial \theta^2}\right), 0 < r < r_0,$

$0 < \theta < \pi, t > 0; U_r(r_0, \theta, t) = 0, 0 < \theta < \pi, t > 0;$
$-\kappa r^{-1}U_\theta(r, 0, t) = q, 0 < r < r_0, t > 0;$
$\kappa r^{-1}U_\theta(r, \pi, t) = q, 0 < r < r_0, t > 0;$
$U(r, \theta, 0) = f(r, \theta), 0 \le r < r_0, 0 < \theta < \pi$

20. $\dfrac{(U_L - U_0)x}{L} + U_0$

21. $\dfrac{-q_0 x}{\kappa} + C, C$ arbitrary, provided $q_L = -q_0$

22. (a) True; (b) Not necessarily true

26. (a) $\dfrac{-\kappa A(U_{out} - U_{in})}{L}$;   (b) 660 W

27. (a) $\dfrac{-\kappa(U_{out} - U_{in})}{r\ln(r_{out}/r_{in})}$;   (b) 2.36×10^4 W

33. (a) $\dfrac{U_a[\kappa + b\mu \ln(b/r)] + b\mu U_m \ln(r/a)}{\kappa + b\mu \ln(b/a)}$

34. $\dfrac{-I^2 r^2}{4\kappa\pi^2 a^4 \sigma} + \dfrac{I^2}{4\pi^2 a^2 \sigma}\left(\dfrac{1}{\kappa} + \dfrac{2}{\kappa^*}\ln\left(\dfrac{b}{a}\right) + \dfrac{2}{b\mu^*}\right) + U_m,$

$0 \le r \le a; \dfrac{I^2}{2\kappa^*\pi^2 a^2 \sigma}\ln\left(\dfrac{b}{r}\right) + \dfrac{I^2}{2\pi^2 a^2 \sigma b\mu^*} + U_m,$

$a \le r < b$

Section 1.3

3. $\dfrac{\partial^2 y}{\partial t^2} = c^2\dfrac{\partial^2 y}{\partial x^2} - \dfrac{\beta}{\rho}\dfrac{\partial y}{\partial t} + g, 0 < x < L, t > 0,$

$(g < 0, \beta > 0); -\dfrac{\tau\partial y}{\partial x} + k_1 y = 0, x = 0, t > 0;$

$\tau\dfrac{\partial y}{\partial x} + k_2 y = 0, x = L, t > 0; y(x, 0) = f(x),$

$0 < x < L; y_t(x, 0) = g(x), 0 < x < L$

6. $\dfrac{\partial^2 y}{\partial t^2} = c^2\dfrac{\partial^2 y}{\partial x^2}, 0 < x < L, t > 0; y(0, t) = 0, t > 0;$

$E\dfrac{\partial y(L, t)}{\partial x} = F, t > 0; y(x, 0) = 0, 0 < x < L;$

$y_t(x, 0) = 0, 0 < x < L$

9. $\dfrac{\partial^2 y}{\partial t^2} = c^2\dfrac{\partial^2 y}{\partial x^2} + g, 0 < x < L, t > 0 (g < 0);$

$y(0, t) = y(L, t) = 0, t > 0; y(x, 0) = y_t(x, 0) = 0,$

$0 < x < L$

Static deflection: $y = \dfrac{gx(L - x)}{2c^2}$

11. $\dfrac{\partial^2 y}{\partial t^2} = c^2\dfrac{\partial^2 y}{\partial x^2} + g, 0 < x < L, t > 0 (g < 0);$

$y(0, t) = 0, t > 0; \tau\dfrac{\partial y(L, t)}{\partial x} = F_L, t > 0;$

$y(x, 0) = y_t(x, 0) = 0, 0 < x < L$

Static deflection: $y = \dfrac{gx(2L - x)}{2c^2} + F_L x/\tau$

13. $L + \dfrac{gL^2}{2c^2}$

14. $L + \dfrac{gL^2}{2c^2} + AL\rho g/k; A =$ cross-sectional area of bar

Section 1.4

4. $\dfrac{\partial^2 z}{\partial r^2} + \dfrac{1}{r}\dfrac{\partial z}{\partial r} + \dfrac{1}{r^2}\dfrac{\partial^2 z}{\partial \theta^2} = \dfrac{-\rho g}{\tau}, 0 < r < r_1, 0 < \theta < \alpha$

$(g < 0); z(r, 0) = 0, 0 < r < r_1; z(r, \alpha) = 0,$
$0 < r < r_1; z(r_1, \theta) = f(\theta), 0 < \theta < \alpha$

5. $\dfrac{\partial^2 z}{\partial t^2} = c^2\left(\dfrac{\partial^2 z}{\partial r^2} + \dfrac{1}{r}\dfrac{\partial z}{\partial r} + \dfrac{1}{r^2}\dfrac{\partial^2 z}{\partial \theta^2}\right) + g - \dfrac{\beta}{\rho}\dfrac{\partial z}{\partial t},$

$0 < r < r_1, -\pi < \theta \le \pi, t > 0 (g < 0, \beta > 0);$
$z(r_1, \theta, t) = 0, -\pi < \theta \le \pi, t > 0; z(r, \theta, 0) = f(r, \theta),$
$0 \le r < r_1, -\pi < \theta \le \pi; z_t(r, \theta, 0) = 0, 0 \le r < r_1,$
$-\pi < \theta \le \pi$

8. $z(r) = \dfrac{\rho g(r_2^2 - r^2)}{4\tau}$

9. (a) $z'' + r^{-1}z' = \dfrac{-f(r)}{\tau}, 0 < r < r_2; z(r_2) = 0$

(f) $\dfrac{k(9r_2r^2 - 4r^3 - 5r_2^3)}{36\tau}$

Section 1.5

1. $\dfrac{\partial^2 y}{\partial t^2} + c^2 \dfrac{\partial^4 y}{\partial x^4} = g, 0 < x < L, t > 0 \left(c^2 = \dfrac{EI}{\rho}\right);$

$y(0, t) = y_x(0, t) = 0, t > 0; y_{xx}(L, t) = y_{xxx}(L, t) = 0,$
$t > 0; y(x, 0) = f(x), 0 < x < L; y_t(x, 0) = 0,$
$0 < x < L$

5. (a) $\dfrac{d^4 y}{dx^4} = \dfrac{F}{EI}, 0 < x < L,$

$y(0) = y''(0) = 0 = y(L) = y''(L)$

$y(x) = \dfrac{Fx(x^3 - 2Lx^2 + L^3)}{24EI}$

(b) 9.2×10^{-9} m   **(c)** 1.68×10^9 N/m

Section 1.6

1. $\dfrac{\partial^2 V}{\partial x^2} + \dfrac{\partial^2 V}{\partial y^2} = 0, 0 < x < L, 0 < y < L'; V(0, y) = 0,$

$0 < y < L'; V(L, y) = 100, 0 < y < L'; V(x, 0) = 0,$
$0 < x < L; V(x, L') = 100, 0 < x < L$

Section 1.8

2. Elliptic, $w_{vv} + w_{\eta\eta} = \left(\dfrac{1}{4}\right)\left[-3w_v - 6w_\eta + \left(\dfrac{\eta}{2} - v\right)w\right]$

4. Hyperbolic,

$w_{v\eta} = \left(\dfrac{w}{8}\right)[(3 + 2\sqrt{2})w_v + (3 - 2\sqrt{2})w_\eta]$

13. (b) $w_{v\eta} = \dfrac{-(w_v + w_\eta)}{6\eta + 6v}$ **(c)** $w_{vv} + w_{\eta\eta} = \dfrac{-w_v}{3v}$

(d) $u_{yy} = 0$

17. $w_{v\eta} = \dfrac{w_\eta}{v}$ **19.** $v_{vv} + v_{\eta\eta} = \dfrac{45v}{64}$

20. $v_{v\eta} = \dfrac{v}{64}$ **21.** $v_{vv} = -2v_\eta$

Section 2.1

2. $\dfrac{8L^2}{3} - 1 + \dfrac{8L^2}{\pi^2} \sum_{n=1}^{\infty} \left(\dfrac{1}{n^2} \cos\dfrac{n\pi x}{L} - \dfrac{\pi}{n} \sin\dfrac{n\pi x}{L}\right)$

3. $\dfrac{2L^2}{3} - 1 + \dfrac{8L^2}{\pi^2} \sum_{n=1}^{\infty} \dfrac{(-1)^n}{n^2} \cos\dfrac{n\pi x}{L}$

6. $\dfrac{3L}{4} + \dfrac{L}{\pi^2} \sum_{n=1}^{\infty} \left(\dfrac{3[1 + (-1)^{n+1}]}{n^2} \cos\dfrac{n\pi x}{L} + \dfrac{\pi}{n} \sin\dfrac{n\pi x}{L}\right)$

9. $1 + \sin x - \cos 2x$ **11.** $\dfrac{1}{2} + \dfrac{1}{2} \cos 4x$

14. $\dfrac{3}{\pi} - \dfrac{1}{2} \sin x - \dfrac{6}{\pi} \sum_{n=1}^{\infty} \dfrac{1}{4n^2 - 1} \cos 2nx$

16. No   **17.** $\dfrac{L^2}{3} + \dfrac{2L^2}{\pi^2} \sum_{\substack{n=-\infty \\ n \neq 0}}^{\infty} \dfrac{(-1)^n}{n^2} e^{-n\pi xi/L}$

18. $\dfrac{e^4 - 1}{2} \sum_{n=-\infty}^{\infty} \left(\dfrac{2 - n\pi i}{n^2\pi^2 + 4}\right) e^{-n\pi xi/2}$

Section 2.2

2. $\dfrac{\pi}{2} - \dfrac{4}{\pi} \sum_{n=1}^{\infty} \dfrac{1}{(2n-1)^2} \cos(2n-1)x$

4. $\dfrac{2L^2}{3} - 1 + \dfrac{8L^2}{\pi^2} \sum_{n=1}^{\infty} \dfrac{(-1)^n}{n^2} \cos\dfrac{n\pi x}{L}$

6. $\dfrac{2L}{\pi} \sum_{n=1}^{\infty} \dfrac{(-1)^n}{n} \sin\dfrac{n\pi x}{L}$ **9.** $\dfrac{1}{2} \sin\dfrac{2\pi x}{L}$

10. $\dfrac{8L^2}{\pi^3} \sum_{n=1}^{\infty} \dfrac{1}{(2n-1)^3} \sin\dfrac{(2n-1)\pi x}{L}$

11. $-\dfrac{L}{2} + \dfrac{4L}{\pi^2} \sum_{n=1}^{\infty} \dfrac{1}{(2n-1)^2} \cos\dfrac{(2n-1)\pi x}{L}$

13. $\dfrac{L^2}{6} - \dfrac{L^2}{\pi^2} \sum_{n=1}^{\infty} \dfrac{1}{n^2} \cos\dfrac{2n\pi x}{L}$

15. $\dfrac{1}{2} + \dfrac{2}{\pi} \sum_{n=1}^{\infty} \dfrac{(-1)^{n+1}}{2n-1} \cos\dfrac{(2n-1)\pi x}{L}$

16. $\dfrac{2}{\pi} - \dfrac{4}{\pi} \sum_{n=1}^{\infty} \dfrac{1}{4n^2 - 1} \cos 2nx$

19. (a) Yes; **(b)** Not necessarily

21. (b) Yes   **22. (b)** Yes

Section 2.3

2. (b) No

4. (a) Does not generally converge uniformly

(b) Does not generally converge uniformly

(c) Does converge uniformly

Section 3.1

1. Linear and homogeneous   **2.** Not linear

3. Not linear   **4.** Not linear

5. Linear and homogeneous

6. Linear and nonhomogeneous

7. Linear and nonhomogeneous

8. Not linear

9. Linear and homogeneous

10. Linear and homogeneous

Section 3.2

1. U_0

3. (a) $\dfrac{4L}{\pi^2}\displaystyle\sum_{n=1}^{\infty}\dfrac{(-1)^{n+1}}{(2n-1)^2}e^{-(2n-1)^2\pi^2 kt/L^2}\sin\dfrac{(2n-1)\pi x}{L}$

(b) $\dfrac{4\kappa}{\pi}\displaystyle\sum_{n=1}^{\infty}\dfrac{(-1)^n}{2n-1}e^{-(2n-1)^2\pi^2 kt/L^2};\ 0;$

$\dfrac{-4\kappa}{\pi}\displaystyle\sum_{n=1}^{\infty}\dfrac{(-1)^n}{2n-1}e^{-(2n-1)^2\pi^2 kt/L^2}$

(c) $\dfrac{4\kappa}{\pi}\displaystyle\sum_{n=1}^{\infty}\dfrac{(-1)^n}{2n-1}=-\kappa,0,\kappa;0,0,0$

5. (a) $\dfrac{4\kappa}{\pi}\displaystyle\sum_{n=1}^{\infty}\dfrac{(-1)^n}{2n-1}e^{-(2n-1)^2\pi^2 kt/L^2};$ (b) $-\kappa$

7. $\dfrac{4L}{5\pi^2}\displaystyle\sum_{n=1}^{\infty}\dfrac{(-1)^{n+1}}{(2n-1)^2}\cos\dfrac{(2n-1)\pi ct}{L}\sin\dfrac{(2n-1)\pi x}{L}$

8. $\dfrac{8L^3}{\pi^4 c}\displaystyle\sum_{n=1}^{\infty}\dfrac{1}{(2n-1)^4}\sin\dfrac{(2n-1)\pi ct}{L}\sin\dfrac{(2n-1)\pi x}{L}$

10. $\displaystyle\sum_{n=1}^{\infty}\left(a_n\cos\dfrac{n\pi ct}{L}+b_n\sin\dfrac{n\pi ct}{L}\right)\sin\dfrac{n\pi x}{L},$ where

$a_n=\dfrac{2}{L}\displaystyle\int_0^L f(x)\sin\dfrac{n\pi x}{L}dx,$

$b_n=\dfrac{2}{n\pi c}\displaystyle\int_0^L g(x)\sin\dfrac{n\pi x}{L}dx$

13. $\dfrac{a_0+b_0 t}{2}+\displaystyle\sum_{n=1}^{\infty}\left(a_n\cos\dfrac{n\pi ct}{L}+b_n\sin\dfrac{n\pi ct}{L}\right)\cos\dfrac{n\pi x}{L},$

where $a_n=\dfrac{2}{L}\displaystyle\int_0^L f(x)\cos\dfrac{n\pi x}{L}dx,$

$b_n=\dfrac{2}{n\pi c}\displaystyle\int_0^L g(x)\cos\dfrac{n\pi x}{L}dx,\ b_0=\dfrac{2}{L}\displaystyle\int_0^L g(x)dx$

16. $\dfrac{L^*-L}{2}-\dfrac{4(L^*-L)}{\pi^2}\displaystyle\sum_{n=1}^{\infty}\dfrac{1}{(2n-1)^2}\cos\dfrac{(2n-1)\pi ct}{L}$

$\times\cos\dfrac{(2n-1)\pi x}{L}$

17. $\dfrac{400}{\pi}\displaystyle\sum_{n=1}^{\infty}\dfrac{1}{(2n-1)\sinh\dfrac{(2n-1)\pi L}{L'}}$

$\times\sinh\dfrac{(2n-1)\pi(L-x)}{L'}\sin\dfrac{(2n-1)\pi y}{L'}$

20. $-\dfrac{400L'}{\pi^2}\displaystyle\sum_{n=1}^{\infty}\dfrac{1}{(2n-1)^2\cosh\dfrac{(2n-1)\pi L}{L'}}$

$\times\sinh\dfrac{(2n-1)\pi(L-x)}{L'}\sin\dfrac{(2n-1)\pi y}{L'}$

21. $100x+B;\ 100x-50L$　　22. No

24. $\dfrac{4qL}{\pi^2\kappa}\displaystyle\sum_{n=1}^{\infty}\dfrac{1}{(2n-1)^2}\operatorname{sech}\dfrac{(2n-1)\pi L'}{L}$

$\times\sinh\dfrac{(2n-1)\pi(L'-y)}{L}\sin\dfrac{(2n-1)\pi x}{L}$

26. $\dfrac{-2kL}{\pi}\displaystyle\sum_{n=1}^{\infty}\dfrac{1}{n}\operatorname{csch}\dfrac{n\pi L'}{L}\sinh\dfrac{n\pi(L'-y)}{L}\sin\dfrac{n\pi x}{L}$

$-\dfrac{2kL}{\pi}\displaystyle\sum_{n=1}^{\infty}\dfrac{1}{n}\operatorname{csch}\dfrac{n\pi L}{L'}\sinh\dfrac{n\pi(L-x)}{L'}\sin\dfrac{n\pi y}{L'}$

Section 3.3

3. $U_0+\dfrac{(U_L-U_0)x}{L}-\dfrac{2}{\pi}\displaystyle\sum_{n=1}^{\infty}\dfrac{U_0+(-1)^{n+1}U_L}{n}$

$\times e^{-n^2\pi^2 kt/L^2}\sin\dfrac{n\pi x}{L}+\dfrac{I^2 x(L-x)}{2A^2\sigma\kappa}$

$+\dfrac{4}{\pi}\displaystyle\sum_{n=1}^{\infty}\left(\dfrac{20}{2n-1}-\dfrac{L^2 I^2}{(2n-1)^3\pi^2 A^2\sigma\kappa}\right)$

$\times e^{-(2n-1)^2\pi^2 kt/L^2}\sin\dfrac{(2n-1)\pi x}{L}$

6. $20+\dfrac{kI^2 t}{A^2\sigma\kappa}$　　7. $20+\dfrac{k}{2A^2\sigma\kappa\alpha}(1-e^{-2\alpha t})$

9. $\dfrac{4}{\pi}\displaystyle\sum_{n=1}^{\infty}\left(\dfrac{10}{2n-1}e^{-(2n-1)^2\pi^2 kt/L^2}\right.$

$+\dfrac{kL^2}{\kappa(2n-1)[2n-1)^2\pi^2 k-\alpha L^2]}$

$\left.\times[e^{-\alpha t}-e^{-(2n-1)^2\pi^2 kt/L^2}]\right)\sin\dfrac{(2n-1)\pi x}{L}$

13. $\dfrac{kx(x-L)}{2\rho c^2}+\displaystyle\sum_{n=1}^{\infty}\left(a_n\cos\dfrac{n\pi ct}{L}+b_n\sin\dfrac{n\pi ct}{L}\right)$

$\times\sin\dfrac{n\pi x}{L},\ a_n=\dfrac{2}{L}\displaystyle\int_0^L\left(f(x)+\dfrac{kx(L-x)}{2\rho c^2}\right)$

$\times\sin\dfrac{n\pi x}{L}dx,\ b_n=\dfrac{2}{n\pi c}\displaystyle\int_0^L g(x)\sin\dfrac{n\pi x}{L}dx$

15. (a) No;

(c) $\dfrac{Fx}{E}+\dfrac{8LF}{\pi^2 E}\displaystyle\sum_{n=1}^{\infty}\dfrac{(-1)^n}{(2n-1)^2}$

$\times\sin\dfrac{(2n-1)\pi x}{2L}\cos\dfrac{(2n-1)\pi ct}{2L}$

16. $\dfrac{(\rho + k)gx}{24EI}(x^3 - 2Lx^2 + L^3) - \dfrac{4(\rho + k)gL^4}{EI\pi^5}$

$\times \displaystyle\sum_{n=1}^{\infty} \dfrac{1}{(2n-1)^5} \sin\dfrac{(2n-1)\pi x}{L} \cos\dfrac{(2n-1)^2\pi^2 ct}{L^2}$

21. $\dfrac{g(L^2 - x^2)}{2\kappa} + \dfrac{16L^2}{\pi^3}\displaystyle\sum_{n=1}^{\infty}\dfrac{1}{(2n-1)^3}$

$\times \left(\dfrac{g(-1)^n}{\kappa} + 2(-1)^n + (2n-1)\pi\right)$

$\times \operatorname{sech}\dfrac{(2n-1)\pi L'}{2L}\cosh\dfrac{(2n-1)\pi(L'-y)}{2L}$

$\times \cos\dfrac{(2n-1)\pi x}{2L}$

Section 4.1

3. $\dfrac{n^2\pi^2}{16}, n \geq 0; \dfrac{1}{2}, \left(\dfrac{1}{\sqrt{2}}\right)\cos\left(\dfrac{n\pi x}{4}\right)$

5. $\dfrac{(2n-1)^2\pi^2}{4}, n > 0; \sqrt{2}\cos\dfrac{(2n-1)\pi x}{2}$

7. $\dfrac{n^2\pi^2}{81}, n > 0; \left(\dfrac{\sqrt{2}}{3}\right)\sin\dfrac{n\pi(x-1)}{9}$

8. $n^2\pi^2 + \dfrac{1}{4}, n > 0; \sqrt{2}\,e^{x/2}\sin(n\pi x)$

10. $\dfrac{n^2\pi^2}{L^2}, n \geq 0; 1, A\cos\dfrac{n\pi x}{L} + B\sin\dfrac{n\pi x}{L}$

14. Sometimes

Section 4.2

2.

$\sin \lambda_n L$	$\cos \lambda_n L$
$\dfrac{(-1)^{n+1}\lambda_n\left(\dfrac{h_1}{l_1} + \dfrac{h_2}{l_2}\right)}{\left[\left(\lambda_n^2 + \dfrac{h_1^2}{l_1^2}\right)\left(\lambda_n^2 + \dfrac{h_2^2}{l_2^2}\right)\right]^{1/2}}$	$\dfrac{(-1)^{n+1}\left(\lambda_n^2 - \dfrac{h_1 h_2}{l_1 l_2}\right)}{\left[\left(\lambda_n^2 + \dfrac{h_1^2}{l_1^2}\right)\left(\lambda_n^2 + \dfrac{h_2^2}{l_2^2}\right)\right]^{1/2}}$
$\dfrac{(-1)^{n+1}(h_1/l_1)}{\sqrt{\lambda_n^2 + (h_1/l_1)^2}}$	$\dfrac{(-1)^{n+1}\lambda_n}{\sqrt{\lambda_n^2 + (h_1/l_1)^2}}$
$\dfrac{(-1)^{n+1}\lambda_n}{\sqrt{\lambda_n^2 + (h_1/l_1)^2}}$	$\dfrac{(-1)^n(h_1/l_1)}{\sqrt{\lambda_n^2 + (h_1/l_1)^2}}$
$\dfrac{(-1)^{n+1}(h_2/l_2)}{\sqrt{\lambda_n^2 + (h_2/l_2)^2}}$	$\dfrac{(-1)^{n+1}\lambda_n}{\sqrt{\lambda_n^2 + (h_2/l_2)^2}}$
0	$(-1)^n$
$(-1)^{n+1}$	0

$\sin \lambda_n L$	$\cos \lambda_n L$
$\dfrac{(-1)^{n+1}\lambda_n}{\sqrt{\lambda_n^2 + (h_2/l_2)^2}}$	$\dfrac{(-1)^n(h_2/l_2)}{\sqrt{\lambda_n^2 + (h_2/l_2)^2}}$
$(-1)^{n+1}$	0
0	$(-1)^n$

7. $\dfrac{4L}{\pi^2}\displaystyle\sum_{n=1}^{\infty}\left(\dfrac{\pi(-1)^{n+1}}{2n-1} - \dfrac{2}{(2n-1)^2}\right)\cos\dfrac{(2n-1)\pi x}{2L}$

10. $\dfrac{16L^2}{\pi^3}\displaystyle\sum_{n=1}^{\infty}\left(\dfrac{\pi(-1)^{n+1}}{(2n-1)^2} - \dfrac{2}{(2n-1)^3}\right)\sin\dfrac{(2n-1)\pi x}{2L}$

11. $0, 1 + \dfrac{n^2\pi^2}{L^2}(n > 0); \sqrt{\dfrac{2}{e^{2L} - 1}},$

$\dfrac{\sqrt{2L}e^{-x}}{\sqrt{n^2\pi^2 + L^2}}\left(\dfrac{n\pi}{L}\cos\dfrac{n\pi x}{L} + \sin\dfrac{n\pi x}{L}\right)$

16. $\dfrac{(2n-1)^2\pi^2}{4(\ln b)^2}; \sqrt{\dfrac{2}{\ln b}}\cos\left[\dfrac{(2n-1)\pi \ln x}{2\ln b}\right]$

18. 9.84006, 39.3603, 88.5606, 157.441

20. (a) $\dfrac{4}{\pi}\displaystyle\sum_{n=1}^{\infty}\dfrac{(-1)^{n+1}}{2n-1}\cos\dfrac{(2n-1)\pi x}{L};$ (b) 0;

(c) 1, -1

22. No   24. Yes   25. Yes

Section 4.3

7. $X'' + \lambda^2 X = 0, 0 < x < L,$
$X(0) = 0 = X'(L) + 200X(L);$
$Y'' + \beta^2 Y = 0, 0 < y < L',$
$Y'(0) = 0 = Y'(L')$

9. $X'' + \lambda^2 X = 0, 0 < x < L,$
$X(0) = 0 = X'(L)$
$Y(0) = 0 = Y(L')$
$Y'' + \beta^2 Y = 0, 0 < y < L',$

Section 5.2

2. $\displaystyle\sum_{n=1}^{\infty} c_n e^{-(2n-1)^2\pi^2 kt/(4L^2)}\sqrt{\dfrac{2}{L}}\cos\dfrac{(2n-1)\pi x}{2L},$

$c_n = \sqrt{\dfrac{2}{L}}\displaystyle\int_0^L f(x)\cos\dfrac{(2n-1)\pi x}{2L}dx$

6. (b) $\dfrac{4L}{5\pi^2}\displaystyle\sum_{n=1}^{\infty}\dfrac{1}{(2n-1)^2}\left((-1)^n + 2\sin\dfrac{(2n-1)\pi}{4}\right)$

$\times \cos\dfrac{(2n-1)\pi ct}{2L}\sin\dfrac{(2n-1)\pi x}{2L}$

(continued)

(c) $\dfrac{16L^3}{\pi^3 c}\displaystyle\sum_{n=1}^{\infty}\dfrac{1}{(2n-1)^3}\left(\dfrac{4}{(2n-1)\pi}+(-1)^n\right)$

$\times\sin\dfrac{(2n-1)\pi ct}{2L}\sin\dfrac{(2n-1)\pi x}{2L}$

7. (a) $\displaystyle\sum_{n=1}^{\infty}(a_n\cos\omega_n t+b_n\sin\omega_n t)\sqrt{\dfrac{2}{L}}\sin\dfrac{n\pi x}{L}$,

$\omega_n=\sqrt{\dfrac{n^2\pi^2 c^2}{L^2}+\dfrac{k}{\rho}}$,

$a_n=\sqrt{\dfrac{2}{L}}\displaystyle\int_0^L f(x)\sin\dfrac{n\pi x}{L}\,dx$,

$b_n=\dfrac{\sqrt{2/L}}{\omega_n}\displaystyle\int_0^L g(x)\sin\dfrac{n\pi x}{L}\,dx$

Section 5.3

2. (b) $50+\dfrac{4L^2}{\pi^3}\displaystyle\sum_{n=1}^{\infty}\dfrac{1}{(2n-1)^3\sinh(2n-1)\pi}$

$\times\cosh\dfrac{(2n-1)\pi y}{L}\cos\dfrac{(2n-1)\pi x}{L}$

(c) No solution

3. (b) $f_1(x-L)+f_2$

6. (a) $\displaystyle\sum_{n=1}^{\infty}a_n r^n\sqrt{\dfrac{2}{\pi}}\sin n\theta$,

$a_n=\dfrac{1}{a^n}\displaystyle\int_0^{\pi}f(\theta)\sqrt{\dfrac{2}{\pi}}\sin n\theta\,d\theta$

(b) $\dfrac{4}{\pi}\displaystyle\sum_{n=1}^{\infty}\dfrac{1}{2n-1}\left(\dfrac{r}{a}\right)^{2n-1}\sin(2n-1)\theta$;

$\dfrac{4}{\pi}\mathrm{Tan}^{-1}\left(\dfrac{r}{a}\right)$

8. $\dfrac{2}{\pi}-\dfrac{4}{\pi}\displaystyle\sum_{n=1}^{\infty}\dfrac{1}{4n^2-1}\left(\dfrac{r}{a}\right)^{2n}\cos 2n\theta$

17. (b) $\displaystyle\sum_{n=1}^{\infty}a_n r^{n/2}\dfrac{1}{\sqrt{\pi}}\sin\dfrac{n\theta}{2}$,

$a_n=R^{-n/2}\displaystyle\int_0^{2\pi}f(\theta)\dfrac{1}{\sqrt{\pi}}\sin\dfrac{n\theta}{2}\,d\theta$

(c) $\sqrt{\dfrac{r}{R}}\sin\left(\dfrac{\theta}{2}\right)$

20. $\dfrac{V_1+V_2}{2}+\pi^{-1}(V_1-V_2)\mathrm{Tan}^{-1}\left(\dfrac{2ar\sin\theta}{a^2-r^2}\right)$

Section 5.4

1. $\dfrac{2}{\sqrt{LL'}}\displaystyle\sum_{m=1}^{\infty}\sum_{n=1}^{\infty}c_{mn}e^{-(n^2/L^2+m^2/L'^2)\pi^2 kt}\sin\dfrac{n\pi x}{L}\sin\dfrac{m\pi y}{L'}$,

$c_{mn}=\dfrac{2}{\sqrt{LL'}}\displaystyle\int_0^{L'}\int_0^{L}f(x,y)\sin\dfrac{n\pi x}{L}\sin\dfrac{m\pi y}{L'}\,dx\,dy$

5. $\dfrac{16U_0}{\pi^2}\displaystyle\sum_{m=1}^{\infty}\sum_{n=1}^{\infty}\dfrac{e^{-k\pi^2[(2n-1)^2/L^2+(2m-1)^2/(4L''^2)]t}}{(2n-1)(2m-1)}$

$\times\sin\dfrac{(2n-1)\pi x}{L}\dfrac{\sin(2m-1)\pi z}{2L''}$

7. $\dfrac{4U_0}{\pi}\displaystyle\sum_{n=1}^{\infty}\dfrac{e^{-(2n-1)^2\pi^2 kt/L^2}}{2n-1}\sin\dfrac{(2n-1)\pi x}{L}$

11. (b) $\dfrac{2L}{\pi^4}\displaystyle\sum_{m=1}^{\infty}\sum_{n=1}^{\infty}\dfrac{(-1)^{n+m}}{(2n-1)^2(2m-1)^2}$

$\times\cos\dfrac{c\pi\sqrt{(2n-1)^2+(2m-1)^2}\,t}{L}$

$\times\sin\dfrac{(2n-1)\pi x}{L}\sin\dfrac{(2m-1)\pi y}{L}$

17. $\dfrac{4L}{\pi^2\kappa}\displaystyle\sum_{n=1}^{\infty}\dfrac{1}{(2n-1)^2\sinh(2n-1)\pi}$

$\times\left(Q\cosh\dfrac{(2n-1)\pi(L-z)}{L}+q\cosh\dfrac{(2n-1)\pi x}{L}\right)$

$\times\sin\dfrac{(2n-1)\pi y}{L}$

Section 5.5

3. $W=\text{constant}$

4. $\lambda_{mn}^2=\dfrac{(2n-1)^2\pi^2}{4L^2}+\dfrac{m^2\pi^2}{L'^2}$,

$W_{mn}=\dfrac{2}{\sqrt{LL'}}\sin\dfrac{(2n-1)\pi x}{2L}\sin\dfrac{m\pi y}{L'}$

6. $\lambda_{mn}^2=\dfrac{(2n-1)^2\pi^2}{4L^2}+\dfrac{(2m-1)^2\pi^2}{4L'^2}$,

$W_{mn}=\dfrac{2}{\sqrt{LL'}}\cos\dfrac{(2n-1)\pi x}{2L}\sin\dfrac{(2m-1)\pi y}{2L'}$

Section 6.1

1. $\dfrac{8\sqrt{2L^3}}{(2n-1)^2\pi^2}\left((-1)^{n+1}(L-1)-\dfrac{2L}{(2n-1)\pi}\right)$

6. $\dfrac{2\sqrt{2L}}{(2n-1)^2\pi^2-4L^2}[(-1)^{n+1}(2n-1)\pi\sin L-2L]$

7. $\tilde{f}(0)=\dfrac{e^L-1}{\sqrt{L}}$, $\tilde{f}(\lambda_n)=\dfrac{-\sqrt{2L^3}}{n^2\pi^2+L^2}(1+(-1)^{n+1}e^L)$

9. $\tilde{f}(\lambda_2)=\sqrt{\dfrac{L}{8}}$, $\tilde{f}(\lambda_n)=0$ for $n\neq 2$

11. $2x$ 12. $-3x^2$ 13. $2\sqrt{2}$ 14. $2x-1$

Section 6.2

1. $\dfrac{U_L x}{L} + \displaystyle\sum_{n=1}^{\infty} c_n e^{-n^2\pi^2 kt/L^2} \sin\dfrac{n\pi x}{L},$

$c_n = \dfrac{2(-1)^n U_L}{n\pi} + \dfrac{2}{L}\displaystyle\int_0^L f(x)\sin\dfrac{n\pi x}{L}\,dx$

2. See the answer to Exercise 9 in Section 3.3.

5. $U_0 + \dfrac{8U_0}{\pi^2}\displaystyle\sum_{n=1}^{\infty}\dfrac{(-1)^n e^{-(2n-1)^2\pi^2 kt/(4L^2)}}{(2n-1)^2}$

$\times \sin\dfrac{(2n-1)\pi x}{2L}$

10. $\dfrac{2gL}{\kappa\pi^2}\displaystyle\sum_{n=1}^{\infty}\dfrac{1-e^{-n^2\pi^2 kt/L^2}}{n^2}\sin\dfrac{n\pi b}{L}\sin\dfrac{n\pi x}{L}$

14. $\dfrac{qx}{\kappa} + U_0 + \dfrac{8}{\pi^2\kappa}\displaystyle\sum_{n=1}^{\infty}\dfrac{(-1)^n(U_0\kappa + qL)}{(2n-1)^2}$

$\times e^{-(2n-1)^2\pi^2 kt/(4L^2)}\sin\dfrac{(2n-1)\pi x}{2L}$

15. (a) $U_0 + \dfrac{q(L-x)}{\kappa} - \dfrac{8qL}{\kappa\pi^2}\displaystyle\sum_{n=1}^{\infty}\dfrac{1}{(2n-1)^2}$

$\times e^{-(2n-1)^2\pi^2 kt/(4L^2)}\cos\dfrac{(2n-1)\pi x}{2L}$

(b) $U_0 + \dfrac{8qL}{\kappa\pi^2}\displaystyle\sum_{n=1}^{\infty}\dfrac{1}{(2n-1)^2}$

$\times \left(e^{-(2n-1)^2\pi^2 k(t-t_0)/(4L^2)} - e^{-(2n-1)^2\pi^2 kt/(4L^2)}\right)$

$\times \cos\dfrac{(2n-1)\pi x}{2L}$

(c) U_0

23. $\dfrac{4F_0 L^2}{\rho\pi}\displaystyle\sum_{n=1}^{\infty}\dfrac{1}{(2n-1)[(2n-1)^2\pi^2 c^2 - \omega^2 L^2]}$

$\times \left(\sin\omega t - \dfrac{L\omega}{(2n-1)\pi c}\sin\dfrac{(2n-1)\pi ct}{L}\right)$

$\times \sin\dfrac{(2n-1)\pi x}{L}$ for the nonresonance case. When

$\omega = m\pi c/L$, replace the mth term in the above series

with $\dfrac{2F_0 L}{m^2\pi^2\rho c}\left(\dfrac{L}{m\pi c}\sin\dfrac{m\pi ct}{L} - t\cos\dfrac{m\pi ct}{L}\right)\sin\dfrac{m\pi x}{L}$

25. $\dfrac{(2n-1)\pi c}{2L}$ **27.** $\dfrac{(2n-1)\pi c}{2L}$ **29.** $\dfrac{n\pi c}{L}$

31. $\omega = \dfrac{n\pi c}{L}$ or $\phi = \dfrac{n\pi c}{L}$; if $\omega = \phi$ and $A_0 = B_0$, then

$\omega = \phi = \dfrac{(2n-1)\pi c}{L}$; if $\omega = \phi$ and $A_0 = -B_0$, then

$\omega = \phi = \dfrac{2n\pi c}{L}$

38. $\dfrac{t^2}{2}\left(\dfrac{c^2 F_0}{\tau L} + g\right) + M(x) - \dfrac{1}{2}[M(x+ct) + M(x-ct)],$

where $M(x)$ is the even, $2L$-periodic extension of

$\dfrac{F_0 x^2}{2L\tau}$

42. (a) $\dfrac{\sigma x(L-x)}{2\varepsilon_0} - \dfrac{4\sigma L^2}{\varepsilon_0\pi^3}$

$\displaystyle\sum_{n=1}^{\infty}\dfrac{\sinh\dfrac{(2n-1)\pi y}{L} + \sinh\dfrac{(2n-1)\pi(L'-y)}{L}}{(2n-1)^3\sinh\dfrac{(2n-1)\pi L'}{L}}$

$\times \sin\dfrac{(2n-1)\pi x}{L}$

(b) $\dfrac{2L}{\varepsilon_0\pi^2}\displaystyle\sum_{n=1}^{\infty}\dfrac{\sigma_n}{n^2}\left(1 - \dfrac{\sinh\dfrac{n\pi y}{L} + \sinh\dfrac{n\pi(L'-y)}{L}}{\sinh\dfrac{n\pi L'}{L}}\right)$

$\times \sin\dfrac{n\pi x}{L},\ \sigma_n = \displaystyle\int_0^L \sigma(x)\sin\dfrac{n\pi x}{L}\,dx$

(c) $\dfrac{2L^3}{\varepsilon_0\pi^3}\displaystyle\sum_{n=1}^{\infty}\dfrac{(-1)^n}{n^3}\left(\dfrac{L'\sinh\dfrac{n\pi y}{L}}{\sinh\dfrac{n\pi L'}{L}} - y\right)\sin\dfrac{n\pi x}{L}$

Section 6.3

2. (a) $\dfrac{2}{L'\pi^3}\displaystyle\sum_{n=1}^{\infty}$

$\times \dfrac{\pi^2 L'n^2[U_1 + U_2(-1)^{n+1}] - L^2(\kappa_2^{-1}\phi_2 + \kappa_1^{-1}\phi_1)[1 + (-1)^{n+1}]}{n^3}$

$\times (1 - e^{-n^2\pi^2 kt/L^2})\sin\dfrac{n\pi x}{L} + \dfrac{8L^2 L'}{\pi^3}$

$\times \displaystyle\sum_{m=1}^{\infty}\sum_{n=1}^{\infty}\dfrac{\kappa_2^{-1}\phi_2(-1)^{m+1} - \kappa_1^{-1}\phi_1}{(2n-1)[(2n-1)^2 L'^2 + m^2 L^2]}$

$\times (1 - e^{-[(2n-1)^2/L^2 + m^2/L'^2]\pi^2 kt})\sin\dfrac{(2n-1)\pi x}{L}$

$\times \cos\dfrac{m\pi y}{L'}$

(b) $U_1 + \dfrac{(U_2 - U_1)}{L}x - \dfrac{2}{\pi}\displaystyle\sum_{n=1}^{\infty}\dfrac{U_1 + U_2(-1)^{n+1}}{n}$

$\times e^{-n^2\pi^2 kt/L^2}\sin\dfrac{n\pi x}{L}$

6. $\dfrac{16AL^2}{\rho\pi^2}\displaystyle\sum_{m=1}^{\infty}\sum_{n=1}^{\infty}$

$$\dfrac{\cos\omega t-\cos\dfrac{c\pi\sqrt{(2n-1)^2+(2m-1)^2}\,t}{L}}{\left(\begin{array}{l}(2n-1)(2m-1)\\ \times\{c^2\pi^2[(2n-1)^2+(2m-1)^2]-\omega^2L^2\}\end{array}\right)}$$

$$\times\sin\dfrac{(2n-1)\pi x}{L}\sin\dfrac{(2m-1)\pi y}{L}$$

7. Same solution as for Exercise 6 except that the $m=1$ and $n=1$ term is replaced with

$$\dfrac{4\sqrt{2}\,AL}{\rho\pi^3 c}t\sin\dfrac{\sqrt{2}\,\pi ct}{L}\sin\dfrac{\pi x}{L}\sin\dfrac{\pi y}{L}$$

10. Same solution as for Exercise 6 except that the $(m,n)=(1,3)$ and $(m,n)=(3,1)$ terms are replaced with

$$\dfrac{8AL}{3\sqrt{10}\,\rho\pi^3 c}t\sin\dfrac{\sqrt{10}\,\pi ct}{L}$$

$$\times\left(\sin\dfrac{\pi x}{L}\sin\dfrac{3\pi y}{L}+\sin\dfrac{3\pi x}{L}\sin\dfrac{\pi y}{L}\right)$$

Section 7.2

2. $\dfrac{2}{\pi}\displaystyle\int_0^{\infty}\dfrac{e^{-k\lambda^2 t}}{\lambda^3}(2\sin\lambda L-\lambda L(1+\cos\lambda L))\cos\lambda x\,d\lambda$

5. $\dfrac{1}{2\sqrt{k\pi t}}\displaystyle\int_0^{L}u(L-u)e^{-(u-x)^2/(4kt)}\,du$

6. $\dfrac{1}{2\sqrt{k\pi t}}\displaystyle\int_0^{\infty}f(u)\!\left(e^{-(u-x)^2/(4kt)}-e^{-(u+x)^2/(4kt)}\right)du$

11. $\dfrac{1}{2c}\displaystyle\int_{x-ct}^{x+ct}g(u)\,du$, where $g(x)$ is extended as an odd function

13. (b) $\dfrac{2V_0}{\pi}\mathrm{Tan}^{-1}\!\left(\dfrac{\sin(\pi x/L)}{\sinh(\pi y/L)}\right)$

15. $\dfrac{2}{\pi}\displaystyle\int_0^{\infty}\dfrac{1}{\lambda}\cos\dfrac{\lambda(a+b-2x)}{2}\sin\dfrac{\lambda(b-a)}{2}\,d\lambda$

17. $\dfrac{4b}{\pi a^2}\displaystyle\int_0^{\infty}\dfrac{1}{\lambda^3}(\sin\lambda a-a\lambda\cos\lambda a)\cos\lambda x\,d\lambda$

19. $\dfrac{1}{\sqrt{k\pi}}\displaystyle\int_0^{\infty}e^{-\lambda^2/(4k)}\cos\lambda x\,d\lambda$

20. $\dfrac{2}{\pi}\displaystyle\int_0^{\infty}\dfrac{1}{\lambda}(\sin\lambda b-\sin\lambda a)\cos\lambda x\,d\lambda;$

$\dfrac{2}{\pi}\displaystyle\int_0^{\infty}\dfrac{1}{\lambda}(\cos\lambda a-\cos\lambda b)\sin\lambda x\,d\lambda$

Section 7.3

5. (a) $\mathscr{F}\{f^{(n)}(x)\}=(i\omega)^n\mathscr{F}\{f(x)\}$

10. (b) $\mathscr{F}_S\{\tilde{f}(x)\}=\left(\dfrac{\pi}{2}\right)f(\omega);\ \mathscr{F}_C\{\tilde{f}(x)\}=\left(\dfrac{\pi}{2}\right)f(\omega)$

12. $\dfrac{2a}{\omega^2+a^2}$ **13.** $\dfrac{n!}{(a+i\omega)^{n+1}}$

14. $\dfrac{2}{\omega}e^{-i\omega(a+b)/2}\sin\dfrac{\omega(b-a)}{2}$

16. $\dfrac{4b}{a\omega^2}\sin^2\!\left(\dfrac{\omega a}{2}\right)$ **17.** $\dfrac{-4b}{a\omega^2}\cos a\omega+\dfrac{4b}{a^2\omega^3}\sin a\omega$

19. $\dfrac{1}{\omega}(\cos a\omega-\cos b\omega);\ \dfrac{1}{\omega}(\sin b\omega-\sin a\omega)$

20. $\dfrac{4b}{a\omega^2}\sin\omega c\sin^2\!\left(\dfrac{a\omega}{2}\right);\ \dfrac{4b}{a\omega^2}\cos\omega c\sin^2\!\left(\dfrac{a\omega}{2}\right)$

26. (a) (i) $\begin{cases}(x^2/2)e^{-8x} & x\geq 0\\ 0 & x<0\end{cases}$

    (ii) $\begin{cases}(b/a)(x-a)[H(x-a)-1] & x>0\\ 0 & x<0\end{cases}$

(b) No

Section 7.4

1. (b) (i) $\dfrac{1}{2}\mathrm{erf}\!\left(\dfrac{x+a}{2\sqrt{kt}}\right)-\dfrac{1}{2}\mathrm{erf}\!\left(\dfrac{x-a}{2\sqrt{kt}}\right)$

    (ii) $1-\dfrac{1}{2}\mathrm{erf}\!\left(\dfrac{x+a}{2\sqrt{kt}}\right)+\dfrac{1}{2}\mathrm{erf}\!\left(\dfrac{x-a}{2\sqrt{kt}}\right)$

2. (a) $\bar{U}\,\mathrm{erfc}\!\left(\dfrac{x}{2\sqrt{kt}}\right)$

3. $\dfrac{Q_0}{\kappa}\left[2\sqrt{\dfrac{kt}{\pi}}\,e^{-x^2/(4kt)}-x\,\mathrm{erfc}\!\left(\dfrac{x}{2\sqrt{kt}}\right)\right]$

4. (b) $U_0\,\mathrm{erf}\!\left(\dfrac{x}{2\sqrt{kt}}\right);$ **(c)** $\bar{U}\,\mathrm{erfc}\!\left(\dfrac{x}{2\sqrt{kt}}\right)$

10. (a) (i) $\displaystyle\sum_{n=1}^{\infty}C_n e^{-n\pi x/L'}\sin\dfrac{n\pi y}{L'},$

$$C_n=\dfrac{2}{L'}\int_0^{L'}f(y)\sin\dfrac{n\pi y}{L'}\,dy$$

    (ii) $\dfrac{2}{\pi}\displaystyle\int_0^{\infty}\dfrac{\tilde{g}(\omega)\sinh\omega y}{\sinh\omega L'}\sin\omega x\,d\omega,$

$$\tilde{g}(\omega)=\int_0^{\infty}g(x)\sin\omega x\,dx$$

    (iii) $\dfrac{2}{\pi}\displaystyle\int_0^{\infty}\dfrac{\tilde{g}(\omega)\sinh\omega(L'-y)}{\sinh\omega L'}\sin\omega x\,d\omega,$

$$\tilde{g}(\omega)=\int_0^{\infty}g(x)\sin\omega x\,dx$$

    (iv) Sum of solutions in (i), (ii), and (iii)

12. (a) U_0;

(b) $C + \dfrac{4L'Q_0}{\pi^2 \kappa} \displaystyle\sum_{n=1}^{\infty} \dfrac{(-1)^{n+1}}{(2n-1)^2} e^{-(2n-1)\pi x/L'}$

$\times \cos\dfrac{(2n-1)\pi y}{L'}$

(c) U_m

15. $\dfrac{V_L x}{L} + \dfrac{1}{\varepsilon} e^{-y}\left(\dfrac{\sin(L-x) + \sin x}{\sin L} - 1\right)$

$+ \dfrac{2}{\pi} \displaystyle\sum_{n=1}^{\infty}\left(\dfrac{V_L(-1)^n}{n} - \dfrac{L^2[1+(-1)^{n+1}]}{n\varepsilon(n^2\pi^2 - L^2)}\right)e^{-n\pi y/L}$

$\times \sin\dfrac{n\pi x}{L}$

17. (d) $\dfrac{2}{\pi}\operatorname{Tan}^{-1}\left(\dfrac{x}{y}\right)$

18. (a) $\dfrac{y}{\pi}\displaystyle\int_{-\infty}^{\infty}\dfrac{f(u)}{(x-u)^2 + y^2}\,du$

(b) $\dfrac{1}{2} + \dfrac{1}{\pi}\operatorname{Tan}^{-1}\left(\dfrac{x}{y}\right)$

Section 8.2

1. (a) 120   **(b)** 2.9812   **(c)** 7.3619
(d) −5.7386   **(e)** 0.6891   **(f)** −1.0276

Section 8.3

3. (a) 0.9604   **(b)** 0.6201   **(c)** 0.3688
(d) 0.0955   **(e)** 0.4448   **(f)** −0.2769
(g) 0.4333   **(h)** 0.1190

Section 8.4

2. (a) $2r_2^{\nu-1}\displaystyle\sum_{n=1}^{\infty}\dfrac{J_\nu(\lambda_{\nu n}r)}{\lambda_{\nu n}J_{\nu+1}(\lambda_{\nu n}r_2)}$

(b) $2\nu r_2^\nu\displaystyle\sum_{n=1}^{\infty}\dfrac{J_\nu(\lambda_{\nu n}r)}{[(\lambda_{\nu n}r_2)^2 - \nu^2]J_\nu(\lambda_{\nu n}r_2)}$

3. $\dfrac{2}{r_2}\displaystyle\sum_{n=1}^{\infty}\dfrac{J_1(\lambda_n r_2)J_0(\lambda_n r)}{\lambda_n\left[1 + \left(\dfrac{h_2}{\lambda_n l_2}\right)^2\right][J_0(\lambda_n r_2)]^2}$; when $l_2 = 0$,

$\dfrac{2}{r_2}\displaystyle\sum_{n=1}^{\infty}\dfrac{J_0(\lambda_n r)}{\lambda_n J_1(\lambda_n r_2)}$; when $h_2 = 0$, $\dfrac{r_2}{\sqrt 2}R_0(r)$

5. (b) $\dfrac{n^2\pi^2}{r_2^2}$; $\sqrt{\dfrac{2}{r_2}}r^{-1}\sin\left(\dfrac{n\pi r}{r_2}\right)$

6. (b) $\sqrt 3\,r_2^{-3/2}$, $\dfrac{\sqrt 2\sqrt{1+\lambda_n^2 r_2^2}}{\lambda_n r_2^{3/2}r}\sin\lambda_n r$

7. (b) $(rN)^{-1}\sin\lambda_n r$,

$2N^2 = r_2\left(1 + \dfrac{h_2 r_2/l_2 - 1}{\lambda_n^2 r_2^2 + (1 - h_2 r_2/l_2)^2}\right)$

8.

Condition at $r = r_2$	Eigenvalue Equation	NR_{mn}	$2N^2$
$h_2 l_2 \neq 0$	$0 = 2\lambda r_2 J'_{m+1/2}(\lambda r_2)$ $+ \left(\dfrac{2h_2 r_2 - l_2}{l_2}\right)J_{m+1/2}(\lambda r_2)$	$\dfrac{J_{m+1/2}(\lambda_{mn}r)}{\sqrt r}$	$r_2^2\left[1 - \left(\dfrac{m+1/2}{\lambda_{mn}r_2}\right)^2 + \left(\dfrac{2h_2 r_2/l_2 - 1}{2\lambda_{mn}r_2}\right)^2\right][J_{m+1/2}(\lambda_{mn}r_2)]^2$
$h_2 = 0$	$0 = 2\lambda r_2 J'_{m+1/2}(\lambda r_2)$ $- J_{m+1/2}(\lambda r_2)$	$\dfrac{J_{m+1/2}(\lambda_{mn}r)}{\sqrt r}$	$r_2^2\left[1 - \left(\dfrac{m+1/2}{\lambda_{mn}r_2}\right)^2 + \left(\dfrac{1}{2\lambda_{mn}r_2}\right)^2\right][J_{m+1/2}(\lambda_{mn}r_2)]^2$
$l_2 = 0$	$0 = J_{m+1/2}(\lambda r_2)$	$\dfrac{J_{m+1/2}(\lambda_{mn}r)}{\sqrt r}$	$r_2^2[J'_{m+1/2}(\lambda_{mn}r_2)]^2 = r_2^2[J_{m+3/2}(\lambda_{mn}r_2)]^2$

Section 8.5

1. $1, x, \dfrac{3x^2-1}{2}, \dfrac{5x^3-3x}{2}, \dfrac{35x^4-30x^2+3}{8},$

$\dfrac{63x^5-70x^3+15x}{8}, \dfrac{231x^6-315x^4+105x^2-5}{16}$

10. (b) $\dfrac{(3x^2-1)Q_0}{2} - \dfrac{3x}{2}, \dfrac{(5x^3-3x)Q_0}{2} - \dfrac{5x^2}{2} + \dfrac{2}{3},$

$\dfrac{(35x^4-30x^2+3)Q_0}{8} - \dfrac{35x^3}{8} + \dfrac{55x}{24}$

(c) $P_2 Q_0 - \dfrac{3x}{2}, P_3 Q_0 - \dfrac{5x^2}{2} + \dfrac{2}{3}, P_4 Q_0 - \dfrac{35x^3}{8} + \dfrac{55x}{24}$

Section 8.6

1. $\dfrac{1}{2} + \displaystyle\sum_{n=1}^{\infty} \dfrac{(-1)^{n-1}(2n-2)!(4n-1)}{2^{2n}n!(n-1)!} P_{2n-1}(\cos\phi)$

2. $\dfrac{\sqrt{2}}{5}\left(\dfrac{1}{\sqrt{2}}\right) + \dfrac{4\sqrt{10}}{35}\left(\sqrt{\dfrac{5}{2}}P_2(\cos\phi)\right)$

$+ \dfrac{8\sqrt{2}}{105}\left(\left(\dfrac{3}{\sqrt{2}}\right)P_4(\cos\phi)\right)$

3. $\dfrac{1}{4} + \dfrac{1}{2}\cos\phi + \displaystyle\sum_{n=1}^{\infty} \dfrac{(-1)^{n-1}(2n-2)!(4n+1)}{2^{2n+1}(n-1)!(n+1)!} P_{2n}(\cos\varphi)$

4. $\dfrac{1}{2} + \displaystyle\sum_{n=1}^{\infty} \dfrac{(-1)^{n-1}(2n-2)!(4n+1)}{2^{2n}(n-1)!(n+1)!} P_{2n}(\cos\phi)$

5. $\lambda_n = 2n(2n-1),\ n \geq 1;\ \sqrt{4n-1}\,P_{2n-1}(\cos\phi)$

6. $\lambda_n = 2n(2n+1),\ n \geq 0;\ \sqrt{4n+1}\,P_{2n}(\cos\phi)$

Section 9.1

1. (b) $\dfrac{2U_0}{r_2} \displaystyle\sum_{n=1}^{\infty} \dfrac{e^{-k\lambda_n^2 t}J_0(\lambda_n r)}{\lambda_n J_1(\lambda_n r_2)}$

(c) $\dfrac{8}{r_2} \displaystyle\sum_{n=1}^{\infty} \dfrac{1}{\lambda_n^3}e^{-k\lambda_n^2 t}\dfrac{J_0(\lambda_n r)}{J_1(\lambda_n r_2)}$

2. (b) $\dfrac{1}{\pi r_2^2}\displaystyle\int_{-\pi}^{\pi}\int_0^{r_2} rf(r)\,dr\,d\theta =$ average value of $f(r)$
over the circle $r \leq r_2$

6. $\sqrt{2}\displaystyle\sum_{n=1}^{\infty} A_n e^{-k\lambda_n^2 t}\dfrac{J_0(\lambda_n r)}{J_1(\lambda_n)}$, where

$A_n = \dfrac{\sqrt{2}}{J_1(\lambda_n)}\displaystyle\int_0^1 rf(r)J_0(\lambda_n r)\,dr$

8. $\dfrac{2}{r_2\sqrt{L}} \displaystyle\sum_{m=1}^{\infty}\sum_{n=1}^{\infty} A_{mn}e^{-k[\lambda_n^2 + (2m-1)^2\pi^2/(4L^2)]t}\dfrac{J_0(\lambda_n r)}{J_1(\lambda_n r_2)}$

$\times \cos\dfrac{(2m-1)\pi z}{2L},\ A_{mn} = \dfrac{2}{r_2\sqrt{L}J_1(\lambda_n r_2)}$

$\times \displaystyle\int_0^L\int_0^{r_2} rf(r,z)J_0(\lambda_n r)\cos\dfrac{(2m-1)\pi z}{2L}\,dr\,dz$

9. (b) $\dfrac{2U_0 h_2 l_2}{r_2} \displaystyle\sum_{n=1}^{\infty} \dfrac{e^{-k\lambda_n^2 t}}{h_2^2 + l_2^2\lambda_n^2}\dfrac{J_0(\lambda_n r)}{J_0(\lambda_n r_2)}$

10. (b) $\dfrac{2U_0 r_2}{\pi r}\displaystyle\sum_{n=1}^{\infty}\dfrac{(-1)^{n+1}}{n}e^{-n^2\pi^2 kt/r_2^2}\sin\dfrac{n\pi r}{r_2}$

12. (b) $\dfrac{2U_0\mu r_2}{\kappa r}\displaystyle\sum_{n=1}^{\infty}\dfrac{(-1)^{n+1}\sqrt{\lambda_n^2 r_2^2 + (1-\mu r_2/\kappa)^2}}{\lambda_n\left[\lambda_n^2 r_2^2 + \dfrac{\mu r_2}{\kappa}\left(\dfrac{\mu r_2}{\kappa} - 1\right)\right]}$

$\times e^{-k\lambda_n^2 t}\sin\lambda_n r$

16. $\dfrac{4Lr_2^2}{\pi^2}\displaystyle\sum_{m=1}^{\infty}\dfrac{1}{(2m-1)^2}e^{-(2m-1)^2\pi^2 kt/(4L^2)}\cos\dfrac{(2m-1)\pi z}{2L}$

$-\dfrac{32L}{\pi^2}\displaystyle\sum_{n=1}^{\infty}\sum_{m=1}^{\infty}\dfrac{e^{-k[\lambda_n^2 + (2m-1)^2\pi^2/(4L^2)]t}}{(2m-1)^2\lambda_n^2}$

$\times \dfrac{J_0(\lambda_n r)}{J_0(\lambda_n r_2)}\cos\dfrac{(2m-1)\pi z}{2L}$

17. (a) $\dfrac{\sqrt{2}}{r_2 J_1(\lambda_n r_2)}\displaystyle\int_0^{r_2} rf(r)J_0(\lambda_n r)\,dr$

19. $\dfrac{8}{r_2}\displaystyle\sum_{n=1}^{\infty}\dfrac{J_0(\lambda_n r)}{\lambda_n^3 J_1(\lambda_n r_2)}\cos c\lambda_n t$

20. $\dfrac{2v_0}{cr_2}\displaystyle\sum_{n=1}^{\infty}\dfrac{J_0(\lambda_n r)}{\lambda_n^2 J_1(\lambda_n r_2)}\sin c\lambda_n t$

24. (b) No;　　**(c)** $\dfrac{J_0(kr)}{J_0(kr_2)}$

27. (b) $\dfrac{2U_0\mu\kappa}{r_2}\displaystyle\sum_{n=1}^{\infty}\dfrac{1}{(\mu^2 + \lambda_n^2\kappa^2)\sinh\lambda_n L}$

$\times \sinh\lambda_n(L-z)\dfrac{J_0(\lambda_n r)}{J_0(\lambda_n r_2)}$

29. $V_0\left(\dfrac{1}{2} + \displaystyle\sum_{n=1}^{\infty}\dfrac{(-1)^{n-1}(4n-1)(2n-2)!}{2^{2n}n!(n-1)!}\right.$

$\left.\times \left(\dfrac{r}{r_2}\right)^{2n-1}P_{2n-1}(\cos\phi)\right)$

30. $\dfrac{V_0 + V_1}{2} - (V_0 - V_1)\displaystyle\sum_{n=1}^{\infty}\dfrac{(-1)^n(4n-1)(2n-2)!}{2^{2n}n!(n-1)!}$

$\times \left(\dfrac{r}{r_2}\right)^{2n-1}P_{2n-1}(\cos\phi)$

33. (d) $\dfrac{4U_0}{\pi}\displaystyle\sum_{n=1}^{\infty}\dfrac{1}{2n-1}\dfrac{I_0[(2n-1)\pi r/L]}{I_0[(2n-1)\pi r_2/L]}\sin\dfrac{(2n-1)\pi z}{L}$

34. (c) $A_0 + \dfrac{2}{L}\displaystyle\sum_{n=1}^{\infty} A_n I_0\left(\dfrac{n\pi r}{L}\right)\cos\dfrac{n\pi z}{L}$, where

$A_0 = \dfrac{1}{L}\displaystyle\int_0^L f(z)\,dz,$

$A_n = \dfrac{1}{I_0(n\pi r_2/L)}\displaystyle\int_0^L f(z)\cos\dfrac{n\pi z}{L}\,dz$

(d) U_0

35. (c) $\dfrac{Q}{4\pi\varepsilon_0 a}\displaystyle\sum_{n=0}^{\infty}\dfrac{(-1)^n(2n)!}{2^{2n}(n!)^2}\left(\dfrac{r}{a}\right)^{2n}P_{2n}(\cos\phi),\ r < a;$

$\dfrac{Q}{4\pi\varepsilon_0 r}\displaystyle\sum_{n=0}^{\infty}\dfrac{(-1)^n(2n)!}{2^{2n}(n!)^2}\left(\dfrac{a}{r}\right)^{2n}P_{2n}(\cos\phi),\ r > a$

36. (c) $\dfrac{Q}{2\pi\varepsilon_0 a}\left(1 - \dfrac{r}{a}\cos\phi + \displaystyle\sum_{n=1}^{\infty} \dfrac{(-1)^{n+1}(2n-2)!}{2^{2n-1}n!(n-1)!}\right.$

$\left.\times \left(\dfrac{r}{a}\right)^{2n} P_{2n}(\cos\phi)\right), r < a;\ \dfrac{Q}{4\pi\varepsilon_0 a}$

$\times \displaystyle\sum_{n=0}^{\infty} \dfrac{(-1)^n(2n)!}{2^{2n}n!(n+1)!}\left(\dfrac{a}{r}\right)^{2n+1} P_{2n}(\cos\phi),$

$r > a$

Section 9.2

2. (b) $\dfrac{Q}{4\kappa r_2}(2r^2 - r_2^2 + 8kt) - \dfrac{2Q}{\kappa r_2}\displaystyle\sum_{n=1}^{\infty}\dfrac{e^{-k\lambda_n^2 t}}{\lambda_n^2}\dfrac{J_0(\lambda_n r)}{J_0(\lambda_n r_2)}$

3. (b) $\dfrac{2g}{r_2\kappa}\displaystyle\sum_{n=1}^{\infty}\dfrac{1 - e^{-k\lambda_n^2 t}}{\lambda_n^3}\dfrac{J_0(\lambda_n r)}{J_1(\lambda_n r_2)}$

(c) $\dfrac{g}{4\kappa}(r_2^2 - r^2) - \dfrac{2g}{r_2\kappa}\displaystyle\sum_{n=1}^{\infty}\dfrac{e^{-k\lambda_n^2 t}}{\lambda_n^3}\dfrac{J_0(\lambda_n r)}{J_1(\lambda_n r_2)}$

4. (b) $\dfrac{kgt}{\kappa}$

5. (b) $\dfrac{2\mu}{r_2}\displaystyle\sum_{n=1}^{\infty}\left(\dfrac{g + \kappa U_m\lambda_n^2}{\mu^2 + \kappa^2\lambda_n^2}\right)\left(\dfrac{1 - e^{-k\lambda_n^2 t}}{\lambda_n^2}\right)\dfrac{J_0(\lambda_n r)}{J_0(\lambda_n r_2)}$

(c) $U_m + \dfrac{g}{4}\left(\dfrac{r_2^2}{\kappa} + \dfrac{2r_2}{\mu} - \dfrac{r^2}{\kappa}\right)$

$- \dfrac{2\mu}{r_2}\displaystyle\sum_{n=1}^{\infty}\left(\dfrac{g + \kappa U_m\lambda_n^2}{\mu^2 + \kappa^2\lambda_n^2}\right)\dfrac{e^{-k\lambda_n^2 t}}{\lambda_n^2}\dfrac{J_0(\lambda_n r)}{J_0(\lambda_n r_2)}$

6. (b) $\dfrac{g}{6\kappa}(r_2^2 - r^2) + \dfrac{2r_2^3 g}{\pi^3\kappa r}\displaystyle\sum_{n=1}^{\infty}\dfrac{(-1)^n}{n^3}e^{-n^2\pi^2 kt/r_2^2}\sin\dfrac{n\pi r}{r_2}$

(c) $f_1\left(1 + \dfrac{2r_2}{\pi r}\displaystyle\sum_{n=1}^{\infty}\dfrac{(-1)^n}{n}e^{-n^2\pi^2 kt/r_2^2}\sin\dfrac{n\pi r}{r_2}\right)$

7. (b) $\dfrac{3kf_1 t}{\kappa r_2} + \dfrac{f_1}{10\kappa r_2}(5r^2 - 3r_2^2) + \dfrac{2f_1}{\kappa r_2 r}$

$\times \displaystyle\sum_{n=1}^{\infty}\dfrac{(-1)^{n+1}}{\lambda_n^3}\sqrt{1 + \lambda_n^2 r_2^2}$

$e^{-k\lambda_n^2 t}\sin\lambda_n r$

10. $-\dfrac{2\sin\theta}{r_2}\displaystyle\sum_{n=1}^{\infty}\dfrac{1 - e^{-k\lambda_n^2 t}}{\lambda_n}\dfrac{J_1(\lambda_n r)}{J_0(\lambda_n r_2)}$

16. $\dfrac{2Ac}{r_2}\displaystyle\sum_{n=1}^{\infty}\dfrac{c\lambda_n\sin\omega t - \omega\sin c\lambda_n t}{c^2\lambda_n^2 - \omega^2}\dfrac{J_0(\lambda_n r)}{J_1(\lambda_n r_2)},$

$\omega \neq c\lambda_m;\ \dfrac{A(-c\lambda_m t\cos c\lambda_m t + \sin c\lambda_m t)J_0(\lambda_m r)}{r_2\lambda_m J_1(\lambda_m r_2)}$

$- \dfrac{2A}{r_2}\displaystyle\sum_{\substack{n=1 \\ n\neq m}}^{\infty}\dfrac{\lambda_n\sin c\lambda_m t - \lambda_m\sin c\lambda_n t}{\lambda_m^2 - \lambda_n^2}\dfrac{J_0(\lambda_n r)}{J_1(\lambda_n r_2)},$

$\omega = c\lambda_m$

20. For $\beta \neq \dfrac{\pi}{2}, \pi, \dfrac{3\pi}{2},$

$\dfrac{4\sigma\beta^2}{\pi\varepsilon}\displaystyle\sum_{n=1}^{\infty}\dfrac{r^2}{(2n-1)[(2n-1)^2\pi^2 - 4\beta^2]}$

$\times\left[1 - \left(\dfrac{r}{r_0}\right)^{(2n-1)\pi/\beta - 2}\right]\sin\dfrac{(2n-1)\pi\theta}{\beta};$

when $\beta = \dfrac{\pi}{2},$

$\dfrac{\sigma r^2}{\varepsilon\pi}\ln\left(\dfrac{r_0}{r}\right)\sin 2\theta$

$+ \dfrac{\sigma}{\pi\varepsilon}\displaystyle\sum_{n=2}^{\infty}\dfrac{r^2}{(2n-1)[(2n-1)^2 - 1]}$

$\times\left[1 - \left(\dfrac{r}{r_0}\right)^{4n-4}\right]\sin 2(2n-1)\theta;$

when $\beta = \pi,$

$\dfrac{4\sigma}{\pi\varepsilon}\displaystyle\sum_{n=1}^{\infty}\dfrac{r^2}{(2n-1)[(2n-1)^2 - 4]}\left[1 - \left(\dfrac{r}{r_0}\right)^{2n-3}\right]$

$\times \sin(2n-1)\theta;$

when $\beta = \dfrac{3\pi}{2},$

$\dfrac{9\sigma r^2}{8\varepsilon\pi}\left[\left(\dfrac{r_0}{r}\right)^{4/3} - 1\right]\sin\dfrac{2\theta}{3} - \dfrac{\sigma r^2}{3\pi\varepsilon}\ln\left(\dfrac{r}{r_0}\right)$

$\times \sin 2\theta + \dfrac{9\sigma}{\pi\varepsilon}\displaystyle\sum_{n=3}^{\infty}\dfrac{r^2}{(2n-1)[(2n-1)^2 - 9]}$

$\times\left[1 - \left(\dfrac{r}{r_0}\right)^{4(n-2)/3}\right]\sin\dfrac{2(2n-1)\theta}{3}$

23. (a) $gr_2\beta = 2q + 2\beta Q$

(b) $\dfrac{A}{\sqrt{\beta}} - \dfrac{gr^2}{4\kappa} + \dfrac{gr\cos(\beta - \theta)}{\kappa\sin\beta} + \dfrac{2q\beta^2 r_2}{\kappa\pi}$

$\times \displaystyle\sum_{n=1}^{\infty}\dfrac{(r/r_2)^{n\pi/\beta}}{n(n^2\pi^2 - \beta^2)}\cos\dfrac{n\pi\theta}{\beta}$

Section 9.3

1. $\dfrac{ag}{\kappa}\displaystyle\int_0^{\infty}\dfrac{1}{\lambda^2}(1 - e^{-\kappa\lambda^2 t})J_1(\lambda a)J_0(\lambda r)\,d\lambda$

2. $\bar{U} - \dfrac{4\bar{U}}{\alpha}\displaystyle\sum_{n=1}^{\infty}\left(\int_0^{\infty}\dfrac{1}{\lambda}e^{-k\lambda^2 t}J_{(2n-1)\pi/\alpha}(\lambda r)\,d\lambda\right)$

$\times \sin\dfrac{(2n-1)\pi\theta}{\alpha}$

5. $\dfrac{aQ}{\kappa}\displaystyle\int_0^{\infty}\dfrac{1}{\lambda}e^{-\lambda z}J_1(\lambda a)J_0(\lambda r)\,d\lambda$

6. $a\bar{U}\displaystyle\int_0^{\infty}e^{-\lambda z}J_1(\lambda a)J_0(\lambda r)\,d\lambda$

Section 10.1

1. (b) (i) $\dfrac{6}{(s+5)^4}$; (ii) $\dfrac{s+1}{s^2+2s+5}+\dfrac{2}{s^2-6s+13}$;

(c) (i) $\left(\dfrac{1}{2}\right)e^t\sin 2t$; (ii) $\left(\dfrac{1}{\sqrt{\pi t}}\right)e^{-3t}$

2. (b) (i) $\dfrac{e^{-3s}(s+1)}{s^2}$; (ii) $\dfrac{e^{-as}}{s}$; (iii) $\dfrac{1-e^{-as}}{s}$;

(c) (i) $\begin{cases}0 & 0<t<2\\ t-2 & t>2\end{cases}$;

(ii) $\begin{cases}0 & 0<t<3\\ \sin(t-3) & t>3\end{cases}$

3. (b) (i) $\dfrac{8}{s^3}+\dfrac{2}{s^2-4}$; (ii) $\dfrac{s-4}{s^2-8s+32}$;

(c) (i) $\left(\dfrac{1}{9}\right)\cos\left(\dfrac{\sqrt{2}\,t}{3}\right)$; (ii) $\left(\dfrac{1}{\sqrt{29}}\right)e^{3t/4}\sinh\left(\dfrac{\sqrt{29}\,t}{4}\right)$

4. (b) (i) $\dfrac{1-e^{-as}(1+as)}{s^2(1-e^{-as})}$; (ii) $\dfrac{1-e^{-as}}{s(1+e^{-as})}$

6. $1-e^{-t}$

8. $\left(\dfrac{2}{7}\right)\cosh\sqrt{2}\,t-\left(\dfrac{\sqrt{2}}{14}\right)\sinh\sqrt{2}\,t-\dfrac{2}{7}e^{-4t}$

10. $\dfrac{2}{s^2}-\dfrac{e^{-s}(s+1)}{s^2}$ **12.** $\dfrac{1-e^{-as}}{s^2(1+e^{-as})}$ **14.** $\dfrac{e^{-as}}{s}$

16. $2e^{2t}-e^t$ **17.** $e^{-t}+e^{t/2}-e^{-t/2}-1$

19. $0, t<2$; $e^{-(t-2)}-e^{-2(t-2)}, t>2$

20. $\dfrac{e^{-t}}{3}+\left(\dfrac{e^{t/2}}{3}\right)\left[\sqrt{3}\sin\left(\dfrac{\sqrt{3}\,t}{2}\right)-\cos\left(\dfrac{\sqrt{3}\,t}{2}\right)\right]$

22. $0, t<1$; $1-\cos(t-1), 1<t<2$; $\cos(t-2)-\cos(t-1), t>2$

23. $\dfrac{e^{-t}(4t^3-t^4)}{24}$ **25.** $\dfrac{\sinh 2t+2t\cosh 2t}{4}$

26. $\left(\dfrac{1}{2}\right)e^t+\left(\dfrac{1}{2}\right)e^{-t}\left[\cosh\sqrt{2}\,t+\left(\dfrac{4}{\sqrt{2}}\right)\sinh\sqrt{2}\,t\right]$

27. $e^{-t}-\cos t+\sin t$ **28.** $2(1+t)e^{-t}+t-2$

30. $\dfrac{\cos 2t+4\cos 3t+4\sin 3t}{5}$

32. $\dfrac{1}{a}\displaystyle\int_0^t f(u)\sinh a(t-u)\,du+A\cosh at+B\sinh at$

35. (b) $s\tilde f(s)-f(0+)$

Section 10.2

3. (b) $U_0+(\bar U-U_0)\operatorname{erfc}\left(\dfrac{x}{2\sqrt{kt}}\right)$

4. (b) $U_0+\dfrac{Q_0}{\kappa}\left[2\sqrt{\dfrac{kt}{\pi}}\,e^{-x^2/(4kt)}-x\operatorname{erfc}\left(\dfrac{x}{2\sqrt{kt}}\right)\right]$

5. (b) $U_m\left[\operatorname{erfc}\left(\dfrac{x}{2\sqrt{kt}}\right)-e^{\mu x/\kappa+k\mu^2 t/\kappa^2}\right.$

$\left.\times\operatorname{erfc}\left(\dfrac{x}{2\sqrt{kt}}+\dfrac{\mu\sqrt{kt}}{\kappa}\right)\right]$

6. (c) $\left(\dfrac{U_0}{2}\right)\left[1+\operatorname{erf}\left(\dfrac{x}{2\sqrt{kt}}\right)\right]$

8. $f_1\left(t-\dfrac{x}{c}\right)H\left(t-\dfrac{x}{c}\right)$

Section 10.3

1. $\dfrac{t(t+2)e^t}{2}$ **3.** $\dfrac{3t-1+e^{-3t}}{9}$

5. $\dfrac{2\sin 2t-\sin t}{3}$ **7.** $\dfrac{2t^2\cosh 2t+3t\sinh 2t}{16}$

9. $\left(\dfrac{1}{2}\right)te^t\sin t$

11. $\dfrac{2}{\pi}\displaystyle\sum_{n=1}^{\infty}\dfrac{(-1)^{n+1}}{n}e^{-n^2\pi^2 t}\sin n\pi x$

13. $\dfrac{8}{\pi^3}\displaystyle\sum_{n=1}^{\infty}\dfrac{1}{(2n-1)^3}\cos(2n-1)\pi t\sin(2n-1)\pi x$

15. $\dfrac{1}{2\pi}\sin\dfrac{\pi t}{2}\sin\dfrac{\pi x}{2}+\dfrac{2}{\pi^2}\displaystyle\sum_{n=1}^{\infty}\dfrac{(-1)^n}{4n^2-1}\sin n\pi t\sin n\pi x$

16. $\dfrac{1}{2\pi^2}[\sin\pi t(\sin\pi x-2\pi x\cos\pi x)-2\pi t\cos\pi t\sin\pi x]$

$+\dfrac{2}{\pi^2}\displaystyle\sum_{n=2}^{\infty}\dfrac{(-1)^n}{n^2-1}\sin n\pi t\sin n\pi x$

Section 10.4

1. $e^{-m^2\pi^2 kt/L^2}\sin\dfrac{m\pi x}{L}$ **2.** U_0

5. $\dfrac{ke^{-\alpha t}}{\kappa\alpha}\left(-1+\dfrac{\cos\sqrt{\alpha/k}\,(L/2-x)}{\cos\sqrt{\alpha/k}\,L/2}\right)$

$+\dfrac{4kL^2}{\kappa\pi}\displaystyle\sum_{n=1}^{\infty}\dfrac{e^{-(2n-1)^2\pi^2 kt/L^2}}{(2n-1)[\alpha L^2-(2n-1)^2\pi^2 k]}$

$\times\sin\dfrac{(2n-1)\pi x}{L}$

6. (a) Add the following series to the solution of Exercise 5:

$\dfrac{40}{\pi}\displaystyle\sum_{n=1}^{\infty}\dfrac{1}{2n-1}e^{-(2n-1)^2\pi^2 kt/L^2}\sin\dfrac{(2n-1)\pi x}{L}$

9. $U_L\left(\dfrac{x}{L} + \dfrac{2}{\pi}\displaystyle\sum_{n=1}^{\infty}\dfrac{(-1)^n}{n}e^{-n^2\pi^2kt/L^2}\sin\dfrac{n\pi x}{L}\right)$;

$$U_L\sum_{n=0}^{\infty}\left[\mathrm{erf}\left(\dfrac{(2n+1)L+x}{2\sqrt{kt}}\right) - \mathrm{erf}\left(\dfrac{(2n+1)L-x}{2\sqrt{kt}}\right)\right]$$

16. $U_0\left(1 - \dfrac{x}{L}\right) - \dfrac{2}{\pi}\displaystyle\sum_{n=1}^{\infty}\dfrac{U_0 + (-1)^n L}{n}e^{-n^2\pi^2kt/L^2}$

$\times \sin\dfrac{n\pi x}{L}$

18. $\dfrac{8kL^2}{\pi^3}\displaystyle\sum_{n=1}^{\infty}\dfrac{1}{(2n-1)^3}\cos\dfrac{(2n-1)\pi ct}{L}\sin\dfrac{(2n-1)\pi x}{L}$

22. $\dfrac{F_0}{\rho\omega^2\sin\dfrac{\omega L}{c}}\left(\sin\dfrac{\omega x}{c} + \sin\dfrac{\omega(L-x)}{c} - \sin\dfrac{\omega L}{c}\right)\sin\omega t$

$+\dfrac{4F_0\omega L^3}{\rho c\pi^2}\displaystyle\sum_{n=1}^{\infty}\dfrac{1}{(2n-1)^2[\omega^2L^2-(2n-1)^2\pi^2c^2]}$

$\times \sin\dfrac{(2n-1)\pi ct}{L}\sin\dfrac{(2n-1)\pi x}{L}$

31. $\dfrac{A\sin(\omega x/c)\sin\omega t}{\sin(\omega L/c)} + 2A\omega Lc\displaystyle\sum_{n=1}^{\infty}\dfrac{(-1)^n}{n^2\pi^2c^2 - \omega^2L^2}$

$\times \sin\dfrac{n\pi ct}{L}\sin\dfrac{n\pi x}{L}$ for the nonresonance case.

When $\omega = \dfrac{m\pi c}{L}$, $\dfrac{A(-1)^m}{2m\pi L}\left(2m\pi ct\sin\dfrac{m\pi x}{L}\cos\dfrac{m\pi ct}{L}\right.$

$\left. - L\sin\dfrac{m\pi x}{L}\sin\dfrac{m\pi ct}{L} + 2m\pi x\cos\dfrac{m\pi x}{L}\sin\dfrac{m\pi ct}{L}\right)$

$+\dfrac{2Am}{\pi}\displaystyle\sum_{\substack{n=1\\n\neq m}}^{\infty}\dfrac{(-1)^n}{n^2-m^2}\sin\dfrac{n\pi ct}{L}\sin\dfrac{n\pi x}{L}$

37. $\displaystyle\sum_{n=1}^{\infty}C_n\cos\dfrac{n^2\pi^2ct}{L^2}\sin\dfrac{n\pi x}{L}$, $C_n = \dfrac{2}{L}\displaystyle\int_0^L f(x)\sin\dfrac{n\pi x}{L}dx$

38. (b) $\dfrac{g}{2c^2}\left(\dfrac{2AEL}{k} + 2Lx - x^2\right)$

40. $9.6 \times 10^{-5}\,\mathrm{s}$

Section 10.5

7. (f) $\dfrac{8U_0}{r_2\pi}\displaystyle\sum_{m=1}^{\infty}\sum_{n=1}^{\infty}\dfrac{1}{(2m-1)\lambda_n}e^{-k[\lambda_n^2 + (2m-1)^2\pi^2/L^2]t}$

$\times \dfrac{J_0(\lambda_n r)}{J_1(\lambda_n r_2)}\sin\dfrac{(2m-1)\pi z}{L}$

10. $\dfrac{A}{\rho\omega^2}\left(\dfrac{J_0(\omega r/c)}{J_0(\omega r_2/c)} - 1\right) - \dfrac{2A\omega}{\rho c r_2}\displaystyle\sum_{n=1}^{\infty}\dfrac{\sin c\lambda_n t}{\lambda_n^2(c^2\lambda_n^2 - \omega^2)}$

$\times \dfrac{J_0(\lambda_n r)}{J_1(\lambda_n r_2)}$

Section 11.1

1. 3   **2.** $\sin 1$ **3.** $9 + e^{-3}$ **4.** 0   **5.** 100

6. $-39 - \cos 10$

9. $\dfrac{-x}{\tau}, 0 \le x \le \dfrac{L}{3}$; $\dfrac{-L}{3\tau}, \dfrac{L}{3} \le x \le \dfrac{2L}{3}$; $\dfrac{x-L}{\tau}$,

$\dfrac{2L}{3} \le x \le L$

11. $\dfrac{x^3 - 3Lx^2}{6EI}$

12. $0, 0 \le t \le T$; $\left(\dfrac{1}{\sqrt{kM}}\right)\sin\sqrt{\dfrac{k}{M}}(t - T), t \ge T$

Section 11.3

1. $\dfrac{d}{dx}\left(x\dfrac{dy}{dx}\right) + 3y = F(x)$

2. $\dfrac{d}{dx}\left(e^x\dfrac{dy}{dx}\right) - 2e^x y = e^x F(x)$

5. $\dfrac{d}{dx}\left(e^{4x}\dfrac{dy}{dx}\right) = e^{4x}F(x)$

6. $-X(x - X) - xH(X - x)$

8. $-k^{-1}\csc k\pi[\sin kx \sin k(\pi - X)H(X - x)$
     $+ \sin kX \sin k(\pi - x)H(x - X)]$

10. $[5(1 + 4e^{10})]^{-1}[(e^{-x} - e^{4x})$
     $\times (4e^{10-X} + e^{4X})H(X - x) + (e^{-X} - e^{4X})$
     $\times (4e^{10-x} + e^{4x})H(x - X)]$

11. $\left(\dfrac{1}{4}\right)e^{-(x+X)}[(2\cos 2x + \sin 2x)\sin 2XH(X - x)$
     $+ (2\cos 2X + \sin 2X)\sin 2xH(x - X)]$

13. $\{2k[1 - \cos k(\beta - \alpha)]\}^{-1}\{[\sin k(\beta - \alpha - X + x)$
     $+ \sin k(X - x)]H(X - x)$
     $+ [\sin k(\beta - \alpha - x + X)$
     $+ \sin k(x - X)]H(x - X)\}$

16. $(6EI)^{-1}[(x - X)^3H(x - X) - x^3 + 3Xx^2]$

18. $(6EI)^{-1}\left[(x - X)^3H(x - X)\right.$

     $+ \dfrac{x^3(3L^2X^2 - L^4 - 2LX^3)}{L^4}$

     $\left. + \dfrac{3x^2(X^3 - 2LX^2 + L^2X)}{L^2}\right]$

22. $-\dfrac{2L}{\pi^2}\displaystyle\sum_{n=1}^{\infty}\dfrac{1}{n^2}\sin\dfrac{n\pi X}{L}\sin\dfrac{n\pi x}{L}$

Ĥ

Section 11.4

1. $(\kappa L)^{-1}[x(L-X)H(X-x) + X(L-x)H(x-X)]$

4. $\dfrac{kx(L-x)}{2\tau}$

6. $\dfrac{k}{32\tau}\begin{cases} 8xL & 0 \le x \le L/4 \\ -L^2 + 16Lx - 16x^2 & L/4 \le x \le 3L/4 \\ 8L(L-x) & 3L/4 \le x \le L \end{cases}$

8. $\dfrac{1}{4\tau}\begin{cases} 2kx(L-x) - 4\bar{k}x & 0 \le x \le L/4 \\ 2kx(L-x) - \bar{k}L & L/4 \le x \le 3L/4 \\ 2kx(L-x) - 4\bar{k}(L-x) & 3L/4 \le x \le L \end{cases}$

11. $\dfrac{L(2\rho c^2 + \rho gL + mg)}{2\rho c^2}$

14. $\dfrac{1}{48EI}\begin{cases} 8x^3 - 12Lx^2 & 0 \le x \le L/2 \\ L^3 - 6L^2x & L/2 \le x \le L \end{cases}$

16. $\dfrac{wx(L-x)(x^2 - Lx - L^2)}{24EI}$

18. $\dfrac{w(4Lx^3 - 6L^2x^2 - x^4)}{24EI} + \dfrac{W}{24EI}$

$\times \begin{cases} Lx^2(2x - 3L) & 0 \le x \le L/4 \\ -x^4 + 3Lx^3 - (27L^2x^2/8) & \\ \quad + (L^3x/16) - (L^4/256) & L/4 \le x \le 3L/4 \\ (5L^4/16) - (13L^3x/8) & 3L/4 \le x \le L \end{cases}$

21. $\dfrac{x}{2}\sin x - \dfrac{\sin x}{2\cos 1}(\sin 1 + \cos 1)$

$\quad + \dfrac{m_2 \sin x + m_1 \cos(1 - x)}{\cos 1}$

23. $\dfrac{x}{k^2} + \dfrac{(\beta - \alpha)[\cos k(x - \alpha) - \cos k(\beta - x)]}{2k^2[1 - \cos k(\beta - \alpha)]}$

25. $\left(\dfrac{1}{4}\right)e^{2x}(1 - \cos 2x)$

Section 11.5

1. $E + \dfrac{L^2}{\kappa\pi^2}\cos\dfrac{\pi x}{L}$

3. (a) $\left(D + \dfrac{x}{4}\right)\sin 2x;$

(b) $\left(D + \dfrac{x}{4}\right)\sin 2x + m_1 \cos 2x$

5. $D\sin\dfrac{n\pi x}{L} + \dfrac{L}{n\pi}\displaystyle\int_x^L F(X)\sin\dfrac{n\pi(X - x)}{L}\,dX$

when $k = n\pi/L$

7. $D\sin\dfrac{(2n-1)\pi x}{2L} + \dfrac{2L}{(2n-1)\pi}\displaystyle\int_x^L F(X)$

$\quad \times \sin\dfrac{(2n-1)\pi(X - x)}{2L}\,dX$

when $k = (2n-1)\pi/(2L)$

Section 11.6

1. $\dfrac{1}{M}\displaystyle\int_0^t (t - T)F(T)\,dT + x_0 + v_0 t$

2. $\dfrac{1}{M\omega}\displaystyle\int_0^t e^{-\beta(t - T)/(2M)}\sin\omega(t - T)F(T)\,dT$

$\quad + e^{-\beta t/(2M)}\left[x_0\cos\omega t + \left(\dfrac{v_0}{\omega} + \dfrac{\beta x_0}{2M\omega}\right)\sin\omega t\right]$

Section 12.2

4. $\dfrac{-4}{\pi r_0^2}\displaystyle\sum_{m=1}^{\infty}\sum_{n=1}^{\infty}\dfrac{J_m(\lambda_{mn}r)J_m(\lambda_{mn}R)\sin m\Theta \sin m\Theta}{\lambda_{mn}^2[J_{m+1}(\lambda_{mn}r_0)]^2}$

6. $\dfrac{-8}{LL'L''}\displaystyle\sum_{j=1}^{\infty}\sum_{m=1}^{\infty}\sum_{n=1}^{\infty}$

$\quad \sin\dfrac{n\pi x}{L}\sin\dfrac{n\pi X}{L}\sin\dfrac{j\pi y}{L'}\sin\dfrac{j\pi Y}{L'}$

$\quad \times \sin\dfrac{m\pi z}{L''}\sin\dfrac{m\pi Z}{L''}$

$\quad \times \dfrac{}{\dfrac{n^2\pi^2}{L^2} + \dfrac{j^2\pi^2}{L'^2} + \dfrac{m^2\pi^2}{L''^2}}$

11. $\dfrac{1}{4\pi}\ln\left(\dfrac{[r_0^4 + r^2R^2 - 2r_0^2rR\cos(\theta + \Theta)]}{[r_0^4 + r^2R^2 - 2r_0^2rR\cos(\theta - \Theta)]}\dfrac{\times [R^2 + r^2 - 2rR\cos(\theta - \Theta)]}{\times [R^2 + r^2 - 2rR\cos(\theta + \Theta)]}\right)$

12. $\displaystyle\sum_{m=-\infty}^{\infty}\sum_{n=-\infty}^{\infty}\dfrac{(-1)^{n+m+1}}{4\pi}$

$\quad \times \ln[(x - x_n)^2 + (y - y_m)^2],$

$\quad x_n = \dfrac{L}{2} + nL + (-1)^n\left(x - \dfrac{L}{2}\right),$

$\quad y_m = \dfrac{L'}{2} + mL' + (-1)^m\left(Y - \dfrac{L'}{2}\right)$

15. $\dfrac{1}{4L}\ln\left[\dfrac{\left(r_0^4 + r^2R^2 - 2r_0^2rR\cos\dfrac{\pi(\theta + \Theta)}{L}\right)}{\left(r_0^4 + r^2R^2 - 2r_0^2rR\cos\dfrac{\pi(\theta - \Theta)}{L}\right)}\dfrac{\times\left(R^2 + r^2 - 2rR\cos\dfrac{\pi(\theta - \Theta)}{L}\right)}{\times\left(R^2 + r^2 - 2rR\cos\dfrac{\pi(\theta + \Theta)}{L}\right)}\right]$

18. $\dfrac{4}{LL'} \displaystyle\sum_{m=1}^{\infty} \sum_{n=1}^{\infty} \dfrac{1}{k^2 - \dfrac{n^2\pi^2}{L^2} - \dfrac{m^2\pi^2}{L'^2}}$

$\times \sin\dfrac{n\pi X}{L} \sin\dfrac{m\pi Y}{L'} \sin\dfrac{n\pi x}{L} \sin\dfrac{m\pi y}{L'}$

20. $\dfrac{4}{\pi r_0^2} \displaystyle\sum_{m=1}^{\infty} \sum_{n=1}^{\infty} \dfrac{1}{k^2 - \lambda_{mn}^2}$

$\times \dfrac{J_m(\lambda_{mn}R)J_m(\lambda_{mn}r)\sin m\Theta \sin m\theta}{[J_{m+1}(\lambda_{mn}r_0)]^2}$

22. $\dfrac{8}{LL'L''} \displaystyle\sum_{j=1}^{\infty} \sum_{m=1}^{\infty} \sum_{n=1}^{\infty}$

$\times \dfrac{1}{k^2 - \dfrac{n^2\pi^2}{L^2} - \dfrac{j^2\pi^2}{L'^2} - \dfrac{m^2\pi^2}{L''^2}}$

$\times \sin\dfrac{n\pi X}{L} \sin\dfrac{j\pi Y}{L'} \sin\dfrac{m\pi Z}{L''}$

$\times \sin\dfrac{n\pi x}{L} \sin\dfrac{j\pi y}{L'} \sin\dfrac{m\pi z}{L''}$

Section 12.3

3. $\displaystyle\int_0^{L'}\int_0^L G(x,y;X,Y)F(X,Y)\,dX\,dY$

$+ \dfrac{2}{L'} \displaystyle\sum_{n=1}^{\infty} B_n \operatorname{csch}\dfrac{n\pi L}{L'} \sinh\dfrac{n\pi x}{L'} \sin\dfrac{n\pi y}{L'}$

$+ \dfrac{2}{L} \displaystyle\sum_{n=1}^{\infty} A_n \operatorname{csch}\dfrac{n\pi L'}{L} \sinh\dfrac{n\pi y}{L} \sin\dfrac{n\pi x}{L},$

$A_n = \displaystyle\int_0^L f(X) \sin\dfrac{n\pi X}{L}\,dX,$

$B_n = \displaystyle\int_0^{L'} g(Y) \sin\dfrac{n\pi Y}{L'}\,dY$

Section 12.4

1. (a) $C - \dfrac{2}{\pi} \displaystyle\sum_{n=1}^{\infty} \dfrac{A_n}{n\sinh(n\pi L/L')} \cosh\dfrac{n\pi(L-x)}{L'}$

$\times \cos\dfrac{n\pi y}{L'}, \quad A_n = \displaystyle\int_0^{L'} f(Y)\cos\dfrac{n\pi Y}{L'}\,dY;$

(b) $-\dfrac{2}{\pi} \displaystyle\sum_{n=1}^{\infty} \dfrac{\cos(n\pi/4) - \cos(3n\pi/4)}{n\sinh(n\pi L/L')}$

$\times \cosh\dfrac{n\pi(L-x)}{L'} \cos\dfrac{n\pi y}{L'}; \; 0$

3. $C + \dfrac{L(x+y) - (x^2+y^2)}{4\kappa}$

4. (e) $C + \dfrac{1}{4\pi} \displaystyle\int_{-\pi}^{\pi}\int_0^{r_0} RF(R,\Theta)$

$\times \ln\left(\dfrac{[r^2 + R^2 - 2rR\cos(\theta-\Theta)]}{\dfrac{\times [r_0^4 + r^2R^2 - 2r_0^2rR\cos(\theta-\Theta)]}{r_0^4 r^2}}\right)$

$\times dR\,d\Theta - \dfrac{r_0}{2\pi}\displaystyle\int_{-\pi}^{\pi} K(\Theta)$

$\times \ln\left(\dfrac{r^2 + r_0^2 - 2r_0 r\cos(\theta - \Theta)}{r_0 r}\right)d\Theta$

Section 12.6

1. $\dfrac{2k}{\kappa L} \displaystyle\sum_{n=1}^{\infty} e^{-n^2\pi^2 k(t-T)/L^2} \sin\dfrac{n\pi X}{L} \sin\dfrac{n\pi x}{L}$

3. $\dfrac{2k}{\kappa L} \displaystyle\sum_{n=1}^{\infty} e^{-(2n-1)^2\pi^2 k(t-T)/(4L^2)}$

$\times \cos\dfrac{(2n-1)\pi X}{2L} \cos\dfrac{(2n-1)\pi x}{2L}$

Section 12.7

1. $\dfrac{1}{\rho}\left(\dfrac{t-T}{L} + \dfrac{2}{\pi c}\displaystyle\sum_{n=1}^{\infty}\dfrac{1}{n}\sin\dfrac{n\pi c(t-T)}{L}\right.$

$\left.\times \cos\dfrac{n\pi X}{L} \cos\dfrac{n\pi x}{L}\right)$

3. $\dfrac{4}{\rho\pi c}\displaystyle\sum_{n=1}^{\infty}\dfrac{1}{2n-1}\sin\dfrac{(2n-1)\pi c(t-T)}{2L}$

$\times \sin\dfrac{(2n-1)\pi X}{2L}\sin\dfrac{(2n-1)\pi x}{L}$

7. (b) $\dfrac{2F_0 L}{\rho\pi^2 c^2}\displaystyle\sum_{n=1}^{\infty}\dfrac{1}{n^2}\left(1-\cos\dfrac{n\pi ct}{L}\right)\sin\dfrac{n\pi x_0}{2L}\sin\dfrac{n\pi x}{L}$

(c) $\dfrac{2F_0 L}{\rho\pi^2 c^2}\displaystyle\sum_{n=1}^{\infty}\dfrac{(-1)^{n+1}}{(2n-1)^2}\left(1-\cos\dfrac{(2n-1)\pi ct}{L}\right)$

$\times \sin\dfrac{(2n-1)\pi x}{L}$

(d) Same answer as for (b), but with the $n = m$ term absent

Index